FUNDAMENTALS
OF CHEMISTRY

FUNDAMENTALS OF CHEMISTRY

Michael A. Wartell

James Madison University

Jack D. Cummins

Metropolitan State College

 Willard Grant Press

Boston, Massachusetts

© Copyright 1980 by Willard Grant Press, Statler Office Building,
20 Providence Street, Boston, Massachusetts 02116

Willard Grant Press is a division of Wadsworth, Inc.

Library of Congress Cataloging in Publication Data

Wartell, Michael A
    Fundamentals of chemistry.

    Includes index.
    1. Chemistry.   I.   Cummins, Jack D.,
joint author.   II.   Title.
QD31.2.W35   540   79-25473
ISBN   0-87150-736-6

*Art drawn by ANCO/Boston. Text and cover design by David Foss, in collaboration
with the Willard Grant Press production staff. Cover photo courtesy of Lawrence
Schauffler. Composed in monophoto Times Roman and Helvetica by Syntax International, Ltd. Photo research by Ronni Linowitz and Jane Goedecke. Acquisition editor:
Jane Goedecke. Developmental editor: Mary Le Quesne. Printed and bound by Halli-
day Lithograph. Cover printed by New England Book Components, Inc.*

PREFACE

Many schools offer introductory chemistry courses for students with little or no background in this subject. The objectives of these courses, however, are not always the same. Some are designed to prepare students for a full year of general chemistry, and so concentrate on the chemical and mathematical skills that will be required later. Others form part of a survey course for nursing and allied health students. In these sequences, emphasis is placed on topics important to this audience, such as solution chemistry. A third group may be taking a beginning course to satisfy a science graduation requirement. These students are interested in some of the applications of chemistry in areas they are familiar with.

Our aim in writing *Fundamentals of Chemistry* was twofold: first, to explain chemistry to students in a way they can understand and learn; second, to do this in a form that will allow each instructor to adapt the presentation to the particular objectives of his or her course.

The time and care that went into the writing and editing were aimed at producing a text at the correct level in terms of language as well as content. Special attention was given to the clarity of definitions of new words and to making them easily recognisable on the page. End-of-chapter glossaries reinforce the importance of these terms and aid in review.

Learning objectives are given at the beginning of every chapter to focus the student's attention and help organize his or her studying.

Problem-solving is, of course, a key to success in learning chemistry. We have incorporated into the text carefully laid out step-by-step examples which are easily identifiable within the chapters. Each step is labeled and explained. As students work through the chapter and become more proficient, we show them how the solving of problems can be streamlined.

Each chapter ends with a sufficient number of problems to allow the student ample practice. Answers to half the problems are provided at the back of the book. Worked-out solutions to those same problems can be found in the study guide. In this way the student will have every opportunity to master the problem-solving skills so essential to the study of chemistry.

Three more or less "optional" chapters have been included to accommodate various interests and needs. Chapter 15 is a brief introduction to organic chemistry, based on functional groups. Chapter 16 deals in a nontechnical way with the ever-current topic of pollution. Chapter 17 discusses nuclear energy from a chemical point of view.

One point of interest: general oxidation-reduction reactions are covered in Chapter 9. We have chosen, however, to place the section on the balancing of oxidation-reduction reactions in an appendix. This topic is often beyond the scope of introductory courses. However, it is an important concept and one that deserves to be included in the book. Therefore, we have left the choice to the instructor.

As was mentioned above, a study guide accompanies the text. In addition to solutions to text problems, it contains two other elements: a chapter review, which uses the learning objectives as the basis for another look at the important concepts in the book; and chapter tests with answers.

A laboratory manual, by H.A. Neidig and J.N. Spencer, Lebanon Valley College, is also available. Most experiments are designed to be completed in two hours. Special emphasis has been placed on safety and helping students avoid common problems and mistakes.

We would like to thank the following individuals for their many helpful suggestions and comments made during their reviews of our manuscript: Robert Becker, Mankato State University; Kevin D. Cadogan, California State University, Hayward; Paul Calgher, Foothill College; Ellene Tratras Contis, Eastern Michigan University; Myron Cucci, Monroe Community College; Donald Dugre, City College of San Francisco; Richard D. Gonzalez, University of Rhode Island; Charles Heaton, Northern Arizona University; Michael Knoll, Vincennes University Junior College; Eileen Lewis, Canada College; Glenn H. Miller, University of California, Santa Barbara; Thomas M. Murphy, University of Maryland; Dexter Plumlee, Northern Virginia Community College; Donna Z. Randall, University of Wisconsin, Green Bay; Tamar Susskind, Oakland Community College; Daniel White, American River College; and Florence Wolters-Chew, Cuyahoga Community College.

Special appreciation and thanks are offered to Mary Blumling, Yvonne Tucker and Debbie Rittenhouse for all their help in the preparation and development of the text.

Michael A. Wartell
James Madison University

Jack D. Cummins
Metropolitan State College, Denver

CONTENTS

5 Nomenclature

6 The Mole Concept

7 Chemical Reactions

8 Working Chemical Problems

16 Pollution 417

17 Nuclear Energy 435

A Balancing Redox Equations 461

B Answers to Selected Problems 469

Index 479

FUNDAMENTALS OF CHEMISTRY

Learning Objectives for Chapter 1

Define **chemistry, matter, energy, chemical change, physical change.**

Explain the relations among the sciences.

Explain the scientific method.

Given a simple situation or problem, explain how the scientific method can be used in solving it.

1 CHEMISTRY

In a world that revolves around technology, it is difficult to imagine daily life without the modern conveniences we take for granted. Picture what it would be like to function without electricity, telephones, or rapid transportation. Each of these "modern conveniences" and an incredible number of others have been made possible by the work of research scientists and inventors. The theories and applications of chemistry, one of the sciences, have been important parts of this work. However, the information assembled is not knowledge inherent to mankind. The equations and principles you will become familiar with and others in scientific use are presented and accepted as facts; but that knowledge has been compiled through years of experimentation and review by men and women who were prompted through curiosity and impelled by determination. Although this information is now worked with familiarly, much of it was completely unknown to our scientist ancestors just a century ago. Most of what you will be learning was unknown two centuries ago. For example, oxygen was not discovered until the eighteenth century; even as the United States was struggling for independence, civilization was unaware of this life-sustaining substance! It is astonishing to realize that the human race, which now sends rockets to the moon, could not identify the components of air two hundred

Figure 1.1 Lightning is an example of a naturally–occurring chemical reaction. Man's understanding of chemistry has enabled him to use chemical reactions to achieve great advances in technology. (Courtesy of the National Oceanic and Atmospheric Administration)

years ago. In spite of the tremendous progress that has been made in the scientific world, experimentation and research is increasingly called for. New knowledge brings new questions to be answered. Many phenomena are still unexplained, and presumably even more are still unrecognized. When you have a fundamental background of chemistry, you will have a basis for appreciating the all-encompassing world of science.

1.1 Chemistry, A Natural Science

Chemistry is the study of the composition, structure, properties, and reactions of the constituents of the universe. The universe can be thought of as composed of matter and energy. **Matter** is what an object is composed of; it is any substance that occupies space and has mass. Familiar examples of matter are **solids** like wood, steel, and sand; **liquids** like water, alcohol, and syrup; and **gases** like air, helium for balloons, and odorous substances in perfume. **Energy** is the ability to do work. It appears in many forms that affect daily existence—like light, heat, motion, electricity, and sound—and in other, less familiar forms. All forms have in common that they can be used to do work. Chemists study matter and also changes in matter and the energy changes that accompany them. They consider changes like the digestion of food in the stomach, the rusting of a piece of iron, and the production of light by a star, all of which involve chemical changes. **Chemical changes** are processes that bring about changes in the composition of substances. Food is digested and converted to waste products, iron is changed to rust, and matter in a star is changed as light is produced. Chemists try to study the almost uncountable number of chemical changes and kinds of matter in the universe. They try to explain how different types of matter interact, of what matter is composed, and how matter changes during chemical processes.

Physical changes affect the form of a substance but not the composition. These as well as chemical changes are important to chemists because they help in understanding the minute, internal structure of matter. Examples of activities that cause physical change are crushing a rock into smaller pieces, cutting a piece of paper, breaking a glass, and carving wood. The shape and size of an object is changed but the composition is not.

Chemistry is one of several natural sciences. If we consider natural science the study of matter, energy, and their interrelations and transformations, then we can include mathematics, physics, chemistry, geology, and biology within the broader designation. None of these areas stands alone. Each discipline calls on the other four from time to time for ideas, areas of study, and fundamental concepts. Mathematics, the study of numbers, symbols and their interrelations, is the most fundamental natural science, since its concepts are basic to all the other fields but independent of them. Mathematicians often look to the other natural sciences, however, for applications for their work. Physics, the study of the interrelation of matter and energy, uses mathematical concepts to explain fundamental principles and observations.

Both geology and biology use chemical, physical, and mathematical concepts. Geologists study the origin, history, and structure of the earth, trying to predict and explain such phenomena as formation of minerals. Biologists study life forms and life processes: how muscles work, how plants and animals grow, and how life forms reproduce. Chemistry, too, relies heavily on the other natural sciences. Mathematical ideas and symbols are used in almost every aspect of chemistry to clarify explanations and to help in developing usable theories. The physicists' studies of the microscopic properties of matter and of the equations describing the universe are fundamental to the chemists' studies of matter on a macroscopic scale.

The discipline of chemistry is divided into several subjects, showing even more clearly the relation of chemistry to the rest of the sciences. These subjects include:

1. Physical chemistry, the study of applying basic physical and mathematical principles to chemistry.
2. Organic chemistry, the study of substances containing carbon.
3. Biochemistry, the study of matter and chemical changes related to living organisms.
4. Inorganic chemistry, the study of other substances besides those studied by organic chemists and biochemists.
5. Analytical chemistry, the identification and study of quantities of components present in various substances.

These areas of chemistry often widely overlap. Tradition more than force has led to labeling the various fields. Many narrower subfields of chemistry have been created, such as geochemistry, or applying chemical principles to geology, and pharmacy, or the study of the use of substances as medicines.

1.2 The Scientific Method: One Way of Solving Problems

What distinguishes a science (like chemistry) from any other field of study? Many people believe it is the approach to how problems are solved, a method first expounded by the scientific community. Scientists try to get knowledge and organize it using a careful, logical approach, called the **scientific method**.

Anyone can study things, look at them, and find out what they do and how they act under different conditions. Scientists, however, pride themselves on studying objects and situations by aiming at specific goals and using specific methods. This leads to prediction of what may happen in previously untried situations. Thus, a scientist is not satisfied with trying an experiment only once, observing the effects, and reporting them. The scientist must be certain the factors involved are understood well enough to ensure that the same event will happen every time the set of conditions is duplicated. Hence, many observations are made to be sure the proposed explanation is correct. Imagine leaving a gold coin on a windowsill under a full moon and returning to find that it had disappeared. A nonscientific conclusion based on the observation might be that moonlight causes gold to disappear. Further observation and repetition of the conditions of the experiment, however, would provide a better explanation for the occurrence, like the presence of a thief.

A chemist, as a scientist, wants to be precise about the way objects and events are described. If such effort is made, errors due to carelessness or prejudice will be less likely to occur. Use of the scientific method assures unbiased results. The method embraces making a **hypothesis**, or proposed explanation for a phenomenon, before experimenting, and also providing a **theory** later—an explanation using the results of experimentation to account for a phenomenon.

It is advantageous to understand the scientific method, not only because this is how many scientific discoveries have been made but also because once something unusual has been noticed, it is important to have an organized approach to follow in studying the discovery. Even though great scientific discoveries have been made with luck, hunches, and flashes of genius, as well as by strict adherence to the scientific method, after the initial discovery, the scientific method is useful for studying further and expanding that discovery.

The fundamental steps of the scientific method are:

1. Define the problem to be studied.
2. Correlate the known facts and propose an expected result or a hypothesis.
3. Conduct experiments to prove or disprove the hypothesis.
4. Propose an explanation (theory or model) to account for the results.

As chemical concepts have become increasingly complex, chemists have begun to study existing hypotheses and theories to expand them or to understand the factors involved more completely. In studying hypotheses, scientists regard their responsibilities as the following:

1. Make observations of experiments.
2. Draw conclusions.
3. Report results.

You see that this restates the steps in the scientific method. Scientists, as they follow this approach, compile data and groups of ideas that can be used to support an old theory or create a new one—another way of using the scientific method.

What does it mean to study a hypothesis or a particular thing or event? It means that to find out what a substance is made of or how it undergoes a change, experiments are carefully chosen and performed to examine specific parts of the problem. The results of such experiments are analyzed and gathered into a concise final statement. Thus one can get precise descriptions of substances and events that are uncolored by bias or mistakes.

1.3   A Short Historical Survey

Chemical concepts and ideas were used by human beings long before historians began to keep records. Prehistoric humans made brass, glass, dyes, beer, and many other substances, using recipes that had been passed along from one generation to another. These recipes were really guides to chemical preparations that had been discovered through a long procedure of trial and error and not through scientific investigation. The recipes do show a knowledge of chemical processes, however, even though early man founded explanations for the results primarily in religion and superstition.

Greek philosophers (600 B.C.–200 A.D.) were the first to study nature carefully and to try to explain natural phenomena. They observed all sorts of natural events and devised many interesting ideas about why substances acted as they did, but their explanations of results showed a lack of understanding. The Greeks believed that everything could be explained and thus devised explanations for everything they observed, no matter how little they knew of the subject. Despite their deficiencies, the Greeks contributed immensely to science. Their intense curiosity prompted a systematized approach to studying phenomena that was a model for scientists in later ages. Their contributions were important also because their explanations of natural phenomena were not based on religious lore.

The age of alchemy (200 B.C.–1600 A.D.) overlaps and follows the height of Greek scientific investigation. Alchemy, however, was hardly a scientific endeavor by any definition of science. Alchemists had two main goals: (1) discovery of a way of changing common metals into gold; and (2) discovery of a substance that, when used, would cure all ills and bring eternal youth to the user. They used trial and error, magical incantations, good-luck charms, and anything else they could think of to produce the desired substances, performing many experiments and observing the results. While no alchemist ever discovered a way of changing common metals into gold or a path to eternal youth, many new techniques and useful drugs were discovered by accident. The time of the alchemists marks the birth of iatrochemistry, using substances to cure ills. Iatrochemical experiments (mostly aimed at finding the elixir of eternal youth) were done almost randomly. New substances made, discovered, or mixed were eaten, rubbed on the body, or inhaled by human beings. The

Figure 1.2 The
alchemist Thomas
Norton at work.
(Courtesy of B. T.
Batsford Ltd from
their publication
*Everyday Life in
Medieval Times,*
by Marjorie
Rowling,
published in 1968)

alchemist then observed the results, which often included death or permanent
disability. Fortunately, alchemists quickly ran out of humans on whom experiments could be performed. Some alchemical discoveries were useful, but not
many were really significant. The spirit of experimentation grew during this
time, but the careful, logical approach of the scientific method had not yet
appeared.

During the eighteenth century, the age of modern chemistry began, with
the discovery of oxygen in the 1770s by Joseph Priestley and Antoine Lavoisier.
In making this discovery, Priestley and Lavoisier used the scientific method to
develop and evaluate their findings. Because this method was used extensively,
the 1770s are usually called the beginning years of modern chemistry. The
age of modern chemistry is the time when chemistry could be classified a science,
not art or superstition.

After the discovery of oxygen, chemists during the late eighteenth century
and most of the nineteenth were concerned with discovering and purifying new
substances and classifying them by properties. Many of the simplest substances
in nature (called elements) were then recognized, grouped by properties, and
assigned places on the periodic table. The periodic table is a tabular classification of the one hundred and six simplest substances in nature; the chart was
substantially developed during the late nineteenth century, and new substances
have since been added with their discovery. Many other, more complex substances (called compounds), which are various combinations of elements, were
also discovered or prepared during the early development. The nineteenth
century can be characterized as a time when chemists extensively expanded
their knowledge of the substances present in nature.

In the late 1800s, scientists began experimentation to determine whether
atoms, or the smallest particles composing elements, could be separated into
even smaller particles. About 1900, these experiments began to succeed, and
the proton and electron were discovered. The elements, substances thought to
be the simplest in nature, were found to be composed of even simpler substances,
subatomic particles. In 1932 a third simple particle, the neutron, was discovered.

During the 1970s, theories involving even more fundamental particles were proposed. The discovery of the quark (pronounced *kwork*, *like cork*), proposed as the most fundamental unit in the universe, was reported in 1977. Also during this time, many theories about the behavior of protons and electrons and about the basic structure of substances were proposed.

Chemical knowledge has advanced at an almost unbelievable rate during the twentieth century. Chemists have studied the chemical constituents of living organisms and have developed theories explaining many aspects of biological processes. These studies have resulted in new and improved chemical treatments for diseases, improved understanding of nutrition, and a much clearer idea about how environmental factors such as pollution affect organisms. Chemists have discovered an assortment of new plastics, synthetic fibers, and other materials that are now a familiar part of our day-to-day existence. Chemists have helped in the development of nuclear energy for both wartime and peacetime uses. During the twentieth century, chemists have discovered new rocket fuels, plant foods, paints, ceramics, construction materials, and innumerable other useful substances. If chemistry and science continue to progress at the fantastic rate of the twentieth century, the new discoveries that may be made are almost unimaginable.

A realization necessary for understanding chemistry and science in general is that each new discovery is made possible by previous discoveries. Sir Isaac Newton, a physicist of the seventeenth century, once said that his discoveries were possible because he was "standing on the shoulders of giants." His work was based on the many experiments that earlier scientists had performed. Each new experiment and new theory contributes a piece to a continually expanding puzzle. Each time a question is answered, many new questions form, and as these new questions are answered, knowledge expands rapidly. This is why scientific knowledge has increased so extensively in the twentieth century.

Figure 1.3 Scientists today can convert one element to another element, and create new elements, using particle accelerators and other tools of modern science. The photo shows the interior of the main accelerator at the Fermi National Accelerator Laboratory, Batavia, Illinois. (Fermilab photo)

1.4 Understanding Chemistry,
A Note to Students

In this textbook, we try to make chemistry as interesting for you as possible so that if you work at it, you can understand the material presented. We hope the ideas presented here will stir your interest in the field, and even though you may not become a chemistry major, you will learn to appreciate the study and importance of chemistry. Further, we hope that as you study chemistry, you will discover that it is very exciting to find out how and why things happen. In doing this, you learn a chemical language so that you will know some of the words and concepts chemists use in their field. Also, you will become familiar with the simple mathematics used in working on chemical problems; Chapter 2 discusses numbers, units, and fundamental mathematical manipulation.

Chemical symbols and words are a part of the chemical language. Chapters 3 through 8 introduce chemical symbols and words.

Once the basic operations and the language of chemistry are known, many interesting problems can be solved and important uses for chemistry can be found. Chapters 9 through 17 explain some of these problems and uses.

We are trying to make chemistry as easy as possible. But you must do your part too. You can make the study of chemistry much easier for yourself by developing good study habits. This means studying regularly, carefully working out all problems, and questioning, rereading, and discussing all the material within the text. Be sure you understand each section before you go on to the next.

Glossary

Biology	The study of life forms and life processes.
Chemistry	The study of the composition, structure, properties, and reactions of the constituents of the universe.
Chemical change	A process that brings about change in the composition of a substance.
Energy	The ability to do work.
Geology	The study of the origin, history, and structure of the earth.
Hypothesis	A prediction or educated guess about the results of an experiment yet to be performed.
Mathematics	The study of numbers and symbols and their relations.
Matter	The material of which the universe is composed.
Physical change	A change that results in the change of size, shape, or form but not composition of a substance.
Physics	The study of matter and energy and their relations.
Theory	An explanation offered to account for the results of an experiment based on observed facts.

Learning Objectives for Chapter 2

Define the following: **International System of Units, SI, exponential notation, exponent, scientific notation, significant figure, unit factor, weight, mass, density, specific gravity, Celsius temperature scale, Kelvin temperature scale, heat, specific heat, calorie.**

Express numbers in exponential notation.

Determine the accuracy of a written number, using the definition of significant figures.

Determine the number of significant figures in a number, using the rules for counting significant figures.

Determine the number of significant figures appropriate in a sum, a difference, a product, and a quotient.

Round off numbers.

Explain the unit factor method for solving problems.

Write unit factors for any equivalency.

Explain the metric system of measurement units and the relevant prefixes.

Using unit factors, convert measurements within each of the metric and English systems and between them.

Explain the relation between weight and mass.

Using appropriate equations, convert among Celsius, Kelvin, and Fahrenheit temperature scales.

2 BASIC TOOLS FOR CHEMISTRY

For science to function, information must be transmitted back and forth among many scientific investigators working in their individual research areas and also among great numbers of people not directly involved in such endeavors. Since large volumes of information must be transferred and since accuracy is important, scientists try to describe their studies in a way that minimizes mistakes and bias. Precise communication, however, is difficult, since thought processes and language are often unorganized and vague. The problem in communication is partly overcome by using numbers. Numbers represent simple statements that do not lend themselves to misinterpretation. To begin and continue a discussion of chemistry, one must understand numbers and their meaning.

Figure 2.1 Numbers communicate facts and allow scientists to discuss their studies precisely and clearly. This programmable thermostat uses numbers in a variety of ways. (Photo courtesy of Honeywell, Inc.)

2.1

Numbers and Units

Numbers are often stated with numerals instead of words. This practice contributes to worldwide communication, since numerals are the same in most languages. Numbers are often associated with measurements of length, weight, volume, temperature, and velocity. Accurate communication of numerical information is important in science.

Although the digits in numerical communication are important, the numerals themselves are of little use if the units to which they refer are not understood. Discussions using numbers must include appropriate and understandable units. While "six miles" and "six inches" both describe lengths, they are vastly different distances, information that the numeral alone would not communicate. Units for measurement have been a problem for man since he first began to record events or describe the surroundings. How many people understand the calendar of the ancient Aztecs? How long is a cubit? (A cubit is defined as the distance from a person's elbow to the tip of that person's middle finger.) Was the length of a cubit different two thousand years ago and does it now differ from one person to another? Why does it take longer to run the 100-meter dash than the 100-yard dash?

To solve the communication problem, groups of people throughout the world have worked to develop a standard system of measurement units that all countries can adopt. This means that ultimately no matter where a person goes, whether it is to the tip of South Africa or Alaska, at the Arctic Circle, the same units will be used to describe the physical surroundings. This set of measurement units is called the **International System of Units**, abbreviated SI (for **Système International**, the French). The system was established to simplify exchange of information and materials between countries. Many of its units are derived from the metric system of measurement. These worldwide measurement units are important to us, since many are basic units in chemistry and since the United States is now converting many measurements to these units.

2.2

Exponential Notation and Significant Figures

Two important ideas have so far been presented. The first is that numbers help in accurate scientific communication; and the second is that appropriate units must accompany these numbers so that communication is readily understandable. There is a particular way of writing numbers informatively and accurately.

Exponential Notation

Writing numbers may at first seem like something to be learned in elementary school; it is a process already familiar to most people. Expressing very large or very small numbers, however, is usually not necessary in daily existence. Scientists, on the other hand, often use extremely large or extremely small numbers. A shorthand form, called exponential notation, can keep such numbers from being unwieldy.

An example of a large number that a scientist might find useful is the distance to the nearest star. The nearest star, except for the sun, is 80,000,000,000,000 miles away from the earth. Writing this many digits and trying to read them is difficult, confusing, and subject to error. Counting and writing zeros is also time-consuming. The same problem exists when very small numbers are used. For example, a disease-causing virus particle might be as small as 0.000002 inch in diameter. Again, the number is awkward, owing to the many zeros. Exponential notation offers a sensible alternative.

> Exponential notation consists in multiplying a number by an appropriate power of ten.

This statement can be best understood by studying some examples. The number 400 can be written as an exponential by these steps.

Step 1: Write the number as 4 multiplied by 100.
$$400 = 4 \times 100$$

Step 2: Break the 100 into individual multipliers of 10.
$$4 \times 100 = 4 \times 10 \times 10$$

Step 3: Express the tens as a power.
$$4 \times 10 \times 10 = 4 \times 10^2$$

In the example, 4×10^2 expresses the number 400 in exponential notation. The superscript 2 is called an **exponent**, or **power**. It indicates the number of tens by which the 4 is multiplied. Again, $10^2 = 10 \times 10 = 100$.

Exponential notation is further refined to **scientific notation**, where only one digit in the multiplier is allowed to the left of the decimal point. In illustration of this point, the number 473×10^7 is written in exponential notation. The same number written in scientific notation is

$$4.73 \times 10^9$$

The term **exponential notation** is more general, and we shall use this form throughout our study. For consistency, we shall write most numbers with only one digit to the left of the decimal point.

Example 2.1   Write 96,000 as an exponential.

Step 1 $96,000 = 9.6 \times 10,000$
Step 2 $9.6 \times 10,000 = 9.6 \times 10 \times 10 \times 10 \times 10$
Step 3 $9.6 \times 10 \times 10 \times 10 \times 10 = 9.6 \times 10^4$

The number 96,000 written in exponential notation is 9.6×10^4. The 4 in 10^4 is the exponent. It shows that 9.6 is multiplied by 10 four times.

Using exponential notation does not make writing the numbers 400 or 96,000 much simpler; however, writing the number that represents the distance to the nearest star in miles is much easier by this notation. In the several examples that follow, Steps 1 and 2 are combined.

Example 2.2   The distance to the star nearest Earth, outside the solar system, is 80,000,000,000,000 miles. Write this number as an exponential.
This number can be written as follows:

Steps 1 and 2 $80,000,000,000,000 = 8 \times 10 \times 10 \times 10 \times 10 \times 10 \times 10 \times$
$10 \times 10 \times 10 \times 10 \times 10 \times 10 \times 10$
Step 3 $80,000,000,000,000 = 8 \times 10^{13}$

The exponent, 13, is gotten by counting the number of zeros following the 8, or the number of places that the decimal point has been moved to the left. You can see that it is much simpler to write

$$8 \times 10^{13}$$

than it is to write 80,000,000,000,000 and the number is less likely to be misunderstood.

In another example, the steps are reduced to counting zeros.

Example 2.3   Write 84,500,000,000,000,000,000,000 in exponential notation.

Step 1   The number is the same as 845 multiplied by

$$100,000,000,000,000,000,000$$

Steps 2 and 3   The large number is 10^{20}, so one exponential form is 845×10^{20}. However, to continue the practice of having only one number to the left of the decimal point, the number is now written

$$845 \times 10^{20} = 8.45 \times 100 \times 10^{20} = 8.45 \times 10^{22}$$

Notice that in the final answer, the decimal point was moved until there was only one digit to the left of the decimal point. The shortened number was then multiplied by 10 raised to the twenty-second power. The exponent equaled the number of places that the decimal point was moved to the left.

Example 2.4

Write 46,700 in exponential notation.

Steps 1 and 2 Begin at the right and count the number of digits until only one digit remains to the left of the decimal:

$$4 \quad 6 \quad 7 \quad 0 \quad 0$$
$$4 \quad 3 \quad 2 \quad 1$$

The number 4.67 remains.

Step 3 The number is multiplied by 10 raised to the number of places counted. For 46,700, the number is 4, and the exponential notation is 4.67×10^4.

Small numbers can also be expressed as exponentials. Begin with 0.01. This number can also be written as

Step 1: $\qquad 0.01 = \dfrac{1}{100}$

Step 2: $\qquad \dfrac{1}{100} = \dfrac{1}{10 \times 10}$

Step 3: $\qquad \dfrac{1}{10 \times 10} = \dfrac{1}{10^2}$

Step 4: $\qquad \dfrac{1}{10^2} = 1 \times 10^{-2}$

When a negative exponent appears, it means that the associated number, in this case 10, can be rewritten as a fraction with the numerator 1 and the denominator 10, raised to the appropriate positive exponent. Thus 10^{-2} means exactly the same as $1/10^2$, which also means $\frac{1}{100}$. When 100 is divided into 1, the resulting quotient is 0.01, the original number.

When you are writing small numbers as exponentials, you can still count decimal places. The following examples show this.

Example 2.5

Write 0.000 000 17 in exponential notation.

Steps 1, 2, and 3 Begin by moving the decimal point seven places to the right.

$$0. \quad 0 \quad 0 \quad 0 \quad 0 \quad 0 \quad 0 \quad 1 \quad 7$$
$$\qquad 1 \quad 2 \quad 3 \quad 4 \quad 5 \quad 6 \quad 7$$

Only one numeral remains to the left of the decimal point.

Step 4   Write the exponential as 10 raised to the negative number of places counted.

$$0.000\,000\,17 = 1.7 \times 10^{-7}$$

Remember that 10^{-7} is the same as

$$\frac{1}{10 \times 10 \times 10 \times 10 \times 10 \times 10 \times 10}$$

Example 2.6   Write 0.000 000 000 009 31 as an exponential.

Steps 1, 2, and 3   The decimal point is moved twelve places to the right.
Step 4 $0.000\,000\,000\,009\,31 = 9.31 \times 10^{-12}$

Table 2.1 summarizes the use of some exponentials to express large and small numbers.

Table 2.1

Number	Exponential Notation	Shorthand Exponential Notation
1 000 000	1×10^6	10^6
1000	1×10^3	10^3
100	1×10^2	10^2
10	1×10^1	10
1	1×10^0	1
0.1	1×10^{-1}	10^{-1}
0.01	1×10^{-2}	10^{-2}
0.000 001	1×10^{-6}	10^{-6}

Often, to save time, exponential notation is shortened even further. If the multiplier is 1, it can be omitted. Thus, 1×10^3 is written simply 10^3; or 1×10^{-6} is written 10^{-6}. These shorthand notations are also shown in Table 2.1.

A rule of thumb is that when the exponent is positive, the decimal place has been moved to the left and the number is larger than 1; and when the exponent is negative, the decimal has been moved to the right and the number is smaller than one.

Writing a positive exponent on the 10 is the same as multiplying the number by 10 raised to that power. Writing a negative exponent on the 10 is the same as dividing the number by 10 raised to that power.

Significant Figures

Knowing how to write numbers as exponentials is extremely important; however, knowing how many numerals to show in the factor portion of a number is also important. The following example underlines this problem. When solving the problem

$$2 \times \tfrac{1}{3} = 0.6666 \ldots$$

how does one know when to stop writing sixes? The number of figures written is not governed by the number of display boxes on a calculator nor is it arbitrary. There are definite rules that apply to choosing how many numerals to write in the solution to a problem; these rules determine the number of significant figures. This is very important because the number of digits expressed in a number indicates the accuracy of the measurement from which the number was derived. Only the significant figures are expressed.

What are significant figures? The number of **significant figures** in a number is the number of digits that are certain in that number, plus one more digit.

Since the number can represent a measurement, the following example helps to explain the definition (Figures 2.2a and 2.2b).

Figure 2.2a Using an unmarked stick one yard long, the car measures 5.2 yards in length. The final digit, 2, is estimated and is, therefore, uncertain.

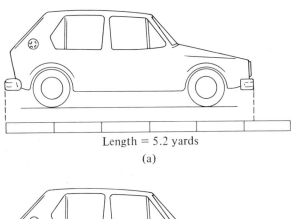

Length = 5.2 yards

(a)

Figure 2.2b Using a yardstick marked off in tenths of yards, the car measures 5.23 yards in length. The digit 2 can now be measured exactly because the stick is marked. The digit 3 is now estimated and uncertain.

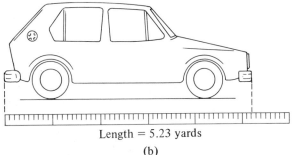

Length = 5.23 yards

(b)

Suppose a stick were cut to a length of 1 yard, and used to measure the length of a car. The car's length turns out to be 5 stick lengths plus a little bit more. How much the car exceeds 5 yd is uncertain because the stick has no other markings on it. The extra can be estimated at less than half a stick length. The measurement is recorded as 5.2 yd because there is some uncertainty about the part of a yard exceeding five. It has been estimated to be 0.2 yd. There are two significant figures in the statement. The second numeral, 2, is the uncertain digit in the definition. The number has been written in a way that indicates an estimation. In this way, scientists place certain limits on an uncertain figure. Unless a statement is made otherwise, the understanding is that the uncertain digit does not vary by more than one unit up or down. Hence the statement that the car is 5.2 yd long means that it could not possibly be longer than 5.3 yd nor shorter than 5.1 yd. The limit of certainty of knowledge is the possible range of length. A shorter way of stating this length is 5.2 $\pm$ 0.1 yd, which means between 5.3 and 5.1 yd.

Suppose now that lines are drawn on the stick to divide it into ten equal sections. On measurement, the car is found to be 5 yd long plus two sections and a little more. This measurement is more accurate than the last. The length of the car can be stated as 5.23 yd. The 5 and the 2 are certain digits. The 3 is uncertain. The car could be as short as 5.22 yd or as long as 5.24 yd. The shorter way of stating the measurement is 5.23 $\pm$ 0.01 yd. The 5.23 shows three significant figures. The number of significant figures can be expanded as more accurate measurements are made, but there is always a limit. The last digit is plus or minus 1.

The usefulness of significant figures can now be seen. It would make little sense to report the length of a car as 5.2300 yd if the measuring device used could not measure that accurately.

Counting Significant Figures

To express the result of a calculation, it is often necessary to know the number of significant figures contained by each number in that calculation. The following set of rules can be used to count the significant figures in a number.

1. All other numbers besides zero are significant. For example, 636, 8.74, and 58.7 all have three significant figures.
2. Zeros may or may not be significant, depending on where they are located relative to the decimal point. If the 0 is used to locate a decimal point, it is usually not significant. However, zeros that result from counting a specific number of items are significant.

Note that as an explanation of Rule 2, the zero in 0.587 is not significant. It is used to **emphasize** the location of the decimal point.

The zeros in 86,000 may or may not be significant, since they **determine** the location of the decimal point. The zeros are significant if the number represents a definite quantity such as a counting of 86,000 jelly beans or other objects; if the number is a measurement, however, the zeros are assumed not to be significant. In this book the same number with three significant zeros is written 86,000. or 8.6000×10^4. Therefore, as a measured value, the number 86,000 has only two significant figures.

The zeros in 8.00 are significant since they are to the right of the decimal point. They show that the measurement was made to the nearest hundredth. The number 8.00, then, has 3 significant figures. Likewise, 80.0 has three significant figures. This time a zero to the left is significant because there is also a zero to the right of the decimal point. Also, 8.00×10^2 has three significant figures. The zeros show accuracy and do not locate the decimal point. This measurement can be expressed in nonexponential form as 800. Similarly, 30. has two significant figures.

The number 0.0065 has only two significant figures. The first three zeros only locate the decimal point. The number 0.006 50 however, has three significant figures. The zero to the right of the number is significant. Several examples of determining significant figures are shown in Table 2.2.

Table 2.2   Examples of Significant Figures

Number	Uncertainty	Significant Figures
458	458 ± 1	3
600	600 ± 100	1
6.00×10^2	$600. \pm 1$	3
420.0	420.0 ± 0.1	4
8×10^4	$80,000 \pm 10,000$	1
0.001	0.001 ± 0.001	1
0.00560	$0.005\,60 \pm 0.000\,01$	3
5.0040	5.0040 ± 0.0001	5
60.040	60.040 ± 0.001	5

There is one exception to the examples that have been shown. This exception is exact numbers. If a room contains 12 people, it contains 12 people exactly. There is no error of plus or minus one person. A count, not a measurement, has been made. A jar of jelly beans may contain, by actual count, 100 beans. It is assumed that there is no error. These numbers are labeled exact numbers and contain an infinite number of significant figures. The most common instance of exact numbers is in converting from one unit to another. There are exactly 3 feet in 1 yard by definition. It is not necessary to indicate the significant figures by adding a decimal point and numerous zeros. The 3 in this case is assumed to have an infinite number of significant figures.

Example 2.7	Determine the number of significant figures in 983.
	There are three significant figures, because according to rule 1, all numerals except zero are significant.
Example 2.8	Determine the number of significant figures in 90,730.
	There are four significant figures in this number. According to rule 2, the first zero is internal in the number and does not locate the decimal point. It is significant. The second zero locates the decimal point. It is not significant.
Example 2.9	Determine the number of significant figures in 0.009 30.
	There are three significant figures in this number. According to rule 2, the first three zeros (reading from left to right) locate the decimal point and are not significant. The last zero is significant.
Example 2.10	Determine the number of significant figures in 8.600×10^3.
	There are four significant figures in this number. According to rule 2, the zeros do not locate the decimal and are significant.

Now that the number of significant figures in individual numbers can be determined, the number of significant figures necessary in an answer resulting from a calculation can be found. Two different rules apply. The first rule covers addition and subtraction, and the second, multiplication and division.

Significant Figures in Sums and Differences

The number of significant figures in the answer to an addition or a subtraction problem is determined by the number in the problem that has the smallest number of significant figures to the right of the decimal point.

Example 2.11	Add 2.56 and 4.3, expressing the answer with appropriate significant figures.
	Step 1 Add or subtract the numbers retaining all figures.

$$\begin{array}{r} 2.56 \\ +4.3 \\ \hline 6.8\boxed{6} \end{array}$$

Step 2   Choose the number having the smallest number of significant figures to the right of the decimal and round off the answer. The answer is

6.9, having two significant figures. The number is rounded off, since 4.3 has only one digit to the right of the decimal point.

Example 2.12 Add 8.78, 4.326, and 7.1, expressing the answer with appropriate significant figures.

Step 1   8.78
                 4.326
                 7.1
                 ———
                 20.2 06

Step 2   The answer is 20.2. The number 7.1 has only one digit to the right of the decimal point; therefore the answer can have only one number to the right of the decimal. Notice, however, that the answer 20.2 itself contains three significant figures.

In this final example, add the following numbers. Expressing the answer with the appropriate number of significant figures should become a habit in any calculation.

Example 2.13 Add 100., 0.056, and 0.22

Step 1   100.
                    0.056
                    0.22
                 ————
                 100. 276

Step 2   The answer is 100.. There are no numerals to the right of the decimal.

It is important to realize that when a problem is solved and digits are ignored, they are being ignored for the sake of accurate communication. In the last example, 100.276 is the numerically correct answer. Giving the answer as 100. communicates the degree of certainty of the total, not the numerical accuracy. Numerically, the answer is obviously wrong.

Significant Figures in Multiplication and Division

The rule governing the number of significant figures in the answer to a multiplication or a division problem is more complex than the rule for addition or subtraction. In almost all cases, however, the correct number of significant figures for the answer can be obtained by using a single rule:

> The answer in a multiplication or a division problem can contain no more significant figures than the number in the calculation with the fewest significant figures.

The following examples illustrate this rule.

Example 2.14

Multiply 42.6 times 8.0.

Step 1   Carry out the multiplication.

$$\begin{array}{r} 42.6 \\ \times\ 8.0 \\ \hline 34\,0.8 \end{array}$$

Step 2   Choose the number in the problem having the smallest number of significant figures and round off the answer to that number.

The correct answer is expressed as 340. There are two significant figures in the answer. The number 42.6 contains three significant figures; 8.0 contains only two. Thus, the answer can have only two significant figures.

Example 2.15

Solve the problem $\dfrac{7560.7}{27}$

Step 1 $\dfrac{7560.7}{27} = 28\,0.03$

Step 2   The answer should be reported as 280, with two significant figures; the denominator has but two significant figures.

The next example involves an exact number.

Example 2.16

If there are three feet in a yard, how many feet are in 1623 yards?

Step 1 $1623 \times 3 = 4869$
Step 2   The correct answer is 4869 feet. In this calculation, the number of significant figures in the answer is determined by the number of significant figures in 1623. The number 1623 has four significant figures. The 3 indicating number of feet in a yard is an exact number; it means that there are exactly three feet in one yard, and therefore the number can be thought of as having an infinite number of significant figures.

When several calculations are performed sequentially, a convenient rule for deciding how many digits to retain at each step in the solution is the following: **Always carry one extra digit beyond those that are significant and then round off at the end of the problem.**

Example 2.17   Solve the problem $863 \times 42 \div 265 = ?$

Step 1   The problem is solved first by multiplying:

$$863 \times 42 = 36{,}246$$

If this were the final answer, the answer would have two significant figures and be expressed 36,000. Because there are further steps, three figures are kept for the next step. Using 36,200, the next step is:

$$36{,}200 \div 265 = 136.6$$

Step 2   The correct answer is 140, with two significant figures. The number 42 with its two significant figures controls the number of significant figures in the answer. It is the least accurate number in the original problem.

Example 2.18   Solve the problem $3.76 \times 4.28 \times 4.1 \div 5.832 = ?$

Step 1   The solution is

$$3.76 \times 4.28 = 16.0928 = 16.09 \text{ (rounded)}$$
$$16.09 \times 4.1 = 65.969 = 66.0 \text{ (rounded)}$$
$$66.0 \div 5.832 = 11.316872 \ldots$$

Step 2   Answer $= 11$

Notice that throughout the calculation, in each step one extra figure beyond the correct number of significant figures was carried.

Using calculators makes stepwise rounding off unnecessary. With a calculator, the final answer can simply be rounded to the appropriate number of significant figures according to the rules already stated.

One last word about rounding numbers. If the last digit is larger than 5, round up. If the last digit is smaller than 5, round down. If the last digit is 5, round up if the previous digit is odd; round down if the previous digit is even. Examples are shown in Table 2.3.

Table 2.3 Rounding Off Numbers

Number		Rounded Number
363	round down to	360
368	round up to	370
365	round down to	360
355	round up to	360

2.3 Measurement Units

Scientists are responsible for describing observations of experiments. Any numerical description of a measurement requires units. Imagine, for example, the confusion resulting from a report that the distance between two places was 12. The natural question is, Twelve what?—Twelve inches, twelve feet, twelve yards, twelve miles, or twelve light-years? There are many pieces of information like this and each must have units attached. Examples include length, volume, weight, velocity, temperature, time, and an uncountable number of others. We shall examine two sets of measurement units, the English system of units and the metric system. We are familiar with the English units inches, feet, miles; quarts, gallons; ounces, pounds; miles per hour; degrees Fahrenheit; and seconds, minutes, and hours. The Metric system of units includes meters; liters; grams; meters per second; degrees Centigrade; and seconds, minutes, and hours. It is the basis for the International System of Units (SI). First, however, we must know how to convert units, so that the relations between the systems can be more easily understood.

Unit Conversions: The Unit Factor Method

Conversion among measurement units is important because it is more convenient to use some units than others; 1 year is a much simpler statement than 31,536,000 seconds. Conversion is also important because a useful tool in solving most problems is the unit factor, which can be most easily understood by solving conversion problems.

Many units express time. These units are the same in both the English system and the metric system. Some of them are seconds, minutes, hours, days, weeks, months, years, and centuries. Several equivalencies among these units should be familiar. We can easily convert 60 seconds to 1 minute, 60 minutes to an hour, 24 hours to 1 day, and 365 days to a year. Each of these relations can be used to make others. It might be necessary, for instance, to know the number of seconds passing in 30 minutes. The following thought process would get the information:

1. There are 60 seconds in 1 minute.
2. The number of seconds in 30 minutes must be greater than the number of seconds in one minute.
3. Multiplying 30 minutes by 60 seconds in 1 minute should give the answer.

$$30 \times 60 = 1800 \text{ seconds in 30 minutes}$$

Another solution, suitable for more complicated problems, consists in using mathematical statements instead of words. The mathematical statements are called conversion factors, or unit factors. They can be developed in the following way. In mathematical terms, the given unit equivalencies are:

$$60 \text{ s} = 1 \text{ min} \quad 60 \text{ min} = 1 \text{ h} \quad 24 \text{ h} = 1 \text{ d} \quad 365 \text{ d} = 1 \text{ yr} \quad 100 \text{ yr} = 1 \text{ c}$$

In these statements, s means seconds, min means minutes, h stands for hours, d represents days, yr means years, and c symbolizes centuries. The statements are shorter than word statements, but both mean exactly the same thing. The numbers, symbols, and abbreviations save space and require less writing.

Look more closely at $60 \text{ s} = 1 \text{ min}$. The statement is an equation. An equation has two equivalent pieces of information separated by an equals sign. Both sides of the equation can be divided by the same number, and still one side of the equation will equal the other side. To see this, divide both sides by 1 min. Stated mathematically, this is

$$\frac{60 \text{ s}}{1 \text{ min}} = \frac{1 \text{ min}}{1 \text{ min}}$$

It can be rewritten:

$$\frac{60 \text{ s}}{1 \text{ min}} = 1 \qquad \text{since} \qquad \frac{1 \text{ min}}{1 \text{ min}} = 1$$

Logically, 60 s/1 min equals 1, since 60 s and 1 min span exactly the same time even though they are expressed in different units (Figures 2.3a and 2.3b).

Figure 2.3a Sixty minutes are equivalent to one hour.

Figure 2.3b Sixty seconds are equivalent to one minute.

(a)
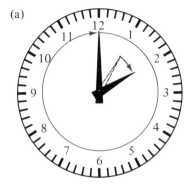

(b)
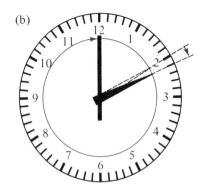

The equation can be treated differently, dividing both sides by 60 seconds. This gives

$$\frac{60 \text{ s}}{60 \text{ s}} = \frac{1 \text{ min}}{60 \text{ s}} \qquad \text{or} \qquad 1 = \frac{1 \text{ min}}{60 \text{ s}}$$

If
$$\frac{60 \text{ s}}{1 \text{ min}} = 1 \qquad \text{and} \qquad 1 = \frac{1 \text{ min}}{60 \text{ s}}$$

then
$$\frac{60 \text{ s}}{1 \text{ min}} = 1 = \frac{1 \text{ min}}{60 \text{ s}}$$

This final equation defines a unit factor. A **unit factor** is a multiplier that is used to convert units. It is possible to multiply a measurement by an appropriate unit factor without changing the value of that measurement. Only the units on the measurement change.

As you ponder this information, try solving some conversion problems.

Example 2.19

A time measurement is stated as 30 min. How many seconds are equivalent to 30 min?

Step 1 Choose an appropriate unit factor. The conversion of minutes to seconds can be made using the unit factor just derived:

$$\frac{60 \text{ s}}{1 \text{ min}} = 1 = \frac{1 \text{ min}}{60 \text{ s}}$$

Step 2 Use the unit factor, checking unit cancellation so that the minutes cancel and the seconds remain. The cancellation is shown along with the numerical solution to the problem:

$$30 \text{ min} \times \frac{60 \text{ s}}{1 \text{ min}} = 1800 \text{ s}$$

$$30 \text{ min} = 1800 \text{ s}$$

Multiplying by the unit factor 60 s/1 min has canceled units in the numerator and denominator of the fraction. The value of the measurement has not changed because it was multiplied by a unit factor equal to 1. Only the units have changed.

If the wrong side of the unit factor equation had been selected, the result would have been

$$30 \text{ min} \times \frac{1 \text{ min}}{60 \text{ s}} = \frac{30 \text{ min} \times \text{min}}{60 \text{ s}}$$

Does anything cancel out? No! The problem has not been solved properly since the units remaining after the multiplication don't make any sense.

Unit factors, properly used, not only make conversion from one set of units to another possible but also show when a mistake involving the units has been made. The answer must always contain the units called for, and all extra units must cancel. If you are having trouble understanding the cancellation, look more closely at the mathematics in the example. The fractions were multiplied. Another example of multiplication of fractions is

$$\frac{3}{4} \times \frac{8}{9} = \frac{24}{36} = \frac{2}{3}$$

The multiplication was accomplished by multiplying the numerators first and then the denominators. The fraction was then reduced. The solution can be made much simpler, however, by cross canceling as shown below.

$$\frac{1_{\,3}}{1^{\,4}} \times \frac{2_{\,8}}{3^{\,9}} = \frac{2}{3}$$

Units can be canceled in exactly the same way as numbers. This was done in the conversion from minutes to seconds. To see this, consider this question: If an average pound of apples contains $7\frac{1}{3}$ apples, how many apples are there in 3 lb? The unit factor to be used is

$$\frac{7\frac{1}{3} \text{ apples}}{1 \text{ lb}} = 1 = \frac{1 \text{ lb}}{7\frac{1}{3} \text{ apples}}$$

Selecting the left-hand side gives

$$3 \cancel{\text{ lb}} \times \frac{7\frac{1}{3} \text{ apples}}{1 \cancel{\text{ lb}}} = 22 \text{ apples}$$

Note the cancellation of units.

Now look back at the time equivalencies given earlier. Several other unit factors are possible with these equations:

$$\frac{60 \text{ min}}{1 \text{ h}} = 1 = \frac{1 \text{ h}}{60 \text{ min}}$$

$$\frac{24 \text{ h}}{1 \text{ d}} = 1 = \frac{1 \text{ d}}{24 \text{ h}}$$

$$\frac{365 \text{ d}}{1 \text{ yr}} = 1 = \frac{1 \text{ yr}}{365 \text{ d}}$$

$$\frac{100 \text{ yr}}{1 \text{ c}} = 1 = \frac{1 \text{ c}}{100 \text{ yr}}$$

Consider a slightly more complicated example of the use of unit factors.

Example 2.20   How many hours pass in two years?

Step 1   The problem asks for conversion of two years to hours. Two unit factors are used in sequence, chosen so that the units cancel. One converts years to days and the second converts days to hours. They are 365 d/1 yr and 24 h/1 d.

Step 2
$$2 \text{ yr} \times \frac{365 \text{ d}}{1 \text{ yr}} = 730 \text{ d}$$

$$730 \text{ d} \times \frac{24 \text{ h}}{1 \text{ d}} = 17{,}520 \text{ h}$$

or in one sequence,

$$2 \text{ yr} \times \frac{365 \text{ d}}{1 \text{ yr}} \times \frac{24 \text{ h}}{1 \text{ d}} = 17{,}520 \text{ h}$$

Note the unit cancellation in both cases.

Measurement According to the Metric System

The English system of measurement units is the one people in the United States are most familiar with. Table 2.4 shows familiar English system measurement units and equivalencies.

The metric system is a more convenient system of measuring than the English system because it is based on factors of 10, like the system used for money in the United States. Think for a moment about the United States monetary system. The basic unit is the dollar. The dollar is broken into 100 units, each unit called a cent. Ten cents make a dime. Ten dimes make a dollar. Ten 1-dollar bills equal a 10-dollar bill. Ten 10-dollar bills equal a 100-dollar bill. Notice that the units progress by factors of 10. Odd values like the quarter, the 5-dollar bill, and the 20-dollar bill, are thrown in for convenience; they are merely fractions or multiples of the basic unit, the dollar. The metric system has a similar basis. A basic unit is defined. From this basic unit, other units

Table 2.4 Familiar English System Measurement Units and Their Equivalencies

Measurement	Units	Equivalencies	Unit Factors
Length	inch (in.)	12 in. = 1 ft	$\dfrac{12\ \text{in.}}{1\ \text{ft}} = 1 = \dfrac{1\ \text{ft}}{12\ \text{in.}}$
	foot (ft) yard (yd)	3 ft = 1 yd	$\dfrac{3\ \text{ft}}{1\ \text{yd}} = 1 = \dfrac{1\ \text{yd}}{3\ \text{ft}}$
	mile	5280 ft = 1 mile	$\dfrac{5280\ \text{ft}}{1\ \text{mile}} = 1 = \dfrac{1\ \text{mile}}{5280\ \text{ft}}$
Volume	pint (pt) quart (qt)	2 pt = 1 qt	$\dfrac{2\ \text{pt}}{1\ \text{qt}} = 1 = \dfrac{1\ \text{qt}}{2\ \text{pt}}$
	gallon (gal)	4 qt = 1 gal	$\dfrac{4\ \text{qt}}{1\ \text{gal}} = 1 = \dfrac{1\ \text{gal}}{4\ \text{qt}}$
Weight	ounce (oz) pound (lb)	16 oz = 1 lb	$\dfrac{16\ \text{oz}}{1\ \text{lb}} = 1 = \dfrac{1\ \text{lb}}{16\ \text{oz}}$
	ton (t)	2000 lb = 1 t	$\dfrac{2000\ \text{lb}}{1\ \text{t}} = 1 = \dfrac{1\ \text{t}}{2000\ \text{lb}}$

are created by taking fractions or multiples of the basic unit. These fractions or multiples are always some factor of 10.

Length

The basic unit of length in the metric system of units is the meter. (A meter is slightly larger than a yard; 1 meter = 1.09 yd.)

The meter is divided into 10 equal parts, as shown in Figure 2.4. Each part is $\frac{1}{10}$ of the original meter and is called a decimeter. Notice that the original unit (meter) remains in the name, but a prefix, **deci-**, has been added. **Deci-** means $\frac{1}{10}$ of a given unit. It can be stated as a decimal (0.1 m) or as an exponential (1×10^{-1} m).

Figure 2.4 Each meter contains 10 decimeters.

decimeter

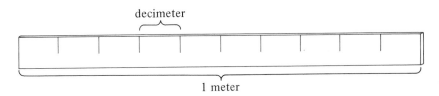

1 meter

The decimeter can also be divided into 10 equal parts, as shown in Figure 2.5. The new unit which is one-tenth of a decimeter or one-hundredth

Figure 2.5 Each decimeter contains 10 centimeters.

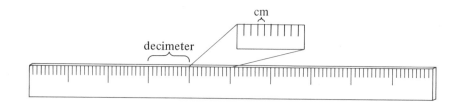

of a meter is called a centimeter. **Centi-** means $\frac{1}{100}$ of a basic unit. This is also 0.01 times the basic unit or 1×10^{-2} times the basic unit.

Dividing each centimeter into 10 parts gives the millimeter. **Milli-** means $\frac{1}{1000}$ of a basic unit. This is also 0.001 times the basic unit, or 1×10^{-3} times the basic unit.

What happens when the basic units are multiplied by tens instead of divided by tens? Ten meters equals one dekameter. (See Figure 2.6.) The basic unit remains, but a new prefix precedes it. **Deka-** means 10 times the basic unit. (Ten times can also be stated as 10^1.)

Figure 2.6 Each dekameter contains 10 meters.

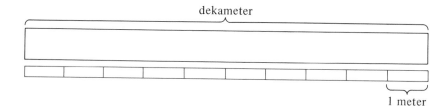

Ten dekameters equals one hectometer. **Hecto-** means 100 times the basic unit, or 10^2 times the basic unit. If there are 10 meters in a dekameter and 10 dekameters in a hectometer, there must be 100 meters in the hectometer.

Ten hectometers equals one kilometer. One kilometer equals 1000 meters, or 10^3 meters. **Kilo-** means 10^3 times the basic unit.

Table 2.5 lists the metric prefixes (which apply to all basic units), the abbreviation for the prefix, and the factor by which the basic unit is multiplied to get the given unit.

Table 2.5 Basic Metric Prefixes

Prefix	Abbreviation	What You Multiply the Basic Unit by
Kilo-	k	1000 (10^3)
Hecto-	h	100 (10^2)
Deka-	dk	10 (10^1)
Deci-	d	0.1 (10^{-1})
Centi-	c	0.01 (10^{-2})
Milli-	m	0.001 (10^{-3})

Using Unit Factors to Convert Lengths in the Metric System

Converting length measurements within the metric system can be done through unit factors. This is like conversion within the English system. However, the unit factors for metric length conversions, since all are factors of 10, are simpler than the unit factors in the English system.

Some units of length of the metric system are more common in chemistry than others. The millimeter, centimeter, meter, and kilometer are the most popular. There are 10 millimeters in 1 centimeter, 100 centimeters in 1 meter, and 1000 meters in 1 kilometer. Stated as equations, these conversions are:

$$10 \text{ millimeters} = 1 \text{ centimeter}$$

$$100 \text{ centimeters} = 1 \text{ meter}$$

$$1000 \text{ meters} = 1 \text{ kilometer}$$

The resulting unit factors are:

$$\frac{10 \text{ mm}}{1 \text{ cm}} = 1 = \frac{1 \text{ cm}}{10 \text{ mm}}$$

$$\frac{100 \text{ cm}}{1 \text{ m}} = 1 = \frac{1 \text{ m}}{100 \text{ cm}}$$

$$\frac{1000 \text{ m}}{1 \text{ km}} = 1 = \frac{1 \text{ km}}{1000 \text{ m}}$$

The examples show how these unit factors are used.

Example 2.21

Convert 3000 millimeters to centimeters.

Step 1 The unit factor to be used is 1 cm/10 mm.
Step 2 Canceling units yields

$$3000 \text{ mm} \times \frac{1 \text{ cm}}{10 \text{ mm}} = 300 \text{ cm}$$

The calculation is relatively easy because dividing or multiplying by 10 simply requires moving the decimal point to the left or right.

In the following examples, Steps 1 and 2 are combined to give a one-step solution.

Example 2.22

Convert 0.5 kilometer to centimeters.

Steps 1 and 2 The conversion requires two unit factors to convert km → m → cm.

$$0.5 \text{ km} \times \frac{1000 \text{ m}}{1 \text{ km}} \times \frac{100 \text{ cm}}{1 \text{ m}} = 50,000 \text{ cm}$$

Example 2.23

Convert 5000 mm to kilometers.

Steps 1 and 2 Several unit factors may be used. The trail to the answer could be mm → cm → m → km.

$$5000 \text{ mm} \times \frac{1 \text{ cm}}{10 \text{ mm}} \times \frac{1 \text{ m}}{100 \text{ cm}} \times \frac{1 \text{ km}}{1000 \text{ m}} = 0.005 \text{ km}$$

Conversion between the English and the Metric Systems

Exactly how big is a millimeter, a centimeter, a meter, or a kilometer compared with similar English-system length units? Another conversion equation helps to answer this question:

$$2.54 \text{ cm} = 1 \text{ in.}$$

Expressed as a unit factor, the equation is

$$\frac{2.54 \text{ cm}}{1 \text{ in.}} = 1 = \frac{1 \text{ in.}}{2.54 \text{ cm}}$$

The relation 2.54 cm = 1 in. indicates that a centimeter is smaller than an inch. The information contained in the unit factor is shown in Figure 2.7 and

Figure 2.7

2.54 cm = 1 in.

$$2.54 \frac{\text{cm}}{\text{in.}} = 1 = \frac{1 \text{ in.}}{2.54 \text{ cm}}$$

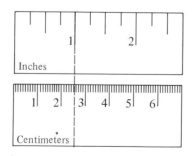

Inches

Centimeters

Figure 2.8 Conversion factors can be thought of as bridges between two systems of measurement. Here the centimeter–inch conversion factor is illustrated, but the conversion bridge idea is applicable to any conversion.

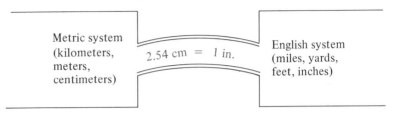

Metric system (kilometers, meters, centimeters)   2.54 cm = 1 in.   English system (miles, yards, feet, inches)

can be thought of as a bridge between the metric system and the English system (Figure 2.8). The English system is one path, the metric system is another path, and the equation 2.54 cm = 1 in. is the bridge between. The bridge 2.54 cm = 1 in. was selected because many of the measurements a chemist makes are expressed in centimeters. Therefore it is convenient to convert between systems at this point. If this were a course in physics, some other unit factor might have been chosen as a conversion point between the two systems.

Conversion between systems consists of moving along a path to the bridge, crossing, and moving along the new path to the desired unit.

Example 2.24

A man is 1750 mm tall. How tall is he in feet?

Step 1 Choose and use unit factors to reach the unit factor that bridges the systems. The bridge is at centimeters, so first convert millimeters to centimeters by a unit factor.

$$1750 \text{ mm} \times \frac{1 \text{ cm}}{10 \text{ mm}} = 175 \text{ cm}$$

Step 2 Use the bridge unit factor.

$$175 \text{ cm} \times \frac{1 \text{ in.}}{2.54 \text{ cm}} = \frac{175}{2.54} \text{ in.} = 68.9 \text{ in.}$$

Step 3 Choose and use unit factors to reach the desired measurement, converting inches to feet.

$$68.9 \text{ in.} \times \frac{1 \text{ ft}}{12 \text{ in.}} = \frac{68.9}{12} \text{ ft} = 5.74 \text{ ft}$$

The man is about average in height. The units were set up so that they conveniently canceled in sequence and only the unit required in the answer remained. The whole problem could have been done in one continuous series of steps.

$$1750 \text{ mm} \times \frac{1 \text{ cm}}{10 \text{ mm}} \times \frac{1 \text{ in.}}{2.54 \text{ cm}} \times \frac{1 \text{ ft}}{12 \text{ in.}} = 5.74 \text{ ft}$$

The same logic can be used to convert from feet to millimeters or meters to miles or miles to kilometers. Use the same procedure—head for the bridge on one path, cross to the other path, and convert to the unit needed in the answer.

Table 2.6 shows several other metric–English length conversions, to indicate the relative sizes of metric and English units.

Table 2.6

Conversion of Metric Length to English Length
1.61 km = 1 mile
1 m = 39.4 in.
25.4 mm = 1 in.

Volume Measurement in the Metric System

In the metric system, the basic unit of volume is the liter. (A quart is slightly smaller than a liter; 1 L = 1.06 qt.) Following the procedure used with length in the metric system, one can measure volume in milliliters, deciliters, liters, dekaliters, hectoliters, and kiloliters. Chemists commonly use two of the possibilities, milliliters and liters. There are 1000 milliliters in a liter; or as unit factors,

$$\frac{1000 \text{ mL}}{1 \text{ L}} = 1 = \frac{1 \text{ L}}{1000 \text{ mL}}$$

or

$$\frac{10^3 \text{ mL}}{1 \text{ L}} = 1 = \frac{1 \text{ L}}{10^3 \text{ mL}}$$

Following are some examples of conversion within the metric system of volume.

Example 2.25

How many milliliters of milk can a 2.27 L milk bottle hold?

Step 1   To convert 2.27 L to milliliters, one must use the appropriate unit factor: 1000 mL/1 L.

Step 2   Using this factor, we get

$$2.27 \cancel{\text{ L}} \times \frac{1000 \text{ mL}}{1 \cancel{\text{ L}}} = 2270 \text{ mL}$$

Example 2.26

A typical injection of medicine might contain 0.5 mL of liquid. How many liters is this?

Step 1   Use the appropriate unit factor, 1 L/1000 mL.

Step 2 $$0.5 \text{ mL} \times \frac{1 \text{ L}}{1000 \text{ mL}} = 0.0005 \text{ L} = 5 \times 10^{-4} \text{ L}$$

A bridge between the systems is the equation 1 L = 1.06 qt, or in unit factor notation,

$$\frac{1.06 \text{ qt}}{1 \text{ L}} = 1 = \frac{1 \text{ L}}{1.06 \text{ qt}}$$

Example 2.27 illustrates volume conversion between the English and metric systems.

Example 2.27   An American tourist in Europe fills his automobile tank with 30.0 L of petrol. He would like to know how many gallons this corresponds to since he understands gallons better.

Step 1   To convert 30.0 L to gallons, one uses the bridge factor immediately, so step 1 is skipped.

Step 2   The appropriate unit factor is used to cross the bridge.

Step 3   Other unit factors are used to convert within the new system. The steps are shown as one calculation.

$$30.0 \text{ L} \times \frac{1.06 \text{ qt}}{1 \text{ L}} \times \frac{1 \text{ gal}}{4 \text{ qt}} = 7.95 \text{ gal}$$

The answer is 7.95 gal. Either the tank wasn't low or the man had a Volkswagen!

The process is as simple for volume as it was for length. The units may not be as familiar but the way of solving the problem is the same.

It is interesting that there are other volume measurement units. In the English system, there are cubic inches, cubic feet, and cubic yards. In the metric system, units such as cubic centimeters (cm^3) and cubic meters are common. Cubic centimeters are widely used in health-related fields. The volume of a hypodermic syringe, for example, is almost always measured in cubic centimeters. This unit (formerly abbreviated cc) is defined as the volume occupied by a cube that is 1 cm on each edge. The volume of such a cube is calculated by multiplying length times width times height:

$$1 \text{ cm} \times 1 \text{ cm} \times 1 \text{ cm} = 1 \text{ cm}^3$$

The cubic centimeter is equivalent to another unit of volume already discussed, the milliliter. The volume 1 cubic centimeter equals the volume

1 milliliter, or 1 cm³ = 1 mL. In unit factor notation, this is

$$\frac{1 \text{ cm}^3}{1 \text{ mL}} = 1 = \frac{1 \text{ mL}}{1 \text{ cm}^3}$$

Glassware most often used for volume measurements is shown in Figure 2.9.

Figure 2.9 Common volume measurement equipment.

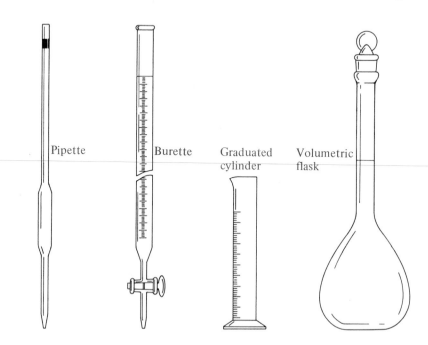

Pipette   Burette   Graduated cylinder   Volumetric flask

Relation of Weight to Mass and Mass Measurement in the Metric System

Weight in metric units is still another important group of measurements. **Weight** is a specialized term that is part of the more general idea of mass. The nonscientist ordinarily measures weights of objects, since a weight measurement is enough for communicating information needed in everyday exchanges. Scientists, on the other hand, use mass, because it is a universal measure and can be used in all situations. The definitions of mass and weight are:

> **Mass:** The quantity of matter in an object, measured relative to its inertia.* Inertia is the resistance of an object to being set in motion by a force acting on it.

---

* The word *object* is used as a totally general term. It could refer to a solid block, a pile of powder, a puddle of liquid, a cloud of gas, or any other form of matter.

Weight: A unit of force obtained by multiplying the mass of a body by the acceleration due to gravity.

If you look at these definitions closely, you will find that weight is proportional to mass and that mass is a measure of the amount of matter in an object. You will also notice that the acceleration due to gravity is included in the definition of weight. The acceleration due to the pull of gravity on an object varies, depending on whether the object is on the earth, on the moon, on Jupiter, or in deep space. Weight measures the pull of gravity on an object. An equation relates mass and weight:

$$\text{Weight} = \text{mass} \times \text{acceleration of gravity}$$

If the acceleration due to gravity does not change, weight and mass are related by a constant, and they simply express the same measurement in two different ways. On the earth, weight and mass are interchangeable concepts, related by a unit factor.

The question can be asked, Why bother distinguishing weight from mass? The answer involves the fundamental difference between these two concepts. The mass of an object remains constant throughout the universe. Weight, on the other hand, changes as the acceleration due to gravity changes. The moon is smaller than the earth; it attracts objects less strongly because the acceleration due to gravity is smaller on the moon than on the earth. A smaller gravity means that objects weigh less. A 64-lb rock on earth weighs only 3.2 lb on the moon. The mass is the same because the amount of matter in the object does not change. The weight changes from the earth to the moon because the acceleration due to gravity changes. On earth, mass and weight are related by the acceleration due to gravity, which is a constant. Therefore, the measurement units can be used interchangeably.

Balances like the instruments in Figure 2.10 are used to measure mass or weight. Scientists, since they must be precise, prefer to differentiate the two properties, and they most often use the mass units of the metric system. In the metric system, mass is commonly measured in the units milligrams, grams, and kilograms. The conversions within the metric system are

$$10^3 \text{ mg} = 1000 \text{ mg} = 1 \text{ g}$$
$$10^3 \text{ g} = 1000 \text{ g} = 1 \text{ kg}$$

or in unit factor notation,

$$\frac{1000 \text{ mg}}{1 \text{ g}} = 1 = \frac{1 \text{ g}}{1000 \text{ mg}} \quad \text{or} \quad \frac{10^3 \text{ mg}}{1 \text{ g}} = 1 = \frac{1 \text{ g}}{10^3 \text{ mg}}$$

$$\frac{1000 \text{ g}}{1 \text{ kg}} = 1 = \frac{1 \text{ kg}}{1000 \text{ g}} \quad \text{or} \quad \frac{10^3 \text{ g}}{1 \text{ kg}} = 1 = \frac{1 \text{ kg}}{10^3 \text{ g}}$$

Figure 2.10 3 types of balances: (a) analytical balance, (b) single pan top loading balance, (both courtesy of Mettler Instrument Corp., Hightstown, NJ); (c) triple beam balance (courtesy of Ohaus Scale Corp.).

(a)

(b)

(c)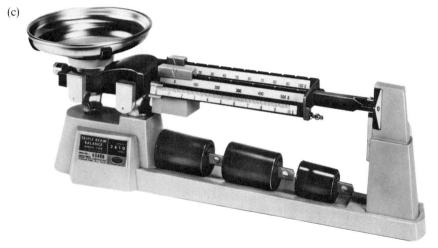

Most commonly, English weight units are used to express values that are equivalent to metric mass units. Therefore the equation 454 g = 1 lb states that an object having a mass of 454 g is attracted toward the earth to the extent that it weighs 1 lb.

The bridge unit factor is

$$\frac{1 \text{ lb}}{454 \text{ g}} = 1 = \frac{454 \text{ g}}{1 \text{ lb}}$$

Weight and mass are equivalent on earth, so the unit factor can be used and is mathematically correct, although not philosophically correct.

Table 2.7

Conversion of Metric Mass to English Weight
1 kg = 2.20 lb
28.4 g = 1 oz
908 kg = 1 ton
454 g = 1 lb

Additional English-metric relations are shown in Table 2.7. These relations are the bridges between the two systems. The following examples show conversions within and between the systems.

Example 2.28

A European magnetic cartridge for a stereo is said to track best at 1.50 g. If the only measuring device available is calibrated in ounces, how can the tracking weight be set?

The question requires conversion of grams to ounces so that the measurement can be made. The bridge unit factor is needed for crossing over. The bridge is at grams, so step 1 can be skipped. Step 2 chooses the bridge factor and step 3 converts from pounds to ounces. The conversion can be done on one line.

$$1.50 \text{ g} \times \frac{1 \text{ lb}}{454 \text{ g}} \times \frac{16 \text{ oz}}{1 \text{ lb}} = \frac{24.0 \text{ oz}}{454} = 0.0529 \text{ oz}$$

The units are canceled for ease in solving the problem.

Individual steps will not be shown in the following examples. Example 2.31 shows very small weight measurements.

Example 2.29

What is the mass in grams of a 115-lb woman?

The problem requires conversion of 115 lb to grams. Using the bridge gives

$$115 \text{ lb} \times \frac{454 \text{ g}}{1 \text{ lb}} = 52,200 \text{ g}$$

The number 52,200 is very large, much larger than 115. In this case, the kilogram is a more convenient unit to use than the gram. Converting to kilograms gives

$$52,200 \text{ g} \times \frac{1 \text{ kg}}{1000 \text{ g}} = 52.2 \text{ kg}$$

This is an easier number to remember. This woman has a mass of about 50 kg.

Example 2.30	Calculate the mass in grams of a 0.13-oz pencil.

Using the bridge and the proper unit factors, we get

$$0.13 \ \cancel{oz} \times \frac{1 \ \cancel{lb}}{16 \ \cancel{oz}} \times \frac{454 \ g}{1 \ \cancel{lb}} = 3.7 \ g$$

The mass of the pencil is 3.7 g.

Example 2.31	How many ounces does a 1.0×10^{-6} g germ weigh?

Using the appropriate unit factors yields

$$1.0 \times 10^{-6} \ \cancel{g} \times \frac{1 \ \cancel{lb}}{454 \ \cancel{g}} \times \frac{16 \ oz}{1 \ \cancel{lb}} = 3.5 \times 10^{-8} \ oz$$

2.4   Density: A Combination Measurement

Several common measurements need units that are called combination units. Combination units consist of two or more simple units that are either multiplied or divided. We are familiar with some from previous examples. Velocity measurements require a combination unit, like m/sec or mi/h. The combination unit for velocity consists of the quotient of two simple units, distance and time.

In the physical comparison of objects of similar size but of different materials, density is often measured. Density is a fundamental physical property of all matter. It relates the mass of an object to its volume. In comparing, for instance, a marble made of glass with a marble of the same size made of steel (a "steelie"), the obvious difference is the weight or mass of the steelie. It weighs more than the glass marble. To be more precise, the steelie is said to be more dense than the glass marble; in other words, steel is more dense than glass. Being more dense means that a specific volume of the more dense material has greater mass than the same volume of the less dense material. In other words, when two materials are of similar weight, the less dense material occupies more volume. This can be seen in comparing the volumes of 1 ton of lead and 1 ton of feathers (Figure 2.11).

Density is formally defined as mass per unit volume (density = mass/volume). For example, 1 mL of water has a mass of about 1 g. Therefore, 1 g water occupies a volume of 1 mL and the density of water is 1 g/mL. Densities of objects or substances are usually measured by one of two different methods. Both methods consist in weighing a sample of the substance and then finding the volume of that sample. Consider how we find the density of a regularly shaped object.

Figure 2.11 Density differences are often significant.

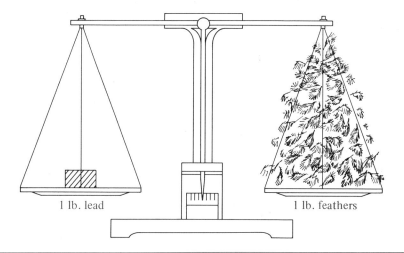

1 lb. lead   1 lb. feathers

Example 2.32

People often say "as heavy as lead," where they mean "as dense as lead." The density of lead can be found by measuring its mass and volume. A cube of lead that is 2.0 cm on each side is found to have mass 90.4 g. Calculate the density of this cube.

To ascertain density, one must divide mass by volume. The measurements for the calculation have already been made.

Step 1   Determine mass. The mass of the cube has been determined by weighing.

Step 2   Determine volume. The volume of the cube can be calculated from the measurement of one side. The volume is length times width times height. Since all these dimensions are the same in a cube,

$$2.0 \text{ cm} \times 2.0 \text{ cm} \times 2.0 \text{ cm} = 8.0 \text{ cm}^3$$

Thus, 8.0 cm³ of lead has a mass of 90.4 g.

Step 3   Calculate density by dividing mass by volume. For the density of the lead cube:

$$\text{Density} = \frac{\text{mass}}{\text{volume}} = \frac{90.4 \text{ g}}{8.0 \text{ cm}^3} = 11 \frac{\text{g}}{\text{cm}^3}$$

This density can also be expressed as 11 g/mL, since cubic centimeters and milliliters are equivalent. Note that grams per milliliter, too, can be used as a unit factor. Recalling the first sentence in the example and comparing the densities of lead and water, we find we have determined that lead is 11 times as dense as water. (The density of water is 1 g/mL.) Therefore, "as heavy as lead" has meaning only if you are comparing equal volumes of lead and another substance, like water.

There is another method for measuring density, which can be used for an irregular object.

Example 2.33

There was once a goldsmith who was charged with making a crown for his king. The crown was prepared from supposedly pure gold and presented to the king. The king, who was very skeptical, suspected that the goldsmith had cheated him, not using pure gold to make the crown but keeping out some of the gold and mixing in copper to make up the difference. Archimedes, the king's chief chemist, was called in to find out whether or not the crown was pure gold.

To judge the matter, Archimedes compared the density of the crown with the density of pure gold. He realized that if the crown were pure gold, the densities would be the same. Archimedes could have outlined steps for determining the density of the crown as follows.

Step 1 Since density = mass/volume, the mass must be determined by weighing the crown.

Step 2 The volume is more difficult to find, since the crown's dimensions are too complicated to measure by a meter stick. The best way to measure the volume is to find out how much water the crown will move out of the way or displace. Water is placed in a cylinder that is marked off in milliliters (Figure 2.12). The total number of milliliters of water is recorded, and the crown is put in the water. The height of the water after the crown is submerged is determined, and the final number of milliliters read. By subtracting the initial reading from the final reading, the volume of water displaced and consequently the volume of the crown can be found.

Step 3 The density of the crown is then determined by dividing its mass by its volume.

Figure 2.12 Volume measurement by water displacement.

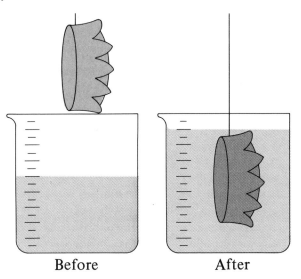

Before   After

By the way, the results from the experiment showed the density of the crown to be different from the density of pure gold; the king therefore ordered that the goldsmith receive a punishment befitting the crime of defrauding the king. The moral of the story is that if the goldsmith had realized that his deceit could be detected, he would have had practical confirmation that honesty is the best policy.

The method described for finding the volume of an irregular object by submerging it in liquid leads to another way of expressing mass-volume relation. This relation is called **specific gravity**. The difference between specific gravity and density is that the mass, instead of being divided by the volume of the substance in question, is divided by the mass of an equal volume of water. Since 1 cm^3 of water has approximately a 1-g mass, this volume of water has relevance in calculations with units of mass; therefore density and specific gravity are often interchangeable. The one big difference is that specific gravity has no units; the units cancel. For instance, the density of copper is about 9 g/cm^3. One cubic centimeter of copper displaces 1 cm^3, or 1 mL, of water. One milliliter of water has a mass of 1 g. Now substitute the mass of the water displaced (1 g) for the volume of the copper.

$$\text{Specific gravity copper} = \frac{9 \text{ g}}{1 \text{ g}} = 9$$

There are no units.

> **Specific gravity** is defined as the mass of an object divided by the mass of the volume of water displaced by the total volume of that object. In most situations, specific gravity is approximately equal to density.

Density can be expressed in many different units, including grams per cubic centimeter, kilograms per liter, pounds per gallon, or any combination of weight and volume units. It's just as simple to convert among these units as it is to convert among the units we are already familiar with.

Example 2.34

Calculate the density of water in pounds per gallon, knowing that its density is 1.00 g/mL.

The problem can be separated into two parts; grams must be converted to pounds and milliliters must be converted to gallons. It can be done step by step, canceling units along the way.

Step 1   Convert grams to pounds:

$$1.00 \frac{g}{\text{mL}} \times \frac{1 \text{ lb}}{454 \, g} = \frac{1 \text{ lb}}{454 \text{ mL}}$$

DENSITY: A COMBINATION MEASUREMENT   Sec. 2.4   **45**

Step 2   Convert milliliters to gallons; head for the bridge and cross, being sure that the units cancel.

$$\frac{1 \text{ lb}}{454 \text{ mL}} \times \frac{1000 \text{ mL}}{1 \text{ L}} \times \frac{1 \text{ L}}{1.06 \text{ qt}} \times \frac{4 \text{ qt}}{1 \text{ gal}} = 8.31 \frac{\text{lb}}{\text{gal}}$$

Canceling units is very helpful in solving problems correctly, so their use should be routine. Unit factors were used throughout in Example 2.34, also a useful routine.

Example 2.35   Fifteen grams of a certain liquid is needed to make a cleaning solution. A container marked off in milliliters is available, but a balance is not. The density of the liquid is known to be 2.5 g/mL. Explain how 15 g of the liquid can be measured.

The solution to the problem consists in determining how many milliliters correspond to 15 g. Common sense indicates that if each milliliter weighs 2.5 g, then 6 mL will weigh 15 g. But common sense is not enough to solve complicated problems. Using a unit factor to solve the problem, we find the number of milliliters:

$$15 \text{ g} \times \frac{1 \text{ mL}}{2.5 \text{ g}} = 6.0 \text{ mL}$$

Thus, 6.0 mL is equivalent to 15 g. The problem has been solved and the units are correct.

Many density-related problems can be solved in this way.

Example 2.36   Suppose a tenant wanted to put a water bed in his apartment. The manager says that the maximum load that the floor can handle in that area is 575 lb; collapse will occur with a greater weight. The water bed holds 115 gal water. Will the floor collapse?

The weight of the water bed must be calculated. Since the density of water is 8.31 lb/gal, the water bed weighs

$$115 \text{ gal} \times 8.31 \frac{\text{lb}}{\text{gal}} = 956 \text{ lb}$$

The water bed idea will have to be given up.

Example 2.37   A gun enthusiast is making bullets from tire-balancing weights. He knows that each bullet requires 2.00 cm³ of lead. If a filling station gives him 1.00 kg of lead, how many bullets can he cast?

Since the slugmaker knows the volume of each bullet, the first calculation must be determining the total volume of lead contained in 1.00 kg lead. This is done by using the density of lead, 11.3 g/cm³.

$$1.00 \text{ kg} \times \frac{1000 \text{ g}}{1 \text{ kg}} = 1000 \text{ g}$$

$$1000 \text{ g} \times \frac{1 \text{ cm}^3}{11.3 \text{ g}} = 88.5 \text{ cm}^3 \text{ of lead}$$

The slugmaker now calculates how many slugs can be made from this volume. If 2.00 cm³ are used for each bullet, then

$$88.5 \text{ cm}^3 \times \frac{1 \text{ bullet}}{2.00 \text{ cm}^3} = 44.3 \text{ bullets}$$

or 44 bullets from the lead. Note that 2.00 cm³/bullet is a unit factor.

Comparing densities of common substances allows us to understand the concept better. Table 2.8 lists several common substances and their densities.

Table 2.8   Densities of Common Substances

Substance	Density[a] (g/mL)
Water[b]	1.0
Ice[b]	0.917
Cork	0.2
Oak charcoal	0.57
Cardboard	0.69
Kerosene	0.82
Milk	1.02
Sugar	1.59
Diamond	3.3
Iron	7.86
Lead	11.3
Gold	19.3

[a] Defined at 25 °C, sea level.
[b] Notice that ice is less dense than water. This is why it floats.

DENSITY: A COMBINATION MEASUREMENT   Sec. 2.4   **47**

2.5 Temperature, Measured by Three Unit Systems

Temperature is a measure of the hotness or coldness of an object. Questions scientists ask that call for temperature in the answer are ones like: At what temperature does water boil? How hot is flowing lava? How cold is the surface of the moon? In these measurements, the units used are also important. In describing temperatures, several different measurement units are used.

The temperature units commonly used in the United States are Fahrenheit degrees. The Fahrenheit temperature scale is associated with the English system. You will recognize some Fahrenheit temperatures: body temperature, 98.6 °F; the freezing point of pure water, 32 °F; the boiling point of pure water at sea level, 212 °F. If you look closely at the last two measurements—pure water freezes at 32 °F and boils at sea level at 212 °F—you will notice that on the Fahrenheit scale, there are 180° between the boiling point and the freezing point of water.

Another temperature scale, which is used throughout Europe and much of the rest of the world, is the Celsius scale. On this scale, there are only 100° (called degrees Celsius) between the freezing point and the boiling point of water. Water freezes at 0 °C and at sea level boils at 100 °C. "Water freezes at 32 °F" and "Water freezes at 0 °C" are equivalent statements.

To develop a conversion between the two temperature scales, it is significant that there is exactly the same distance between the freezing point and the boiling point on each scale. However, there are 100 divisions between boiling and freezing on the Celsius scale and 180 divisions between the same two temperatures on the Fahrenheit scale (Figure 2.13). This means that Fahrenheit degrees are smaller than Celsius degrees. Since 180 Fahrenheit degrees span the same space as 100 of the Celsius degrees, each Fahrenheit degree is $\frac{100}{180} = \frac{5}{9}$ of a Celsius degree. This is the first step toward converting between the scales. To account for the difference in the size of 1° on the two scales, the number of Fahrenheit degrees must be multiplied by $\frac{5}{9}$ to get the number of Celsius degrees. By the same token, to convert from Celsius degrees to Fahrenheit degrees, the number of Celsius degrees must be multiplied by $\frac{9}{5}$.

We now have the unit factor,

$$\frac{9\,°F}{5\,°C} = 1 = \frac{5\,°C}{9\,°F}$$

There is another problem in converting between the two scales. The Fahrenheit scale is set off from the Celsius scale at the freezing point of water by 32°. At high temperatures, the scales differ by more than 32° and at lower temperatures, the scales seem to differ by fewer degrees. In fact, $-40°$ on the Fahrenheit thermometer is exactly equivalent to $-40°$ on the Celsius ther-

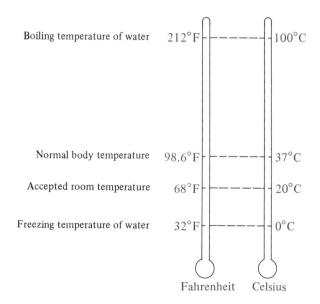

Figure 2.13 Fahrenheit and Celsius scales compared. The numbers are different but they measure the same temperature.

Boiling temperature of water   212°F — — — — 100°C

Normal body temperature   98.6°F — — — — 37°C

Accepted room temperature   68°F — — — — 20°C

Freezing temperature of water   32°F — — — — 0°C

Fahrenheit   Celsius

mometer. In other words, the two scales cross at this point. This crossing point can be used as another clue in developing an equation relating the two scales.

The conversion of 212 °F to 100 °C will be used to illustrate the equation developed from the above facts. The answer is known, so the method can be checked. Start with the original temperature, 212 °F. Now add 40 to this number (the scales cross at $-40°$).

$$212° + 40 = 252$$

There are fewer divisions on the Celsius scale by a factor of $\frac{5}{9}$ than on the Fahrenheit scale, so multiply by $\frac{5}{9}$.

$$\tfrac{5}{9}(252) = 140$$

Subtracting the original 40 added produces

$$140 - 40 = 100$$

In general the equation to convert from degrees Fahrenheit to degrees Celsius is

$$t_C = \tfrac{5}{9}(t_F + 40) - 40$$

where t_F = temperature in degrees Fahrenheit and t_C = temperature in degrees Celsius. This equation can be used to convert any Fahrenheit temperature to Celsius temperature.

The same logic can be used to develop an equation to convert Celsius temperature to Fahrenheit temperature. That equation is

$$t_F = \tfrac{9}{5}(t_C + 40) - 40$$

Here also t_F represents the Fahrenheit temperature and t_C represents the Celsius temperature.

The only difference between the two equations is the use of the factors $\tfrac{5}{9}$ and $\tfrac{9}{5}$. In converting to Fahrenheit, the number of divisions is **increased**, so $\tfrac{9}{5}$ is used. In converting to Celsius, the number of divisions is **decreased**, so $\tfrac{5}{9}$ is used. Adding the 40 before multiplying by either $\tfrac{9}{5}$ or $\tfrac{5}{9}$ puts both scales on the same basis.

In the several examples, there are no steps, since solving these problems consists in substituting values in an equation.

Example 2.38

Comfortable room temperature is 68 °F. What must the equivalent European thermostat setting be to ensure similar comfort?

It is necessary to convert 68 °F to the Celsius scale. Using the equation,

$$t_C = \tfrac{5}{9}(t_F + 40) - 40$$

and substituting the given values, we get

$$t_C = \tfrac{5}{9}(68 + 40) - 40$$
$$= \tfrac{5}{9}(108) - 40$$
$$= 60 - 40$$
$$= 20\ ^\circ C$$

The thermostat should be set at 20 °C.

Consider the opposite problem.

Example 2.39

The label on a German-made guitar amplifier claims that it cannot be operated above 45 °C. Is it necessary to rent another amplifier for use at a summer afternoon concert where the temperature will probably be 100 °F?

The problem is solved by converting 45 °C to degrees Fahrenheit and comparing that answer with 100 °F. We use the equation and substitute the given value:

$$t_F = \tfrac{9}{5}(t_C + 40) - 40$$
$$= \tfrac{9}{5}(45 + 40) - 40$$
$$= \tfrac{9}{5}(85) - 40$$
$$= 153 - 40$$
$$= 113 \,°F \approx 110 \,°F$$

If the temperature does not go above 110 °F the amplifier will be all right. It is easy to convert from °F to °C so long as the equations are known and the relation between the two temperature scales is understood.

Example 2.40

Many weather forecasters are now giving temperatures on the Celsius scale. If the temperature reading were reported as −5 °C, what would the equivalent Fahrenheit temperature be?

$$t_F = \tfrac{9}{5}(t_C + 40) - 40$$
$$= \tfrac{9}{5}(-5.0 + 40) - 40$$
$$= \tfrac{9}{5}(35) - 40$$
$$= 63 - 40$$
$$= 23 \,°F$$

The air is moderately cold but not unbearably so.

Another temperature scale often used by scientists is the Kelvin, or gas, scale. This scale has been selected for the International System of Units. It is related to the Fahrenheit and Celsius scales, as Figure 2.14 shows. On the Kelvin scale, the distance between the boiling point of water and the freezing point is 100°. Therefore, a Kelvin degree is exactly the same size as a Celsius degree. Since 273.15 on the Kelvin scale corresponds to 0 on the Celsius scale, the conversion between Kelvin and Celsius must be

$$t_K = t_C + 273.15$$

where t_K = temperature measured in degrees Kelvin and t_C = temperature in degrees Celsius.

In everyday use, the decimal fraction 0.15 is often ignored because it is small compared with the total temperature. In all but the most exacting work, the equation is used in the form $t_K = t_C + 273$. Kelvin temperatures are written K (not °K) according to the SI system. The zero on the Kelvin scale corresponds to the lowest temperature attainable.

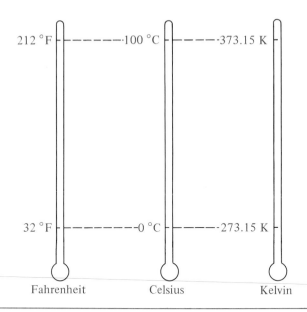

Figure 2.14 Fahrenheit, Celsius and Kelvin temperature scales compared.

212 °F ––––––– 100 °C ––––– 373.15 K

32 °F ––––––– 0 °C ––––– 273.15 K

Fahrenheit   Celsius   Kelvin

Example 2.41

Convert 500 K to the equivalent temperature on the Fahrenheit scale.

First convert to Celsius.

$$t_K = t_C + 273$$
$$500 = t_C + 273$$
$$t_C = 500 - 273 = 227 \,°C$$

Now convert from Celsius to Fahrenheit.

$$t_F = \tfrac{9}{5}(227 + 40) - 40$$
$$= \tfrac{9}{5}(267) - 40$$
$$= 481 - 40$$
$$= 441 \,°F$$

The temperature 500 K corresponds to 441° on the Fahrenheit scale.

Example 2.42

Theoretically, the lowest possible temperature is 0 K. Calculate the equivalent temperatures on the Celsius and Fahrenheit scales.

Use the K → °C formula.

$$t_C = t_K - 273$$
$$= -273 \,°C$$

Now the °C → °F formula—

$$t_F = \tfrac{9}{5}(t_C + 40) - 40$$
$$= \tfrac{9}{5}(-273 + 40) - 40$$
$$= \tfrac{9}{5}(-233) - 40$$
$$= -419 - 40$$
$$= -459 \, °F$$

Both answers are referred to by most people as "below zero" temperatures.

2.6   Heat

A concept related to temperature is heat. Heat is a form of energy that cannot be viewed with the unaided eye, but its effects can be measured. When heat flows into an object, the object becomes warmer; an increase in the temperature of the object is seen. When heat flows from an object, it becomes cooler; a decrease in its temperature can be measured. These effects are seen every day. A pot of water being heated on a stove exemplifies heat flowing to an object. The effect on the water is an increase in temperature. Energy has been transferred from the stove burner through the metal of the pot to the water. The burner becomes hot thus causing the pot to get hot, and ultimately the water. Common sense indicates that this will happen. The energy that was transferred is called "heat," and it is only one of many different types of energy. The opposite effect occurs when ice is dropped into water at room temperature. Heat flows from the water to the ice and eventually the ice melts.

Heat is measured by the effect that it has on substances, particularly water. The calorie is one of the basic units of heat energy. It is defined as the amount of heat required to raise the temperature of 1 g of water 1 °C.* Calories are units of the metric system and metric system prefixes can be used. For instance, 1000 calories = 1 kilocalorie.

The **kilocalorie** is known as the Calorie (with capital C), or food calorie, to the many who are concerned with weight loss or gain as related to diet. Various foodstuffs can be classified in terms of the energy they produce. A carrot, for example, may contain 10 Calories. This means that the carrot,

---

* Calorie is specifically defined for the one Celsius degree between 14.5 and 15.5 °C. This specification must be made, since for different starting temperatures, differing quantities of heat must be added to raise the temperature of 1 g of water 1 °C.

when eaten, supplies energy to the body equivalent to the energy needed to heat 10,000 g of water 1 °C, or 100 g of water 100 °C. If the normal intake of food equals 2000 food calories a day, this is equivalent to 2 million calories, or enough energy to raise 27,000 g of water from room temperature (25 °C) to boiling (100 °C). In pounds, that weight of water is

$$27,000 \text{ g} \times \frac{1 \text{ lb}}{454 \text{ g}} = 59 \text{ lb water}$$

Two thousand Calories is often quoted as the average food intake necessary to maintain weight.

Another example of heat energy concerns the hot-water heating system of a house. The furnace heats the water, supplying it with heat energy (measured in calories). The hot water circulates throughout the house and cools off, giving off the same number of calories that were originally added. When these calories are lost by the water, they warm the air and heat the house.

Another example is the cooling of a car engine. Cool water circulates through the engine and takes heat (calories) away from the engine. The water then goes to the radiator to transfer that heat to the air.

The concept of heat exchange can be extended to other things besides water if an idea called "specific heat" is used. Specific heat relates to the ability of any substance to take up heat.

> More precisely, **specific heat** is the amount of heat energy, measured in calories, required to raise the temperature of one gram of a substance one degree Celsius. Water furnishes the standard, since its specific heat is 1 cal/g · °C, measured at 15 °C.

Specific heats of several metals are shown in Table 2.9; the designations are unitless. From the table, you can see that while 1 cal is required to raise the temperature of water 1 °C, only 0.031 cal is required to raise an equal mass of gold 1 °C and 0.215 cal is required to raise 1 g aluminum 1 °C. Of the five metals, gold translates heat into temperature change most efficiently and aluminum translates it least efficiently.

Table 2.9 Specific Heats of Common Metals

Substance	Specific Heat (Relative to Water)
Gold	0.031
Lead	0.038
Silver	0.057
Iron	0.106
Aluminum	0.215

2.7 The International System of Units (SI)

Metric units and to a lesser extent English measurement units are used worldwide; however, communication problems created by different measurement units have made it necessary to try to standardize units of measurement. Representatives from many countries have decided which units will be part of a world system. The system that they developed is called the International System of Units (abbreviated SI). The world is now converting to the SI system.

The SI units include several standard metric system measurement units, since the metric system of units is the most widely used in the world. Some of these are shown in Table 2.10.

Table 2.10 Common SI Units

Type of Unit	SI Unit	Metric Unit	Conversion
Length	meter	meter	
Volume	cubic decimeter	liter	1 cubic decimeter = 1000 liters
Mass	kilogram	gram	1 kilogram = 1000 grams
Temperature	Kelvin	Celsius	1 Kelvin degree = 1 Celsius degree
Time	second	second	
Force	newton	dyne	1 dyne = 0.00001 newton
Heat	joule	calorie	1 calorie = 4.184 joule

In spite of general agreement that a standardized system of units is convenient, the changeover to SI in the United States has been slow. This is not strange, however, since the task is so large. The changeover is being aided by pressure from scientific and economic communities in the United States. Progress is apparent in the increasing number of national park signs, highway signs, and food wrappers showing metric units that appear daily (see Figure 2.15). Weather reports include Celsius temperatures regularly. The near future

Figure 2.15 The SI system is replacing the English system. (Photographed by B. Hallett)

should see our fairly complete conversion to SI. The United States government is encouraging rapid conversion so that U.S. goods will be more competitive in world markets. Since the SI units and metric units are similar, and since use of the metric units is traditional in chemistry, metric system units will be emphasized in this textbook. Table 2.11 summarizes equivalencies between the English and metric systems.

Table 2.11

Equivalencies for Conversion Between the Metric and English Systems		
Length	1 cm = 0.3937 in.	1 in. = 2.540 cm
	1 m = 3.281 ft	1 ft = 0.3048 m
	1 km = 0.6214 mile	1 mile = 1.609 km
Volume	1 mL = 2.113×10^{-3} pt	1 pt = 473.26 mL
	1 L = 1.056 qt	1 qt = 0.947 L
Weight and mass	1 g = 0.03527 oz	1 oz = 28.35 g
	1 kg = 2.205 lb	1 lb = 0.4535 kg
		1 ton = 907.2 kg

Glossary

Calorie	A unit of heat measurement. One calorie (cal) is the quantity of heat required to raise the temperature of 1 g of water 1 °C. The food calorie (Calorie) is defined as 1 kilocalorie (kcal).
Celsius temperature scale	Temperature scale by which water freezes at 0° and boils at 100° at sea level.
Density	Mass per unit volume.
English system of measurement	System of measurement based on units such as pound, foot, second, and Fahrenheit degree.
Exponential notation	A method of expressing a number as a series of digits multiplied by 10 raised to an appropriate power.
Fahrenheit temperature scale	Temperature scale by which water freezes at 32° and boils at 212° at sea level.
Gram	A metric system unit of mass. The amount 454 g is equivalent to 1 lb.
Heat	A form of energy. Heat will pass from a hot substance to a cooler substance and will cause a rise in temperature of the cooler substance and a lowering in temperature of the hotter substance.

International System of Measurement (SI)	System of measurement based on units such as meter, kilogram, second, and Kelvin degree.
Kelvin temperature scale	Temperature scale by which water freezes at 273° and boils at 373° at sea level.
Kilogram	The fundamental unit of mass in the International System of Measurement.
Liter	A metric system unit of volume. One liter is equivalent to 1.06 liquid quarts.
Mass	The quantity of matter in a body measured relative to its inertia. Mass is determined for a given body by dividing the weight of the body by the acceleration due to gravity.
Matter	Anything that occupies space and has mass.
Meter	A metric system unit of length. One meter is equivalent to 39.37 in.
Significant figures	The number of digits obtained with certainty in a given measurement plus the first uncertain digit.
Specific gravity	The mass of an object divided by the mass of the volume of water displaced by the total volume of that object.
Specific heat	The quantity of heat (usually measured in calories) required to raise the temperature of 1 g of a substance 1 °C relative to water.
Temperature	The heat content of an object measured on a temperature scale.
Thermometer	An instrument used to indicate temperature.
Weight	The result of the force of gravity acting on a body; weight equals the mass of the body multiplied by the acceleration due to gravity.

Problems

1. Write the following numbers in exponential notation.
   (a) 753,000,000 (b) 275
   (c) 0.000 76 (d) 0.01
   (e) 7 (f) 0.000 000 008 379 5
   (g) 876,395,421 (h) 186,000
   (i) 0.0793 (j) 123,000

2. Write the following numbers as ordinary numbers.
   (a) 10^{-6} (b) 1.35×10^4
   (c) 8.732×10^8 (d) 9.000×10^5
   (e) 5×10^0 (f) 6×10^{25}
   (g) $5.839\ 125 \times 10^{-8}$ (h) 58×10^2
   (i) 5×10 (j) 6.835×10^{-13}

3. How many significant figures are in the following numbers?
   (a) 5700 (b) 63.0
   (c) 0.0051 (d) 9.70×10^4
   (e) 750.0 (f) 6.02×10^{23}
   (g) 5.0060 (h) 0.0100

4. Solve the following problems and write the answers showing the correct number of significant figures. Remember to keep track of significant figures and to round off when necessary.
   (a) $5.76 + 8.43 + 7.465$ (b) 9.00×16
   (c) $83.50 - 43.500$
   (d) $8.76 \times 10^4 \div 5.0 \times 10^4$

5. Write unit factors for the following conversion equalities. For example, the unit factor for the equality 1 ft = 12 in. is

$$\frac{1 \text{ ft}}{12 \text{ in.}} = 1 = \frac{12 \text{ in.}}{1 \text{ ft}}$$

(a) 1 yd = 36 in.
(b) 1 lb = 16 oz
(c) 2 pt = 1 qt
(d) 3 teaspoons (t) = 1 tablespoon (T)
(e) 4 qt = 1 gal
(f) 1 fathom = 6 ft

6. List the common prefixes used by the metric system and the value that the basic unit is multiplied by to obtain the given unit. Example:

Prefix   What you multiply the basic unit by
centi-   0.01

7. Write unit factors for the following conversion equalities.
(a) 1 cm = 10 mm   (b) 1 km = 1000 m
(c) 1 L = 1000 mL   (d) 1 dL = 10 cL
(e) 1 g = 1000 mg   (f) 1 kg = 1000 g

8. Convert the following:
(a) 1 mm = ? cm   (b) 1 dm = ? km
(c) 1 m = ? mm   (d) 1 km = ? cm
(e) 1 cm = ? m   (f) 1 m = ? dkm

9. Convert the following:
(a) 1 cL = ? dL   (b) 1 mL = ? L
(c) 1 L = ? dkL   (d) 1 dkL = ? mL
(e) 1 kL = ? mL   (f) 1 L = ? mL

10. Convert the following:
(a) 1 mg = ? g   (b) 1 hg = ? g
(c) 1 kg = ? g   (d) 1 kg = ? mg
(e) 1 dkg = ? cg   (f) 1 g = ? mg

11. Convert the following:
(a) 500. in. to miles
(b) 2000. oz to tons
(c) 3.00 L to cubic centimeters
(d) 500. gal to quarts

12. Convert the following:
(a) 0.500 mile to kilometers
(b) 700. kg to tons
(c) 5.00 g to ounces
(d) 5.00 g to pounds
(e) 50.0 lb to milligrams

13. Convert the following:
(a) 2.00 ft to centimeters
(b) 4.00 gal to milliliters
(c) 25.0 lb to kilograms
(d) 1.00 pt to liters
(e) 400.0 m to yards

14. At a track meet, the winning distance of the shot put was 672 inches. How many yards was the shot put?

15. A hummingbird weighs 2.00 oz. Convert this to tons.

16. Define (a) mass; (b) weight.

17. How many oranges are contained in a sack of oranges that weighs 4.00 lb if there are 2.50 oranges in each pound? (Assume that the weight of the sack is negligible.) Write the unit factor for the problem.

18. How many yards are in 1.00 mile if there are 5280 ft per mile?

19. A man weighs about 70.0 kg. How many grams does he weigh? How many pounds does he weigh?

20. An automobile can travel 60. miles in 1 h. How many kilometers can it go in 1 h?

21. Explain the difference between density and specific gravity.

22. The Olympic Games traditionally have all measurements made in the metric system. How many yards are run in the one hundred meter dash? How many miles are run in the five thousand meter run?

23. There are 90.0 ft between bases on a baseball diamond. If a game were to be played in Mexico, where the metric system is used, how many meters would a player have to run to reach first base?

24. A Volkswagen can go 25.0 mi on 1.00 gal of gasoline. How many kilometers can it go? How many kilometers could it go on 4.00 L of gasoline?

25. A city block on the average is 300. ft square. How many square inches are contained in a city block? How many square centimeters?

26. Explain how calories and specific heats are related.

27. Convert the following:

(a) $\dfrac{1.0\ \text{lb}}{2.0\ \text{gal}}$ to $\dfrac{\text{oz}}{\text{qt}}$ (b) $\dfrac{3.0\ \text{lb}}{\text{qt}}$ to $\dfrac{\text{g}}{\text{mL}}$

(c) $\dfrac{1.0\ \text{g}}{\text{mL}}$ to $\dfrac{\text{lb}}{\text{gal}}$ (d) $\dfrac{1.0\ \text{kg}}{3.0\ \text{L}}$ to $\dfrac{\text{tons}}{\text{gal}}$

28. The density of carbon tetrachloride, a dry-cleaning agent, is 1.25 g/mL. What is its density in pounds per gallon?

29. Oil has a density of 0.92 g/cm^3. What volume does 800. g of oil occupy?

30. The density of water is 1 g/cm^3, or 1 g/ml. If a jug contains 0.500 L of water, what weight in grams of water does the jug contain?

31. Lead shot for shotguns is prepared by pouring molten lead through a screen at the top of a tower and letting the droplets fall into water. The density of lead is 11.3 g/cm^3. How many grams of lead have fallen into the water tank if 100. L of water have been displaced?

32. The density of gold is 19.3 g/cm^3. How many pounds will 1 ft^3 of gold weigh?

33. Convert the following:
    (a) 89 °F to °C   (b) 315 °C to °F
    (c) -123 °C to °F   (d) 1520 °C to °F
    (e) 1400 °F to K

34. Calculate body temperature in degrees Celsius for a normal, healthy person of body temperature 98.6 °F.

35. Calculate what the temperature is in degrees Fahrenheit when the temperature is 40° below 0 °C.

36. Water in Denver, a mile above sea level, boils at 96 °C on a sunny day. At what temperature Fahrenheit does this water boil?

37. Surprisingly, the human body can withstand dry-air temperatures at 90 °C for periods of 15 min or so. Calculate this temperature in °F and K.

38. A student discovered a new material that could easily be molded into a shape for fishing lures. To be effective, however, the lure must sink in water; thus it must have a density larger than 1.00 g/cm^3. The student found that 0.250 ft^3 of the material weighed 5.00 lb. Will the new material sink or float in water?

Learning Objectives for Chapter 3

Define the following: **atom, element, molecule, compound, proton, neutron, electron, nucleus, periodic chart, atomic number, atomic weight, mass number, atomic mass unit, isotope, periodic property, level, sublevel, orbital, Hund's rule, mole, Avogadro's number.**

Describe the experiments of Thomson, Millikan, and Rutherford concerning atomic structure.

Describe the structure of the atom.

Using the periodic chart, determine the atomic number, atomic weight, number of electrons, and average number of neutrons in an atom of any element.

Explain the model for electronic structure as presented here.

Using a periodic chart, determine the electronic configuration or structure for an atom of any element.

Describe the shapes of types of orbitals.

Describe the physical properties of the elements in general.

Using a periodic chart, determine the weight of one mole of atoms of any element.

Given the weight of a sample of an element, calculate the number of moles of atoms present and the number of atoms present.

3 THE ATOM

During the past century, scientists have engaged in laborious experimentation, analyzing their results to develop ideas about the structure of matter. The development of ideas and theories has been time-consuming and difficult because the tiny particles of which matter is thought to be composed cannot be seen with the unaided eye. Thus, one must imagine how these tiny particles appear and behave and base belief in their existence on the results of experiments that indicate it but do not offer absolute proof.

To spark this imagination, it is helpful to understand how small the fundamental particles of matter are believed to be. You can begin by imagining an iron cube. Iron is the common metal used in numerous aspects of everyday life. Iron metal has a silvery appearance. It looks and feels solid and heavy. It may be used to support a building, build an automobile, or furnish material for a sculpture. In all these different shapes and functions, it is still called iron. The substance always retains a fundamental part of its character, no matter what its form. This part of the character of iron that never changes is determined by the kind of tiny fundamental particles that compose the visible piece of iron. Any visible piece of iron is made up of an incredibly large number of these particles. If the cube of iron in this discussion were 1.0 cm on each side, it would contain approximately 8.5×10^{22} particles, each of which would have the properties of iron. Each particle, if imagined to be a small sphere, would have the diameter 1.3×10^{-7} mm. How large is this number, 8.5×10^{22}? And how small is each particle in comparison with familiar objects? The extreme size of 8.5×10^{22} might be better understood from the following example. If we had 8.5×10^{22} dollar bills, where each dollar bill is about 6 in. long, all these laid end to end would form a ribbon 8,000,000,000,000,000,000 (8.0×10^{18}) miles long. This distance is about 10,000 times the distance to the nearest star outside the solar system.

The small size of the particles can be understood from another comparison. Each line on this page is 0.5–1 mm wide. The unaided human eye can distinguish detail in objects as small as 0.1 mm (one-tenth of a millimeter). Using the best optical microscope available, an observer can distinguish objects as small as 1×10^{-4} mm (one ten-thousandth of a millimeter). The iron atoms we are discussing are 1.3×10^{-7} mm in diameter (approximately one ten-millionth of a millimeter) —much smaller than can be seen using any optical microscope.

These small particles composing the sample of iron are called atoms.

Atoms are the smallest particles of a substance that can exist and still be recognized as that substance.

Atoms can be further divided, but when this is done, the remaining pieces no longer have the properties of iron.

Iron is one of the simplest substances existing in nature because it is composed of only one kind of atom. It is one of the 106 known elements.

Elements are substances composed of only one specific kind of atom.

Thus, an atom is the smallest recognizable particle, in a sample of an element, that still retains the characteristics of the entire sample.

Since there are 106 different known elements, 106 different, specific kinds of atoms exist. Some of these exist naturally and some are man-made. Familiar examples of elements include helium, the "lighter-than-air" substance used to fill balloons; aluminum, the shiny, lightweight metal used in airplane construction; gold, the precious metal; and oxygen, the atmospheric gas that we breathe to live.

A definition of atoms helps lead to a better definition of chemistry. Matter is composed of many types of atoms linked in specific ways and quantities.

The study of chemistry is the study of how and why atoms link to form particles of substances more complex than elements.

It is also the study of the properties of these new substances. Thus, belief in the existence of atoms is fundamental to the study of chemistry as it is known today.

3.1   Atoms and Molecules

When atoms of the same kind or of different kinds combine, an incredibly large number of combinations is possible. This accounts for the diversity of substances around us. An example of one simple combination is the smallest possible particle of water. It is composed of three atoms—one atom of oxygen linked to two atoms of hydrogen (Figure 3.1). Each particle that is recognizable as water is composed of the same three atoms. These particles are called molecules.

Molecules are particles that consist of more than one atom. Each molecule contains its constituent atoms in a definite, fixed, whole-number ratio.

The last statement is often called the law of definite proportions, or the law of constant composition. In accordance with this principle, a water molecule must always contain two atoms of hydrogen and one atom of oxygen. A glass

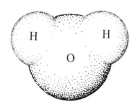

Figure 3.1 If we consider atoms to be tiny balls, the smallest particle of water might look like this. H and O are symbols standing for hydrogen and oxygen.

of water might contain 1×10^{25} water molecules, and each molecule would be exactly the same, containing one oxygen atom and two hydrogen atoms; otherwise it would not be a water molecule.

Even when a single molecule contains hundreds of atoms, the properties of that molecule depend on the presence of those atoms in a specific proportion and linked in a specific way. Any changes in composition or structure change the properties of the molecule.

Some molecules are composed of atoms that are alike. The common substances in the atmosphere, nitrogen and oxygen, exist in two-atom units.

The same atoms can link in different ways to form different compounds.

This statement is often called the law of multiple proportions. For instance, two oxygen atoms can combine to form a molecule of oxygen gas that can be breathed. The linkage of three oxygen atoms, however, yields a molecule of ozone, a poisonous gas that causes tire deterioration on earth and by its presence in the upper atmosphere protects earth dwellers against ultraviolet radiation (Figures 3.2a and 3.2b).

Molecules can be considered from another point of view. If the simplest recognizable component of a substance, its smallest particle, contains more than one atom, it is called a molecule.* Just as atoms or molecules containing only one kind of atom are the smallest recognizable particles in elements,

molecules containing more than one kind of atom are the smallest recognizable particles in substances called **compounds**.

Thus, both elements and compounds can exist as molecules.

A **molecule** is composed of two or more linked atoms, which may be alike or different.

Figure 3.2a Oxygen gas (O_2), the substance in the atmosphere which supports life, is made up of many oxygen molecules.

Each molecule of a given compound contains exactly the same number of each atom as any other molecule of that compound does. Compounds always have their component elements in a simple, definite ratio. Elements and compounds are the two basic kinds of substances of which everything in the universe is made.

_____

* This is a simplified version. The idea will be expanded later to include different kinds of combinations of atoms.

Figure 3.2b Ozone (O_3) is a dangerous pollutant in the lower atmosphere and an important shield in the upper atmosphere. Notice that it and oxygen gas are composed of oxygen atoms, linked in different ways.

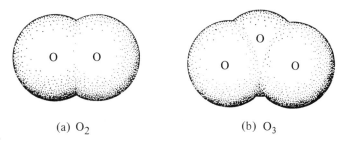

(a) O_2 (b) O_3

The idea that the universe is composed of tiny particles that can be arranged and rearranged is not new. The Greek philosophical school of the atomists proposed such a concept about 400 B.C. The word **atom** is derived from the Greek word **atomos**, meaning "uncut, indivisible." Scientists, however, do not really accept the Greek proposal as the beginning of atomic theory, since the Ancient Greeks failed to establish any set rules concerning the nature of atoms based on experiment. To the Greeks, theorizing about atoms was a philosophical exercise, separated completely from physical measurements. Not until nearly 2000 years later—in the early 1800s, when scientists like John Dalton conducted specific experiments on the behavior of different materials—was elementary atomic theory born. Dalton observed gases and theorized that their behavior could be explained only if the gases were composed of tiny, indivisible particles. He then extended his theory to other forms of matter.

From his experiments, Dalton suggested that invisible atoms existed, that different kinds of atoms had different weights, and that atoms combined in simple ratios (Figure 3.3). Dalton's theories were only partially correct. He did, however, lay the groundwork for the ideas of modern scientists about atoms; hence he is known as the father of atomic theory.

3.2 The Particles that Compose Atoms

There are 106 different kinds of atoms, and they represent 106 elements, each having different properties. How are these atoms different? Experiments indicate that each atom consists of smaller particles. Most of the smaller particles are important to physicists, but only three are really important to the study of present-day chemistry.

The three important particles are the **proton**, the **neutron**, and the **electron**.

Different atoms have different combinations of these "subatomic" particles. (**Subatomic** means "smaller than atomic.") The way in which these three kinds of subatomic particles form atoms is the basis of the model, or theory, of atomic structure.

Since individual atoms cannot be seen directly, scientists create a "mind's-eye" picture or devise a model to explain the results of experiments. These

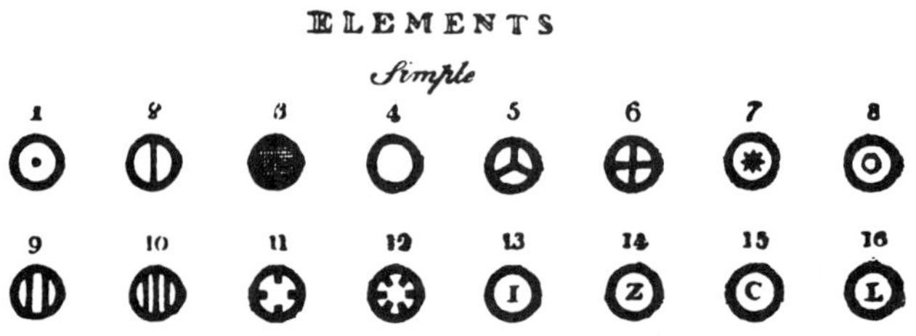

Figure 3.3 A portion of Dalton's table of the elements.

models are supplied with particular features that seem necessary for explaining the properties of larger quantities of matter. The scientists, by observing the results of experiments, can propose a picture of each atom and its properties. These theories or models are ideas, not ironclad facts. The most widely accepted theories of atomic structure vary in mathematical difficulty, depending on how many experimental details are to be described. The theories about atomic structure that we shall examine are mathematically simple but comprehensive enough to allow understanding the material presented.

Atoms consist of protons, neutrons, and electrons. Several experiments carried out in the late 1800s and early 1900s can be studied to develop ideas or models of the particles and their locations in the atom.

Discovery of the Electron

In 1897, J. J. Thomson showed that electrons exist as separate particles, each having a negative charge. He did this in two different ways, using cathode rays, which are streams of electrons emitted from an electrode, or a conductor of electrical charge. By measuring the current produced by the streams of electrons and the effect of imposing a magnetic field on them, Thomson was able to calculate a value for the charge-to-mass ratio for the electron $e/m = -1.76 \times 10^8$ coulombs/gram. A coulomb is a unit of electrical charge. The separate values of the charge and the mass of the electron, however, still remained undetermined.

Around 1910, Millikan performed different experiments on the electron—ones that allowed him to calculate the electron's charge and thus its mass. He actually measured what effect electrons adhering to the surface of oil droplets had on these droplets. From this experiment, he found the charge on the electron to be 1.6×10^{-19} coulombs. From $e/m = -1.76 \times 10^8$ coulombs/g and $e = -1.6 \times 10^{-19}$ coulombs, the mass of the electron can be calculated, and it is found to be 9.1×10^{-28} g.

Discovery of the Proton

Thomson's investigation of the proton in experiments similar to the cathode-ray experiments enabled him to calculate the proton's charge and mass. He found that the proton had a positive charge that exactly equaled the electron's negative charge. The mass of the proton was determined to be 1.67×10^{-24} g.

The actual value of the charge on the electron or the proton is usually not considered when dealing with atoms. Since protons and electrons have a charge ratio of **1:1**, the charge on a single electron is often defined as one negative atomic unit of charge and the charge on the proton as one positive atomic unit of charge.

Discovery of the Neutron

The neutron was discovered sometime later, in the 1930s. The neutron has either no electrical charge or a charge of zero, and it has a mass approximately equal to the mass of a proton. Mass and charge information concerning protons, neutrons, and electrons is summarized is Table 3.1.

The Structure of the Atom

What can be added to the model by looking at the table? A simple calculation shows that most of the mass of an atom must come from protons and neutrons, since the electrons are very light. The ratio of a proton's mass to an electron's mass is (from Table 3.1)

$$\frac{\text{Mass of proton}}{\text{Mass of electron}} = \frac{1.67 \times 10^{-24} \text{ g}}{9.11 \times 10^{-28} \text{ g}} = 1830$$

The ratio of the neutron mass to the electron mass is of the same order as the relation between the proton and electron masses. This means that protons and neutrons are 1830 times heavier than electrons and account for most of the mass of any atom.

What can be added to the theory by considering charges on the particles? The electrical charge on the electron is -1, and the electrical charge on the proton is $+1$. Most everyday objects do not give an electrical shock when touched. Thus, the electrical charge on most substances must be zero. For this to be true, there must be equal numbers of protons and electrons in each atom; the plusses and the minuses must cancel, to yield a zero charge.

Two important points about the structure of atoms have been added to the model: (1) the mass of an atom comes primarily from protons and neutrons; (2) there are equal numbers of protons and electrons in atoms.

The model for an atom's structure has been expanded, but the arrangement of particles is still unknown. Studies about this were Ernest Rutherford's contribution to the atomic model. Lord Rutherford interpreted the results of an experiment, shown in Figures 3.4a and 3.4b, that H. Geiger and E. Marsden

Table 3.1

	Mass (grams)	Charge (atomic units)
Proton	1.67×10^{-24}	$+1$
Neutron	1.67×10^{-24}	0
Electron	9.11×10^{-28}	-1

Figure 3.4a Rutherford's experiment, showing possible paths of alpha particles after striking gold foil.

Figure 3.4b A close-up view of the foil and alpha particles. The closer to the nucleus a particle passes, the greater the degree of reflection.

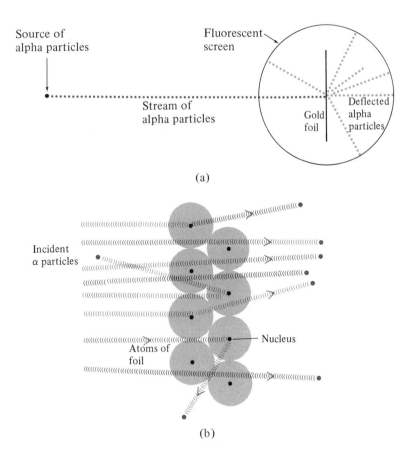

Source of alpha particles

Fluorescent screen

Stream of alpha particles

Gold foil

Deflected alpha particles

(a)

Incident α particles

Atoms of foil

Nucleus

(b)

performed. In this experiment, alpha (α) particles (small, charged, fast-moving particles consisting of two protons and two neutrons) were directed at a thin sheet of gold foil.

Most scientists at that time thought that protons were spread evenly throughout an atom. Neutrons were unknown. Alpha particles are four times as heavy as protons; so if the alpha particle hit just one proton, one would not expect it to bounce back. Thus, if all the particles had passed through the foil, the experiment would have indicated that the model of protons spread evenly throughout the atoms was a good one. This would be much like shooting bullets at a haystack—none would be expected to bounce back.

When Rutherford performed the experiment, he found that a few of the particles did bounce back. What did this mean? If you were shooting bullets at a haystack and one bounced back on occasion you might conclude that there was something very small, very hard, and certainly heavier than the bullet somewhere in that haystack. Rutherford came to a similar conclusion about the atoms. He decided that most of the mass of an atom must be in a very small part of the atom's volume and the rest of the atom must be primarily empty

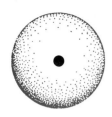

Figure 3.5 The model of the atom: a small, heavy nucleus surrounded by a cloud of light electrons. Most of the atom is empty space.

space. It would then be reasonable that most particles should pass through but once in a while, one should bounce back.

Can the theory be expanded to include this experimental evidence? Certainly. We can picture the atom as having a center that is very small, much smaller than the atom itself (Figure 3.5). *This core, or center, of an atom is called the* **nucleus**. *The nucleus is made up of protons and neutrons.* The central core is surrounded by many other very tiny particles. These tiny particles are electrons. The electrons travel far from the nucleus and are far apart, since like charges repel each other. Thus the atom is primarily empty space. This proposed model explains the results of the Rutherford scattering experiment. The electrons are held to travel so fast around the atom that if it were possible to see an atom, only a blur would appear all around the nucleus. It is almost as if there were a cloud of electrons around the atom.

A review of the model of the atom presented thus far recalls that it consists of a nucleus, with electrons in the surrounding space. The nucleus is composed of two different kinds of heavy particles. Protons have a diameter of about 10^{-12} cm, weigh about 1.67×10^{-24} g each, and have a positive charge. Also in the nucleus are neutrons that are about the same size and mass as protons but lacking charge. The protons and neutrons are held together by very strong forces that scientists have not been able to explain completely. The electrons that surround the nucleus are very much lighter than either protons or neutrons; they weigh about 9.1×10^{-28} g each and have a charge of -1. Each atom has one electron for each proton, since in an atom, each positive charge must be neutralized by an equivalent negative charge. If two protons are found to exist in an atom, then two electrons must be also there. Ten protons in an atom means that ten electrons must be present, to neutralize the positive charge.

3.3   The Periodic Chart: How Atoms of Different Elements Are Related

The model of the atom we have drawn is complete enough for us to continue our study of chemistry. Some main points have not been clarified.

1.   What distinguishes one type of atom from another?
2.   How many neutrons are in the various atoms?
3.   How are the electrons arranged around the nucleus?

These three questions can be answered through studying and understanding the chemists most important reference, the periodic chart. Since elements are substances that are composed of only one kind of atom, and there are 106 known elements, there must be also 106 kinds of atoms. Most of them exist in nature and the rest have been made in the laboratory. Chemists arrange these elements in a very special way on a "periodic chart." A list or a simple table could have been used, but the peculiar arrangement of the periodic chart helps in studying the elements. A person who understands the chart's use can determine much about atomic structure and can predict how atoms of elements interact.

The **periodic** chart is an ordered arrangement of the 106 known elements.

Scientists began to develop the periodic chart in the 1860s. Approximately sixty elements were known then. Dmitri Mendeleev proposed what was later called the periodic law, which stated that if the known elements were arranged in order of increasing weight, the properties of the elements would repeat periodically. This observation led scientists to begin filling in the blank areas in the periodic table of the sixty known elements; eventually the rest of the 106 elements that are known today were discovered and placed.

The modern periodic chart is shown in Figure 3.6. In the chart there are groups of boxes with either one or two letters in each box. (The single letter or first of two is always capitalized.) The boxes are numbered consecutively at the top. Each letter or pair of letters within a box is the symbol for an element. Each element has its own box. For some elements, the letters are just the first one or two letters of their names: H for hydrogen, O for oxygen, N for nitrogen, Ba for barium, and Mo for molybdenum. For others, the symbols come from

Figure 3.6 Periodic table of the elements (based on carbon 12). Elements 104 and 105 were reported in the late 1960s and have been tentatively named Kurchatovium and Hahnium, respectively. Element 106, discovered in 1974, is as yet unnamed.

Periodic Chart of the Elements

IA																	VIII A
1 H 1.0080	II A											III A	IV A	V A	VI A	VII A	2 He 4.003
3 Li 6.940	4 Be 9.013											5 B 10.82	6 C 12.011	7 N 14.008	8 O 16.000	9 F 19.00	10 Ne 20.183
11 Na 22.991	12 Mg 24.32	III B	IV B	V B	VI B	VII B	VIII B			I B	II B	13 Al 26.98	14 Si 28.09	15 P 30.975	16 S 32.066	17 Cl 35.457	18 Ar 39.944
19 K 39.100	20 Ca 40.08	21 Sc 44.96	22 Ti 47.90	23 V 50.95	24 Cr 52.01	25 Mn 54.94	26 Fe 55.85	27 Co 58.94	28 Ni 58.71	29 Cu 63.54	30 Zn 65.38	31 Ga 69.72	32 Ge 72.60	33 As 74.91	34 Se 78.96	35 Br 79.916	36 Kr 83.80
37 Rb 85.48	38 Sr 87.63	39 Y 88.92	40 Zr 91.22	41 Nb 92.91	42 Mo 95.95	43 Tc (99)	44 Ru 101.1	45 Rh 102.91	46 Pd 106.4	47 Ag 107.880	48 Cd 112.41	49 In 114.82	50 Sn 118.70	51 Sb 121.87	52 Te 127.61	53 I 126.91	54 Xe 131.30
55 Cs 132.91	56 Ba 137.36	57 *La 138.92	72 Hf 178.50	73 Ta 180.95	74 W 183.86	75 Re 186.22	76 Os 190.2	77 Ir 192.2	78 Pt 195.09	79 Au 197.0	80 Hg 200.61	81 Tl 204.39	82 Pb 207.21	83 Bi 209.00	84 Po (210)	85 At (210)	86 Rn (222)
87 Fr (223)	88 Ra (226)	89 †Ac (227)	104 Ku (261)	105 Ha (260)													

* Lanthanides	58 Ce 140.13	59 Pr 140.92	60 Nd 144.27	61 Pm (147)	62 Sm 150.35	63 Eu 152.0	64 Gd 157.26	65 Tb 158.93	66 Dy 162.51	67 Ho 164.94	68 Er 167.27	69 Tm 168.94	70 Yb 173.04	71 Lu 174.99

† Actinides	90 Th (232)	91 Pa (231)	92 U 238.07	93 Np (237)	94 Pu (242)	95 Am (243)	96 Cm (247)	97 Bk (249)	98 Cf (251)	99 Es (254)	100 Fm (253)	101 Md (256)	102 No (253)	103 Lw (257)

the Latin or Greek name of the element or they have a historical basis: K for potassium, W for tungsten, Fe for iron, and Na for sodium. The names of the elements are shown with the table to help you identify each element. From now on, symbols as well as the names of the elements will be used when they are mentioned. At the bottom of each box is another number, called the atomic weight.

Atomic Number

| 1 |
| H |
| 1.0079 |

On the periodic chart, the atoms are arranged consecutively by a number appearing at the top center of the box for that element. These numbers start with 1 and continue through 106. Chemists call these numbers atomic numbers.

> The atomic number, which can be abbreviated Z, is defined as the number of protons, or the number of positive charges, in the atomic nucleus.

The atomic number identifies the element and refers only to the number of protons. This answers the first question posed at the beginning of the section.

> The number of protons in an atom distinguishes one type of atom from another.

Each atom of hydrogen, element number 1, has one proton in its nucleus. This means that it also has one electron moving around that nucleus in accordance with the model for atomic structure. Helium (He), atom number 2, has two protons in its nucleus, and thus each atom has two electrons. Skipping further down the chart to element number 86, radon (Rn), one finds that its atoms have 86 protons each in the nucleus (meaning 86 positive charges), so that there must be 86 electrons or negative charges in each atom to balance the positive charges.

Atomic Weight and Mass Number

According to the model, there are also neutrons in the nucleus, and neutrons have no charge. Does the chart indicate how many neutrons are in an atom? The chart does not give exact numbers of neutrons per atom but does show approximate numbers. The discussion that follows answers the second question posed, about the number of neutrons.

> Remember that the mass of an atom comes primarily from the protons and neutrons, since both weigh so much more than electrons. This part of the model leads to the definition of the term mass number.

> The mass number, abbreviated with the letter A, is defined as the sum of the numbers of neutrons and protons in any given atom.

The element hydrogen has many atoms with a mass number of 1, indicating that it has one proton in the nucleus and no neutrons. The element helium has many atoms with a mass number of 4. Its atomic number, 2, shows that each atom has two protons in its nucleus. Helium atoms with mass number 4 must also contain two neutrons. Writing this relation as an equation gives

$$\text{Mass number } \mathbf{A} = \text{no. of protons } \mathbf{Z} + \text{no. of neutrons}$$

$$\text{Number of neutrons} = \mathbf{A} - \mathbf{Z}$$

The atomic number and the number of protons in the nucleus of an atom are one and the same, and they are represented by $\mathbf{Z}$.

Mass numbers of atoms are not shown directly on the periodic chart. However, they can be approximated from the chart. If you look closely at some of the atomic weights, which are printed below the symbols for the elements, you will notice that the atomic weight of sodium (Na) is 22.9898, almost 23. Chlorine (Cl) has an atomic weight 35.453, however, that is not really close to either 35 or 36. It might seem from the discussion that the mass shown on the chart should equal the sum of the masses of protons and neutrons in the atom. An atom cannot contain half a proton or half a neutron. You will see, if you look again at the atomic weights of the elements, that few whole numbers are given for any atomic weights. The apparent paradox can be explained through the definition of atomic weight and isotope.

The mass of the proton, neutron, and electron are all known. One might assume, therefore, that to determine the mass of an atom, one could add the masses of the number of protons present to the number of neutrons present and the number of electrons present. But such a calculation does not give the atomic weights shown on the periodic chart.

If this summation of proton, neutron, and electron weights does not work, how are atomic weights found?

Atomic weight is defined as the relative weight of any atom compared with a single carbon-12 atom.

Scientists have picked an element, carbon, which can have a mass number of 12. The mass number is the sum of the protons and neutrons. Carbon, with mass number 12, called carbon-12, has 6 protons, 6 neutrons, and 6 electrons. This leads to another term, atomic mass units (amu).

One **atomic mass unit** is one-twelfth the total weight of a carbon-12 atom.

One amu equals approximately 1.66×10^{-24} g. Therefore, a carbon-12 atom has an atomic weight of 12 atomic mass units, by definition. An arbitrary number has been assigned to the mass of an atom of carbon. Now the rest of the elements can be assigned masses relative to the mass selected for that carbon-12 atom.

11
Na
22.9898

17
Cl
35.453

6
C
12.01115

This approach is reasonable. Why then is the atomic weight given for carbon on the periodic chart 12.011 amu and not 12.000? The atomic weight of helium isn't 4; it is 4.0026 amu. The atomic weight of lithium (Li) is not 7; it is 6.939 amu. The main reason that these weights are not whole numbers is that atoms of a single element can contain differing numbers of neutrons.

Consider a large number of atoms of any given element. In atoms, the number of protons and electrons must be equal; however, the number of neutrons that may be present in an atom is not restricted by charge consideration. In nature each existing element nearly always has atoms with differing numbers of neutrons.

Atoms having the same number of protons and differing numbers of neutrons are called **isotopes**.

For instance, a lithium atom having three protons and eight neutrons has a mass number of 11. A lithium atom having three protons and four neutrons has a mass number of 7. Both of these atoms are isotopes of lithium. Both exist in nature. An average atomic weight for lithium, based on the frequency of occurrence of all the isotopes of lithium, is 6.939. This average value is important when considering that the samples chemists use are composed of a variety of isotopes. The atomic number Z, the number of protons in a nucleus, is the number that determines which element is which. Any atom with atomic number 3 (having 3 protons) is lithium, regardless of the number of neutrons that are present in the nucleus.

As a second example, there is uranium. Uranium (U) has many different isotopes. There are uranium-235 atoms with mass number equal to 235, uranium-236 with $A = 236$, uranium-237 with $A = 237$, uranium-238 with $A = 238$, and others with higher weights. All these atoms are uranium, since all contain 92 protons. They all exist in nature. The average weight of a uranium atom in a natural sample is 238.03 amu and has been calculated on the basis that more of some isotopes exist in nature than others.

| 92 |
| U |
| 238.03 |

Even carbon, the element on which the whole chart is based, exists in three isotopic forms: carbon-12, carbon-13, and carbon-14. The atomic weight of carbon shown on the chart, 12.01115 amu, represents the average weight of an atom in the mixture of isotopes as they exist in nature. This is the weight given on the chart. Thus, the chart indicates the composition of the nuclei of atoms although it does not show exact values.

The number of neutrons in the nucleus of a given atom determines how that nucleus will act—whether it will be stable or unstable. Certain isotopes of given elements have unstable nuclei. If the nucleus is unstable, it will fall apart and shoot out particles or energy, to try to attain a stable state. If the nucleus does this, the isotope is said to be radioactive.

It is no simple chore to calculate the exact number of neutrons in the nucleus of any given atom. The isotope of the element in question must be specified.

Example 3.1   How many neutrons does an atom of cobalt of mass number 59 have?

Using the formula and referring to the periodic chart for the atomic number, one can establish that

$$\text{Neutrons} = \mathbf{A} - \mathbf{Z} = 59 - 27 = 32 \text{ neutrons}$$

Example 3.2   How many neutrons does a cobalt atom have if it has a mass number of 60?

Using the formula and referring to the periodic chart for the atomic number gives

$$\text{Neutrons} = \mathbf{A} - \mathbf{Z} = 60 - 27 = 33 \text{ neutrons}$$

Example 3.3   What is the mass number for a uranium atom that has 146 neutrons?

Using the formula and referring to the periodic chart for the atomic number, we get

$$\text{Mass number} = \mathbf{Z} + \text{neutrons} = 92 + 146 = 238$$

The second question of our investigation, How many neutrons are present in the atom? has been answered. The average number of neutrons in atoms of an element can be determined through the periodic chart. The number of neutrons present in a single atom can be determined only if the isotopic form is known. As a review, the information contained in a single block of the periodic table is summarized in Figure 3.7.

Figure 3.7 Summary of the components of the periodic chart. Atomic weight is expressed in amu.

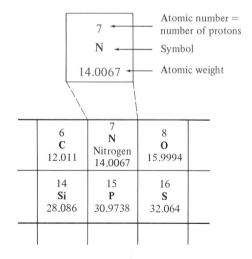

3.4   Electronic Structure

According to theory, the nucleus is the part of the atom that determines what the atom is called and whether it is radioactive. The electrons surrounding the nucleus determine what kind of reactions the atom will undergo. In other words, the arrangement of electrons in an atom determines how the atom will act when it encounters the atoms of another element (or even atoms like itself). Will there be an explosion when the atoms meet? Will there be a slow reaction? Will there be complete lack of reaction?

The electrons that surround the nuclei enable atoms to link and to form various kinds of compounds. The electrons give the atoms their chemical properties. Therefore, it is important to know how these electrons are arranged, what the arrangements mean, and how the periodic chart can be used to predict these arrangements. Let us now see how our third question will be answered— How are electrons arranged around the nucleus?

Imagine the nucleus to be at the center of a sphere that represents the atom; this is pictured in Figure 3.8. The electrons exist within this sphere somewhere, around the nucleus. They are believed to be in constant motion.

In 1913, Niels Bohr developed the basis for a model of the atom. Using the data from experiments on atoms and their emission of light, Bohr theorized that electrons existed in energy levels that could be roughly described as concentric shells around the nucleus of an atom. He further stated that these shells existed only at certain distances from the nucleus, and that no shells were possible at intermediate distances. According to his theory, the number of electrons occupying these discrete energy levels was determined by the distance of the given shell from the nucleus. Shells far from the nucleus could hold more electrons than shells nearer the nucleus. Bohr also theorized that each energy level was distinct and that the relative energies of the levels increased as the distance from the nucleus increased.

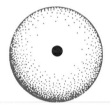

Figure 3.8 An atom pictured as a sphere, with the nucleus at the center.

Figure 3.9 Professor Niels Bohr (photo courtesy of Edgar Fahs Smith Memorial Collection, Van Pelt Library, University of Pennsylvania).

The theory that shells far from the nucleus hold more electrons than shells closer to the nucleus can be understood as follows. The nucleus of an atom is positively charged. (Many protons are in the nucleus, held together by strong forces that overcome the repulsive forces of the protons themselves.) The charge on the nucleus depends on the number of protons within it. Electrons around the nucleus, since they are negatively charged, are attracted to it. However, the number of electrons that can approach the nucleus is limited. As more electrons are attracted to the nucleus, they also approach each other and hence are repelled by the negative charges of neighboring electrons. Thus some electrons are forced to remain in outer levels, even though the nucleus bears strong attractive forces for the electrons.

Another factor limiting the number of electrons that can exist in levels near the nucleus is the geometric structure of the corresponding shells. Picture concentric shells around the nucleus, as shown below. The surface area of each shell increases as the shell's distance from the nucleus increases. Thus the outer shells simply have more room for electron occupation than the inner shells. Only a fraction of the total number of electrons in an atom can occupy the volume available in the inner levels.

Experiments and observations of the properties of atoms have led scientists to expand Bohr's theory of energy levels corresponding to the shells; the subsequent work has emphasized the concept of levels. First, it is held, an electron can occupy only one level at a time. The levels are represented with integers—1, 2, 3, and so on; low-numbered levels correspond to inner concentric shells. An electron occupying energy level 1, for instance, is most likely to be found near the nucleus, spending more time there than an electron occupying energy levels 2 or 3. Since the electrons in an atom are in constant motion, their respective distances from the nucleus vary. That an electron is in a given energy level means that a significant part of its time is spent at the distance from the nucleus corresponding to the Bohr shell. Fewer electrons can occupy low-numbered energy levels, compared with the electrons that are at the higher-numbered levels. Electrons near the nucleus are strongly attracted to its positive charge; hence, it is more difficult to remove them from an atom than it is to remove electrons that are farther from the nucleus.

Theoretically, the nucleus of any atom has numerous levels that the electrons can occupy. The model for electron structure assigns the same levels to all atoms. For atoms with large nuclei, the electron occupation areas are close to the nucleus because of the strong attraction that a nucleus with many protons has for the electrons surrounding it. However, although the level concept exists, atoms of most elements have too few electrons to fill many of them.

Table 3.2 Maximum Possible Number of Electrons in Energy Levels (Shells) of Atom

Level	Electrons
1	2
2	8
3	18
4	32
5	50
⋮	⋮

Each level can hold a maximum number of electrons, as listed in Table 3.2. The low-numbered levels hold fewer electrons than the higher-numbered levels. Electrons are thought to fill levels near the nucleus first before those farther out. In terms of energy, low-numbered energy levels are occupied before higher-numbered levels. In every case shown in Table 3.3, electrons fill the low-numbered levels first and then succeeding levels. This simple filling order does not continue for the elements throughout the periodic chart, however, and the model must be extended to explain the changes.

Before extending the model, it is important to consider the relation of the level concept to the periodic chart. The top three rows of the periodic chart

Table 3.3 Level Occupation for Various Atoms

Atom	Symbol	Number of Protons in Nucleus	Number of Electrons	Number of Electrons in Each Level				
				1	2	3	4	5
Hydrogen	(H)	1	1	1				
Helium	(He)	2	2	2				
Lithium	(Li)	3	3	2	1			
Beryllium	(Be)	4	4	2	2			
Boron	(B)	5	5	2	3			
Carbon	(C)	6	6	2	4			
Nitrogen	(N)	7	7	2	5			
Oxygen	(O)	8	8	2	6			
Fluorine	(F)	9	9	2	7			
Neon	(Ne)	10	10	2	8			
Sodium	(Na)	11	11	2	8	1		
Magnesium	(Mg)	12	12	2	8	2		
Aluminum	(Al)	13	13	2	8	3		
Silicon	(Si)	14	14	2	8	4		
Phosphorus	(P)	15	15	2	8	5		
Sulfur	(S)	16	16	2	8	6		
Chlorine	(Cl)	17	17	2	8	7		
Argon	(Ar)	18	18	2	8	8		

I A																	VIII A
1 **H** 1.0080	II A											III A	IV A	V A	VI A	VII A	2 **He** 4.003
3 **Li** 6.940	4 **Be** 9.013											5 **B** 10.82	6 **C** 12.011	7 **N** 14.008	8 **O** 16.000	9 **F** 19.00	10 **Ne** 20.183
11 **Na** 22.991	12 **Mg** 24.32	III B	IV B	V B	VI B	VII B		VIII B		I B	II B	13 **Al** 26.98	14 **Si** 28.09	15 **P** 30.975	16 **S** 32.066	17 **Cl** 35.457	18 **Ar** 39.944
19 **K** 39.100	20 **Ca** 40.08	21 **Sc** 44.96	22 **Ti** 47.90	23 **V** 50.95	24 **Cr** 52.01	25 **Mn** 54.94	26 **Fe** 55.85	27 **Co** 58.94	28 **Ni** 58.71	29 **Cu** 63.54	30 **Zn** 65.38	31 **Ga** 69.72	32 **Ge** 72.60	33 **As** 74.91	34 **Se** 78.96	35 **Br** 79.916	36 **Kr** 83.80
37 **Rb** 85.48	38 **Sr** 87.63	39 **Y** 88.92	40 **Zr** 91.22	41 **Nb** 92.91	42 **Mo** 95.95	43 **Tc** (99)	44 **Ru** 101.1	45 **Rh** 102.91	46 **Pd** 106.4	47 **Ag** 107.880	48 **Cd** 112.41	49 **In** 114.82	50 **Sn** 118.70	51 **Sb** 121.87	52 **Te** 127.61	53 **I** 126.91	54 **Xe** 131.30
55 **Cs** 132.91	56 **Ba** 137.36	57 ***La** 138.92	72 **Hf** 178.50	73 **Ta** 180.95	74 **W** 183.86	75 **Re** 186.22	76 **Os** 190.2	77 **Ir** 192.2	78 **Pt** 195.09	79 **Au** 197.0	80 **Hg** 200.61	81 **Tl** 204.39	82 **Pb** 207.21	83 **Bi** 209.00	84 **Po** (210)	85 **At** (210)	86 **Rn** (222)
87 **Fr** (223)	88 **Ra** (226)	89 **†Ac** (227)	104 **Ku** (261)	105 **Ha** (260)													

* Lanthanides	58 **Ce** 140.13	59 **Pr** 140.92	60 **Nd** 144.27	61 **Pm** (147)	62 **Sm** 150.35	63 **Eu** 152.0	64 **Gd** 157.26	65 **Tb** 158.93	66 **Dy** 162.51	67 **Ho** 164.94	68 **Er** 167.27	69 **Tm** 168.94	70 **Yb** 173.04	71 **Lu** 174.99

† Actinides	90 **Th** (232)	91 **Pa** (231)	92 **U** 238.07	93 **Np** (237)	94 **Pu** (242)	95 **Am** (243)	96 **Cm** (247)	97 **Bk** (249)	98 **Cf** (251)	99 **Es** (254)	100 **Fm** (253)	101 **Md** (256)	102 **No** (253)	103 **Lw** (257)

Figure 3.10 Atoms of elements in the top three rows of the periodic chart have electrons existing in the first three levels.

are shown in Figure 3.10. The first row shows two elements, the second eight, and the third eight. The first three rows of the periodic chart indicate the level filling order, according to the model. This is an important quality of the periodic chart, which will become even more useful as the model for electronic structure is expanded. The arrangement of electrons on atoms is considered a property that can be inferred from the periodic chart. Such properties are called **periodic properties**.

This simple level model does not work perfectly as the atoms become heavier, since the order of filling of levels changes as more electrons are added. To improve the model, it is necessary to divide the energy levels into smaller units, called sublevels. Each energy level is composed of one or more **sublevels**, and sublevels are divided into even smaller regions of space, called orbitals.

Orbitals are regions in space around the nucleus in which a given electron is most likely to be found. Orbitals can contain no more than two electrons each.

They are defined in complex mathematics, and the model is set up to account for many electrons in a given atom that will not collide or occupy the same space at the same time. A division of levels into sublevels and orbitals is shown in Table 3.4. Each level comprises one or more sublevels, each of which can be separated into orbitals. As an example, the third level is divided into three sublevels—a 3s, a 3p, and a 3d sublevel. The 3s contains one s orbital, the 3p contains three p orbitals, and the 3d contain five d orbitals. The energy-level

Table 3.4

Level	Sublevel	Orbitals Present Type	Orbitals Present Number	Total Possible Occupying Electrons	
1	1s	s	1	2	
2	2s	s	1	2	8
	2p	p	3	6	
3	3s	s	1	2	
	3p	p	3	6	18
	3d	d	5	10	
4	4s	s	1	2	
	4p	p	3	6	32
	4d	d	5	10	
	4f	f	7	14	

number always corresponds to the number of sublevels possible. The first four orbital types are labeled *s*, *p*, *d*, and *f* for historical reasons (standing for **sharp**, **principal**, **diffuse**, and **fundamental**), and the more complex types are designated *g*, *h*, and so on through the alphabet. So far, scientists have not discovered any elements with electrons in orbitals beyond the *f* orbital, but *g* and higher orbitals can be shown experimentally to exist. The *s* orbital in a given level is always the first filled.

The order of filling the sublevels is shown in Figure 3.11. For example, an atom of hydrogen (H) has one electron, which must be in the 1*s* orbital. An atom of oxygen (O), with eight electrons, has two in the 1*s*, two in the 2*s*, and four distributed among three 2*p* orbitals. Each sulfur (S) atom, with sixteen electrons, has two in the 1*s*, two in the 2*s*, six in the three 2*p* orbitals, two in the 3*s*, and four in the three 3*p* orbitals.

How does the idea of levels and orbitals fit the periodic chart? Hydrogen (H) and helium (He) are the only elements in the first row of the chart. Hydrogen atoms have one electron each and helium atoms have two. So according to the filling order, a hydrogen atom has one electron in its 1*s* sublevel, and a helium atom has two electrons in its 1*s* sublevel. Level 1 has only a 1*s* sublevel, and once the sublevel is full, that element marks the end of a row. The rows correspond roughly to the levels and filling order. Thus, each row ends with an element that shows the complete filling of a sublevel.

Among the elements of the second row, lithium atoms have a total of three electrons, so each atom has two electrons in its 1*s* sublevel and one electron in its 2*s* sublevel. This electron configuration is abbreviated as $1s^2 2s^1$. The coefficients 1 and 2 stand for the energy levels that are being filled—the first energy level and the second energy level. The *s* designates the sublevel and the orbital type, and the superscript 2 in $1s^2$ means that there are two electrons in the 1*s* sublevel. (Figure 3.12.) The statement 1*s*, or $1s^1$, means one electron in the 1*s* orbital or sublevel. Beryllium (Be) atoms have four electrons, so each

Figure 3.11 This simple chart shows the order of electrons filling into sublevels. The *p* sublevel circles represent three *p* orbitals, the *d* sublevel circles represent five *d* orbitals, and the *f* sublevel circles represent seven *f* orbitals.

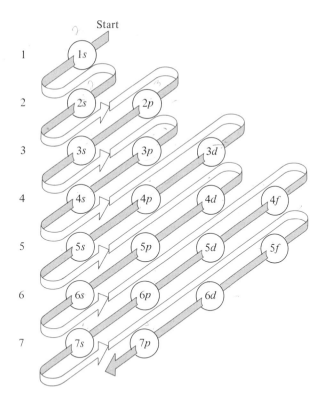

atom has two electrons in its 1*s* sublevel and two in its 2*s* sublevel. (This can be written $1s^2 2s^2$.) Boron (B) atoms have five electrons, so each atom has two electrons in its 1*s*, two in its 2*s*, and one in its 2*p* sublevel (written $1s^2 2s^2 2p$).

Carbon(C) atoms have six electrons each, so each atom has two electrons in its 1*s* sublevel, two electrons in its 2*s* sublevel, and one in each of two 2*p* orbitals. Electrons are thought to fill sublevels (the 2*p* for example) one orbital at a time until each orbital has one electron in it. Only then are electrons paired in orbitals. (This concept is a statement of **Hund's rule**.) Thus, for nitrogen (N) atoms with seven electrons, two are in the 1*s* orbital, two are in the 2*s* orbital, and one each is in the three 2*p* orbitals.

For the rest of the elements in that row, electrons continue to fill the three available 2*p* orbitals, pairing electrons in each; the elements have the electronic

Figure 3.12 The abbreviated method for indicating electron configuration.

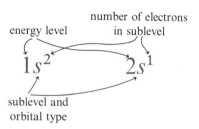

Table 3.5

Element	Electronic Configuration
Carbon (C)	$1s^2 2s^2 2p^2$
Nitrogen (N)	$1s^2 2s^2 2p^3$
Oxygen (O)	$1s^2 2s^2 2p^4$
Fluorine (F)	$1s^2 2s^2 2p^5$
Neon (Ne)	$1s^2 2s^2 2p^6$

structures shown in Table 3.5. That there are three p orbitals in each level after the first one means that a total of six electrons can fit in a p orbital set. At this point, another level and another row come to an end.

One important use of the periodic chart now appears. For the elements in each column, the last electron added to the electronic configuration enters the same type of orbital, although at successively higher energy levels. For elements directly under hydrogen and lithium, the last electron inserted into atoms of each of these elements enters an s orbital. In electronic structures of sodium (Na), potassium (K), rubidium (Rb), cesium (Cs), and francium (Fr), the last orbital filled is always an s type of orbital. This is shown in Table 3.6. Notice that the numbers preceding the s's are the numbers of the level. The elements in the beryllium column behave like this also. For them, the last orbital written in the electronic configuration is an s orbital containing two electrons, as shown in Table 3.7. Consider now the rest of the main families in columns across the periodic chart, groups IIIA through VIIIA. Table 3.8 shows for all groups on the periodic chart the orbital and the number of electrons in the level farthest from the nucleus. Notice that all the elements in this block of the periodic chart have their outermost electrons in the p orbital set.

The chart is arranged so that, looking down the columns, one almost always finds elements that have the same outer orbital structure. These columns of elements are called families, or groups.

About half of all the known elements have been discussed so far. Where do the d and f orbitals come into use? There are five d orbitals at each level above the first two levels, and each set can contain a total of 10 electrons. The

Table 3.6

Element Symbol	Last Term in Electronic Structure
H	$1s^1$
Li	$2s^1$
Na	$3s^1$
K	$4s^1$
Rb	$5s^1$
Cs	$6s^1$

Table 3.7

Element Symbol	Last Term in Electronic Structure
Be	$2s^2$
Mg	$3s^2$
Ca	$4s^2$
Sr	$5s^2$
Ba	$6s^2$
Ra	$7s^2$

Table 3.8

Elements		Last Filled Orbital Type and Number of Electrons
Group IIIA	Boron and elements below	p^1
Group IVA	Carbon and elements below	p^2
Group VA	Nitrogen and elements below	p^3
Group VIA	Oxygen and elements below	p^4
Group VIIA	Fluorine and elements below	p^5
Group VIIIA	Neon and elements below	p^6

$3d$ orbitals (the first of the type available) begin filling at element 21, scandium (Sc). The d orbitals being filled for the elements in the next row (starting at element 39, yttrium (Y)) are the $4d$ orbitals. Elements 57 and 72 through 80 correspond to filling of the $5d$ orbitals. The d orbitals fill progressively for the elements across the table in the direction left to right. As an example, the electronic structure of vanadium (V; number 23) can be written

$$V: \quad 1s^2 2s^2 2p^6 3s^2 3p^6 4s^2 3d^3$$

The designation d^3 means that one electron is present in each of three of the five d orbitals of the $3d$ sublevel. Cadmium (Cd; number 48) furnishes another example; the electronic structure is

$$Cd: \quad 1s^2 2s^2 2p^6 3s^2 3p^6 4s^2 3d^{10} 4p^6 5s^2 4d^{10}$$

What about the f orbitals? There are seven f orbitals per shell, and these seven can hold a total of 14 electrons. The filling of the first such set (the $4f$ orbitals) begins at element 58, cerium (Ce). The $5f$ orbital set begins to fill at element 90, thorium (Th). At this point, it is better to look up electronic structures of elements that have partially filled f orbitals, since it is not easy to predict their electronic structures from the periodic chart.

The elements that have their *d* orbitals filled progressively are called transition elements; they start at scandium (Sc; number 21) and are listed in the direction to the right, ending with zinc (Zn; number 30). The next higher cycle starts at yttrium (Y; number 39) and ends with cadmium (Cd; number 48). They also include lanthanum (La; number 57), and the elements hafnium (Hf; number 72) through mercury (Hg; number 80). These elements are blocked out in a separate part of the chart; and it is reasonable to suspect that there must be something different about their electronic structures. There is something different about filling the *d* levels.

Scandium (number 21) comes right after potassium (number 19) and calcium (number 20). It seems that with atoms of scandium, the fourth main energy level should continue to be filled, since this was the case for potassium and calcium. At scandium, however, additional electrons begin entering the third main energy level—into its five hitherto unused orbitals, called the 3*d*. Electrons are completing the filling of an energy level below an orbital that already had electrons in it. Therefore, if one could look at atoms of the elements from 21 through 30, one would first see the 4*s* electrons and then, at a lower energy level, closer to the nucleus, the 3*d* electrons (Figure 3.13). The arrangement of electrons determines the properties of elements; thus all these elements should have similar properties. It is true that chromium, manganese, iron, cobalt, and nickel all are silvery metals, which are very hard and strong. They are also chemically similar.

The *f* orbital elements are called the lanthanides and the actinides. The seven *f* orbitals may hold a total of 14 electrons. The 4*f* and 5*f* orbitals lie at a lower level than the full *s*, *p*, and *d* orbitals at the time of their filling. The inserted electrons lie deep inside the electronic configuration of the atom, and these elements are even more like one another than the transition elements. The

Figure 3.13 The 3*d* electrons fill in after the 4*s* electrons, so they are really filling into an internal level.

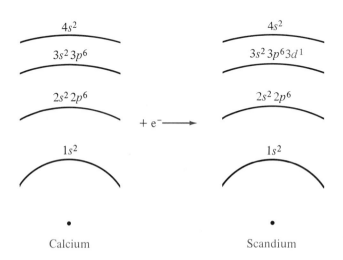

Ch. 3   THE ATOM

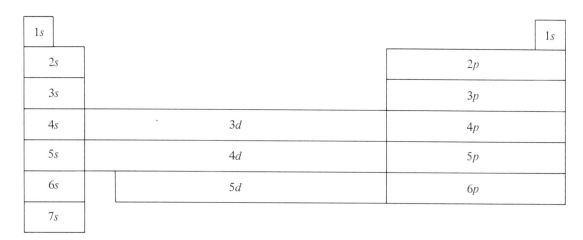

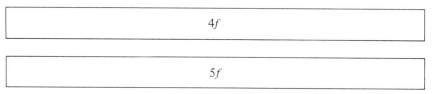

Figure 3.14 Diagram of the periodic chart, showing final orbitals filled in each section.

actinides and lanthanides are grouped and referred to as the inner transition elements.

Practice in writing electronic configurations will help you to become familiar with them. Figure 3.14 shows a periodic chart, in which areas have been blocked out, indicating filled orbitals. Referring to this chart will help as you are learning to write electronic structures.

Example 3.4

Write the electronic configuration for selenium (Se; number 34).

Step 1 Determine where the element lies on the periodic chart. Selenium is in the fourth row among the elements where the p orbitals are filling, giving a $4p$ last term.

Step 2 Determine the final term in the configuration. Since selenium is in the fourth column after the p's begin filling, the final term is $4p^4$.

Step 3 Write the remaining structure. Writing everything between, one gets the structure

$$\text{Se}: \quad 1s^2 2s^2 2p^6 3s^2 3p^6 4s^2 3d^{10} 4p^4$$

Example 3.5

Write the electronic configuration for technetium (Tc; number 43).

Step 1 Technetium is in the fifth row among the elements for which the d orbitals become filled.

Step 2 The last term in the electronic structure is $4d$. Since Tc is five elements from the left in the d orbital block (five columns over from the elements for which d filling starts), the final term is $4d^5$.

Step 3 Filling in the rest of the terms, we get

$$\text{Tc:} \quad 1s^2 2s^2 2p^6 3s^2 3p^6 4s^2 3d^{10} 4p^6 5s^2 4d^5$$

Example 3.6 Write the electronic configuration for plutonium (Pu; number 94).

Step 1 Plutonium is in the second row of elements that fill f orbitals at the bottom of the chart.

Step 2 The last term must be $5f$. Looking this up in Table 3.9, we find that the term is $5f^6$.

Step 3 Filling in the rest of the electrons gives

$$\text{Pu:} \quad 1s^2 2s^2 2p^6 3s^2 3p^6 4s^2 3d^{10} 4p^6 5s^2 4d^{10} 5p^6 6s^2 4f^{14} 5d^{10} 6p^6 7s^2 5f^6$$

Table 3.9 gives the electronic configurations for all the elements, so that you can check practice problems and look up f orbital configurations. A shorthand way of writing the electronic configuration is often used. Whenever a He, Ne, Ar, Kr, or Xe configuration is present, that configuration is indicated by brackets. Subsequent elemental electronic configurations are shown as the symbol plus any additional electrons. For example, instead of writing sodium (Na) as $1s^2 2s^2 2p^6 3s^1$, we use [Ne] instead of $1s^2 2s^2 2p^6$, which is the electronic configuration for Ne, and a $3s^1$ is added. Thus the configuration of Na is shown as

$$[\text{Ne}]3s^1$$

Some electronic structures do not agree with the configuration according to the filling order. For example, copper (Cu; atomic number 29), has the electronic configuration $[\text{Ar}]4s^1 3d^{10}$. The table for writing electronic configurations (Figure 3.11) indicates that it should be $[\text{Ar}]4s^2 3d^9$. This discrepancy and others like it are explained by expanding the model to postulate that half-filled or completely filled sublevels are very stable configurations. Atoms that have nearly half-full or nearly full sublevels allow electrons from nearby sublevels to occupy them to achieve the most stable state. Copper can achieve a full $3d$ sublevel by rearranging a $4s$ electron to the $3d$ sublevel, getting a $[\text{Ar}]4s^1 3d^{10}$ configuration. Similarly, chromium atoms (Cr) have a half-filled $3d$ sublevel if a $4s$ electron is rearranged to the $3d$ sublevel, hence the configuration $[\text{Ar}]4s^1 3d^5$. Experimental evidence indicates that copper and chromium atoms exist in this electronic structure and also other atoms shown in Table 3.9. It is important to remember that a half-filled s sublevel contains one electron, a half-filled p sublevel contains three electrons, a half-filled d sublevel contains five electrons, and a half-filled f sublevel contains seven electrons.

Table 3.9 Electronic Configurations of Atoms of All the Elements

Element	Z	1s	2s	2p	3s	3p	3d	4s	4p	4d	4f	5s	5p	5d	5f	6s	6p	6d	7s
H	1	1																	
He	2	2																	
Li	3	2	1																
Be	4	2	2																
B	5	2	2	1															
C	6	2	2	2															
N	7	2	2	3															
O	8	2	2	4															
F	9	2	2	5															
Ne	10	2	2	6															
Na	11	2	2	6	1														
Mg	12	2	2	6	2														
Al	13	2	2	6	2	1													
Si	14	2	2	6	2	2													
P	15	2	2	6	2	3													
S	16	2	2	6	2	4													
Cl	17	2	2	6	2	5													
Ar	18	2	2	6	2	6													
K	19	2	2	6	2	6		1											
Ca	20	2	2	6	2	6		2											
Sc	21	2	2	6	2	6	1	2											
Ti	22	2	2	6	2	6	2	2											
V	23	2	2	6	2	6	3	2											
Cr	24	2	2	6	2	6	5	1											
Mn	25	2	2	6	2	6	5	2											
Fe	26	2	2	6	2	6	6	2											
Co	27	2	2	6	2	6	7	2											
Ni	28	2	2	6	2	6	8	2											
Cu	29	2	2	6	2	6	10	1											
Zn	30	2	2	6	2	6	10	2											
Ga	31	2	2	6	2	6	10	2	1										
Ge	32	2	2	6	2	6	10	2	2										
As	33	2	2	6	2	6	10	2	3										
Se	34	2	2	6	2	6	10	2	4										
Br	35	2	2	6	2	6	10	2	5										
Kr	36	2	2	6	2	6	10	2	6										
Rb	37	2	2	6	2	6	10	2	6			1							
Sr	38	2	2	6	2	6	10	2	6			2							
Y	39	2	2	6	2	6	10	2	6	1		2							
Zr	40	2	2	6	2	6	10	2	6	2		2							
Nb	41	2	2	6	2	6	10	2	6	4		1							
Mo	42	2	2	6	2	6	10	2	6	5		1							
Tc	43	2	2	6	2	6	10	2	6	6		1							
Ru	44	2	2	6	2	6	10	2	6	7		1							

Table 3.9 (Continued)

Element	Z	1s	2s	2p	3s	3p	3d	4s	4p	4d	4f	5s	5p	5d	5f	6s	6p	6d	7s
Rh	45	2	2	6	2	6	10	2	6	8		1							
Pd	46	2	2	6	2	6	10	2	6	10									
Ag	47	2	2	6	2	6	10	2	6	10		1							
Cd	48	2	2	6	2	6	10	2	6	10		2							
In	49	2	2	6	2	6	10	2	6	10		2	1						
Sn	50	2	2	6	2	6	10	2	6	10		2	2						
Sb	51	2	2	6	2	6	10	2	6	10		2	3						
Te	52	2	2	6	2	6	10	2	6	10		2	4						
I	53	2	2	6	2	6	10	2	6	10		2	5						
Xe	54	2	2	6	2	6	10	2	6	10		2	6						
Cs	55	2	2	6	2	6	10	2	6	10		2	6			1			
Ba	56	2	2	6	2	6	10	2	6	10		2	6			2			
La	57	2	2	6	2	6	10	2	6	10		2	6	1		2			
Ce	58	2	2	6	2	6	10	2	6	10	2	2	6			2			
Pr	59	2	2	6	2	6	10	2	6	10	3	2	6			2			
Nd	60	2	2	6	2	6	10	2	6	10	4	2	6			2			
Pm	61	2	2	6	2	6	10	2	6	10	5	2	6			2			
Sm	62	2	2	6	2	6	10	2	6	10	6	2	6			2			
Eu	63	2	2	6	2	6	10	2	6	10	7	2	6			2			
Gd	64	2	2	6	2	6	10	2	6	10	7	2	6	1		2			
Tb	65	2	2	6	2	6	10	2	6	10	9	2	6			2			
Dy	66	2	2	6	2	6	10	2	6	10	10	2	6			2			
Ho	67	2	2	6	2	6	10	2	6	10	11	2	6			2			
Er	68	2	2	6	2	6	10	2	6	10	12	2	6			2			
Tm	69	2	2	6	2	6	10	2	6	10	13	2	6			2			
Yb	70	2	2	6	2	6	10	2	6	10	14	2	6			2			
Lu	71	2	2	6	2	6	10	2	6	10	14	2	6	1		2			
Hf	72	2	2	6	2	6	10	2	6	10	14	2	6	2		2			
Ta	73	2	2	6	2	6	10	2	6	10	14	2	6	3		2			
W	74	2	2	6	2	6	10	2	6	10	14	2	6	4		2			
Re	75	2	2	6	2	6	10	2	6	10	14	2	6	5		2			
Os	76	2	2	6	2	6	10	2	6	10	14	2	6	6		2			
Ir	77	2	2	6	2	6	10	2	6	10	14	2	6	7		2			
Pt	78	2	2	6	2	6	10	2	6	10	14	2	6	9		1			
Au	79	2	2	6	2	6	10	2	6	10	14	2	6	10		1			
Hg	80	2	2	6	2	6	10	2	6	10	14	2	6	10		2			
Tl	81	2	2	6	2	6	10	2	6	10	14	2	6	10		2	1		
Pb	82	2	2	6	2	6	10	2	6	10	14	2	6	10		2	2		
Bi	83	2	2	6	2	6	10	2	6	10	14	2	6	10		2	3		
Po	84	2	2	6	2	6	10	2	6	10	14	2	6	10		2	4		
At	85	2	2	6	2	6	10	2	6	10	14	2	6	10		2	5		
Rn	86	2	2	6	2	6	10	2	6	10	14	2	6	10		2	6		
Fr	87	2	2	6	2	6	10	2	6	10	14	2	6	10		2	6		1
Ra	88	2	2	6	2	6	10	2	6	10	14	2	6	10		2	6		2
Ac	89	2	2	6	2	6	10	2	6	10	14	2	6	10		2	6	1	2

Table 3.9 *(Continued)*

Element	Z	1s	2s	2p	3s	3p	3d	4s	4p	4d	4f	5s	5p	5d	5f	6s	6p	6d	7s
Th	90	2	2	6	2	6	10	2	6	10	14	2	6	10		2	6	2	2
Pa	91	2	2	6	2	6	10	2	6	10	14	2	6	10	2	2	6	1	2
U	92	2	2	6	2	6	10	2	6	10	14	2	6	10	3	2	6	1	2
Np	93	2	2	6	2	6	10	2	6	10	14	2	6	10	4	2	6	1	2
Pu	94	2	2	6	2	6	10	2	6	10	14	2	6	10	6	2	6		2
Am	95	2	2	6	2	6	10	2	6	10	14	2	6	10	7	2	6		2
Cm	96	2	2	6	2	6	10	2	6	10	14	2	6	10	7	2	6	1	2
Bk	97	2	2	6	2	6	10	2	6	10	14	2	6	10	8	2	6	1	2
Cf	98	2	2	6	2	6	10	2	6	10	14	2	6	10	10	2	6		2
Es	99	2	2	6	2	6	10	2	6	10	14	2	6	10	11	2	6		2
Fm	100	2	2	6	2	6	10	2	6	10	14	2	6	10	12	2	6		2
Md	101	2	2	6	2	6	10	2	6	10	14	2	6	10	13	2	6		2
No	102	2	2	6	2	6	10	2	6	10	14	2	6	10	14	2	6		2
Lr	103	2	2	6	2	6	10	2	6	10	14	2	6	10	14	2	6	1	2
Ku	104	2	2	6	2	6	10	2	6	10	14	2	6	10	14	2	6	2	2?
Ha	105	2	2	6	2	6	10	2	6	10	14	2	6	10	14	2	6	3	2?
?	106	2	2	6	2	6	10	2	6	10	14	2	6	10	14	2	6	4	2?
?	107	2	2	6	2	6	10	2	6	10	14	2	6	10	14	2	6	4	2?

Shapes of Orbitals

Each of the kinds of orbitals we have considered has a unique shape. These shapes do not exist in space where they can be touched and seen. They are mind's-eye models, which scientists use to describe where they think the electrons spend most of their time in a given orbital. These shapes have been developed by mathematical models that physicists have devised. The models represent theories that best explain experimental results.

If the nucleus is the center, the 1s orbital looks like the sphere shown in Figure 3.15. The other s orbitals in higher levels have the same basic shape.

Figure 3.15 Three-dimensional picture of the 1s orbital.

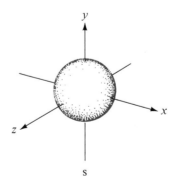

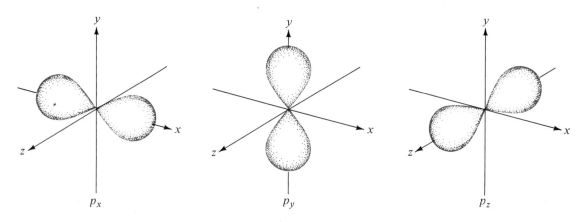

Figure 3.16 Three-dimensional pictures of the three 2p orbitals.

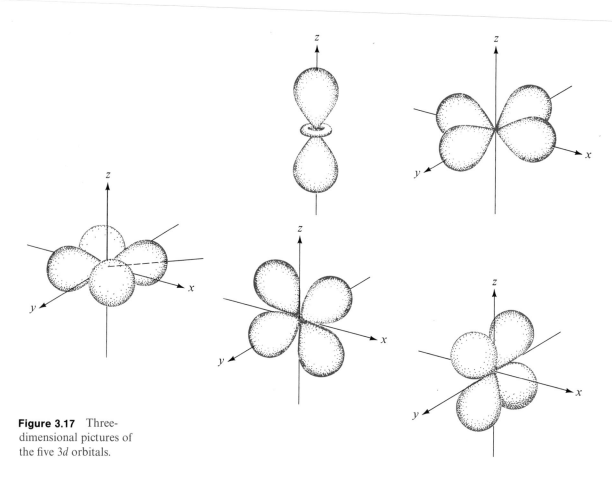

Figure 3.17 Three-dimensional pictures of the five 3d orbitals.

The three $2p$ orbitals appear as in Figure 3.16. The nucleus exists where they cross. Other level p orbitals have about the same shape. The five $3d$ orbitals appear as in Figure 3.17. Other level d orbitals have about the same shape.

It is difficult to draw the seven 4f orbitals, and there is some question about how they look, so they are not shown.

Regardless of the level, the shapes of s, p, d, and f orbitals always look about the same.

3.5 Physical Appearance of the Elements: Introduction to Periodic Properties

The periodic chart is arranged so that elements with similar physical or chemical properties are grouped. A look back at Figure 3.5 will show a zigzag line separating the left two-thirds of the main body of the chart from the right third. To the left of the line are the metals, samples of which appear lustrous, can be bent or shaped, and conduct electricity. To the right of the line are the nonmetals, substances that usually are powdery and nonlustrous and do not conduct electricity.

The A groups on the chart, often called the representative elements, constitute the core group of metals and nonmetals. The B groups are called the transition metals. They are grouped because they chemically and physically resemble each other more than other substances on the chart. The two groupings below the main body are called the lanthanides and the actinides. They are really part of the IIIB group, but convenience in drawing the chart and their very similar properties cause them to be placed in a single group below the chart.

The most important groupings are the vertical columns, or families, of elements. Each column of elements has similar physical and chemical properties. Column IA consists of the active metals, called alkali metals, including sodium and potassium, which explode on contact with water. Column IIA consists of less reactive metals, called alkaline earths. Column IB consists of the noble, or precious, metals, copper (Cu), silver (Ag), and gold (Au). Column VIIA consists of extremely active nonmetals, called halogens, like fluorine (F) and chlorine (Cl), which are very corrosive. Column VIIIA consists of almost totally nonreactive gases, called the noble gases. Such properties as the ones described are called periodic properties and can be predicted from the behavior of similar atoms of elements within columns on the periodic chart.

3.6

Counting Atoms:
Introduction to the Mole

Since atoms are very tiny and weigh very little, it is impossible to "weigh out" single atoms even on the most sophisticated balances. It is necessary, nonetheless, for chemists to be able to approximate the number of atoms in measurable samples of substances. Since controlled chemical reactions are involved in making almost everything used in day-to-day existence—food substances, plastics, paints, building materials—it is important for chemists to be able to mix proper quantities of raw materials for the reactions. Part of the information given in the periodic chart, the atomic weight, helps chemists to do this.

To see how this is done, consider the following statement: **A sample of any element weighing an amount in grams numerically equal to the atomic weight contains the same number of atoms as a similar sample of any other element.**

1.01 g of hydrogen contains as many hydrogen atoms—
- as 26.98 g of aluminum contains aluminum atoms
- as 55.85 g of iron contains iron atoms
- as 196.97 g of gold contains gold atoms

The following calculations show that this is true.

$$1.01 \text{ g H} \times \frac{1 \text{ atom H}}{1.01 \text{ amu}} \times \frac{1 \text{ amu}}{1.66 \times 10^{-24} \text{ g}} = 6.02 \times 10^{23} \text{ atoms}$$

$$26.98 \text{ g Al} \times \frac{1 \text{ atom Al}}{26.98 \text{ amu}} \times \frac{1 \text{ amu}}{1.66 \times 10^{-24} \text{ g}} = 6.02 \times 10^{23} \text{ atoms}$$

$$55.85 \text{ g Fe} \times \frac{1 \text{ atom Fe}}{55.85 \text{ amu}} \times \frac{1 \text{ amu}}{1.66 \times 10^{-24} \text{ g}} = 6.02 \times 10^{23} \text{ atoms}$$

$$196.97 \text{ g Au} \times \frac{1 \text{ atom Au}}{196.97 \text{ amu}} \times \frac{1 \text{ amu}}{1.66 \times 10^{-24} \text{ g}} = 6.02 \times 10^{23} \text{ atoms}$$

The number of atoms present, 6.02×10^{23} atoms is called Avogadro's number, since the scientist Avogadro proposed it. By definition, a **one-mole (1-mol) sample of any substance contains Avogadro's number of units**. As examples,

1 mol gold contains 6.02×10^{23} gold atoms
1 mol water contains 6.02×10^{23} water particles
1 mol pencils contains 6.02×10^{23} pencils

These statements are equalities that can be stated as unit factors.

$$\frac{1 \text{ mol}}{6.02 \times 10^{23} \text{ atoms}} = 1 = \frac{6.02 \times 10^{23} \text{ atoms}}{1 \text{ mol}}$$

$$\frac{1 \text{ mol Au}}{196.97 \text{ g Au}} = 1 = \frac{196.97 \text{ g Au}}{1 \text{ mol Au}}$$

$$\frac{1 \text{ mol Fe}}{55.85 \text{ g Fe}} = 1 = \frac{55.85 \text{ g Fe}}{1 \text{ mol Fe}}$$

$$\frac{1 \text{ mol Al}}{26.98 \text{ g Al}} = 1 = \frac{26.98 \text{ g Al}}{1 \text{ mol Al}}$$

Example 3.7

How many moles of sodium are contained in 20.0 g of sodium? How many atoms are present?

Step 1 Determine the atomic weight by referring to the periodic chart. The atomic weight of Na is 22.99.

Step 2 Calculate the number of moles present using the appropriate unit factor.

$$20.0 \text{ g Na} \times \frac{1 \text{ mol Na}}{22.99 \text{ g Na}} = 0.870 \text{ mol Na}$$

Step 3 Calculate the number of atoms present, using the appropriate unit factor.

$$0.870 \text{ mol Na} \times \frac{6.02 \times 10^{23} \text{ atoms Na}}{1 \text{ mol Na}} = 5.24 \times 10^{23} \text{ atoms Na}$$

Example 3.8

How many moles of uranium (U) are present in 546 g of U?

Step 1 The atomic weight of uranium is 238.03.

Step 2
$$546 \text{ g U} \times \frac{1 \text{ mol U}}{238.03 \text{ g U}} = 2.29 \text{ mol U}$$

Use of the mole allows chemists to "count atoms" in chemical reactions. If you think about the water particles discussed earlier, you will remember that each molecule of water contains one oxygen atom and two hydrogen atoms. To make water from hydrogen and oxygen with no waste, one could cause $2 \times 6.02 \times 10^{23}$ hydrogen atoms to react with 6.02×10^{23} oxygen atoms to form 6.02×10^{23} water particles. In the laboratory, a chemist simply mixes 16 g of oxygen (1 mol of oxygen atoms) with 2.02 g of hydrogen (2 mol of hydrogen atoms) to produce 1 mol of water.

Glossary

Alpha particle	A helium atom nucleus, composed of two protons and two neutrons.
Atom	The smallest particle of an element that can participate in ordinary chemical changes.
Atomic mass unit (amu)	One-twelfth the mass of one atom of carbon-12.
Atomic number	The number of protons in the nucleus of an atom.
Atomic weight	The relative weight of any atom compared with an isotope of carbon, carbon-12. Carbon-12 is assigned a mass of 12 amu.
Avogadro's number	The value 6.02×10^{23} particles/mole.
Cathode rays	Streams of electrons emitted from an electrode as the result of placing a high voltage across two electrodes under partial vacuum.
Coulomb	A unit of electrical charge.
Electron	A subatomic particle that has a mass of approximately 9.1×10^{-28} gram (g) and a negative charge of 1.602×10^{-19} coulomb (C).
Electronic configuration	The arrangement of electrons in an atom.
Element	Substances that cannot be decomposed by the ordinary types of chemical change nor made by chemical union.
Family, or group, of elements	A set of elements that appear in one column on the periodic chart. These elements have similar chemical properties.
Isotopes	Atoms of the same element having differing atomic weights because they have differing numbers of neutrons.
Mass number	An interger that corresponds to the sum of the protons and neutrons in an atom.
Molecule	The smallest particle of an element or a compound that can exist and still be recognized as that element or compound. Molecules contain more than one atom.
Neutron	Subatomic particle that has a mass of approximately 1.67×10^{-24} g and no charge. The neutron is located in the nucleus of the atom.
Nucleus	The positively charged core of the atom.
Proton	A subatomic particle that has a mass of approximately 1.67×10^{-24} g and a positive charge of 1.6×10^{-19} coulomb (c). The proton is located in the nucleus of the atom. The number of protons identifies the element.

Problems

1. Explain the difference between a compound and an element.

2. Explain how the mass and the charge on the electron are determined.

3. Atomic weights are always found by experiment. Why can't scientists determine the atomic weight of an element by adding the weights of the protons, neutrons, and electrons contained in an atom of that element?

4. Describe the Rutherford scattering experiment. What experimental results might Rutherford have expected if the protons and electrons were evenly spread throughout the atom?

5. Write symbols for:
   (a) hydrogen   (b) helium   (c) gold
   (d) silver   (e) copper   (f) sulfur
   (g) iodine   (h) oxygen   (i) nitrogen
   (j) calcium   (k) iron   (l) tungsten
   (m) carbon   (n) bromine   (o) sodium

6. Write names for:
   (a) Pt   (b) P   (c) Zn
   (d) Ne   (e) Co   (f) V
   (g) Cl   (h) B   (i) Si
   (j) U   (k) Rh   (l) F
   (m) Zr   (n) Li   (o) Pu

7. Explain the relation between atomic number and number of protons in atoms.

8. Determine the number of protons in atoms of each of the elements in Problem 6.

9. Determine the number of electrons in atoms of each of the elements in Problem 6.

10. Explain the relation between mass number and number of neutrons in atoms of elements.

11. Explain the relation between electronic orbitals and levels.

12. Complete the following table by filling in the number of protons and electrons and an average number of neutrons in the appropriate boxes.

Element	Protons	Electrons	Neutrons
Au	79	79	118
(a) Al		13	
(b) Ca			20
(c) Br	35		
(d) Ru	44		
(e) Na		11	

13. Using the periodic table, determine the number of protons, electrons, and average number of neutrons in:
    (a) Cr   (b) C   (c) U   (d) Xe
    (e) Rb   (f) Sn   (g) V   (h) S
    (i) W   (j) H

14. Fill in the accompanying chart.

Energy Level	No. of Sublevels	Orbitals Present	Total No. Orbitals Present	Total No. Electrons Possible
1				
2	2	s, p	$1s + 3p = 4$	$2 \times 4 = 8$
3				
4				

15. If the orbitals in a sublevel were shown as follows, with each box representing an orbital, and electrons were shown as dots, show how:

    s ☐
    p ☐ ☐ ☐
    d ☐ ☐ ☐ ☐ ☐
    f ☐ ☐ ☐ ☐ ☐ ☐ ☐

    4 electrons fit in the $3p$ sublevel.
    Answer: $3p$ | :: | · | · |
    (a) 5 electrons fit in the $5f$ sublevel.
    (b) 2 electrons fit in the $3p$ sublevel.
    (c) 6 electrons fit in the $3d$ sublevel.
    (d) 5 electrons fit in the $6d$ sublevel.

16. Write the electronic structures for atoms of the following elements:
    (a) Li   (b) Ca   (c) Ga   (d) As
    (e) Sn   (f) S   (g) Cl   (h) Xe
    (i) Cr   (j) Eu

17. Which elements have atoms with the following electronic structures?
    (a) $1s^2 2s^1$
    (b) $1s^2 2s^2 2p^6 3s^2 3p^5$
    (c) $1s^2 2s^2 2p^6 3s^2 3p^6 4s^2 3d^5$
    (d) $1s^2 2s^2 2p^6 3s^2 3p^6 4s^2 3d^{10} 4p^6 5s^2 4d^{10} 5p^6 6s^2 4f^5$
    (e) $1s^2 2s^2 2p^6 3s^2 3p^6 4s^2 3d^{10} 4p^3$

18. State which sublevel is the last one to be filled with electrons, in atoms of:
    (a) Pt   (b) Po   (c) Sr   (d) Cs
    (e) Rn   (f) V   (g) Gd   (h) As
    (i) Cm   (j) Fe

19. Copper (Cu), silver (Ag), and gold (Au) have been prized as valuable metals since biblical times. Their similar properties result from similarities in electronic configuration. Describe their similar electronic configurations.

20. What do the transition elements have in common in their electron arrangements?

21. Hydrogen, deuterium, and tritium are isotopes of hydrogen. All have one proton but different mass numbers, that is, 1, 2, and 3. How many neutrons are contained in each isotope?

22. The elements contained in the two rows at the bottom of the periodic chart are the lanthanides (58–71) and the actinides (90–103). Some exist in nature. Many are relatively rare and the man-made ones exist only for short periods. All the elements in both rows have a similar electronic structure. Explain.

23. From the electronic configurations of platinum (Pt) and gold (Au), explain why they might have similiar properties. It is interesting that both are extremely precious metals.

24. Using the periodic chart and your own knowledge as a guide, determine the physical appearance of samples of the following elements at room temperature:
    (a) Au—solid, metallic   (b) F
    (c) Hg   (d) H
    (e) O   (f) C
    (g) U   (h) Al
    (i) Ar   (j) Mo

25. (a) How many sodium atoms are contained in 1 mol of sodium?
    (b) How many sodium atoms are contained in 0.50 mol of sodium?
    (c) How many sodium atoms are contained in 2.0 mol of sodium?
    (d) Write a unit factor showing the relation of grams of an element to moles of an element.

26. How many moles of the element are contained in each of the following?
    (a) 9.01 g Be   (b) 14.04 g Si
    (c) 119.01 g U   (d) 80.16 g Ca
    (e) 13.48 g Ag   (f) 9177 g K
    (g) 889.06 g Y   (h) 315.84 g Se
    (i) 14.52 g Ge   (j) 55.84 g Fe

27. Calculate the number of atoms present in each of the examples in Problem 26.

28. (a) A student has 3 pencils in his pocket. How many moles of pencils does he have?
    (b) If one pencil weighs 10 g, how much does a mole of pencils weigh?

Learning Objectives for Chapter 4

Define **ionization potential, electron affinity, ion, cation, anion, noble gas, valence electron, outer duet, outer octet, chemical formula, ionic bond, formula unit, covalent bond, dimer, single bond, double bond, triple bond, molecule, valence, electron dot formula, polyatomic ion, coordinate covalent bond, resonance, bonding electron pair, nonbonding electron pair, bond angle, electronegativity, polar covalent bond, nonpolar covalent bond.**

Using a periodic chart, explain trends in ionization potential of atoms of elements.

Using a periodic chart, explain trends in electron affinity of atoms of elements.

Explain how ionic bonds form.

Explain how covalent bonds form.

Given two elements, predict whether their atoms will bond ionically, covalently, or not at all.

Compare and contrast ionic and covalent bonding.

Using a periodic chart, draw electron dot representations for atoms and formula units.

Predict the shapes of simple molecules.

Using a periodic chart, explain trends in electronegativity of atoms of elements bonded into compounds.

Determine whether bonds are polar or nonpolar.

Determine whether molecules are polar or nonpolar.

4 COMPOUNDS AND BONDING

The model proposed for the atom consists of a positively charged, small, massive nucleus surrounded by a negatively charged cloud of electrons. The electron cloud, which has little mass, occupies a tremendous volume compared with the volume of the nucleus. The electrons can be assigned to specific orbitals. Using this model of the atom, scientists can demonstrate how atoms combine to form the vast numbers of different substances in the universe. The model of the atom can be used to explain compound formation.

Many different models can be proposed to explain how atoms bind together to form compounds. Chemists generally use the simplest available model to interpret an observed phenomenon, since simplicity usually aids in communication and understanding. If such a model does not fit what is observed, the model can be expanded or changed. The bonding model we shall emphasize is based on the transfer of electrons from one atom to another or the sharing of electrons between atoms. By transfer and sharing, atoms attain full sets of orbitals. This is the simplest bonding model that explains the formation and structure of the compounds that we are interested in. More complex bonding theories require more complex models.

All models for atoms that bind together use electronic structure as the starting point for any explanation, and most continue by including the sharing or transfer of electrons between atoms. Therefore, it is necessary to begin our examination of bonding by considering why atoms might lose or gain electrons.

4.1 Electronic Structure and the Behavior of Atoms

The electrons surrounding the nucleus of an atom are attracted to the nucleus with varying degrees of intensity. The strength of attraction for an electron in a given orbital varies with the kind of atom. Thus, scientists have found that

97

some kinds of atoms lose electrons easily whereas other kinds gain electrons. Still other kinds of atoms resist both gain and loss of electrons. Gaining and losing electrons is important, because this is how some compounds are formed.

Ionization Potential

One way to measure an atom's ability to release electrons is to measure the atom's ionization potential.

> **Ionization potential** is defined as the amount of energy needed to remove an electron from an isolated atom.

Low ionization potentials mean easy removal of an electron from an atom. Once one electron is removed, enough energy can be supplied to remove a second electron, a third electron, and so on. Thus, an atom can have a first, a second, a third, and higher ionization potential, up to the number of electrons in the atom. The outermost electron is usually removed from the atom first. The second, third, and further electrons removed are closer to the attracting nucleus and are being removed from an already positive ion. They are attracted more strongly than the first electron. Thus, it is more difficult to remove each succeeding electron. Table 4.1 lists the first, second, and third ionization potentials for several elements. Since the concept of ionization potential is important in chemistry, the trends and implications of the information in Table 4.1 will be examined fully. The units on the ionization potentials given

Table 4.1   Ionization Potentials for the First 18 Elements (KCal/Mol)

At. No.	Element	IP$_1$	IP$_2$	IP$_3$	IP$_4$
1	H	313.6			
2	He	566.8	1254		
3	Li	124.3	1744	2823	
4	Be	214.9	419.9	3548	5020
5	B	191.3	580.0	874.5	5980
6	C	259.6	562.2	1104	1487
7	N	335.1	682.8	1094	1786
8	O	314.0	810.6	1267	1785
9	F	401.8	806.7	1445	2012
10	Ne	497.2	947.2	1500	2241
11	Na	118.5	1091	1652	2280
12	Mg	176.3	346.6	1848	2521
13	Al	434.1	655.9	2767	3593
14	Si	187.9	376.8	771.7	1041
15	P	241.8	453.2	695.5	1184
16	S	258.9	540	807	1091
17	Cl	83.3	300.0	548.9	920.2
18	Ar	363.4	637.0	943.3	1379

in Table 4.1 are kilocalories per mole (kcal/mol). They are useful for comparing values for different elements given in the table.

The first ionization potential for elements 3 through 10 corresponds to the second row of the periodic chart. For the elements in the direction from left to right across this row, the ionization potential becomes larger: Li, 124.3; C, 259.6; Ne, 497.2. This means that with each successive element across the periodic chart, it becomes increasingly difficult to remove the first electron from an atom of the element. This can be explained as follows. The outermost electron in lithium (Li) and thus the first electron removed from lithium is the $2s$ electron. This is an electron from the second energy level. Next is beryllium (Be), whose outermost electron is also in the second energy level. There is one more positive charge (proton) in the nucleus of beryllium, however, than there is in lithium. The result is four positive charges that attract four negative charges, a stronger force than three positive charges attracting three negative charges. It is therefore more difficult to remove the electrons in beryllium than the electrons in lithium. By the same argument, it is more difficult to remove one electron from carbon than from beryllium. Table 4.1 shows this trend. If you were to plot the first ionization potential against the atomic number for elements 3 through 10, you might expect a straight line, as shown by the dotted line in Figure 4.1. This corresponds to the filling of the second energy level. This theoretical straight line would arise from the regular increase of one positive charge added to each successive atom, with the corresponding additional electron located in the same main energy level. In reality, the ionization potential follows the solid line in Figure 4.1. Notice that beryllium (Be), nitrogen (N), and neon (Ne) do not lie on the expected dotted line but slightly above that line. This occurs because half-filled and completely filled sets of orbitals are more stable. Beryllium has a filled $2s$ orbital and is unexpectedly stable, as indicated by its higher ionization potential. It is more difficult to remove an electron from a beryllium atom than might have been expected. Nitrogen ($1s^2 2s^2 2p^3$) has a half-filled $2p$ set of orbitals and also has unexpected stability. Neon ($1s^2 2s^2 2p^6$) has a completely filled second energy level. It is very difficult to remove an electron from neon. Similar arguments extend to half-filled and completely filled d sets of orbitals.

There also exists a trend in first ionization potential for the successive elements down a column on the periodic chart. Look at hydrogen (H), lithium (Li), and sodium (Na). Apparently it becomes increasingly easy to remove that first electron: H (313.6); Li (124.3); and Na (118.5). Why does this happen?

For the elements down a column on the periodic chart, the number of energy levels increases. The outermost electron in hydrogen is in the first energy level ($1s$); the outermost electron in lithium is in the second energy level ($2s$); and the outermost electron in sodium is in the third energy level ($3s$). Moving up in energy levels means moving farther from the nucleus. Thus electrons in higher levels are farther from the nucleus and bound less tightly, and it is easier to remove them.

The trend is for the ionization potential to decrease (that is, electrons are

Figure 4.1 A graph of ionization potential (KCal/Mol) vs. atomic number.

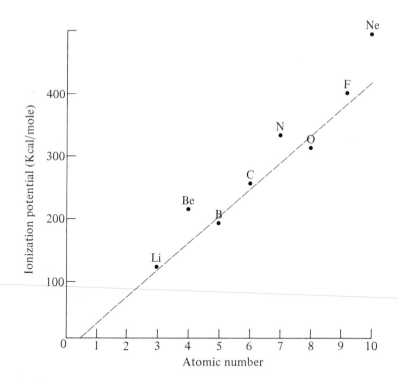

more easily removable) for elements down a column on the periodic table).
General trends on the periodic chart for first electron ionization potentials are
shown in Figure 4.2.

The last trend we examine is the ionization potential of a second, a third,
and other electrons in a given atom. This trend is also affected by the main

Figure 4.2 Periodic trends in first electron ionization potential.

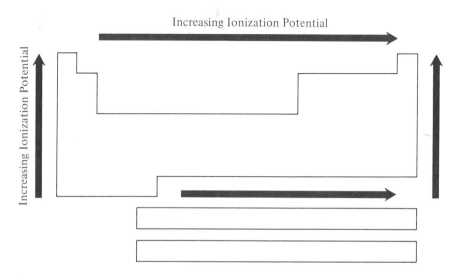

energy level and the orbital of the particular electron being removed. The second electron is more firmly entrenched than the first, the third electron even more so, the fourth still more so. Even larger differences than those within the orbitals exist among the different energy levels and sets of orbitals.

For example, the number corresponding to the removal of the outermost electron from the lithium $2s$ orbital is 124.3. The next electron removed comes from the full $1s$ orbital. The number associated with this ionization increases to 1744. It is more than ten times as difficult to remove the second electron in the lithium atom than the first. In a chemical process, a lithium atom would not be expected to lose more than one electron.

Now look at beryllium. It is relatively easy to remove the outermost electron ($2s^2$), with $IP_1 = 214.9$. The next electron (still in the $2s$ orbital is not so easily removable, which is expected, with $IP_2 = 419.9$. The third electron (a $1s$ electron) requires about ten times as much energy for removal: $IP_3 = 3548$. In a chemical process, beryllium would not be expected to lose more than two electrons easily.

Notice the large difference in the ionization potential of the element boron between the removal of the third and fourth electron. Can you explain this?

The ease or difficulty of removing electrons from atoms affects the way atoms link to form compounds. In your study, it helps to remember the following trends in ionization potentials:

1. In elements located successively across the periodic table, it becomes increasingly difficult to remove electrons from atoms.

2. In elements in the direction down a column, it becomes easier to remove electrons.

3. It becomes increasingly difficult to remove the second, third, and subsequent electrons from the same atom.

Electron Affinity

Electron affinity is the partner of ionization potential. Consideration of it along with ionization potential allows prediction of compound formation.

> **Electron affinity** is defined as the energy released when an electron is added to an isolated atom.

The greater the energy released when an electron is added to an atom, the stronger the attraction of the isolated atom for electrons. High electron affinities occur when an atom has a nearly filled set of orbitals and adding an electron will fill that set, creating a more stable species. Thus, some atoms would not have an electron affinity. That is, they would not accept additional electrons. Table 4.2 lists electron affinities for the first 18 elements. Notice that fluorine has the highest electron affinity and also an electron configuration $1s^2 2s^2 2p^5$. One more electron added produces a full second main energy level,

Table 4.2 Electron Affinities for Elements 1 through 18

Atomic No.	Element	Electron Affinity[a] (arbitrary units)	Atomic No.	Element	Electron Affinity (arbitrary units)
1	H	17.4	10	Ne	. . .
2	He	. . .[b]	11	Na	(12.5)
3	Li	14	12	Mg	. . .
4	Be	. . .	13	Al	(11)
5	B	(7)	14	Si	(32)
6	C	29	15	P	(18)
7	N	. . .	16	S	48
8	O	34	17	Cl	83.3
9	F	79.5	18	Ar	. . .

[a] Parentheses around a number indicate that the value has been calculated and not found experimentally.

[b] Ellipsis dots indicate place in which electron affinity is not expected to exist.

a stable configuration. Chlorine is second highest, with a configuration $1s^22s^22p^63s^23p^5$. The additional electron produces the stable structure $1s^22s^22p^63s^23p^6$. Other elements that have reasonably high electron affinities are hydrogen and carbon. For hydrogen, addition of 1 electron produces a full first main energy level; and for carbon, addition of an electron produces a half-filled $2p$ set of orbitals. Atoms of other elements act similarly. Look at other elements with electron affinities and see whether you can explain why these atoms might have a tendency to add additional electrons.

Remember that electron affinities increase for the elements in the direction from left to right on the periodic chart and from bottom to top on the chart.

A summary of the important ideas so far would stress the following.

First, atoms that contain electrons in half-filled and completely filled sets of orbitals are particularly stable. Second, one or more electrons are removed from an atom when the atom absorbs specific quantities of energy (which become its ionization potential). Some atoms absorb a relatively small amount of energy whereas others absorb a large amount. The electron affinity is a measure of the tendency of an isolated atom to attract an electron toward itself. Both ionization potential and electron affinity are related to the electronic structure of the atom.

The ionization potential indicates how easily electrons are removed from an atom to form a positive ion (a cation). The electron affinity indicates how easily electrons are added to an atom to form a negative ion (anion).

An **ion** is the charged particle that results when electrons are removed from or added to an atom or a group of atoms.

These parts of the model for the electronic structure of atoms are used in studying the two extremes of bonding: ionic bonds and covalent bonds.

The Concept of Bonding

The electronic configurations of atoms offer an explanation for the formation of compounds through bonding between atoms. The elements shown in the extreme right column of the periodic chart are helium (He), neon (Ne), argon (Ar), krypton (Kr), xenon (Xe), and radon (Ra). It is extremely difficult, though not impossible, for atoms of these elements to bond to atoms of their own species or to atoms of any other elements. Their "aloofness," then, a presumed characteristic of nobility, gives them the name **noble gases**. Atoms of each one of these elements have completely filled s and p sublevels in their highest electronic energy level. The electrons in the highest-numbered energy level of an atom are often called **valence electrons**. The highest energy level of helium atoms contains only an s orbital, so two electrons are enough to fill that level of a helium atom. These two electrons are called an **outer duet**. Atoms of other elements in the column have one s and three p orbitals in their highest levels. Eight electrons are required to fill these orbitals, and the electronic configuration is called an **outer octet**. Since the noble gas elements are so nonreactive, the outer duet in helium and outer octet in other noble gas elements must be stable electronic configurations. This high stability is also indicated by the large ionization potential of atoms of these elements compared with others in their rows. Since it is difficult to remove an electron from atoms of noble gases, their configurations must be stable.

The octet structure is the foundation for a model used to explain how atoms react with one another to form compounds and why only some do and others do not. According to the model, atoms of elements located in A columns of the periodic table can react with other atoms as compounds form—losing, gaining, or sharing electrons to attain an octet.

4.2   Ionic Bonding

> **Ionic bonds** result from transfer of one or more electrons from one atom to another.

The ionic bond can be explained in light of the outer octet concept. Consider an atom of lithium (Li), which contains three electrons. If it were to lose one of these electrons, two electrons would be left; they would completely fill the $1s$ orbital, producing an outer duet, like the configuration of helium. The lithium ion would then have three protons and only two electrons (Figure 4.3). Three positive charges from the protons and two negative charges from the

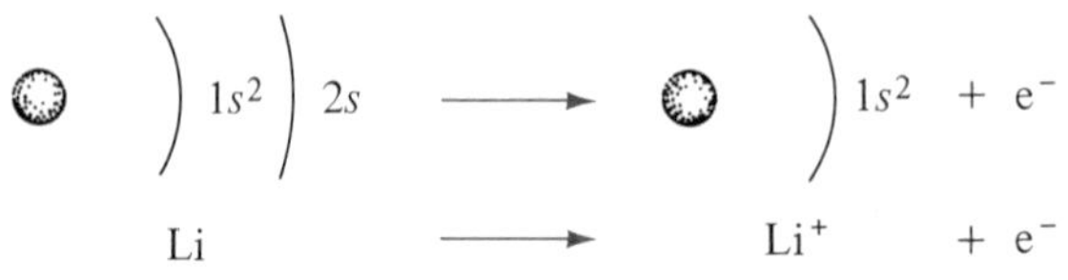

Figure 4.3 A lithium
atom becomes a lithium
ion by losing one
electron. The electrons
are shown in main
energy levels around
the nucleus.

$$\odot \Big)\ 1s^2\ \Big)\ 2s \quad \longrightarrow \quad \odot \Big)\ 1s^2 \ + \ e^-$$

$$\text{Li} \qquad \longrightarrow \qquad \text{Li}^+ \quad + \ e^-$$

electrons would produce a net charge of $+1$ on what was originally a neutral lithium atom. Such a charge is called the ionic charge, and the species formed, an ion.

The **ionic charge** is the charge on an atom after it gains or loses electrons.

A charged lithium particle (lithium ion) is shown as Li^+.

Lithium atoms lose only one electron, since losing more than one electron would destroy the outer duet, an event contrary to the tendency toward maintaining full levels and hence stability. Lithium atoms lose one electron each when forming compounds to attain the particularly stable heliumlike electronic structure.

In another example, the fluorine (F) atom has seven electrons in its outer $2s$ and $2p$ orbitals, $1s^2 2s^2 2p^5$ (Figure 4.4). Adding one electron produces an electronic structure like that of the neon (Ne) atom, $1s^2 2s^2 2p^6$. The original atom now has 9 protons and 10 electrons, a species with a -1 charge. This species is called the fluoride ion, F^-.

Notice that with the lithium atom, an electron was removed to form the full set of orbitals, whereas with the fluorine atom, an electron was added to accomplish the same end. Atoms tend to gain or lose the **minimum number** of electrons possible to achieve a full outer level. Therefore, lithium atoms do not gain seven electrons to attain a neonlike configuration nor do fluorine atoms lose seven electrons to attain a heliumlike configuration.

Elements in columns IIA and VIA behave in a manner similar to lithium (Li) and fluorine (F). A beryllium (Be) atom, for example, can lose two electrons to form Be^{2+}, producing an ion with an electronic structure like helium, $1s^2$. Oxygen atoms can gain two electrons to form O^{2-}, an ion with an electronic structure exactly like neon, $1s^2 2s^2 2p^6$.

Compounds are uncharged. Therefore, if uncharged compounds are to be formed from charged ions (according to the model), the charges on any ions present must be neutralized by the equal and opposite charges of other ions.

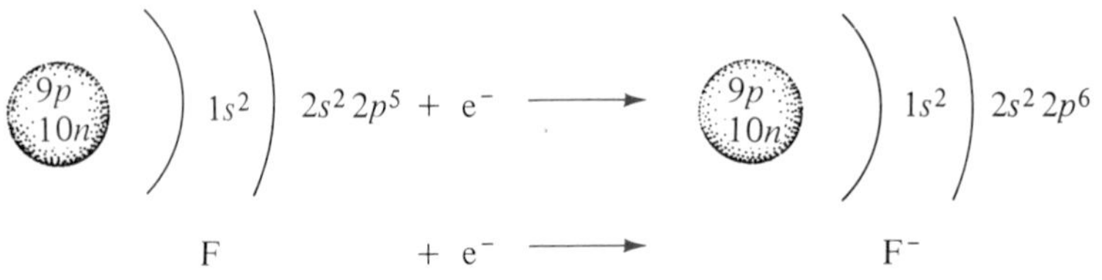

Figure 4.4 A fluorine
atom gains an electron,
becoming a fluoride ion.
The second main energy
level will be full if one
electron is added to a
neutral fluorine atom.
The fluorine atom then
contains 9 positive
charges (protons) and
10 negative charges
(electrons), yielding a net
charge of -1.

$$\left(\begin{array}{c}9p\\10n\end{array}\right) \Big)\ 1s^2\ \Big)\ 2s^2\,2p^5 \ + \ e^- \quad \longrightarrow \quad \left(\begin{array}{c}9p\\10n\end{array}\right) \Big)\ 1s^2\ \Big)\ 2s^2\,2p^6$$

$$\text{F} \qquad\qquad + \ e^- \longrightarrow \qquad\qquad \text{F}^-$$

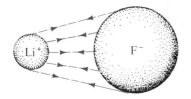

Figure 4.5 The lithium ion and fluoride ion are oppositely charged so they attract one another. This is an example of ionic binding.

This idea is the basis for the model of the ionic bond. If the neutral lithium atom (electronic structure $1s^2 2s^1$) were to donate its outermost electron to a fluorine atom (electronic structure $1s^2 2s^2 2p^5$), both atoms would have full sets of orbitals; the lithium atom would have a $+1$ charge, and the fluorine atom a -1 charge. Since opposite charges attract, the two ions would be attracted to each other, forming the neutral compound lithium fluoride (LiF). You will notice that LiF is a chemical formula. **Chemical formulas** are a shorthand way of representing compounds.

The force holding the two ions together in a pair is an attraction resulting from the opposite ionic charges; this attraction is the ionic bond.

Thus, an **ionic bond** is a bond formed as the result of the electrostatic attraction of two oppositely charged species. (See Figure 4.5.)

Compounds formed in this way are called ionic compounds. The individual components of compounds are usually called molecules. In the most formal definition, however, the ionic pair $Li^+ F^-$ is not a true molecule because the ions are arranged in a crystal. When many lithium and fluoride ions are arranged in a crystal, it is impossible to tell which Li^+ is paired with which F^-. (See Figure 4.6.) Therefore, the term **formula unit** has been established to mean one unit corresponding to the formula of any compound (for example, one Li^+ and one F^-).

Figure 4.6 Schematic diagram of an ionically bonded solid. It is difficult to determine which positive ion is paired with which negative ion.

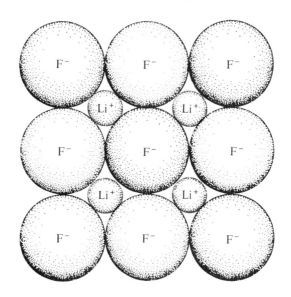

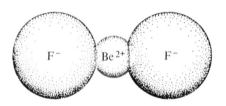

Figure 4.7 Formula
unit formed from
beryllium and fluorine
ions. Ions are shown as
simple balls.

Another formula unit that could be formed by exchanging electrons is a unit composed of the ions Be^{2+} and O^{2-}. The positive charges cancel the negative charges, and the neutral formula unit BeO, called beryllium oxide, is formed.

Beryllium ions and fluoride ions can likewise combine to form a formula unit. In this case (Figure 4.7), two electrons are exchanged, one accepted by each of the two fluorine atoms from a single beryllium atom. The compound formed is represented by the symbol BeF_2 and named beryllium fluoride. The symbol Be represents beryllium, F represents fluorine, and the numeral 2, called a subscript, means there are two fluoride ions in each formula unit of beryllium fluoride.

A similar example of ionic compound formation occurs when the two ions Li^+ and the one ion O^{2-} combine (Figure 4.8). This compound is represented by Li_2O and called lithium oxide.

So far, we have considered only 4 of the 106 known elements relative to compound formation. It would be very difficult to memorize properties of every single one of the 106 known elements. Fortunately, they can be grouped by similar properties. The groups are called families, and they are organized by columns on the periodic table.

Atoms with similar outer electronic structure are placed in the same columns. Thus, the elements in the columns headed by Li, Be, O, and F form compounds in the same way that the first element in the column does. Atoms of elements in column IA, for example, lying under lithium, tend to lose one electron when they form compounds. Atoms of elements in column IIA, under beryllium, tend to lose two electrons when they form compounds. Atoms of elements in column VIA under oxygen tend to gain two electrons in forming compounds. Atoms of elements in column VIIA under fluorine tend to gain one electron in forming compounds. When you realize this, you can predict the chemical behavior of 22 elements. The following examples show how to predict compound formation.

Figure 4.8 Formula
unit formed from lithium
and oxygen ions. Ions
are shown as simple
balls.

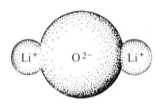

Example 4.1   Determine the formula of the compound formed when rubidium (Rb) and chlorine (Cl) combine.

Step 1   Determine the electronic structure of participating elements and ions formed. The electronic structure of Rb is

$$\text{Rb}: \quad 1s^2 2s^2 2p^6 3s^2 3p^6 4s^2 3d^{10} 4p^6 5s^1$$

and the structure of the rubidium ion is

$$\text{Rb}^+: \quad 1s^2 2s^2 2p^6 3s^2 3p^6 4s^2 3d^{10} 4p^6$$

Note the outer octet. The electronic structure of Cl is

$$\text{Cl}: \quad 1s^2 2s^2 2p^6 3s^2 3p^5$$

and the structure of the chlorine ion is

$$\text{Cl}^-: \quad 1s^2 2s^2 2p^6 3s^2 3p^6$$

Again note the outer octet.

Step 2   Determine how many of each kind of ion must be present to neutralize the charge. One Rb^+ neutralizes one Cl^-, so the formula must be RbCl, rubidium chloride.

Example 4.2   Determine the formula of the compound formed when potassium and sulfur combine.

Step 1   The electronic structure of the potassium atom (K) is

$$1s^2 2s^2 2p^6 3s^2 3p^6 4s^1$$

The potassium ion, K^+, has the structure

$$1s^2 2s^2 2p^6 3s^2 3p^6$$

A potassium (K) atom (located under lithium on the chart) loses an electron to form a stable $+1$ ion, K^+, in the same procedure that a lithium atom undergoes. Note the outer octet for the ion. The electronic structure for the sulfur atom (S) is

$$1s^2 2s^2 2p^6 3s^2 3p^4$$

and the structure for the sulfur ion (S^{2-}) is

$$1s^2 2s^2 2p^6 3s^2 3p^6$$

A sulfur atom can gain two electrons to form a -2 ion, S^{2-}; the oxygen atom has a similar procedure. Note the outer octet for the ion.

Step 2 Two ions K^+ bond to one ion S^{2-} to form a formula unit with zero charge, which is K_2S, called potassium sulfide.

In most compounds, atoms of elements in these four columns behave according to the rules given. Unfortunately, the concept of the ionic bond is complicated by electron interactions. Consequently, an ionic bond is never completely ionic. In a LiCl formula unit, the ion Li^+ does not have a full $+1$ charge and the ion Cl^- does not have a full -1 charge. Instead, they share one electron to some extent, and the electron in question spends most of its time around the chlorine atom, giving the appearance of an ion Cl^-.

4.3   Covalent Bonding

A **covalent bond** is formed when two atoms share two electrons. One must review atomic structure to understand this concept. The element fluorine, which exists in nature as F_2, is a good introduction to the necessary fundamentals. The electronic configuration for a fluorine atom is $1s^2 2s^2 2p^5$. If an electron is not available to fill the $2p$ orbitals, a semblance of a filled outer octet can be obtained if a valence electron is shared with another fluorine atom. Sharing means that two fluorine atoms, each with one electron in one of the p orbitals, both make use of these electrons in their outer level, essentially filling the level. This is shown in Figure 4.9. Sharing these electrons produces the covalent bond; the two electrons occupy both orbitals simultaneously, shared between two fluorine nuclei. Each shared pair of electrons is considered a covalent bond between two atoms. Two shared pairs constitute a double bond. Three shared pairs constitute a triple bond.

Figure 4.9

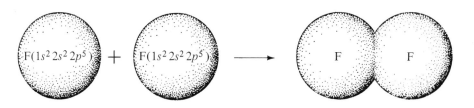

Figure 4.10

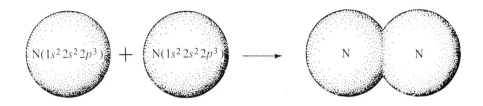

That triple covalent bonds can be formed is seen in molecular nitrogen. Nitrogen in its elemental state exists as N_2. The electronic configuration for nitrogen is $1s^2 2s^2 2p^3$, indicating that three electrons are needed to form a stable ion. The outer octet can be completed, however, if three electrons are shared. The net result is three covalent bonds between the two nitrogens; six electrons are shared between the nuclei. The bond between nitrogen atoms in N_2 is a triple bond (Figure 4.10).

Carbon is unique among the 106 known elements because its atoms can form covalent bonds both with other carbon atoms and with atoms of many other elements. The electronic configuration for carbon is $1s^2 2s^2 2p^2$. A carbon atom, to form an ion with a noble gas configuration, must either lose four electrons or gain four electrons. In reality it does neither. Carbon atoms share their four valence electrons with atoms of other elements to get the noble gas configuration. Four covalent bonds can form. Depending on the atoms to which the carbon atom bonds, the four bonds can be any combination of single, double, and triple bonds; four single bonds; one double bond and two single; one triple bond and one single; or two double bonds.

Sharing with four single bonds is shown by the compound methane (CH_4), commonly known as natural gas. In methane, the four electrons are shared, one each with a hydrogen atom, to form covalent bonds; the hydrogens contribute one electron each (Figure 4.11). The carbon and hydrogen atoms in the compound appear to have a full outer level. Notice that the directions in which the bonds point give a definite shape to the compounds formed from carbon.

Figure 4.11

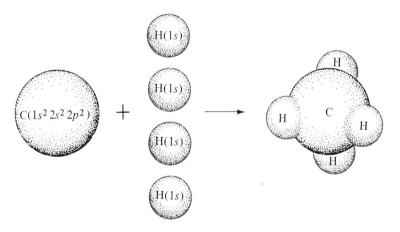

Figure 4.12

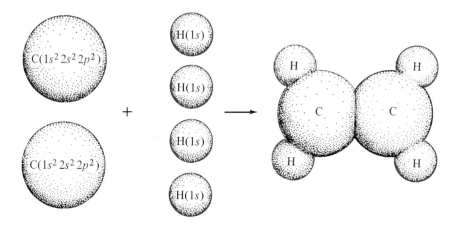

A carbon atom having one double bond and two single bonds is present in a compound like ethene (H_2CCH_2). In ethene, a carbon atom shares two of its electrons with another carbon atom; the result is four shared electrons and a double covalent bond. The remaining two electrons on each carbon atom are shared, one each, with hydrogen atoms (Figure 4.12).

A triple bond is present between the carbon atoms in the compound acetylene (HCCH). The bonding in this compound is explained by postulating six shared electrons between the carbon atoms, three from each carbon atom to form a carbon-carbon triple bond; the fourth carbon electron on each carbon atom is shared with a hydrogen atom (Figure 4.13).

Covalent bonding results in the formation of "molecules." Ionic bonding results in the formation of groups of ions (formula units) whose bonding partners are not obvious. The term **molecule** indicates the smallest unit of a compound in which the atoms are covalently bonded. The term **formula unit** applies to compounds in which there is ionic bonding, although it can also be used to describe molecules.

Some additional examples of covalent bonding follow.

Figure 4.13

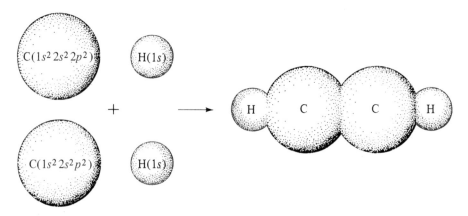

Example 4.3

A molecule can be formed from one carbon and two oxygen atoms (CO_2). Explain this arrangement.

Step 1   Determine the electronic structures of the combining atoms and predict how many electrons must be shared to form the outer octet. The electronic structure of carbon (C) is $1s^2 2s^2 2p^2$. Carbon atoms must share four electrons to attain an outer octet. The electronic structure of oxygen (O) is $1s^2 2s^2 2p^4$. Oxygen atoms must share two electrons each to attain an outer octet.

Step 2   Determine how many of each atom must be present to attain both outer octets. Two oxygen atoms sharing a total of four electrons help complete the carbon outer octet. The oxygen atoms attain a full octet by sharing two each of the carbon's four other electrons.

Notice that there are four electrons between the carbon and each oxygen. This is a double bond, or two bonds, between the carbon and oxygen (Figure 4.14). Two electrons form a single bond between atoms, four electrons form a double bond, and six electrons form a triple bond.

Figure 4.14 A molecule of carbon dioxide formed from carbon and oxygen atoms. This is an example of double bonding. A total of 8 electrons are being shared, forming 4 bonds, 2 bonds to each oxygen atom.

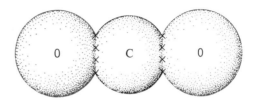

The remaining elements in columns IVA and VA behave like carbon and nitrogen. A compound consisting of three chlorine (Cl) atoms and one phosphorus (P) atom exists, phosphorus trichloride (PCl_3). A compound consisting of four bromine (Br) atoms and one silicon (Si) atom exists, tetrabromosilane ($SiBr_4$). There are many possibilities for combinations.

The column headed by boron, column IIIA, has thus far been neglected. Atoms of elements in this column require a total of only six electrons to have a stable configuration. For example, boron and fluorine form the compound boron trifluoride (BF_3). To do this, each fluorine atom must share one electron, and each boron atom must share three electrons. The result produces eight electrons around each fluorine atom and only six around the boron atom. The molecules of these compounds are called **electron-deficient**, since boron in its simple compounds has only six electrons in its highest electron level instead of eight. Atoms of the element aluminum behave much like boron atoms, as one would expect from the similar electronic configurations.

Elements in column IIIA often form compounds that seem to be more complex than the compounds discussed so far. The compound formed between aluminum and oxygen is an example. Each aluminum atom has three electrons to share. Each oxygen atom has two electrons to share. In this case two aluminum atoms supply six electrons, and three oxygen atoms provide six electrons; the molecules created are composed of two aluminum atoms and three oxygen atoms, producing Al_2O_3. Elements in column IIIA usually form compounds of this type with elements in VIA.

Finally, hydrogen, the common element we have not yet examined, has atoms that share one electron, to attain a heliumlike configuration. In this way, hydrogen atoms form single covalent bonds in compounds.

4.4 Electron Dot Representation of Compounds

To understand covalent bonds more fully, and how this type of bonding affects the chemical properties of materials, you will be helped by a simple schematic representation of a covalent compound. Such a representation is called an electron dot formula. Electron dot formulas provide a picture of a molecule, indicating the location of the valence electrons around each atom. This kind of diagram is very helpful in showing how a particular molecule behaves. Electron dot formulas, although primarily used for covalent compounds, can also be used for ionic compounds.

In writing electron dot formulas, only the outermost, or valence, electrons are used. For the element neon (Ne), the valence electrons are those electrons located in the second main energy level. The electronic configuration is $1s^2 2s^2 2p^6$. In neon, the second main energy level contains eight electrons, two in the $2s$ orbital and six in the three $2p$ orbitals. To symbolize this, one writes the symbol Ne and then puts dots for the eight electrons in pairs around the symbol. The electrons are placed in pairs because each orbital (one s and three p) can hold two electrons. In the atom, the pairs of electrons are as far apart as possible, because their negative charges repel each other. If four pairs of electrons were placed around the symbol for the atom, and these pairs were placed as far apart as possible, they would be at the corners of a tetrahedon. If the three-dimensional representation were compressed into two dimensions, the pairs could be shown as on a map:

N

W   Ne   E

S

Since there are eight electrons grouped in pairs in the outer orbitals of neon, and four directions in which to put them, the electron dot representation for neon is

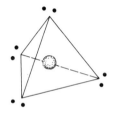

Figure 4.15 A tetrahedron with pairs of electrons at each corner. (The atom is at the center of the tetrahedron.)

It is important to realize that a three-dimensional atom has been projected onto a two-dimensional page (Figure 4.15).

The electrons in inner orbitals are not shown since they do not take part in bonding. For neon, only the $2s$ and $2p$ electrons are shown. All the inert gas elements below neon in column VIIIA of the periodic table have an outer-octet electronic configuration like Ne and can be represented by similar electron dot formulas. For example, xenon is shown as

$$:\overset{..}{\underset{..}{Xe}}:$$

Fluorine has seven electrons in its outer level and is symbolized as F surrounded by seven dots:

$$:\overset{..}{\underset{..}{F}}\cdot$$

The single dot can be placed in any of the four directions. Other VIIA column elements can be symbolized similarly.

The fluoride ion has eight electrons in its outer four orbitals and can be shown as

$$:\overset{..}{\underset{..}{F}}:^-$$

(The minus sign indicates that the ion has one more electron than it has protons.) The ions of the elements below fluorine in group VIIA can be represented in exactly the same way. The iodine atom and the iodide ion for example, are pictured as

$$:\overset{..}{\underset{..}{I}}\cdot \quad \text{and} \quad :\overset{..}{\underset{..}{I}}:^-$$

In Column VIA, oxygen and the oxide ion can be shown as

$$:\overset{..}{\underset{.}{O}}\cdot \quad \text{and} \quad :\overset{..}{\underset{..}{O}}:^{2-}$$

Atoms of nitrogen, carbon, and boron are shown as

$$\cdot\overset{..}{\underset{.}{N}}\cdot \quad \cdot\overset{.}{\underset{.}{C}}\cdot \quad \cdot\overset{.}{B}\cdot$$

Their ions are not shown because they usually share electrons and do not form ions very easily.

Atoms of beryllium and lithium can be shown as

$$\cdot Be\cdot \quad \text{and} \quad Li\cdot$$

Their ions can be shown as

$$Be^{2+} \quad \text{and} \quad Li^+$$

Both of these have no electrons left in what were originally their outer levels.

Example 4.4 Write the electron dot formula for argon (Ar).

Step 1 Find the element on the periodic chart and determine the number of electrons in its outer level. Argon is in column VIIIA and has eight electrons in its third level.

Step 2 Arrange the electrons around the symbol for the element.

$$:\overset{\cdot\cdot}{\underset{\cdot\cdot}{Ar}}:$$

Example 4.5 Write the electron dot formula for phosphorus (P).

Step 1 Phosphorus is in column VA and has five electrons in its third level.

Step 2

The dots around the individual atoms can now be used to picture bond formation. Consider first the fluorine molecule (F_2), which contains a single covalent bond. Fluorine has seven electrons in its outer orbitals. Stability of the atom is increased by completing the outer octet. It is completed as fluorine atoms add an electron and form the charged species F^- or bond covalently to another atom. The electron dot diagram or picture of the locations of the electrons in F_2 is

$$:\overset{\cdot\cdot}{\underset{\cdot\cdot}{F}}:\overset{\times\times}{\underset{\times\times}{F}}\overset{}{\times}$$

with two electrons shared.

The covalent bond consists of a pair of electrons. One shared pair of electrons equals one bond.

Note that there are eight electrons around each fluorine atom and a "single" bond is formed. Dots have been used to illustrate the electrons on one fluorine atom and ×'s have been used to show electrons on the other fluorine atom. This was done only to indicate that one electron was contributed by each fluorine atom to form the bond. All electrons look exactly alike, and once the bond is formed, it is impossible to tell which electron comes from which fluorine. The structure could be represented as

To simplify the electron dot formula further, one uses a line to represent a pair of electrons in a bond. This representation produces the diagram $:\overset{..}{F}—\overset{..}{F}:$, which can be shortened even further to F—F. This extremely shortened notation should be used only when one fully understands the electronic arrangements of the atoms involved.

Example 4.6   Write the electron dot formula for sulfur dichloride (SCl_2).

Step 1   Determine the number of electrons in the outermost level of each atom involved. Sulfur atoms have six electrons in their outermost levels and chlorine atoms have seven.

Step 2   Write the electron dot formula for each atom.

$$:\overset{..}{\underset{.}{S}}\cdot \qquad \cdot\overset{..}{\underset{..}{Cl}}:$$

Step 3   Determine the number of electrons each atom must share and draw the electron dot structure appropriately. Chlorine atoms must share one electron to reach the octet. Sulfur atoms must share two electrons to reach the octet. If the unpaired electrons are shared, the structure is

$$\begin{array}{ccccc} :\overset{..}{\underset{..}{S}}\overset{×\,×}{\underset{×\,×}{\times Cl}}\overset{×}{\underset{×}{}} & & :\overset{..}{S}—\overset{..}{\underset{..}{Cl}}: & & S—Cl \\ \times\overset{}{\underset{×\,×}{Cl}}\overset{×}{\underset{×}{}} & \text{or} & \;\;| & \text{or} & \;\;| \\ & & :\overset{}{\underset{..}{Cl}}: & & Cl \end{array}$$

The molecule has two single covalent bonds, one between each chlorine atom and the sulfur atom.

It is possible to form more than one covalent bond between two elements.

Example 4.7   Draw the electron dot formula for carbon dioxide (CO_2).

Step 1   Carbon atoms have four electrons and oxygen atoms have six electrons in their outer levels.

Step 2 $\cdot\overset{.}{\underset{.}{C}}\cdot \qquad \cdot\overset{..}{\underset{.}{O}}:$

Step 3   Carbon atoms must share four electrons to reach the octet. Oxygen atoms must share two electrons to reach the octet. If the unpaired electrons are shared, the structure is

$$:\overset{..}{\underset{..}{O}}::C::\overset{..}{\underset{..}{O}}: \qquad \text{or} \qquad :\overset{..}{\underset{..}{O}}{=}C{=}\overset{..}{\underset{..}{O}}:$$

Two "double" bonds are formed.

Example 4.8   Draw the electron dot formula for the bonding in nitrogen (N_2).

Step 1   Each nitrogen atom has five electrons in its outer level.

Step 2 $\cdot \overset{\cdot\cdot}{\underset{\cdot}{N}} \cdot$ $\cdot \overset{\cdot\cdot}{N} \cdot$

Step 3   Each nitrogen atom must share three electrons to form the octet. If the unpaired electrons are shared, the structure is

$$:N:::N: \text{or}   :N\equiv N:$$

A triple bond has been formed.

Table 4.3 shows several additional examples.

4.5   Representing Polyatomic Ions

Ions consisting of more than one atom can also be represented with electron dot diagrams. The atoms from which these ions are made are covalently bonded, and the final cluster is charged.

These are called **polyatomic ions**—ions because they are charged, and *polyatomic* because they contain more than one atom.

When one chlorine atom and four oxygen atoms combine, the ion formed is the perchlorate ion, with the formula ClO_4^-. A neutral chlorine atom has seven electrons in its outer orbitals. The neutral oxygen atom contains six electrons in the outer orbitals. For the -1 charge to be created, one additional electron must be added to the cluster. The total number of electrons that must be represented is 32: there are 24 from the four oxygens, 7 from the chlorine, and 1 to produce the charge. To write the electron dot formula, one must first choose a central atom.

Practice is the only way to be sure of choosing the correct central atom, but a few hints will help. Oxygen atoms are rarely connected two in a row; such an arrangement exists only in peroxides. Hydrogens can never be connected two in a row (except in H_2) because they can form only one bond. A good general rule to follow is to make the polyatomic ion appear as symmetrical as possible. This means putting one atom in the center and surrounding it by the other atoms present. Put the other atoms around it, forming single bonds from the central atom to the others.

Thus we should choose chlorine as the central atom for the perchlorate ion. In writing the electron dot formula, the extra electron can arbitrarily be

Table 4.3 Representative Electron Dot Formulas

Compound	Name	Electron Dot Formula for Atoms	Electron Dot Formula for Molecule
1) CO	Carbon monoxide	$\cdot\ddot{C}\cdot\quad \overset{\times\times}{\underset{\times}{:\ddot{O}}}\!\times$	$:C\!:\!\overset{\times}{\underset{\times}{:}}\!O\!:\quad :C\!\equiv\!O:$

(Both C and O have eight electrons around them. The oxygen has contributed more electrons than the carbon, but the total number in the molecule is the same as the total for the uncombined atoms. Oxygen has contributed four electrons to the bond, and carbon has contributed two electrons.)

Compound	Name	Electron Dot Formula for Atoms	Electron Dot Formula for Molecule
2) N_2O_4	Dinitrogen tetraoxide	$\times\!\overset{\times\times}{\underset{\times}{N}}\!\times\quad :\ddot{O}\cdot$	$\ddot{O}\!:\!\overset{\times\times}{\underset{\times\times}{:}}\!N\!\overset{\times}{\underset{\times}{:}}\;N\!:\!\ddot{O}\quad \ddot{O}\!=\!N\!-\!N\!=\!\ddot{O}$

(The total number of electrons in the atoms adds up to the total number of electrons in the molecule. The outer-octet electrons are 24 electrons yielded by four oxygen atoms with 6 electrons each, and 10 electrons yielded by two nitrogen atoms with 5 electrons each. The total is 34 electrons; N_2O_4 has 34 electrons as shown. Double and single bonds exist between O and N, a single bond between N and N. All atoms have eight electrons around them.)

Compound	Name	Electron Dot Formula for Atoms	Electron Dot Formula for Molecule
3) O_2	Molecular oxygen	$:\ddot{O}\cdot$	$\cdot\ddot{O}\!:\!\ddot{O}\cdot\quad :\ddot{O}\!-\!\ddot{O}\cdot$

(Experimentally, molecular oxygen has been shown to have two, unpaired electrons.)

Compound	Name	Electron Dot Formula for Atoms	Electron Dot Formula for Molecule
4) NI_3	Nitrogen triiodide	$\times\!\overset{}{\underset{\times}{N}}\!\times\quad :\ddot{I}:$	$:\ddot{I}\!:\!N\!:\!\ddot{I}:\quad :\ddot{I}\!-\!N\!-\!\ddot{I}:$
5) CCl_4	Carbon tetrachloride	$\times\!\overset{}{\underset{\times}{C}}\!\times\quad :\ddot{C}l\cdot$	$:\ddot{C}l\!:\!C\!:\!\ddot{C}l:\quad :\ddot{C}l\!-\!C\!-\!\ddot{C}l:$
6) BF_3	Boron trifluoride	$\times\!\overset{}{\underset{}{B}}\!\times\quad :\ddot{F}:$	$:\ddot{F}\!:\!B\!:\!\ddot{F}:\quad :\ddot{F}\!-\!B\!-\!\ddot{F}:$

(Remember that boron needs only six electrons.)

placed on the chlorine atom since it is the central atom. Write the symbol for chlorine with seven electrons placed as shown.

$$\overset{\times\;\times}{\underset{\times\;\times}{\times}}\!Cl\!\times$$

Now add the one extra electron indicated by the presence of the negative charge:

$$\text{:}\overset{\times\,\times}{\underset{\times\,\times}{\text{Cl}}}\text{:}^{-}$$

To complete the perchlorate ion formula, bring up an oxygen atom with its six electrons arranged as follows:

$$\text{:}\overset{\cdot\cdot}{\underset{\cdot\cdot}{\text{O}}} \qquad \text{:}\overset{\times\,\times}{\underset{\times\,\times}{\text{Cl}}}\text{:}^{-}$$

A covalent bond is formed, with the chlorine contributing both electrons for the bond:

$$(\text{:}\overset{\cdot\cdot}{\underset{\cdot\cdot}{\text{O}}}\text{:}\overset{\times\,\times}{\underset{\times\,\times}{\text{Cl}}}\text{:})^{-}$$

Notice that there are now eight electrons around the oxygen atom. This kind of covalent bond has a special name, coordinate covalent bond.

> A **coordinate covalent bond** is a covalent bond formed when one atom contributes both electrons to the bond. Once a coordinate covalent bond is formed, it has all the properties of a regular covalent bond and cannot be distinguished from other covalent bonds. The only difference is the way in which it is formed.

To complete the structure, add three more oxygen atoms to form three more coordinate covalent bonds. The situation is now

$$\left(\begin{array}{c} \text{:}\overset{\cdot\cdot}{\text{O}}\text{:} \\ \text{:}\overset{\cdot\cdot}{\text{O}}\text{:}\overset{\times\,\times}{\text{Cl}}\text{:}\overset{\cdot\cdot}{\text{O}}\text{:} \\ \text{:}\overset{\cdot\cdot}{\text{O}}\text{:} \end{array}\right)^{-}$$

All the atoms involved now have eight electrons around them, and the octet rule is thus satisfied. The -1 charge on the ion can be balanced by anything with a $+1$ charge such as the sodium ion, Na^{+}. The result is an ionic bond between the sodium ion and the perchlorate polyatomic ion. The compound described, called sodium perchlorate $(NaClO_4)$, is an example of both ionic and covalent bonding in the same compound.

Another example of how polyatomic ions can be represented is illustrated by the sulfate ion, SO_4^{2-}. This unit contains one sulfur and four oxygen atoms. This polyatomic ion has a -2 charge. Start the structure by writing the sulfur with its six electrons placed as follows:

$$\text{:}\overset{\times\,\times}{\underset{\times}{\text{S}}}\text{:}$$

Now add the two extra electrons indicated by the -2 charge:

$$\times \overset{\times \times}{\underset{\times \times}{\text{S}}} \times \quad 2-$$

The four oxygen atoms are added to form four coordinate covalent bonds:

$$\left(\begin{array}{c} :\ddot{\text{O}}: \\ :\ddot{\text{O}} \times \overset{\times \times}{\underset{\times \times}{\text{S}}} \times \ddot{\text{O}}: \\ :\ddot{\text{O}}: \end{array} \right)^{2-}$$

Notice that each atom now has eight electrons around it. The -2 charge can be balanced by forming ionic bonds with two potassium ions K^+. The compound, written K_2SO_4, is called potassium sulfate. This is another example of a compound in which both ionic and covalent bonding are present.

The nitrate ion, NO_3^- is more complex. It contains one nitrogen atom, three oxygen atoms, and one extra electron. To write the electron dot formula, begin with the nitrogen atom, arranging the electrons as shown, $\overset{\times \times}{\underset{\times}{\text{N}}} :$. Now add the one extra electron to form

$$\overset{\times \times}{\underset{\times \times}{\text{N}}} \overset{\times}{} \quad \bar{}$$

Three coordinate covalent bonds are now formed with the three oxygen atoms:

$$\left(\begin{array}{c} :\ddot{\text{O}}: \\ \overset{\times \times}{\underset{\times \times}{\text{N}}} \times \ddot{\text{O}}: \\ :\ddot{\text{O}}: \end{array} \right)^{-}$$

Notice that the nitrogen atom is surrounded by only six electrons. This problem can be remedied by moving in one of the oxygen electron pairs to form a double bond:

$$\left(\begin{array}{c} \ddot{\text{O}}: \\ \overset{\times \times}{\underset{\times \times}{\text{N}}} \times \ddot{\text{O}}: \\ :\ddot{\text{O}}: \end{array} \right)^{-} \quad \text{or} \quad \left(\begin{array}{c} :\ddot{\text{O}} \\ \diagdown \\ \text{N} = \ddot{\text{O}}: \\ | \\ :\ddot{\text{O}}: \end{array} \right)^{-}$$

All atoms in the ion now have eight electrons around them.

Another way of producing this structure is shown in Example 4.9, which illustrates a method that can be used for all electron dot formulas.

Example 4.9   Write the electron dot formula for the nitrate ion.

Step 1   Add all the valence electrons available for bonding in the ion. For NO_3^-, this would produce:

Contributor	Valence Electrons
N atom	5
3 O atoms	18
Extra e^-	1
	$\overline{24}$

Step 2   Pick out one atom to be the center. This is usually the single atom. For NO_3^-, pick nitrogen. Place one pair of electrons between each pair of atoms.

$$O$$

$$O:N:O$$

Six electrons have now been used, and 18 remain.

Step 3   Distribute the electrons that are left evenly over the remaining atoms, making sure that no atom is surrounded by more than eight electrons.

$$\left(:\ddot{O}:N:\ddot{O}: \right)^-$$
$$:\ddot{O}:$$

Step 4   If there are not eight electrons around each atom, form double and triple bonds to accomplish this. For NO_3^-, the nitrogen does not have eight electrons. Move one oxygen pair in to form a double bond:

$$\left(:\ddot{O}::N:\ddot{O}: \right)^-$$
$$:\ddot{O}:$$

The representation is now complete and correct.

The electron dot diagram for the nitrate ion could also be written

$$\left(\begin{array}{c} :\ddot{O}: \quad :\dot{O}: \\ N \\ :\ddot{O}: \end{array} \right)^-$$
 or
$$\left(\begin{array}{c} :\ddot{O}: \quad :\ddot{O}: \\ N \\ :\ddot{O}: \end{array} \right)^-$$

What has been done for the rearrangements is that the double bond has been moved around the nitrogen from one oxygen to another. All three structures are equivalent. When a rearrangement of electrons is possible, the true structure is not the first, nor the second, nor the third structure presented. It is a combination or hybrid of all three structures. This phenomenon is called **resonance**.

Whenever a molecule can be represented by two or more structures that differ only in the arrangement of electrons, **resonance** exists.

This means that the bonds between the nitrogen atom and the three oxygen atoms are not single bonds, nor double bonds—they are something in between.

One compound containing the nitrate ion is potassium nitrate, the principal ingredient of explosive black powder. It is necessary in writing this formula to have one ion NO_3^- per ion, K^+, and the formula is written KNO_3.

Example 4.10   Write the electron dot formula for the cyanide ion, CN^-.

Step 1   C   4 electrons
N   5 electrons
extra e^- 1 electron
Total   10 electrons

Step 2   C:N. Single bond between C and N; N chosen to be central.

Step 3 $(:C:\ddot{N}:)^-$. Electrons, 10 in number, are distributed around N atom and then around C atom.

Step 4 $(:C:::N:)^-$. Two pairs are moved in to form a triple bond, and thus eight electrons are situated around each atom. This is the correct CN^- structure.

A possible compound containing the cyanide ion is (KCN), from which is produced a deadly cyanide gas (HCN) used in execution gas chambers.

4.6   Predicting the Shapes of Molecules: Bond Angles

Electron dot diagrams can also be used to predict the shapes of individual molecules. The rules used in this prediction are developed from the valence-shell-electron-pair repulsion theory. After the electron dot diagram has been drawn, the rules implied by the information in Table 4.4 are applied.

Understanding the implications of Table 4.4 means understanding the term **nonbonding electron pair**.

Table 4.4 Shapes of Molecules

Bonding Pairs of Electrons	Nonbonding Pairs of Electrons on Center Atom	Shape	Example	Electron Dot Formula[a]
2	0	Linear	$ZnCl_2$	$:\ddot{C}l:Zn:\ddot{C}l:$
3	0	Planar triangle	BCl_3, $AlCl_3$	$\ddot{C}l$ $\ddot{C}l$ $:\ddot{C}l$ $\ddot{C}l:$ B Al $:\ddot{C}l:$ $:\ddot{C}l:$
4	0	Tetrahedral	CCl_4, CBr_4	$:\ddot{C}l:$ $:\ddot{B}r:$ $:\ddot{C}l:C:\ddot{C}l:$ $:\ddot{B}r:C:\ddot{B}r:$ $:\ddot{C}l:$ $:\ddot{B}r:$
3	1	Pyramidal	NH_3, PH_3	$\overset{\times\times}{N}$ $\overset{\times\times}{P}$ H H H H H H
2	2	Bent	H_2O, H_2S	$H:\overset{\times\times}{\ddot{O}}\overset{\times}{}$ $H:\overset{\times\times}{\ddot{S}}\overset{\times}{}$ H H

[a] The bonding pairs on the center atom are shown as black dots and the nonbonding pairs as x's

A **nonbonding pair of electrons** is a pair of electrons that does not form a bond.

The first example of this in the table is the molecule ammonia (NH_3). It has the electron dot formula

$$H:\overset{\times\times}{N}:H$$
$$H$$

The two ×'s represent a nonbonding pair of electrons or an electron pair that is not bonded to anything. This nonbonded pair makes a definite contribution to the shape of the molecule since its negative charge repels other negative charges just as electrons of bonded atoms do.

The first example in order in the table, $ZnCl_2$, has no nonbonding electrons. Besides compounds of boron and aluminum previously discussed, compounds of zinc also exemplify formula units that do not need an outer octet for stability. The zinc atom has the electronic configuration $1s^2 2s^2 2p^6 3s^2 3p^6 4s^2 3d^{10}$. Notice that the third main energy level, $3s^2 3p^6 3d^{10}$, is full, leaving two electrons in the fourth main energy level, the $4s$ sublevel. The two electrons in the $4s$ sublevel are used for bonding in covalent compounds. The chlorine atoms bonded to the Zn atom orient themselves as far apart as possible, at the two extremes of the Zn atom, giving a straight line, or a linear molecule. Another way of stating that the molecule is linear is to say that the bond angle is 180°.

A **bond angle** is an angle defined by an atom in the molecule and two others bonded to it.

In this case, it is

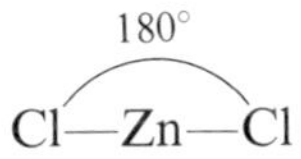

$$\overset{180°}{\overparen{Cl-Zn-Cl}}$$

The bonded atoms have assumed the largest bond angle possible.

Placing the atoms attached to the central atoms or the nonbonding pairs of electrons on the central atom as far apart as possible is the key to drawing the shape of a molecule with this model. In the next example in Table 4.4, BCl_3, the chlorine atoms are arranged as far apart as possible around the central boron. This produces a triangular flat molecule. The configuration is called a planar triangle. The bond angles in this molecule are 120°:

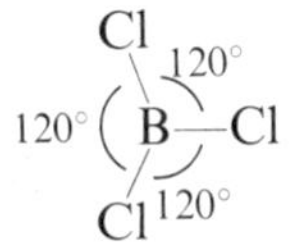

If four atoms are placed around a central atom, as in CCl_4, the tetrahedral shape is produced, since the tetrahedron allows a structure that sets the four bonding atoms at the largest bond angles, 109°.

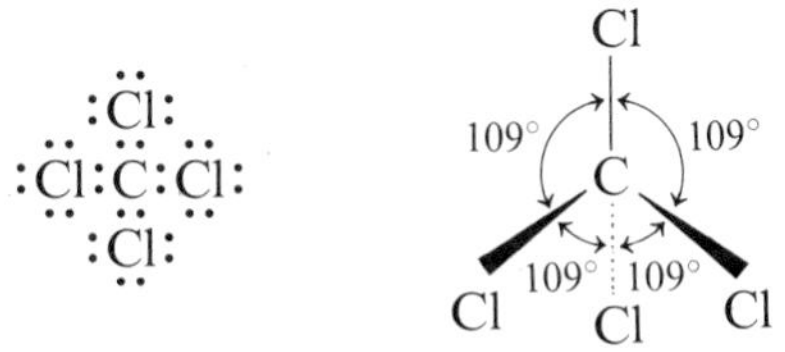

Example 4.11   Predict the shape of SCl_2.

Step 1   Draw the electron dot diagram for the compound. The electron dot diagram is

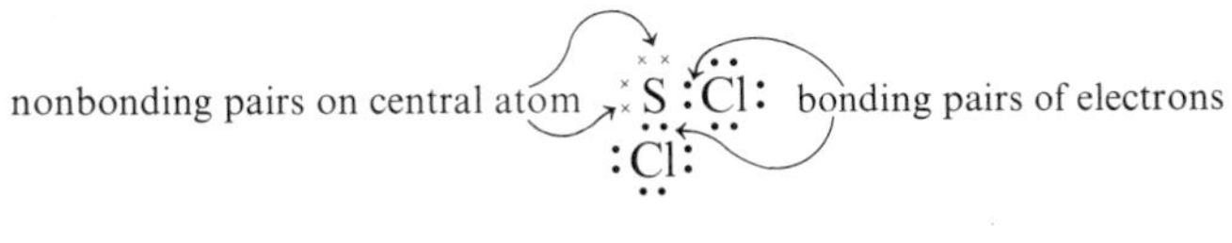

Step 2   Count the number of bonding and nonbonding pairs of electrons present. There are two bonding pairs of electrons and two non-bonding pairs of electrons around the central atom.

Step 3   Using Table 4.4, predict the shape of the molecule. The tetrahedral shape is the basis and the molecule is bent.

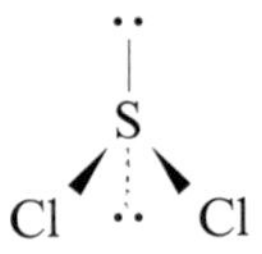

Example 4.12   Predict the shape of CH_4.

    Step 1   The electron dot diagram of CH_4 is

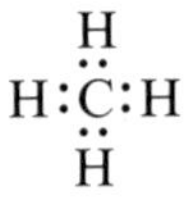

$$\begin{array}{c} H \\ \ddot{} \\ H\!:\!\overset{\cdot\cdot}{\underset{\cdot\cdot}{C}}\!:\!H \\ H \end{array}$$

    Step 2   The molecule contains four bonding pairs and no nonbonding pairs.
    Step 3   The molecule is tetrahedral.

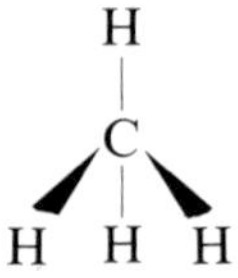

    The tetrahedral shape can be used as the basic shape for any molecule that has any combination of four atoms or nonbonding pairs of electrons around it.

Example 4.13   Predict the shape of ammonia (NH_3).

    Step 1   The electron dot representation is

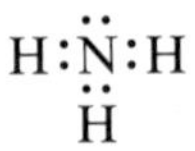

$$H\!:\!\overset{\cdot\cdot}{\underset{\cdot\cdot}{N}}\!:\!H \\ \quad\; H$$

    Step 2   There are three bonding pairs and one nonbonding pair.
    Step 3   The one nonbonding pair and three hydrogen atoms occupy the four points of the tetrahedron around the nitrogen atom. The molecule itself adopts the shape of a pyramid, with the nitrogen

atom at the top. The nonbonding pair actually repels the three bonds, lessening the 109° tetrahedral bond angle. The molecule is pyramidal.

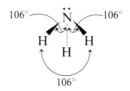

If two bonding atoms and two nonbonding pairs exist around the central atom in the molecule, the tetrahedral shape is still the basis.

Example 4.14   Predict the shape of water (H_2O).

Step 1   The electron dot formula of the water molecule is

$$H:\overset{\cdot\cdot}{\underset{\cdot\cdot}{O}}:$$
$$H$$

Step 2   There are two bonding and two nonbonding pairs.
Step 3   Placing the two nonbonding pairs and the two hydrogen atoms at the four points of a tetrahedron gives the bent molecule

$$\overset{\cdot\cdot}{\underset{\cdot\cdot}{O}}$$
$$H \qquad H$$
$$104.5°$$

The nonbonding pairs repel the bonds and each other to give a 104.5° bond angle, slightly less than tetrahedral.

Example 4.15   Predict the shape of $AlBr_3$.

Step 1   The electron dot diagram of $AlBr_3$ is

$$:\overset{\cdot\cdot}{Br}:$$
$$\overset{\cdot\cdot}{Al}:\overset{\cdot\cdot}{Br}:$$
$$:\overset{\cdot\cdot}{Br}:$$

Step 2   This molecule contains three bonding pairs and no nonbonding pairs.
Step 3   The molecule is a planar triangle.

4.7

Electronegativity ✓

In Section 4.2 the statement was made that no bond can be completely ionic; there is always some sharing of electrons. There can, however, be a completely covalent bond. The amount of ionic and covalent character a bond possesses largely determines how a molecule behaves.

The elements that tend to form ionic bonds are in the first two columns and the last two columns of the periodic table. Some of the elements that tend to form covalent bonds lie between these extremes (the B elements are ignored in this discussion). The elements in column VII can also form covalent bonds and so can many elements in columns V and VI. From this information, what conclusions can you draw about ionic and covalent bond formation? First, the farther apart the columns containing the atoms of interest, the more ionic the bond between the atoms. The closer together the columns containing the atoms, the more covalent the bond between the atoms. Thus, fluorine (F) atoms combine with themselves to form F_2 for a bond that is 100 percent covalent. On the other hand, the compound NaCl forms a bond that is about 90 percent ionic. Remember there is always some sharing regardless of how ionic the bond is.

This can be stated in another way. Atoms of the elements in column VIIA (F, Cl, Br, and I), draw electrons toward themselves very strongly. This produces a configuration resembling a noble gas. Atoms of the elements in column IA (except hydrogen) draw electrons toward themselves less strongly than any of the rest of the elements; these atoms tend to lose electrons to attain the inert gas configuration.

> Elements in column VIIA are very electronegative (attract electrons strongly), and elements in column IA are much less electronegative (attract electrons weakly).

Elements in between have electronegativities between those of column IA and column VIIA, and the electronegativity increases with the elements across the chart from left to right and decreases with the elements from the top of the chart toward the bottom. The relative electronegativity of some common elements decreases in the order

$$F > O > N, Cl > Br > S > I > C, H$$

The concept of electronegativity was developed by Linus Pauling, twice a Nobel laureate and also an advocate of vitamin C. A precise definition of electronegativity is difficult, but the basic idea can be used to explain the behavior of many compounds under a variety of conditions.

Table 4.5 Electronegativities of the Elements

H 2.20																	He
Li 0.97	Be 1.47											B 2.01	C 2.50	N 3.07	O 3.50	F 4.10	Ne
Na 1.01	Mg 1.23											Al 1.47	Si 1.74	P 2.06	S 2.44	Cl 2.83	Ar
K 0.91	Ca 1.04	Sc 1.20	Ti 1.32	V 1.45	Cr 1.56	Mn 1.60	Fe 1.64	Co 1.70	Ni 1.75	Cu 1.75	Zn 1.66	Ga 1.82	Ge 2.02	As 2.20	Se 2.48	Br 2.74	Kr
Rb 0.89	Sr 0.99	Y 1.11	Zr 1.22	Nb 1.23	Mo 1.30	Tc 1.36	Ru 1.42	Rh 1.45	Pd 1.35	Ag 1.42	Cd 1.46	In 1.49	Sn 1.72	Sb 1.82	Te 2.01	I 2.21	Xe
Cs 0.86	Ba 0.97	*	Hf 1.23	Ta 1.33	W 1.40	Re 1.46	Os 1.52	Ir 1.55	Pt 1.44	Au 1.42	Hg 1.44	Tl 1.44	Pb 1.55	Bi 1.67	Po 1.76	At 1.96	Rn
Fr 0.86	Ra 0.97	**															

*La 1.08	Ce 1.06	Pr 1.07	Nd 1.07	Pm 1.07	Sm 1.07	Eu 1.01	Gd 1.11	Tb 1.10	Dy 1.10	Ho 1.10	Er 1.11	Tm 1.11	Yb 1.06	Lu 1.14

**Ac 1.00	Th 1.11	Pa 1.14	U 1.22	Np 1.22	Pu 1.22	Am	Cm	Bk	Cf	Es	Fm	Md
						←			~1.2 (estimated)			→

Pauling himself defined **electronegativity** as the power of an atom in a molecule or formula unit to attract electrons to itself.

Electronegativity should not be confused with electron affinity. They have similar terms but definitely not the same meaning. Electron affinity applies to isolated atoms in the gas phase. Electronegativity applies to atoms bonded into molecules. Table 4.5 shows the periodic table with electronegativity values. Figure 4.16 shows a diagram of the general trends in electronegativity.

The greater the electronegativity value, the greater the tendency for an atom to pull electrons toward it. In general, the greater the difference in electronegativity between two elements, the more ionic the bond between two atoms. The electrons involved in a bond tend to be found most often near atoms of elements with high electronegativities rather than around atoms of elements with low electronegativities. Therefore, electrons are not equally shared unless the electronegativity of the two atoms involved in the bond is equal.

Bonds that are covalent and have electrons shared equally are called **nonpolar covalent bonds**. Nonpolar bonds exist where bonding is between two atoms of the same kind. Examples are H_2, Cl_2, and O_2. It should be clear that there are no electronegativity differences between two atoms of the same kind.

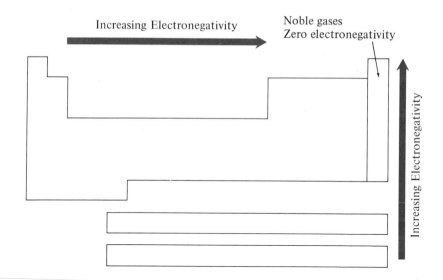

Figure 4.16 General periodic trends in electronegativity.

Increasing Electronegativity

Noble gases
Zero electronegativity

Increasing Electronegativity

Bonds that are covalent but do not have electrons shared equally are called **polar covalent bonds**. The greater the electronegativity difference, the more polar the bond. As the electronegativity difference increases, the bond eventually becomes ionic. The exact point in the changing electronegativity at which a bond becomes ionic instead of very polar covalent has not been determined. Polar covalent bonds are found in HCl, HBr, and HI. Concerning ionic bonds, a bond that is formed between potassium (K) and bromine (Br) will be much more ionic than the bond that is formed between selenium (Se) and bromine. The bond formed between sodium (Na) and chlorine (Cl) will be more ionic than the bond that is formed between sodium and phosphorus (P).

Molecules, like bonds, can be classified as polar or nonpolar. If a molecule contains only nonpolar bonds, it is a nonpolar molecule. Examples are

$$:N{\equiv}N: \qquad :\overset{..}{\underset{..}{Cl}}{-}\overset{..}{\underset{..}{Cl}}: \qquad H{-}H$$

The presence of polar bonds in a molecule, however, does not mean that the molecule must be polar.

In a molecule like carbon dioxide (CO_2), the shape is linear:

$$:\overset{..}{\underset{..}{O}}{=}C{=}\overset{..}{\underset{..}{O}}:$$

Although each bond is polar, the molecule is not, since the symmetry of the molecule is such that the polarities cancel.

A similar situation occurs in methane (CH_4). Its structure is a tetrahedron. Even though the C–H bonds are polar, the shape of the molecule is such that the polarities cancel.

All the following molecules containing polar bonds are polar:

$$\text{H}\!-\!\ddot{\underset{\displaystyle\cdot\cdot}{\text{C}}}\text{l}\!:\qquad \text{H}\!:\!\overset{\displaystyle\cdot\cdot}{\underset{\displaystyle\text{H}}{\text{O}}}\!:\qquad \overset{\displaystyle\ddot{\text{N}}}{\underset{\displaystyle\text{H}}{\text{H}\qquad\text{H}}}$$

In general, molecules containing polar bonds will be polar, but check the symmetry of the molecule to make sure that a special case is not involved.

dipole moment

4.8 Atomic and Ionic Size

Figure 4.17 shows the sizes of atoms given in atomic units for several elements. These values can be compared to the sizes of the corresponding ions listed in Table 4.6. The ionic radii are given for the most stable ions. Notice that the ionic and atomic sizes increase for the elements down a column, since more electrons are filling higher levels in these atoms. For the elements from left to right, atoms become smaller because the charge on the nucleus becomes larger and attracts electrons more strongly. Similarly, for the elements from left to right (last two columns), ions are successively smaller because the nuclear charge increases.

Figure 4.17 Atomic radii ($\times\,10^8$ cm)

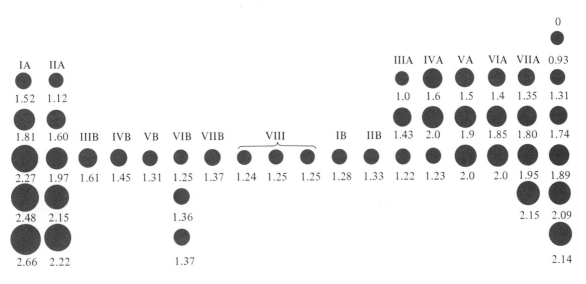

Table 4.6 Ionic Radius Values for Selected Elements ($\times 10^8$ cm)

I (+1)	II (+2)	VI (−2)	VIII (−1)
Li 0.60	Be 0.31	O 1.40	F 1.36
Na 0.95	Mg 0.65	S 1.84	Cl 1.81
K 1.33	Ca 0.99		Be 1.95
Rb 1.48	Sr 1.13		I 2.16

Glossary

Chemical formula	A combination of symbols and subscripts that represents an atom, a molecule, an ion, or a compound.
Coordinate covalent bond	A covalent bond formed when one atom gives both electrons for the bond.
Covalent bond	A bond that is formed when atoms share electrons.
Double bond	A bond that is formed when two atoms share two pairs of electrons between them.
Electron affinity	Energy released when an electron is added to an isolated atom.
Electron dot formula	A diagrammatic representation of the outer shell electrons associated with each atom in a formula unit of a compound or an element.
Electronegativity	The power of an already bonded atom to draw electrons to itself in a compound.
Ion	An electrically charged particle derived from an atom or a group of atoms.
Ionic bond	A bond that is formed when electrostatic attraction exists between two ions.
Ionic charge	The electrical charge on an ion resulting from gain or loss of electrons.
Ionization potential	Amount of energy required to remove an electron from an isolated atom.
Noble gas configuration	The arrangement of electrons within an atom or an ion that consists of an octet of electrons in the outer level of the atom or ion, specifically ns^2np^6, where $n = 2, 3, 4 \ldots$.
Nonpolar bond	A bond that exists when electrons are equally shared.
Octet rule	A rule that describes the tendency of atoms in A groups in the periodic table (except Group IIIA) to attain octets of electrons in their outer levels when they form compounds.

Polar bond   A bond that exists when electrons are unequally shared.

Polyatomic ion   An ion consisting of two or more atomic nuclei bonded covalently.

Triple bond   A bond that is formed when two atoms share three pairs of electrons between them.

Problems

1. Define (a) ionic bond, and (b) covalent bond in your own words.

2. Determine the number of atoms contained in each of the following formula units:
   (a) LiCl
   (b) BCl_3
   (c) $BaCl_2$
   (d) H_2CO_3
   (e) H_3PO_4
   (f) $(NH_4)_2SO_4$
   (g) $Ba_3(PO_4)_2$
   (h) $KClO_4$
   (i) $KMnO_4$
   (j) NaOH

3. Write electronic structures for each of the following ions. *Note:* All have octets in the outer shell.

   (a) O^{2-}
   (b) F^-
   (c) Na^+
   (d) Ca^{2+}
   (e) Br^-
   (f) Mg^{2+}
   (g) Al^{3+}
   (h) N^{3-}
   (i) B^{3+}
   (j) K^+

4. In column I are several electronic structures for ions; in column II are several ions. Match the electronic structures with the correct ions. *Hint:* There are two possible ions for each electronic structure.

I	II
(a) $1s^2$	(a) F^-
(b) $1s^2 2s^2 2p^6$	(b) Be^{2+}
(c) $1s^2 2s^2 2p^6 3s^2 3p^6$	(c) K^+
	(d) O^{2-}
	(e) B^{3+}
	(f) P^{3-}

5. Predict how many atoms of each element of the following pairs should form a formula unit of a compound. (Example: C + O equals a compound formed from one atom of C and 2 atoms of O.)

   (a) C + Br
   (b) Li + Cl
   (c) K + O
   (d) N + Br
   (e) Ba + N
   (f) B + S
   (g) Be + I
   (h) Si + O
   (i) F + F (shared!)
   (j) Sb + I

6. Write the formulas for the ions that will probably form or the number of electrons shared by the following:
   (a) Sr   (b) N   (c) F   (d) B   (e) K

7. Give the total charge for the following structures and name the corresponding elements:
   (a) 12 protons, 11 neutrons, 13 electrons.
   (b) 5 protons, 4 neutrons, 5 electrons.
   (c) 54 protons, 50 neutrons, 52 electrons.
   (d) 75 protons, 78 neutrons, 70 electrons.
   (e) 30 protons, 20 neutrons, 35 electrons.

8. Define **coordinate covalent bond** in your own words.

9. Draw electron dot structures for each of the following:
   (a) H
   (b) O
   (c) Al
   (d) Zn
   (e) C
   (f) N
   (g) Br
   (h) Be
   (i) K
   (j) Ne

10. Using the structures, explain how many electrons the atoms of each element in Problem 11 would lose, gain, or share in bonding.

11. Draw electron dot formulas for:
    (a) Na^+
    (b) S^{2-}
    (c) B^{3+}
    (d) Ba^{2+}
    (e) Si^{4+}
    (f) P^{3-}
    (g) Br^-
    (h) Mg^{2+}
    (i) Cs^+
    (j) Se^{2-}

12. Draw the electron dot structures for the following:
   (a) F_2 (b) HCl   (c) PCl_3
   (d) BCl_3 (e) CCl_4 (f) ClO_3^-
   (g) SO_3^{2-} (h) PO_4^{3-} (i) $ZnCl_2$
   (j) N_2 (k) PH_3 (l) SiH_4
   (m) AsF_3

13. Define (a) electronegativity; (b) electron affinity; (c) ionization potential.

14. Which of the following compounds do you predict would contain primarily ionic bonds or primarily covalent bonds, or both? Explain carefully.
   (a) Cl_2 C   (b) HCl PC (c) Al_2O_3 PC (d) SO_2 C
   (e) N_2 (f) NO_3 C (g) H_2SO_4 (h) MgS
   (i) CO_2 (j) NH_3 (k) $CdCl_2$ (l) KBr

15. Which of the following have double bonds? triple bonds?
   (a) CO_2 (b) PCl_3 (c) SO_2 (d) NO_3^-
   (e) Br_2 (f) N_2 (g) C_2H_4 (h) HCN

16. Predict the larger ion in each pair. Explain your prediction.
   (a) Li^+ or K^+ (b) Be^{2+} or Li^+
   (c) F^- or Br^- (d) S^{2-} or Cl^-
   (e) Sr^{2+} or Br^-

17. Often more than one electron dot diagram can be written for a molecule or ion; this is a way of picturing resonance. One example of resonance is the nitrate ion, NO_3^-. Write electron dot resonance structures for the following:

   (a) Carbonate ion (CO_3^{2-}) (3 structures)
   (b) Sulfur dioxide (SO_2) (2 structures)
   (c) Nitrite ion (NO_2^-) (2 structures)
   (d) Sulfur trioxide (SO_3) (3 structures)

18. Predict the shapes of the following compounds or ions:
   (a) PCl_3 (b) BCl_3 (c) CCl_4
   (d) ClO_3^- (e) SO_3^{2-} (f) PO_4^{3-}
   (g) $ZnCl_2$ (h) PH_3 (i) SiH_4
   (j) AsF_3

19. Carbon (C) in the form of coal combines with oxygen in the air inside a furnace to provide heat for many homes and to generate electricity. Predict a formula for the product of the combination reaction called burning. Predict the shape of the molecule.

20. High-sulfur coal, coal that contains significant quantities of sulfur, combines with oxygen to form a dangerous pollutant, sulfur dioxide (SO_2). Through a series of reactions, SO_2 eventually becomes sulfuric acid (H_2SO_4), which is responsible for lung, throat, and eye irritation and corrosion of metals. Draw electron dot formulas for SO_2 and H_2SO_4 and point out the number of single, double, and triple bonds present. In each compound, is the bonding primarily ionic or covalent? Explain.

21. Common sand is mostly silicon dioxide (SiO_2). Draw its electron dot formula. Determine the shape of each molecule.

Learning Objectives for Chapter 5

Define **chemical formula, binary compound, oxidation number, polyatomic ion, oxyacid.**

Name and write chemical formulas for binary compounds.

Predict formulas for compounds that result from the union of two elements.

Name and write formulas for compounds that contain polyatomic ions.

Name and write formulas for oxyacids.

5 NOMENCLATURE

Chemical nomenclature in various forms has been used and abused for three hundred years. Chemical names and symbols have been used for a wide range of things, from serious scientific communication to word games and bumper stickers. During the 1964 presidential campaign, advertisements for Barry Goldwater for president appeared in the form AuH_2O, combining the symbol for gold (Au) and the symbol for water (H_2O). Many chemistry students have puzzled over the compound HIHOAg until they realized it was the symbol for the famous cry of the Lone Ranger, "Hi Ho Silver."

Only within this century have scientists tried to standardize systems of chemical nomenclature. As a result of their efforts, many compounds are now known by more than one name. An organization composed of representatives of chemists throughout the world has undertaken to develop a worldwide system of nomenclature. This organization, known as the International Union of Pure and Applied Chemistry (IUPAC), has established rules for naming nearly all chemical compounds; it continues to develop new rules as new kinds of compounds are discovered or synthesized. Although we emphasize the IUPAC system of nomenclature, occasionally some **common** names are used, particularly those that are widely accepted.

5.1   The Elements

The elements are all represented by one- or two-letter symbols. In most cases, the letter or letters used to show the elements correspond to initial letters of the element's name. Hydrogen, for example, is given the symbol H; helium, He;

Figure 5.1   Some chemical names and symbols used by early chemists. Modern standardization of chemical symbolism and nomenclature have greatly simplified chemical communication.

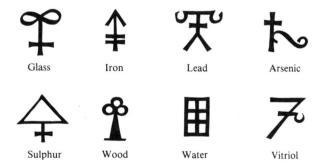

| Glass | Iron | Lead | Arsenic |

| Sulphur | Wood | Water | Vitriol |

calcium, Ca; and so on. Elements have usually been named by their discoverers, and this tradition remains in present-day science. Thus in the past twenty years, elements such as berkelium (Bk) and californium (Cf) reflect the location of their discovery—Berkeley, California. Element number 102, nobelium (No), went nameless for several years as scientists argued over who truly discovered the element and thus had the right to assign a name. Scientists are still arguing about whether the name for element 105 should be hahnium (the American discoverer's choice) or kurchatovium (the Soviet discoverer's choice). Several elements, particularly the substances that ancient peoples described, have symbols based on Latin names, even though the elements do not retain their Latin name. In these cases, the chemical symbol associated with a particular element must be memorized. The most common examples of these last-mentioned elements are listed in Table 5.1 with their symbols.

The elements are divided into two main categories, metals and nonmetals. The dividing line between these classes of elements is a zigzag line down the periodic chart (see front leaf) between the elements beryllium (Be) and boron (B), aluminum (Al) and silicon (Si), germanium (Ge) and arsenic (As), antimony (Sb) and tellurium (Te), and bismuth (Bi) and polonium (Po). The metals lie to the left of this zigzag line and the nonmetals lie to the right. Many rules for naming compounds depend on whether the elements involved are metals or nonmetals. Thus, the chart location of the metallic elements and the nonmetallic elements is important.

A few of the elements exist in nature in units containing a specific number of atoms. Nitrogen in the air, for example, always occurs in units containing two nitrogen atoms. Therefore, the symbol for elemental nitrogen is written as a capital N with a subscript 2, N_2. The subscript indicates that two nitrogen atoms are bound as a unit. Do not confuse N_2 with the expression 2N, which means two separate nitrogen atoms. Table 5.2 lists the common elements, with the number of atoms that make a unit in the elemental state.

Table 5.1 Elements with Unusual Chemical Symbols

English Name	Symbol	Latin Name
Antimony	Sb	Stibium
Copper	Cu	Cuprum
Gold	Au	Aurum
Iron	Fe	Ferrum
Lead	Pb	Plumbum
Mercury	Hg	Hydrargyrum
Potassium	K	Kallium
Silver	Ag	Argentum
Sodium	Na	Natrium
Tin	Sn	Stannum
Tungsten	W	Wolfram

Table 5.2 Common Natural Elements Having More Than One Atom in Each Formula Unit

Element	Formula
Hydrogen	H_2
Nitrogen	N_2
Oxygen	O_2
Fluorine	F_2
Chlorine	Cl_2
Bromine	Br_2
Iodine	I_2
Sulfur	S_8

5.2   Binary Compounds

A **binary compound** is a compound that contains two different elements. The number of elements is the only requirement the definition includes; nothing is said about the number of each kind of element present per unit. Two different elements, and only two, must be present. Thus, a compound containing one calcium atom and one sulfur atom (CaS) is a binary compound, and so is a compound containing two aluminum atoms and three oxygen atoms (Al_2O_3). Be sure you understand what the term binary compound means before you go on.

Binary compounds are divided into two categories—compounds formed between a metal and a nonmetal, and compounds formed between two nonmetals. The system of nomenclature changes as the category of compound changes, so it is important to note the kinds of elements involved. For compounds formed between metals and nonmetals, the following rules apply:

Rule 1   To write the formula for a neutral compound, be sure that the final charge on the compound is zero. To do this, you must assume a charge on each atom in a compound, even if the compounds are mostly covalently bonded. Follow the rule that the atom having the highest electronegativity has the negative charge. Thus, for $AlCl_3$, assume Al^{3+} and Cl^-. In SF_2, assume S^{2+} and F^-. These assumed, or assigned, charges are called oxidation numbers. **Oxidation numbers** are the real or assigned charges on bonded or nonbonded atoms. The oxidation number represents the combining power of an atom. Oxidation numbers of nonbonded atoms are zero. Although some charges are only assigned in this textbook, the units represented will be called ions. (Al^{3+} is not really an ion in $AlCl_3$, but it will be shown as such.)

Rule 2   Write the symbol for the metallic element first, and then the symbol for the nonmetallic element.

Rule 3   Name the metallic element in its entirety. Follow this with the name of the nonmetallic element, changing its ending to **-ide**.

These rules will become clear through a series of examples.

Example 5.1   Name the compound LiF.

Step 1   Separate the components, determining oxidation numbers. The compound is neutral: Li^+, F^-. Notice that the metallic element symbol is written first in the formula and the nonmetallic symbol second.

Step 2   Refer to the rules to name the compound. The compound is called lithium fluoride. The metal name has been written first, followed by the nonmetal name with the ending changed to **-ide**.

Example 5.2   Name the compound $MgCl_2$.

Step 1   The compound is neutral: Mg^{2+}, $2Cl^-$. Notice that the metallic element symbol is written first in the formula and the nonmetallic element symbol second.

Step 2   The compound is called magnesium chloride. The metal name has been written first, followed by the nonmetal name with its ending changed to **-ide**.

If you are having trouble remembering the oxidation numbers of the various ions, use the periodic chart as a guide. The accompanying Table 5.3 lists the generalizations for binary compounds of metal-nonmetal combinations.

The charges shown on the ions in the accompanying examples are used as though a completely ionic compound were formed. It is known that the atoms toward the center of the chart do not form ions, but imagining that they do helps in writing correct formulas.

Table 5.3

Group	*Charge of Stable Ions Formed by Elements*	*Oxidation Number*
IA	+1	+1
IIA	+2	+2
IIIA	+3	+3
VA	−3	−3
VIA	−2	−2
VIIA	−1	−1

Example 5.3	Name the compound Al_2S_3.
	Step 1 The compound is neutral: $2Al^{3+}$, $3S^{2-}$. The metallic element symbol is written first followed by the symbol of the nonmetallic element.
	Step 2 The compound is called aluminum sulfide. The metal name has been written first, followed by the nonmetal name with its ending changed to **-ide**.

Example 5.4	Write the formula for beryllium oxide.
	Step 1 Refer to the rules for naming compounds. The metal name is written first, followed by the nonmetal name with the ending changed to **-ide**.
	Step 2 Determine the oxidation numbers. The oxidation numbers are $+2$ for Be and -2 for O.
	Step 3 Write the formula by balancing oxidation numbers. One of each ion present results in a neutral compound, so the formula must be BeO.

Example 5.5	Write the formula for aluminum bromide.
	Step 1 The metal name is written first, followed by the nonmetal name with an **-ide** ending.
	Step 2 The oxidation numbers or charges on the ions are $+3$ for Al and -1 for Br.
	Step 3 For a neutral compound to be formed, each unit must include three Br^- for each Al^{3+}. The formula is $AlBr_3$.

Example 5.6	Write the formula for calcium nitride.
	Step 1 The metal name is written first, followed by the nonmetal name with an **-ide** ending.
	Step 2 The oxidation numbers of the ions are $+2$ for Ca and -3 for N.
	Step 3 For a neutral compound to be formed, each unit must contain two N^{3-} for every three Ca^{2+}: $3 \times (+2) = +6$; $2 \times (-3) = -6$. The formula is Ca_3N_2.

The rules discussed thus far cover most compounds formed between metals and nonmetals in the A groups on the periodic chart. An additional rule must be added, however, to deal with the transition elements in the B groups on the periodic chart and such elements as tin (Sn) and lead (Pb). Atoms of these elements can have more than one possible oxidation number. For example, the name **nickel oxide** could refer to one of two possible compounds, NiO or Ni_2O_3. (Nickel can exist as Ni^{2+} or Ni^{3+}. Here, oxygen exists as O^{2-}.) To overcome this problem, another rule is necessary.

If a metal in a binary compound can have more than one possible oxidation number, the oxidation number of the metallic element is shown using a roman numeral in parentheses immediately following the name of the metallic element; this usage is called the **Stock notation**. This rule, too, can be explained by examples.

Example 5.7

Name the compound NiO.

Step 1 The compound is neutral. Since oxygen exists as O^{2-} in these compounds, nickel must exist as Ni^{2+}.

Step 2 The name of the compound is nickel(II) oxide. The (II) indicates the $+2$ charge on the nickel.

Example 5.8

Name the compound Ni_2O_3.

Step 1 The compound is neutral. Since oxygen exists as O^{2-} in these compounds, the total charge coming from the oxygen is -6: $3 \times (-2) = -6$. Thus each nickel ion must be $+3$: $2 \times (+3) = +6$.

Step 2 The name of the compound is nickel(III) oxide.

Example 5.9

Name the compound $CuCl_2$.

Step 1 The compound is neutral. Since the chloride ion exists as Cl^-, oxidation number $= -1$, the total charge contributed by the chlorines is -2. The copper ion must be Cu^{2+}, a $+2$ oxidation number.

Step 2 The compound is called copper(II) chloride.

Example 5.10

Write the formula for cobalt(III) fluoride.

Steps 1 and 2 The compound is neutral. The cobalt has a $+3$ oxidation number in this compound and the fluoride ion has a -1 oxidation number.

Step 3 There must be three fluoride ions present to offset the ion Co^{3+}. The formula is written CoF_3.

Example 5.11

Write the formula for manganese(II) sulfide.

Steps 1 and 2 The compound is neutral. The manganese ion in this compound has a $+2$ oxidation number, and the sulfide ion has a -2 oxidation number.

Step 3 One Mn^{2+} is needed for each S^{2-} in the compound. The formula for the compound is MnS.

Ch. 5   NOMENCLATURE

Example 5.12   Write the formula for iron(II) nitride.

Steps 1 and 2   The compound is neutral. The iron ion in this compound has a $+2$ oxidation number and the nitride ion exists as N^{3-}, with a -3 oxidation number.

Step 3   There must be three iron ions for every two nitride ions. The formula for this compound is Fe_3N_2.

The nomenclature for these kinds of compounds is complicated by tradition. Years before the present system came into being, chemists had other ways of naming compounds. Some of these older names are still used so commonly that we must know them. The old method used to distinguish between two different oxidation numbers for metals was to change the ending of the metal to either *-ous* or *-ic*. The *-ous* suffix represents the lower oxidation number and *-ic* the higher. For example, Fe^{2+} is called the ferrous iron, and Fe^{3+} is called the ferric ion. The formula $FeCl_2$, then, designates ferrous chloride, and $FeCl_3$ ferric chloride. There are only a few metals for which one must know the common names, although this system can be applied to most metals. The important ones are listed in Table 5.4.

The rules given and the information regarding the common system of nomenclature should enable you to name binary compounds composed of two different nonmetallic elements. Because such compounds are bonded covalently (see Chapter 4) and seem to form bonds differing in number in the different compounds, the initial set of nomenclature rules is changed slightly.

Rule 1   In a formula, the symbol for the most positive elements, or the least electronegative element (Chapter 4), is written first.

Rule 2   In naming compounds, the number of atoms of each type is specified by prefixes that state how many of each element are present in a formula unit.

Table 5.4   Common names for some metal ions and compounds

Ion		Compound	
Fe^{2+}	Ferrous ion	FeO	Ferrous oxide
Fe^{3+}	Ferric ion	Fe_2O_3	Ferric oxide
Cu^+	Cuprous ion	Cu_2S	Cuprous sulfide
Cu^{2+}	Cupric ion	CuS	Cupric sulfide
Hg_2^{2+}	Mercurous ion[a]	Hg_2Cl_2	Mercurous chloride
Hg^{2+}	Mercuric ion	$HgCl_2$	Mercuric chloride
Sn^{2+}	Stannous ion	$SnCl_2$	Stannous chloride
Sn^{4+}	Stannic ion	$SnCl_4$	Stannic chloride

[a] Mercury plus one (Hg^+) always occurs as a dimer (two mercurys together) so it is symbolized Hg_2^{2+}.

Table 5.5 Prefixes and Compounds

Prefix	Meaning		Compounds
Mono-	One	CO	Carbon monoxide
Di-	Two	SO_2	Sulfur dioxide
Tri-	Three	NI_3	Nitrogen triiodide
Tetra-	Four	N_2O_4	Dinitrogen tetraoxide
Penta-	Five	P_2S_5	Diphosphorus pentasulfide
Hexa-	Six	SF_6	Sulfur hexafluoride
Hepta-	Seven	Cl_2O_7	Dichlorine heptaoxide
Octa-	Eight	Br_3O_8	Tribromine octaoxide
Nona-	Nine	I_4O_9	Tetraiodine nonaoxide
Deca-	Ten	P_4O_{10}	Tetraphosphorus decaoxide

You see that charges are not used in naming, since the elements in nonmetal-nonmetal binary compounds are covalently bonded and have no charges. Table 5.5 lists the prefixes used.

Notice, in the entries of Table 5.5, that if the initial or most positive element occurs only once in the formula unit, the prefix **mono-** is not used. Notice also that the name of the more positive element is written first in its entirety and that the ending on the more negative element is always **-ide**.

Naming and writing formulas for these compounds requires knowing the rules and a familiarity with Table 5.5.

Example 5.13

Name the compound CO_2.

This is a binary compound of two nonmetals. The numerical prefixes are used in the name. Since there is only one carbon atom present in the formula unit, no prefix is used. The compound is called carbon dioxide.

Example 5.14

Name the compound BCl_3.

The compound is a binary compound of two nonmetals. The numerical prefixes are used in the name. The compound is called boron trichloride.

Example 5.15

Write the formula for diarsenic trioxide.

The name indicates that there are two arsenic and three oxygen atoms per formula unit. The formula for the compound is As_2O_3.

Example 5.16

Write the formula for nitrogen tribromide.

The name indicates that there are one nitrogen atom and three bromine atoms in the formula unit. The formula is NBr_3.

5.3 Binary Compounds Containing Hydrogen and Nonmetals

The rules in Section 5.2 cover all the binary compounds except those containing hydrogen and nonmetals. The compounds can be named, as it has already been established: HCl as a gas is named hydrogen chloride. Or if the substance is known to be mixed with water, it can be named as an acid: HCl is then hydrochloric acid.

These compounds are called acids because when added to water they split apart to produce a hydrogen ion, H^+, and a negative ion, characteristic of what acids do. The acid name begins with **hydro**. The prefix indicates that the molecule consists of hydrogen and a nonmetal, with no oxygen present. These compounds are also called binary acids.

Example 5.17 Name the compound HBr.

HBr: hydrogen bromide (if no water present)
hydrobromic acid (if water is mixed with the compound)

Example 5.18 Name the compound H_2S.

H_2S: hydrogen sulfide (if no water is present)
hydrosulfuric acid (if water is mixed with the compound)

Some compounds are exceptions. They have long had common names and still retain them. Two examples are H_2O, water, and NH_3, ammonia.

5.4 Polyatomic Ions

We have already become familiar with examples of ions that contain two or more different elements bonded covalently and possessing a charge (Chapter 4). These units, because of their covalent character, bond together as a stable unit. They have names characteristic of the unit. Table 5.6 lists common polyatomic ions and the charge associated with these ions.

The rules for naming compounds containing these ions are like the rules for naming metal-nonmetal binary compounds, except that the names of polyatomic ions are substituted where appropriate. Examples of such compounds are here listed.

$NaNO_3$	Sodium nitrate	$CaSO_4$	Calcium sulfate
$CuNO_3$	Copper(I) nitrate	$Al(ClO_3)_3$	Aluminum chlorate
$Cu(NO_3)_2$	Copper(II) nitrate	$KMnO_4$	Potassium permanganate
		NH_4Cl	Ammonium chloride

Notice that as usual, the positive element or ion is written out in its entirety. In most compounds shown, the charge on the positive ions is not indicated, since the positive ions can have only one charge. Copper, however, may have either a $+1$ or a $+2$ charge; thus the charge is indicated in parentheses.

There is no shortcut method for naming compounds with polyatomic ions. The ions and the charge associated with each ion must be memorized.

Here are a few more examples.

Table 5.6 Polyatomic Ions

Name of Ion	Formula
Ammonium ion	NH_4^+
Acetate ion	$C_2H_3O_2^-$
Bicarbonate ion	HCO_3^-
Carbonate ion	CO_3^{2-}
Chromate ion	CrO_4^{2-}
Dichromate ion	$Cr_2O_7^{2-}$
Cyanide ion	CN^-
Hydroxide ion	OH^-
Nitrate ion	NO_3^-
Nitrite ion	NO_2^-
Permanganate ion	MnO_4^-
Phosphate ion	PO_4^{3-}
Monohydrogen phosphate ion	HPO_4^{2-}
Dihydrogen phosphate ion	$H_2PO_4^-$
Sulfate ion	SO_4^{2-}
Bisulfate ion (or hydrogen sulfate ion)	HSO_4^-
Sulfite ion	SO_3^{2-}
Bisulfite ion	HSO_3^-
Perchlorate ion	ClO_4^-
Chlorate ion	ClO_3^-
Chlorite ion	ClO_2^-
Hypochlorite ion	ClO^-

Example 5.19			Write the formula for calcium sulfate.
	Step 1		Determine the appropriate oxidation numbers or charges. The formula for the sulfate ion is SO_4 and it has a -2 charge, giving $SO_4{}^{2-}$. Calcium has a $+2$ charge, giving Ca^{2+}.
	Step 2		Write the formula for a neutral compound. Combining one of each of the ions results in a neutral formula unit. The formula is $CaSO_4$.

Example 5.20			Write the formula for ammonium phosphate.
	Step 1		The phosphate ion is $PO_4{}^{3-}$. The ammonium ion is $NH_4{}^+$.
	Step 2		Thus, three ammonium ions must be present to offset the charge on the phosphate ion in a neutral compound. The formula is $(NH_4)_3PO_4$.

Note that parentheses are used and that the ammonium ion is listed first since it has a positive charge.

5.5   Common Oxy Acids

Many of the polyatomic ions listed in Section 5.4 can be associated with a hydrogen ion instead of some other metal ion. When these compounds are mixed with water, they are named as acids, just as the hydrogen-containing binary compounds studied in Section 5.3 were. They are named in a logical way, but learning them is best done by memorization. The common oxy acids are listed in Table 5.7. The associated polyatomic ions are included.

Table 5.7 Common oxy acids

	Acid		*Associated polyatomic ion*
$HC_2H_3O_2$	Acetic acid	$C_2H_3O_2{}^-$	Acetate ion
H_2CO_3	Carbonic acid	$CO_3{}^{-2}$	Carbonate ion
$HClO_4$	Perchloric acid	$ClO_4{}^-$	Perchlorate ion
$HClO_3$	Chloric acid	$ClO_3{}^-$	Chlorate ion
$HClO_2$	Chlorous acid	$ClO_2{}^-$	Chlorite ion
$HClO$	Hypochlorous acid	ClO^-	Hypochlorite ion
HNO_3	Nitric acid	$NO_3{}^-$	Nitrate ion
HNO_2	Nitrous acid	$NO_2{}^-$	Nitrite ion
H_3PO_4	Phosphoric acid	$PO_4{}^{3-}$	Phosphate ion
H_2SO_4	Sulfuric acid	$SO_4{}^{2-}$	Sulfate ion
H_2SO_3	Sulfurous acid	$SO_3{}^{2-}$	Sulfite ion

Glossary

Acid A compound that produces the ions H^+ when it is dissolved in water.

Binary compound A compound whose formula units are composed of atoms of only two elements.

Chemical formula A combination of symbols and subscripts used to represent an atom, a molecule, or an ion.

Oxidation number Real or assigned charges on bonded or nonbonded atoms. The oxidation number represents the combining power of an atom.

Oxy acids Compounds composed of hydrogen ion and oxygen-containing polyatomic ions that dissociate to form some hydrogen ion (H^+) when they are found in water.

Polyatomic ions A grouping of two or more elements bonded covalently and possessing a charge.

Problems

1. Name the following compounds:
   (a) Cl_2 (b) N_2 (c) $CdCl_2$
   (d) HCl (e) MgS (f) KBr
   (g) Al_2O_3 (h) CO_2 (i) PCl_3
   (j) SO_2 (k) NH_3 (l) P_4

2. Name the following compounds:
   (a) $NaCl$ (b) Cl_2O_7 (c) Be_3N_2
   (d) SnS (e) HgO (f) CrS
   (g) SnS_2 (h) BaF_2 (i) Fe_2O_3
   (j) P_2O_5 (k) Li_2S (l) MgI_2

3. Name the following compounds:
   (a) Rb_3P (b) CO (c) K_2S
   (d) $SrSe$ (e) PCl_5 (f) CaO
   (g) MgO (h) BF_3 (i) Hg_2Cl_2
   (j) AlN (k) LiI (l) Co_3N_2

4. Name the following compounds:
   (a) $KHCO_3$ (b) HNO_3 (c) $MgSO_4$
   (d) $MgCO_3$ (e) $KMnO_4$ (f) $NaCN$
   (g) $Na_2Cr_2O_7$ (h) $Al_2(SO_4)_3$
   (i) NH_4NO_3 (j) KOH
   (k) $NaClO$ (l) H_3PO_4

5. Name the following compounds:
   (a) $FePO_4$ (b) $HC_2H_3O_2$
   (c) $Al(HCO_3)_3$ (d) $MnHPO_4$
   (e) KNO_2 (f) Na_2CrO_4
   (g) $NaHCO_3$ (h) $MgSO_3$
   (i) $NaOH$ (j) $HClO_3$
   (k) $Ba(OH)_2$ (l) H_2SO_4

6. Name the following compounds:
   (a) $NaC_2H_3O_2$ (b) $Ca(C_2H_3O_2)_2$
   (c) H_2CO_3 (d) HNO_2
   (e) $Mg(NO_2)_2$ (f) WCO_3
   (g) H_2SO_3 (h) $Cu(NO_3)_2$
   (i) $Ti(SO_4)_2$ (j) $HClO_2$
   (k) NH_4OH (l) $HgCl_2$

7. Write formulas for the following compounds:
   (a) Copper(I) bromide
   (b) Carbon monoxide
   (c) Sodium oxide
   (d) Calcium chloride
   (e) Magnesium sulfide
   (f) Aluminum nitride
   (g) Aluminum phosphide
   (h) Boron trichloride
   (i) Sulfur trioxide
   (j) Nitrogen gas

8. Write formulas for the following compounds:
   (a) Rubidium sulfide
   (b) Mercuric sulfide
   (c) Manganese(IV) fluoride
   (d) Lead(IV) iodide
   (e) Nickel(II) sulfide
   (f) Stannous nitride
   (g) Ferrous iodide
   (h) Magnesium phosphide
   (i) Mercury(I) oxide
   (j) Aluminum sulfide

9. Write formulas for the following compounds:
   (a) Ammonium bicarbonate
   (b) Ferric nitrite
   (c) Magnesium acetate
   (d) Sulfurous acid
   (e) Calcium phosphate
   (f) Copper(I) acetate
   (g) Aluminum sulfate
   (h) Nitric acid
   (i) Silver nitrate
   (j) Acetic acid

10. Write formulas for the following compounds:
   (a) Ferrous sulfide
   (b) Lithium sulfite
   (c) Lead(IV) hydroxide
   (d) Carbonic acid
   (e) Potassium permanganate
   (f) Hypochlorous acid
   (g) Sodium dichromate
   (h) Aluminum hypochlorite
   (i) Lithium chromate
   (j) Perchloric acid

11. Write formulas for the following compounds:
   (a) Hydrosulfuric acid
   (b) Acetic acid
   (c) Copper(II) sulfate
   (d) Beryllium carbonate
   (e) Nitrous acid
   (f) Sodium cyanide
   (g) Iron(II) hydroxide
   (h) Gold(III) sulfate
   (i) Tin(IV) nitrate
   (j) Potassium dihydrogen phosphate

12. The following compounds have common names. Name them as though you were following the standard nomenclature rules precisely.
   (a) H_2O, water
   (b) NH_3, ammonia
   (c) H_2SO_4, sulfuric acid
   (d) NaOH, lye
   (e) HCl, muriatic acid

13. Fill in the following grid with appropriate formulas and name the compounds formed.

	Cl^-	O^{2-}	SO_4^{2-}	NO_2^-	ClO_4^-	PO_4^{3-}	CO_3^{2-}
(a) Mg							
(b) B							
(c) Co(II)							
(d) Pb(IV)							
(e) NH_4^+							
(f) Sr							
(g) Li							

14. Fill in the following grid with correct formulas.

	Fluoride	Sulfide	Chlorate	Permanganate	Hydroxide
(a) Potassium					
(b) Calcium					
(c) Aluminum					
(d) Tin(II)					
(e) Ammonium					

Learning Objectives for Chapter 6

Define **mole, Avogadro's number, formula weight, molecular weight, percentage composition, empirical formula.**

Using the periodic chart, determine the atomic weight for an element and explain its possible meanings.

Given the weight of a sample of an element, calculate the number of moles or atoms or both of the element present.

Using the periodic chart, calculate the weight of a single atom of an element.

Using the periodic chart, calculate the formula weight of formula units of compounds.

Given the weight of a sample of a compound, calculate the number of moles or formula units or both of the compound present.

Using a periodic chart, calculate the percentage composition of a compound.

Given an elemental analysis, calculate the empirical formula of a compound.

Given an elemental analysis and formula weight, calculate the exact formula of a compound.

6 THE MOLE CONCEPT

6.1 What Is a Mole?

Individual atoms cannot be seen directly; thus, chemists rarely concern themselves with one atom, two atoms, or even hundreds of atoms. Still, when a chemical formula is written, the number of atoms per formula unit is specified. The molecular formula H_2O indicates that two atoms of hydrogen combine with one atom of oxygen. These seemingly opposing concerns about atoms are really not inconsistent. If a water molecule always contains two hydrogen atoms and one oxygen atom, then millions of billions of water molecules will maintain the same ratio. That is, there will always be twice as many hydrogen atoms as oxygen atoms in water. It is apparent that it is difficult to count atoms. It is much easier to weigh out a large number of atoms. Then, by knowing how much one atom weighs, one can determine the number of atoms present. It is not unlike buying cherries at the store. Rarely does a buyer count the cherries; normally a scale is used, and the cherries are bought by the pound. A pound of cherries may contain 74 cherries, give or take a few. The point is, if you needed to prepare a thousand fruit bags, each containing one apple and five cherries, you would not go to the store and count out five thousand cherries, you would determine the number of cherries per pound, and buy that many pounds of cherries.

Since it is impossible to conduct experiments on individual formula units, molecules, and atoms or weigh them out, it is necessary to define some terms that make experiments possible. A formula like $BaCl_2$ represents a three-atom formula unit comprising one barium atom and two chlorine atoms. But how could someone who was given a pressure bottle of chlorine gas and a pile of pure barium calculate what weight of each element should be allowed to react so that the ratio of Cl to Ba atoms would be kept 2:1?

149

Chemists have developed a clever way of "counting" atoms by weighing them. This method consists of defining the mole.

One **mole** of any substance contains **Avogadro's number** (6.02×10^{23}) of particles of that substance.

The definition relates the mole to the weight of a sample of an element in the following way.

The **atomic weight** of an element expressed in grams is the mass of one mole of that element

(Figure 6.1). Thus, a sample of an element containing the atomic weight expressed in grams contains Avogadro's number of atoms. In considering some examples, remember that atomic weights are found on the periodic chart.

Example 6.1

Find the atomic weight of fluorine on the periodic chart and explain its meaning.

The atomic weight of fluorine (F) is 18.998 amu. This can be taken to mean that 18.998 g of fluorine is one mole and contains 6.02×10^{23} fluorine atoms.

Example 6.2

Find the atomic weight of iron on the periodic chart and explain its meaning.

One atom of iron (Fe) has a mass of 55.847 amu. A 55.847-g sample of iron contains 6.02×10^{23} atoms of iron. This weight of iron is one mole (1 mol) of iron.

Notice that Avogadro's number has been written out to only three significant figures. Scientists know Avogadro's number much more accurately than this, but for most work, greater accuracy is not needed. It is also convenient to round most atomic weights to three significant figures. This simplifies calculations without introducing appreciable errors. Therefore, 1 mol of fluorine atoms weighs 19.0 g and 1 mol of iron weighs 55.8 g.

Figure 6.1 Although they do not weigh the same amount, there are equal numbers of atoms (6.02×10^{23}) in the two samples.

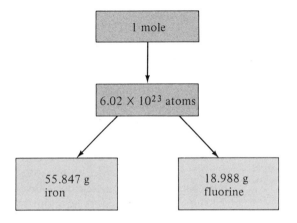

Example 6.3

How many atoms are contained in a 1.0-g sample of iron?

Step 1   Find the atomic weight of iron on the periodic chart and write the appropriate unit factor. There are 55.8 g in 1 mol of iron and 1 mol contains 6.02×10^{23} atoms; this can be stated in unit factor notation as

$$\frac{55.8 \text{ g Fe}}{1 \text{ mol Fe}} = 1 = \frac{1 \text{ mol Fe}}{55.8 \text{ g Fe}}$$

Step 2   Use the unit factor to calculate the number of moles present. There is only 1.0 g present, so there must be less than 1 mol. Multiplying gives

$$1.0 \text{ g Fe} \times \frac{1 \text{ mol Fe}}{55.8 \text{ g Fe}} = 0.018 \text{ mol Fe}$$

This number is the fraction of a mole of Fe in 1.0 g. (Notice that this problem has been solved using unit factors and canceling units.)

Step 3   Use the unit factor relating moles and number of atoms to find the answer. Since there is 0.018 mol in 1.0 g of iron, there must also be that fraction times Avogadro's number of atoms in 1.0 g iron, or

$$0.018 \text{ mol Fe} \times \frac{6.02 \times 10^{23} \text{ atoms Fe}}{1 \text{ mol Fe}} = 1.1 \times 10^{22} \text{ atoms Fe}$$

Example 6.4

How many atoms are contained in a 150-g sample of phosphorus (P)?

Step 1   From the periodic chart, we know that 1 mol of phosphorus weighs 31.0 g. The unit factor is

$$\frac{31.0 \text{ g P}}{1 \text{ mol P}} = 1 = \frac{1 \text{ mol P}}{31.0 \text{ g P}}$$

Step 2   There are 150 g present, so the calculation is

$$150 \text{ g P} \times \frac{1 \text{ mol P}}{31.0 \text{ g P}} = 4.8 \text{ mol P}$$

Step 3   To calculate the number of atoms present, multiply the number of moles by Avogadro's number.

$$4.8 \text{ mol P} \times \frac{6.02 \times 10^{23} \text{ atoms P}}{1 \text{ mol P}} = 2.9 \times 10^{24} \text{ atoms P}$$

Avogadro's number and the weight of 1 mol of an element can be used conveniently to find the approximate weight of a single atom.

Example 6.5   Calculate the weight of a single aluminum atom.

The weight of one atom of aluminum can be calculated in the following way:

$$\frac{27.0 \text{ g Al}}{1 \text{ mol Al}} \times \frac{1 \text{ mol Al}}{6.02 \times 10^{23} \text{ atoms Al}} = \frac{4.49 \times 10^{-23} \text{ g Al}}{1 \text{ atom Al}}$$

One atom of aluminum weighs approximately 4.49×10^{-23} g.

Example 6.6   Calculate the weight of a single atom of lead.

One atom of lead weighs

$$\frac{207.2 \text{ g Pb}}{1 \text{ mol Pb}} \times \frac{1 \text{ mol Pb}}{6.02 \times 10^{23} \text{ atoms Pb}} = \frac{3.44 \times 10^{-22} \text{ g Pb}}{1 \text{ atom Pb}}$$

One atom of lead weighs approximately 3.44×10^{-22} g. Comparing the answer with Example 6.5 indicates that one atom of lead is nearly eight times heavier than one atom of aluminum.

The mole concept and Avogadro's number are very useful because they allow one to count atoms by weighing large quantities of them. The following statements elaborate on this.

Allowing 6.02×10^{23} sodium atoms (Na) to react with 6.02×10^{23} chlorine atoms (Cl), should yield 6.02×10^{23} formula units of sodium chloride (NaCl). This can also be stated in the following way. Adding 1 mol of sodium atoms to 1 mol of chlorine atoms produces 1 mol of sodium chloride.

As the mole is used to refer to compounds, it means the formula unit weight expressed in grams.

Very often chemists define molecular weights instead of formula weights. Molecular weights are nearly the same as formula weights. The difference is that **formula weight** is used to refer to compounds, ionic substances, and elements, and **molecular weight** should be used only to refer to covalent compounds.

In fact, **mole** is an abbreviation of the term **gram-molecular weight**, the formula weight of a molecule expressed in grams. In this text, **formula weight** is used to refer to all compounds, and it means the weight of one formula unit of any compound or element.

The mole concept is general. One mole can refer to Avogadro's number of atoms, Avogadro's number of formula units, Avogadro's number of pencils, Avogadro's number of bananas, or Avogadro's number of anything.

One determines the formula weight of a compound by adding the atomic weights of all the atoms in each formula unit. These examples will show you how to calculate formula weights.

Example 6.7

Calculate the formula weight of sodium chloride (NaCl).

Step 1 Refer to the periodic chart to find the atomic weights of the atoms present: Na, 23.0; Cl, 35.5.

Step 2 Count the number of each atom present, according to the formula, and add together that number of atomic weights. There is one Na atom and one Cl atom present in each formula unit.

$$
\begin{array}{lll}
1 \text{ Na:} & 1 \times 23.0 = 23.0 \text{ amu} \\
1 \text{ Cl:} & 1 \times 35.5 = \underline{35.5 \text{ amu}} \\
& & 58.5 \text{ amu} = \text{formula weight of NaCl}
\end{array}
$$

Example 6.8

Calculate the formula weight of barium fluoride (BaF_2).

Step 1 Ba, 137.0; F, 19.0.

Step 2
$$
\begin{array}{lll}
1 \text{ Ba:} & 1 \times 137.0 = 137.0 \text{ amu} \\
2 \text{ F:} & 2 \times 19.0 \;= \underline{\;38.0 \text{ amu}} \\
& & 175.0 \text{ amu} = \text{formula weight of } BaF_2
\end{array}
$$

Example 6.9

Calculate the formula weight of lithium sulfate (Li_2SO_4).

Step 1 Li, 6.94; S, 32.0; O, 16.0.

Step 2
$$
\begin{array}{lll}
2 \text{ Li:} & 2 \times 6.94 = 13.9 \text{ amu} \\
1 \text{ S:} & 1 \times 32.0 = 32.0 \text{ amu} \\
4 \text{ O:} & 4 \times 16.0 = \underline{64.0 \text{ amu}} \\
& & 109.9 \text{ amu} = \text{formula weight of } Li_2SO_4
\end{array}
$$

Example 6.10

Calculate the formula weight of magnesium hydroxide ($Mg(OH)_2$). (Everything in the parentheses has to be multiplied by the subscript.)

Step 1 Mg, 24.3; O, 16.0; H, 1.0.

Step 2
$$
\begin{array}{lll}
1 \text{ Mg:} & 1 \times 24.3 = 24.3 \text{ amu} \\
2 \text{ O:} & 2 \times 16.0 = 32.0 \text{ amu} \\
2 \text{ H:} & 2 \times 1.0 \;= \underline{\;2.0 \text{ amu}} \\
& & 58.3 \text{ amu} = \text{formula weight of } Mg(OH)_2
\end{array}
$$

Example 6.11

Calculate the formula weight of aluminum dichromate ($Al_2(Cr_2O_7)_3$).

Step 1 Al, 27.0; Cr, 52.0; O, 16.0.

Step 2
$$2 \text{ Al}: \quad 2 \times 27.0 = 54.0 \text{ amu}$$
$$6 \text{ Cr}: \quad 6 \times 52.0 = 312.0 \text{ amu}$$
$$21 \text{ O}: \quad 21 \times 16.0 = 336.0 \text{ amu}$$
$$\overline{702.0 \text{ amu}} = \text{formula weight of } Al_2(Cr_2O_7)_3$$

With these examples as a guide, you can calculate the formula weight of any compound.

With the calculated formula weights, converting to moles is easy. For example, one mole of NaCl weighs 58.4 g. One mole of BaF_2 weighs 175.0 g. One mole of Li_2SO_4 weighs 109.9 g. One mole of $Mg(OH)_2$ weighs 58.3 g. One mole of $Al_2(Cr_2O_7)_3$ weighs 702.0 g. Since one mole of any substance contains 6.02×10^{23} formula units of that substance, one mole of atoms contains 6.02×10^{23} atoms. In general, then

$$1 \text{ mol atoms} = 6.02 \times 10^{23} \text{ atoms}$$
$$1 \text{ mol of formula units} = 6.02 \times 10^{23} \text{ formula units}$$

and

$$\text{Weight of 1 mol atoms} = \text{atomic weight in grams}$$
$$\text{Weight of 1 mol formula units} = \text{formula weight in grams}$$

Exactly as the number of atoms in a sample of an element has been calculated, the number of formula units in a sample of a compound can be calculated.

Example 6.12

How many moles of HCl are present in an 11-g sample of HCl?

Step 1   Calculate the formula weight of HCl and thus the weight of 1 mol of HCl.

$$1 \text{ H}: \quad 1 \times 1.0 = 1.0$$
$$1 \text{ Cl}: \quad 1 \times 35.5 = 35.5$$
$$\overline{36.5}$$

Thus, 1 mol HCl weighs 36.5 g.

Step 2   Use the appropriate unit factor to reach the final answer:

$$11 \text{ g HCl} \times \frac{1 \text{ mol HCl}}{36.5 \text{ g HCl}} = 0.30 \text{ mol HCl}$$

Example 6.13

How many moles of Li_2SO_4 are present in 25.0 g Li_2SO_4?

Step 1   The weight of 1 mol Li_2SO_4 is 109.9 g.

Step 2 $$25.0 \text{ g } Li_2SO_4 \times \frac{1 \text{ mol } Li_2SO_4}{109.9 \text{ g } Li_2SO_4} = 0.227 \text{ mol } Li_2SO_4$$

Example 6.14   ~~How many formula units~~ of BaF_2 are in 5.0 g of this compound?

(handwritten: atom)

Step 1   In Example 6.8, it was calculated that the formula weight of BaF_2 is 175.0. Five grams must be some fraction of a mole.

Step 2 $5.0 \text{ g } BaF_2 \times \dfrac{1 \text{ mol } BaF_2}{175.0 \text{ g } BaF_2} = 0.029 \text{ mol } BaF_2$

Step 3   Use a second unit factor to determine the number of ~~formula units~~ present.   *(handwritten: atoms)*

$$0.029 \text{ mol } BaF_2 \times \frac{6.02 \times 10^{23} \text{ formula units } BaF_2}{1 \text{ mol } BaF_2}$$

$$= 1.7 \times 10^{22} \text{ formula units of } BaF_2$$

The procedure is really just as easy as working with atoms.

Example 6.15   How many formula units are in a 5.0×10^2 g sample of magnesium hydroxide?

Step 1   The gram-formula weight of $Mg(OH)_2$ is 58.3 g.

Step 2   The number of moles is

$$5.0 \times 10^2 \text{ g } Mg(OH)_2 \times \frac{1 \text{ mol } Mg(OH)_2}{58.3 \text{ g } Mg(OH)_2} = 8.6 \text{ mol } Mg(OH)_2$$

Step 3   The number of formula units is

$$8.6 \text{ mol } Mg(OH)_2 \times \frac{6.02 \times 10^{23} \text{ formula units } Mg(OH)_2}{1 \text{ mol } Mg(OH)_2}$$

$$= 5.2 \times 10^{24} \text{ formula units } Mg(OH)_2$$

Example 6.16   How many grams are present in 2.3 mol of HCl?

Step 1   The formula weight of HCl is 36.5.

Step 2 $2.3 \text{ mol } HCl \times \dfrac{36.5 \text{ g } HCl}{1 \text{ mol } HCl} = 84 \text{ g } HCl$

Example 6.17   Calculate the weight in grams of 0.35 mol $Al_2(Cr_2O_7)_3$.

Step 1   The formula weight of aluminum dichromate is 702.0.

Step 2 $0.35 \text{ mol } Al_2(Cr_2O_7)_3 \times \dfrac{702.0 \text{ g } Al_2(Cr_2O_7)_3}{1 \text{ mol } Al_2(Cr_2O_7)_3} = 250 \text{ g } Al_2(Cr_2O_7)_3$

Elemental Composition by Percentage

A compound like sodium chloride (NaCl) is not half sodium and half chlorine by weight, since the atoms have different atomic weights. What percentage by weight of NaCl is sodium and what percentage is chlorine? This problem can be solved by using the atomic weights of the atoms and the formula weight of the compound to calculate the percentage composition. The percentage composition of a compound is defined as the percentage that each element contributes to the total compound weight. It is calculated using

$$\text{Percentage of one element} = \frac{\text{weight of element present in 1 mol of compound}}{\text{weight of 1 mol of compound}} \times 100$$

A 1-mol sample of NaCl weighs 58.5 g. These 58.5 grams consist of 23.0 g of sodium atoms and 35.5 g of chlorine atoms. The percentage of sodium in sodium chloride is the weight of sodium divided by the total weight of the compound, with the resulting answer being multiplied by 100.

$$\frac{23.0 \text{ g}}{58.5 \text{ g}} \times 100 = 39.3\% \text{ sodium}$$

The percentage of chloride is obtained by dividing the weight of chloride by the total weight and multiplying by 100.

$$\frac{35.5 \text{ g}}{58.5 \text{ g}} \times 100 = 60.7\% \text{ chloride}$$

One can also get the percentage of chloride simply by subtracting the percentage of sodium from 100%.

$$\begin{array}{r} 100.0\% \\ - 39.3\% \text{ sodium} \\ \hline 60.7\% \text{ chloride} \end{array}$$

Example 6.18 Calculate the percentage of fluoride in barium fluoride (BaF$_2$).

Step 1 Determine the formula weight of BaF$_2$ and express this as the weight of one mole.

$$\text{Wt 1 mol BaF}_2 = 175.0 \text{ g}$$

Step 2   Determine the weight of fluorine present in 1 mol BaF_2

$$\text{Wt F in 1 mol BaF}_2 = 2 \times 19.0 \text{ g} = 38.0 \text{ g}$$

Step 3   Divide the weight of fluorine present by formula weight of BaF_2 to get the final answer.

$$\text{Percentage F} = \frac{38.0 \text{ g}}{175.0 \text{ g}} \times 100 = 21.7\%$$

The percentage of barium can be found by subtraction.

$$
\begin{array}{r}
100.00\% \\
-\ 21.7\% \ \text{fluoride} \\
\hline
78.3\% \ \text{barium}
\end{array}
$$

Example 6.19   Calculate the percentage of oxygen in 1 mol magnesium hydroxide.

Step 1   Wt 1 mol $\text{Mg(OH)}_2 = 58.3$ g
Step 2   Wt oxygen in 1 mol $\text{Mg(OH)}_2 = 2 \times 16.0 = 32.0$ g

Step 3 $\text{Percentage oxygen} = \dfrac{32.0 \text{ g}}{58.3 \text{ g}} \times 100 = 54.9\%$

The percentage of hydrogen can be calculated by the following equation:

$$\frac{2.00 \text{ g}}{58.3 \text{ g}} \times 100 = 3.43\% \text{ hydrogen}$$

The sum of the percentage of oxygen and the percentage of hydrogen subtracted from 100 gives the percentage of magnesium in the compound.

$$100\% - (54.9\% + 3.43\%) = 41.7\% \text{ magnesium}$$

Example 6.20   Calculate the percentage of oxygen in barium nitrate.

Step 1   Wt 1 mol $\text{Ba(NO}_3)_2 = 261.3$ g
Step 2   Wt O in 1 mol of $\text{Ba(NO}_3)_2 = 96.0$ g

Step 3 $\text{Percentage N} = \dfrac{96.0 \text{ g}}{261.3 \text{ g}} \times 100 = 36.7\%$

6.3   Empirical Formulas

Since chemical formulas are ratios of the numbers of moles of the different atoms present, the percentage composition of a compound can be used to determine the empirical, or simplest, formula of a compound. For example, hydrogen peroxide exists as H_2O_2. Its simplest, or empirical, formula is HO. Many times in the laboratory a chemist must take a sample of material and determine the percentage of each element present. From these data, the simplest formula or empirical formula of a compound can be calculated. Such a calculation is carried out as follows.

Example 6.21

A chemist states that the sample of solid submitted for analysis contains 63.9% chlorine and 36.1% calcium. What is its empirical formula?

Step 1   Imagine a 100-g sample. In this sample, 63.9 g Cl and 36.1 g Ca are present (63.9 g + 36.1 g = 100 g).

Step 2   Calculate the number of moles of each substance present in a 100-g sample. The number of moles of each of chlorine and calcium in the sample can be found by:

$$\text{mol Ca} = 36.1 \text{ g Ca} \times \frac{1 \text{ mol Ca}}{40.1 \text{ g Ca}} = 0.900 \text{ mol Ca}$$

$$\text{mol Cl} = 63.9 \text{ g Cl} \times \frac{1 \text{ mol Cl}}{35.5 \text{ g Cl}} = 1.80 \text{ mol Cl}$$

Step 3   State the answer from Step 2 as a formula and convert to whole numbers. Technically the compound is $Ca_{0.90}Cl_{1.80}$. The problem now boils down to finding the simplest whole-number ratio of Ca to Cl. This is done by taking the smallest number of moles, in this case the Ca, and dividing each of the moles present (including the smallest one itself) by that number. This calculation yields

$$\frac{0.900 \text{ mol}}{0.900 \text{ mol}} \text{Ca} = 1.0 \text{ Ca}$$

$$\frac{1.80 \text{ mol}}{0.900 \text{ mol}} \text{Cl} = 2.0 \text{ Cl}$$

Step 4   State the simplest formula. The ratio of calcium to chlorine is 1 to 2, so the simplest formula must be $CaCl_2$.

Example 6.22	A compound contains 2.10% hydrogen, 32.1% sulfur, and 65.2% oxygen. What is the simplest formula for the compound?

Step 1 Start by assuming a 100-g sample containing 2.10 g H, 32.1 g S, and 65.2 g O.

Step 2 Calculate the number of moles of each element present.

$$\text{mol H} = 2.10\ \cancel{g} \times \frac{1\ \text{mol H}}{1.0\ \cancel{g}} = 2.1\ \text{mol H}$$

$$\text{mol S} = 32.7\ \cancel{g} \times \frac{1\ \text{mol S}}{32.1\ \cancel{g}} = 1.02\ \text{S}$$

$$\text{mol O} = 65.2\ \cancel{g} \times \frac{1\ \text{mol O}}{16.0\ \cancel{g}} = 4.08\ \text{mol O}$$

Step 3 Technically the compound is $H_{2.1}S_{1.02}O_{4.08}$.

The sulfur is present in the smallest number of moles. Therefore, the number of moles of each element is divided by the number of moles of sulfur.

$$\frac{1.02\ \text{mol}}{1.02\ \text{mol}} S \approx 1\ S \qquad \frac{2.1\ \text{mol}}{1.02\ \text{mol}} H = 2.1 \approx 2\ H \qquad \frac{4.08\ \text{mol}}{1.02\ \text{mol}} O \approx 4\ O$$

Real experimental data rarely give ratios that are exact, since analytical errors cannot be completely eliminated. The ratios usually, however, are close enough to whole numbers that a decision can be made about what the ratio is supposed to be. The number for H is so close to 2 that one can safely assume that the ratio is 1:2:4.

Step 4 The simplest formula for the compound is H_2SO_4.

Example 6.23	Analysis reported a compound to contain 43.7% phosphorus and 56.3% oxygen. What is the simplest formula for the compound?

Step 1 Assume 43.7 g P and 56.3 g O are present.

Step 2 $\text{mol P} = 43.7\ \cancel{g} \times \dfrac{1\ \text{mol P}}{31.0\ \cancel{g}} = 1.41\ \text{mol P}$

$$\text{mol O} = 56.3\ \cancel{g} \times \frac{1\ \text{mol O}}{16.0\ \cancel{g}} = 3.52\ \text{mol O}$$

Step 3 The formula is $P_{1.41}O_{3.52}$. Reducing the ratios to whole numbers gives

$$\frac{1.41\ \text{mol}}{1.41\ \text{mol}} P = 1\ P \qquad \frac{3.52\ \text{mol}}{1.41\ \text{mol}} O = 2.5\ O$$

The ratio is not to a whole number, and we must find the simplest whole number ratio in the calculation. The formula can be corrected by multiplying both numbers by two:

$$1\,P \times 2 = 2\,P \qquad 2.5\,O \times 2 = 5\,O$$

Step 4   The simplest formula is P_2O_5.

The finding in Example 6.23 is still only the simplest formula and not necessarily the true formula. The true formula could just as well be P_4O_{10}, which has the same ratio of phosphorus to oxygen as P_2O_5. The only way to ascertain the true formula is to determine the formula weight of the compound. In this case, if the formula weight were found to be 142, the true formula would be P_2O_5. If the formula weight were determined by experiment to be 284, then P_4O_{10} would be the correct formula.

Finding an exact formula is illustrated in the Example 6.24.

Example 6.24

Analysis of a 5.0-g sample of an unknown compound showed that it contained 4.6 g of carbon and 0.40 g of hydrogen. Its formula weight was found to be about 78. What is the formula?

Step 1   In this case, a total weight is given as 5.0 g, so this is used as the base weight.

Step 2   The ratios of moles of carbon and hydrogen must be found.

$$4.6\,g \times \frac{1\ \text{mol C}}{12.0\,g} = 0.38\ \text{mol C}$$

$$0.40\,g \times \frac{1\ \text{mol H}}{1.0\,g} = 0.40\ \text{mol H}$$

Step 3 $C_{0.38}H_{0.40}$
Reducing this formula yields

$$\frac{0.38\ \text{mol}}{0.38\ \text{mol}}\,C = 1\,C \qquad \frac{0.40\ \text{mol}}{0.38\ \text{mol}}\,H = \text{approximately 1 H}$$

Step 4   The simplest formula for this molecule is C_1H_1.

Step 5   Compare the formula weight for the simplest formula to that given as exact to determine the correct formula. The molecular weight of the compound C_1H_1, is

$$
\begin{array}{ll}
C & 12.0 \\
H & \underline{1.00} \\
 & 13.0
\end{array}
$$

and the unknown compound has formula weight 78. How many units of 13.0 are contained in 78? This is found by dividing 78 by 13.0:

$$\frac{78}{13.0} = 6.0$$

The molecule must contain 6 units of CH, so that its actual formula is C_6H_6.

The simplest formula was calculated by using the weights of the elements present instead of the percentages of each element present.

Example 6.25 is more complicated.

Example 6.25

A 7.50-g sample of a solid material is found to contain 1.24 g nitrogen and 2.03 g sodium, and also oxygen, which cannot be weighed directly. The formula weight of the material is 85 g/mol. Find the formula of the compound.

Step 1 There are 2.03 g sodium, 1.24 g nitrogen, and an unknown weight of oxygen present. The weight of oxygen can be calculated by subtracting the weight of the sodium and the weight of nitrogen from the total weight of the sample.

$$\text{Total wt} = \text{wt sodium} + \text{wt nitrogen} + \text{wt oxygen}$$

$$7.50 \text{ g} = 2.03 \text{ g} + 1.24 \text{ g} + \text{wt oxygen}$$

$$\text{Wt oxygen} = 7.50 \text{ g} - 2.03 \text{ g} - 1.24 \text{ g}$$

$$\text{Wt oxygen} = 4.23 \text{ g}$$

Step 2 The number of moles of each element present can be found.

$$\text{mol sodium} = 2.03 \text{ g Na} \times \frac{1 \text{ mol Na}}{23.0 \text{ g Na}} = 0.0883 \text{ mol Na}$$

$$\text{mol nitrogen} = 1.24 \text{ g N} \times \frac{1 \text{ mol N}}{14.0 \text{ g N}} = 0.0886 \text{ mol N}$$

$$\text{mol oxygen} = 4.23 \text{ g O} \times \frac{1 \text{ mol O}}{16.0 \text{ g O}} = 0.264 \text{ mol O}$$

Step 3 $Na_{0.0883}N_{0.0886}O_{0.264}$.
To convert these numbers into whole number ratios, divide each answer by 0.0883.

$$\frac{0.0883 \text{ mol}}{0.0883 \text{ mol}} \text{Na} = 1 \text{ Na} \qquad \frac{0.0886 \text{ mol}}{0.0883 \text{ mol}} \text{N} = 1 \text{ N}$$

$$\frac{0.264 \text{ mol}}{0.0883 \text{ mol}} \text{O} = 2.99 \text{ O} = 3 \text{ O}$$

Step 4   The empirical formula is $NaNO_3$, the formula weight of which is 85.0 g/mol. Thus, $NaNO_3$ must be the actual formula for the compound.

To find the true formula of a compound, then, two pieces of information are necessary: the molecular weight of the compound and either the actual weights or the percentages of the elements in the compound.

Many more important uses for the mole concept will appear throughout our study of chemical reactions.

Glossary

Avogadro's number   The number of formula units of a substance contained in one mole of that substance. Numerically, this is 6.02×10^{23}.

Empirical formula   Chemical formula with subscripts in the lowest possible ratio of whole numbers.

Formula weight   The sum of the atomic weights of the elements in the formula of a substance.

Mole   The formula weight of a substance expressed in grams. It corresponds to 6.02×10^{23} formula units.

Molecular weight   The sum of the atomic weights of the elements in a covalent compound.

Problems

1. In your own words explain the similarities and differences between gram-atomic weight, formula weight, and the mole.

2. Find the atomic weight or formula weight of each of the following:
   (a) Si
   (b) C
   (c) F_2
   (d) Br_2
   (e) HI
   (f) K_2S
   (g) NaOH
   (h) $Ba(NO_3)_2$
   (i) $Ca_3(PO_4)_2$
   (j) P_4O_{10}

3. Find the atomic weight or formula weight of each of the following:
   (a) P_4
   (b) S_8
   (c) Cr
   (d) $KMnO_4$
   (e) Al_2O_3
   (f) $HC_2H_3O_2$
   (g) $Mg(IO_3)_2$
   (h) SiF_4
   (i) $Al_2(SO_4)_3$
   (j) K_3AsO_4

4. How many moles are contained in each of the following?
   (a) 5.00 g of Al
   (b) 16.0 g of O_2
   (c) 10.0 g of H_2
   (d) 20.0 kg of P
   (e) 100 mg of Ba

5. How many moles are contained in each of the following?
   (a) 62.0 g of H_3PO_4
   (b) 5.00 × 10⁻³ g of HCl
   (c) 250 g of $BaCl_2$
   (d) 1.70 × 10⁻⁴ g of Li_2SO_4
   (e) 10.0 g of $Al(OH)_3$

6. How many atoms or formula units are contained in each of the following?
   (a) 1 mol of Si
   (b) 0.030 mol of Fe
   (c) 7.30 mol of U
   (d 4.0 mol of CH_4 (methane)
   (e) 65 mol of CaI_2

7. How many atoms or formula units are contained in each of the following?
   (a) 2.5 mol of HCl
   (b) 0.025 mol of BaI_2
   (c) 1.00 × 10⁻² mol of $Ca(OH)_2$
   (d) 6.00 × 10²⁰ mol of $Fe(OH)_3$
   (e) 167 mol of CO_2

8. How many atoms or formula units are contained in each of the following?
   (a) 1.00 g of Cr
   (b) 15.0 g of Si
   (c) 0.03 g of N_2
   (d) 3.00 × 10⁻³ g of Br_2
   (e) 1.00 × 10²³ g of Cl_2O

9. How many atoms or formula units are contained in each of the following?
   (a) 300 g of $HClO_3$
   (b) 1.50 × 10¹⁵ g of K_3PO_4
   (c) 10.0 g of $Al(NO_3)_3$
   (d) 2.00 g of $(NH_4)_3PO_4$
   (e) 1.00 × 10⁻¹⁰ g of SiO_2

10. List the total number of atoms in the following quantities of material:
    (a) 3 mol of Al
    (b) 69.25 g of PCl_3
    (c) 16 mol of $Ca_3(PO_4)_2$
    (d) 320 g of $Fe(OH)_3$
    (e) 645 formula units of $MgCO_3$

11. Calculate the percentage composition of each of the following compounds (that is, the percentage by weight of the elements present):
    (a) $BaCl_2$
    (b) KF
    (c) $AlCl_3$
    (d) H_3PO_4
    (e) $FeCl_3$

12. Calculate the percentage composition of each of the following compounds (percentage by weight of the elements present):
    (a) KOH
    (b) $Mg(OH)_2$
    (c) $AlPO_4$
    (d) $Ba_3(PO_4)_2$
    (e) $KMnO_4$

13. Explain how the empirical formula of a compound is related to the actual formula of a compound.

14. Find the empirical formulas for the following compounds:
    (a) 66.7% C, 11.1% H, 22.2% O
    (b) 5.9% H, 94.1% O

15. Find the empirical formulas for the following compounds:
    (a) 25.5% Mg, 74.5% Cl
    (b) 3.7% H, 37.8% P, 58.5% O

16. Find the empirical formulas for the following compounds:
    (a) 79.9% Cl, 20.1% Al
    (b) 50.0% S, 50.0% O

17. The following empirical formulas were found and associated with their correct formula weight. What is the true formula of each compound?
    (a) HgCl, formula weight 471 Hg_2Cl_2
    (b) P, formula weight 124 P_4
    (c) SiO_2, formula weight 60.0
    (d) Br, formula weight 160
    (e) NO_2, formula weight 184

18. A compound containing boron and hydrogen was analyzed and found to be 78.0% boron and 22.0% hydrogen. The formula weight was found to be 27.6 amu. What is the correct formula for the compound?

19. A compound containing 1.50 g of Al and 6.00 g of Cl has a formula weight of 267. What is the true formula for the compound?

Learning Objectives for Chapter 7

Define **chemical reaction, reactant, product, chemical equation, balanced chemical equation, conservation of matter, spontaneous reaction, nonspontaneous reaction, free energy, enthalpy, exothermic reaction, endothermic reaction, entropy.**

Write and balance simple chemical equations.

State the meanings of balanced chemical equations.

Explain the relation of entropy, enthalpy, and free energy.

Explain the relation between free energy and reaction spontaneity.

Given a reaction enthalpy change, determine whether the reaction is endothermic or exothermic.

7 CHEMICAL REACTIONS

⭐ A **chemical reaction** is any event in which chemical bonds are formed or broken, or both.

This definition indicates that in a chemical reaction something must happen to individual atoms, molecules, or ions. Grinding a rock into particles of dust, for example, is a long way from changing the character of the individual molecules of the rock. The grinding only produces very small particles of rock. Such an event is not a chemical reaction.

The formation of compounds from elements, the decomposition of compounds into elements, and the formation of new compounds from other compounds are examples of chemical reactions. The character of the basic unit (atom or molecule or formula unit) changes. Our environment is filled with chemical reactions. The striking of a match and the burning of the matchstick are chemical reactions involving oxygen in air. Much of the food you eat undergoes chemical reaction in your body, providing energy so you can move and exist. The temperature of the environment inside buildings is often stabilized through chemical reaction. (Heating usually involves burning coal, oil, or some other fuel. Electricity produced as a result of some chemical reaction is often used in cooling.) A car travels down the road thanks to chemical reaction (gasoline combining with oxygen). Trees grow because of chemical reaction (complex biochemical reactions). The movement of your eyes in reading this page is caused by chemical reaction (once again, biochemical reactions). There are an almost uncountable number of chemical reactions constantly in process, not only in our environment but within our bodies.

In all these different chemical reactions, two things always happen. First, starting material (**reactants**) is converted to new and different material (**products**). Second, energy is either absorbed or released.

Knowing how much reactant is consumed in a chemical reaction and how much product to expect is vitally important to a chemist. A chemist may, for

(a)

Figure 7.1 Three examples of chemical reactions involving oxygen: (a) a photographic flash bulb, which uses a reaction of magnesium and oxygen to produce energy in the form of light; (b) a forest fire, which causes atmospheric oxygen to react in the combustion process; and (c) a steel mill, where oxygen combines chemically with impurities in iron ore, in the process of converting it to steel. (Photos courtesy of (a) Eastman Kodak, (b) USDA Forest Service, and (c) Bethlehem Steel Corporation)

(b)

(c)

example, want to prepare a drug that has as a basis rare reactant materials. It is important for the chemist to know how much of each material to start with to produce the drug so as not to waste valuable chemicals. Such a calculation means knowing the chemical equation involved. Once you know how a chemical equation for a reaction is written, and what information can be obtained from such an equation, you will be able to calculate detailed information about the quantities of materials used and produced in chemical reactions.

<table>
<tr><td>7.1</td></tr>
</table>

Writing Chemical Equations

Chemists use **chemical equations** to show, by symbols, which substances react and which products are produced in a reaction. Correctly written, chemical equations help to determine exactly what weights of reactants are needed for a particular reaction. The reaction of hydrogen (H_2) and oxygen (O_2) to form water (H_2O) is used to introduce the concept of writing chemical equations.

A first try at stating this reaction in symbols might be something like

$$H_2 + O_2 \rightarrow H_2O$$

This representation seems reasonable since the symbols correspond to those learned for these compounds. The combination of hydrogen and oxygen is indicated by the plus sign between their symbols. Water is formed in the reaction as the reactants disappear. This is indicated by an intervening arrow extending from the reactants (H_2 and O_2) toward the product (H_2O). The reactants can be written $H_2 + O_2$ or $O_2 + H_2$; the order does not matter.

The chemical statement, on its simplest level, says that one molecule of hydrogen (H_2) reacts with one molecule of oxygen (O_2) to form one molecule of water (H_2O). There are, however, two atoms of hydrogen and two atoms of oxygen on the reactant side. On the product side, there are two atoms of hydrogen and only one atom of oxygen. The right-hand side of the equation has one fewer oxygen atom than the left-hand side, so the sides are not really equal. The equation is not yet complete; a **balance** has not been achieved.

> A **balanced chemical equation** has the same number and kinds of atoms on the left side as it does on the right.

If all the reactants and all the products are shown, then balancing must be handled by adjusting the number of reactant and product units so that the total number of atoms of each kind appear on each side of the equation. Balancing the sides of a chemical equation is one way of showing conservation of matter.

> **Conservation of matter** means that during a chemical reaction, the total weight of reactants must equal the total weight of products.

The atoms are rearranged during the reaction, but none is created or destroyed, and the total number of atoms present remains the same. The equation is balanced in the following way.

First consider the water molecule. It contains hydrogen and oxygen in the ratio two atoms of hydrogen to one of oxygen. On the left-hand side of this unbalanced chemical statement, there are equal numbers of hydrogen and oxygen atoms; therefore, the numbers must be adjusted. The ratios can be made equal by writing

$$2H_2 + O_2 \rightarrow H_2O$$

Now the unbalanced equation states that two molecules of hydrogen react with one molecule of oxygen to form one molecule of water. Both sides are in the correct ratio, but there are twice as many atoms of each reactant as there are atoms of product. If the whole right-hand side of the equation is doubled, the equation becomes balanced:

$$2H_2 + O_2 \rightarrow 2H_2O$$

The equation is read, "Two molecules of hydrogen react with one molecule of oxygen to form two molecules of water." The numbers in front of the chemical formulas are called coefficients, and they define the number of units of that formula necessary in the equation. Notice that there is no number prefixed to the O_2 symbol. The absence of a number implies that the coefficient is the number 1. For example, $3NH_3$ means three molecules of ammonia; $5Fe$ means five atoms of iron; $2NaCl$ means two formula units of sodium chloride. These numbers can also mean three moles of ammonia, five moles of iron, and two moles of sodium chloride. In other words:

the coefficients in an equation indicate the relative proportions of the chemicals that react and form.

The numbers written as subscripts must be distinguished from the numbers written as coefficients. The numbers written as subscripts on the right indicate the number of atoms of a kind bonded into the formula unit. For example, in $2NaNO_3$, one formula unit of the compound consists of one sodium atom, one nitrogen atom, and three oxygen atoms. The number 2 is the coefficient and means that there are two units of sodium nitrate to be considered. The 3 is a subscript, indicating the number of oxygen atoms.

Our example about the formation of water was balanced by **inspection**. This means that we looked at it, decided what had to be done, and added the proper coefficients. Essentially, we used trial and error. It is very important that chemical equations be balanced. Otherwise the equations would imply that matter was either being created from nothing or disintegrating into nothing. Also, these statements would be meaningless in calculating quantities of reactants and products involved.

Try to picture hydrogen and oxygen combining. Figures 7.2 and 7.3 illustrate three molecules, two hydrogen and one oxygen, combining to form

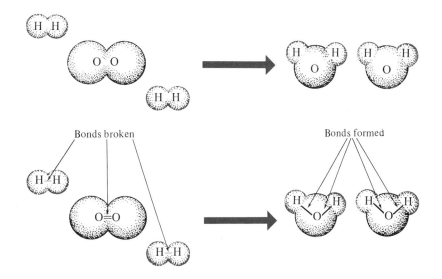

Figure 7.2 When one molecule of oxygen (O_2) reacts with two molecules of hydrogen (H_2), two molecules of water (H_2O) are formed.

Figure 7.3 In the H_2 + O_2 reaction, four bonds are broken, and four are formed.

Bonds broken

Bonds formed

two water molecules. Four bonds have been broken, two H–H and one O–O; and four O–H bonds have been formed. Some other examples of equation balancing follow.

Example 7.1   Hydrochloric acid (HCl) reacts with sodium hydroxide (NaOH), the compound known as lye, to form sodium chloride (NaCl) and water (H_2O). Write the balanced chemical equation for this reaction and state its meaning.

Step 1   Write formulas for reactants and products, separating them by plus signs and an arrow.

$$HCl + NaOH \rightarrow NaCl + H_2O$$

Step 2   To determine where to begin balancing, count the numbers of atoms of each element present on each side. In this case, the numbers of atoms on each side of the equation are equal. The equation is already balanced. There are two hydrogen atoms, one chlorine atom, one sodium atom, and one oxygen atom on each side. The equation is read, "One molecule of hydrogen chloride reacts with one formula unit of sodium hydroxide to form one formula unit of sodium chloride and one molecule of water."

Example 7.2   Phosphorus (P) and chlorine (Cl_2) react to form phosphorus trichloride (PCl_3). Write a balanced equation for this reaction.

Step 1   Begin by writing reactants and products.

$$P + Cl_2 \rightarrow PCl_3$$

Step 2   There are unequal numbers of atoms on either side. There are 2 Cl atoms on the left and 3 Cl atoms on the right. The number of P atoms is the same on each side.

Step 3   Adjust the numbers of atoms present using coefficients. The ratio of phosphorus to chlorine in PCl_3 is $1:3$. Adjust the reactant side of the equation accordingly, since the ratio of atoms in compounds does not change.

$$2P + 3Cl_2 \rightarrow PCl_3$$

Step 4   Reinspect the equation and adjust more coefficients if necessary. There are now twice as many of each type of atom on the left as on the right. Doubling the right-hand side balances the equation:

$$2P + 3Cl_2 \rightarrow 2PCl_3$$

In balancing an equation, only the coefficients change. The subscripts cannot be changed.

Example 7.3   Aluminum and oxygen react to form aluminum oxide. Write a balanced equation for this reaction.

Step 1 $Al + O_2 \rightarrow Al_2O_3$

Step 2   There is 1 Al on the left and 2 Al on the right. There are 2 O on the left and 3 O on the right.

Step 3   Adjust the left side ratio to fit the Al_2O_3 ratio:

$$4Al + 3O_2 \rightarrow Al_2O_3$$

Notice that $4Al:6O$ is the same as $2\ Al:3O$.

Step 4   Double the right side to make both sides equal:

$$4Al + 3O_2 \rightarrow 2Al_2O_3$$

7.2   Importance of Balanced Equations

It is of little significance to discuss individual molecules in reaction with one another because it is impossible to observe individual molecules or atoms. What is important, however, is that the formula units are reacting with each other in a certain, set ratio. For the HCl + NaOH reaction, they react in the

Figure 7.4 The ratios
in chemical reactions are
similar to this example.
For every bolt, two nuts
are needed. No matter
how many bolts there
are, twice as many nuts
are always needed to get
the right nut and bolt
assembly. In the H_2 +
O_2 reaction, no matter
how many oxygen
molecules are used,
there are always twice as
many hydrogen
molecules used.

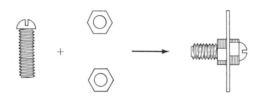

ratio of 1:1. For the reaction $2H_2 + O_2 = 2H_2O$ they react in the ratio 2:1. This information is obtained from the balanced equation. (See Figure 7.4 for a related example.)

Thus, it is possible to say that one molecule of HCl reacts with one formula unit of NaOH, or that 10 molecules of HCl react with 10 formula units of NaOH, or that 10^6 molecules of HCl react with 10^6 formula units of NaOH, or most important, that 6.02×10^{23} molecules of HCl react with 6.02×10^{23} formula units of NaOH. Because 6.02×10^{23} formula units equals one mole, this last statement can also be expressed as: 1 mol of HCl reacts with 1 mol of NaOH to form 1 mol of NaCl and 1 mol of H_2O. Such statements provide the chemist with a convenient way of treating quantities in a chemical reaction.

How is this information useful? Weighing out 40.0 g (1 mol) of NaOH and 36.5 g (1 mol) of HCl and allowing the reaction to take place causes the formation of 18.0 g (1 mol) of H_2O and 58.4 g (1 mol) of NaCl, with no measurable amounts of either NaOH or HCl left over. Similarly, 5 mol of NaOH might have been added to 5 mol of HCl or 0.5 mol of NaOH to 0.5 mol of HCl to yield a specific amount of product with no waste. The important thing is that the weight of a mole of anything is known. Thus, molecules do not have to be counted to choose the right proportions of reactants. It is necessary, however, to balance the chemical equation if you want to calculate the correct number of moles involved.

The hydrogen plus oxygen reaction, $2H_2 + O_2 \rightarrow 2H_2O$, can be read, "Two molecules of hydrogen react with one molecule of oxygen to produce two molecules of water." The ratio of molecules of hydrogen, oxygen, and water is 2:1:2. Hence, the reaction can be read, "Two moles of hydrogen gas (H_2; 4.0 g) reacts with 1 mol of oxygen gas (O_2; 32.0 g) to give 2 mol of water (H_2O; 36.0 g)."

It is also important to note that the sum of the reactant masses must equal the sum of the product masses. In this example, the sum of the masses of H_2 and O_2 (4.0 g + 32.0 g = 36.0 g) equals the mass of the water (36.0 g). If only 1 mol of hydrogen molecules were available, the equation would indicate that 0.5 mol of oxygen molecules (16.0 g) would be consumed to form 1 mol of water (18.0 g).

The balanced chemical equation is used to calculate the various ratios in which reactants are used and products are formed.

7.3 Practice in Balancing and Reading Chemical Equations

Here are three more examples of the techniques of balancing equations by inspection.

Example 7.4	The rusting of iron is the reaction of iron (Fe) with oxygen (O_2) to form rust, iron(III) oxide (Fe_2O_3). Balance the equation and state its meanings.

Step 1 $Fe + O_2 \rightarrow Fe_2O_3$

Step 2   The equation is not balanced. There is one iron atom on the left and two iron atoms on the right.

Step 3   Using the $2Fe:3O$ ratio from Fe_2O_3, multiply the oxygen on the left by 3 and the Fe on the left by 4. This multiplication gives six oxygen atoms on the left side:

$$4Fe + 3O_2 \rightarrow Fe_2O_3$$

Step 4   Now there are four iron atoms on the left and only two on the right, so the right must be multiplied by 2:

$$4Fe + 3O_2 \rightarrow 2Fe_2O_3$$

The equation is now balanced. What does the equation say?

In the reaction of iron and oxygen to form iron(III) oxide, the reactants and products disappear and form in the ratio of atoms and molecules

$$4Fe:3O_2:2Fe_2O_3.$$

This can be 4 atoms of $Fe:3$ molecules of $O_2:2$ molecules of Fe_2O_3 or 40 atoms of $Fe:30$ molecules of $O_2:20$ molecules of Fe_2O_3 or 4 mol of $Fe:3$ mol of $O_2:2$ mol of Fe_2O_3 or 2 mol of $Fe:1.5$ mol of $O_2:1$ mol of Fe_2O_3 or any set of possible conditions so long as the ratio of molecules is 4 to 3 to 2, iron to oxygen to iron(III) oxide.

Example 7.5	Write and balance the equation for the reaction of nitrogen (N_2) and hydrogen (H_2) to form ammonia (NH_3). State its meanings.

Step 1 $N_2 + H_2 \rightarrow NH_3$

Step 2   There are two hydrogen atoms on the left and three on the right. There are two nitrogen atoms on the left and one on the right.

Step 3   Preserving the $1N:3H$ ratio in ammonia, multiply the H_2 by 3:

$$N_2 + 3H_2 \rightarrow NH_3$$

Step 4   The left side of the equation now contains twice as many of each type of atom as the right side. Multiply the NH_3 by 2:

$$N_2 + 3H_2 \rightarrow 2NH_3$$

The equation is now balanced.

The equation states that nitrogen and hydrogen molecules react to form ammonia molecules in the ratio 1:3:2. Just as with the Fe_2O_3 reaction, the equation states the ratio of reactants used and products formed.

Example 7.6   Write and balance the equation for the reaction of MnO_2 and HBr to form $MnBr_2$, Br_2, and H_2O.

Step 1 $MnO_2 + HBr \rightarrow MnBr_2 + Br_2 + H_2O$
Step 2   There is one Br atom on the left and four on the right. There is one Mn atom on the left and one on the right. There are two O atoms on the left and one on the right. There is an H atom on the left and two on the right.
Step 3   Preserving the ratio in H_2O, multiply H_2O by 2 and HBr by 4.

$$MnO_2 + 4HBr \rightarrow MnBr_2 + Br_2 + 2H_2O$$

Note that the ratio $H:O$ on both sides is now

left   right
$4:2 \rightarrow 4:2$

Step 4   Counting atoms shows that the equation is now balanced. Even in this complicated equation, the simple method works.

Continuing practice is the best way to learn balancing chemical equations, and the problems at the end of the chapter are intended to help you practice.

7.4   Spontaneous and Nonspontaneous Reactions

Chemical reactions can be classified as spontaneous or nonspontaneous. A **spontaneous reaction**, once started, will continue until the reactants are consumed. Often, spontaneous reactions require work initially but continue by themselves once they are started. For a **nonspontaneous reaction**, energy must be added continuously during the reaction. A burning matchstick is an example of a spontaneous reaction. Once started, the burning continues. Work is required in striking the match, but the matchstick burns until it is extinguished or until the whole stick has burned. The opposite reaction is nonspontaneous. Reconstructing a matchstick from its burned remains requires a constant input of energy, or work. Imagine how difficult it would be to accomplish this reverse reaction.

The reaction of hydrogen (H_2) and oxygen (O_2) to form water (H_2O) is spontaneous. To start the reaction, however, energy must be added. (Hydrogen and oxygen can exist together for years yet form very little water.) A lighted match inserted into a hydrogen-oxygen mixture provides the necessary energy. Once this reaction is begun, it proceeds to completion. For the reverse reaction, water does not decompose spontaneously to form hydrogen and oxygen. Electricity (a form of work) must be continuously passed through water to cause decomposition. As soon as the flow of electricity ceases, the decomposition stops. The reaction is not spontaneous.

Spontaneity is an important concept since it indicates which chemical reactions will proceed naturally and which require energy to be put in constantly. You can imagine how important it is to know the answers to such questions as whether pure metal can be chemically removed from newly mined ore, whether natural gas can be economically produced from coal, whether certain food additives will be digested harmlessly, whether specific industrial processes will pollute the atmosphere, and innumerable other problems that chemists must meet. Their best approach is through considering individual reactions.

7.5 Free Energy

Free energy is a numerical measure of the spontaneity of a reaction. A chemist, knowing the change in free energy for a given reaction, can determine whether the reaction is spontaneous. The symbol for free energy change is ΔG. (The Greek letter Δ, *delta*, means "change in.") The actual numerical value of ΔG is not significant for us now, but the general idea of using ΔG is important. First, there is one value of the free energy associated with the products, called $G_{products}$, and one value of the free energy associated with the reactants, called $G_{reactants}$. The value ΔG is the difference between $G_{products}$ and $G_{reactants}$, and it can be read as the difference between the free energy of the products and the free energy of the reactants. It is the change in free energy that accompanies the reaction.

If $G_{reactants}$ is larger than $G_{products}$, the reaction is **spontaneous**, and ΔG is negative. On the other hand, if $G_{products}$ is greater than $G_{reactants}$, the reaction is not spontaneous, and ΔG is positive. Look at it this way. If there is a step down in free energy from reactants to products, $G_{reactants} > G_{products}$, and the reaction is spontaneous—it happens. This is shown in Figure 7.5. On the other hand, if the change is a step up, $G_{products} > G_{reactants}$, and the reaction does not

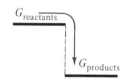

Figure 7.5 A spontaneous reaction is like going down a step in free energy, and $G_p - G_r < 0$.

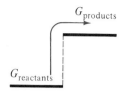

Figure 7.6 A nonspontaneous reaction is like going up a step in free energy, and $G_p - G_r > 0$.

proceed unless enough work is done to force the reaction (Figure 7.6). Consider a situation in which water flows downhill. Water flows downhill spontaneously. This means that $G_{\text{bottom hill}} - G_{\text{top hill}} < 0$. For water flowing uphill, $G_{\text{top hill}} - G_{\text{bottom hill}} > 0$, and the process is not spontaneous. In another example, the reaction to form water from hydrogen and oxygen, $G_{H_2O} - (G_{H_2} + G_{O_2}) < 0$, and the reaction is spontaneous.

In review, free energy can be used to predict the spontaneity of a reaction. Free energy itself, however, is not a simple term. The numerical value of the free-energy change results from a combination of two other kinds of energy involved in chemical reactions: enthalpy and entropy.

7.6   Enthalpy, Entropy, and Free Energy

The **enthalpy change** is the heat absorbed or released during a chemical reaction; it is symbolized by ΔH. It is the difference between the **enthalpy**, or heat content, of the products and the enthalpy of the reactants. The change in enthalpy is the chief factor that determines the change in free energy. When a match burns, it releases heat, and the change in enthalpy (heat) for the reaction is negative. The heat content of the products is lower than the heat content of the reactants.

$$\Delta H = H_{\text{products}} - H_{\text{reactants}} < 0$$

When $\Delta H < 0$ for a reaction, the reaction is said to be **exothermic** (heat-releasing). An exothermic reaction is usually spontaneous.

Some well-known examples of reactions in which heat is released are the reaction of oxygen with many things (burning), the explosion of a stick of dynamite, the reaction that takes place in setting off a highway flare, and the dissolving of acids in water.

On the other hand, some reactions absorb heat and cause their surroundings to become cooler. These reactions are **endothermic**.

$$\Delta H = H_{\text{products}} - H_{\text{reactants}} > 0$$

In this case, the reaction requires heat, so the sign on the enthalpy change is positive. An example of this sort of process is the dissolution of a salt, sodium nitrate ($NaNO_3$), in water. As the sodium nitrate dissolves, it removes heat energy from its surroundings (the water), and the water becomes cooler. Many reactions that are endothermic acquire the heat needed by absorbing it from the material immediately surrounding the reaction. Endothermic reactions are usually not spontaneous. It is important to realize that the heat absorbed or released during a chemical reaction is routinely measured in the laboratory. The quantity of heat released when food substances are burned in oxygen defines the food Calorie, a measure of the food value of a substance.

Entropy

The less important term determining free energy is entropy.

Entropy is energy that is related to disorder; it is a way to express unavailable energy that cannot be measured. The energy related to entropy cannot be converted into either work or heat. It is symbolized by the letter S. In a spontaneous reaction, the reactants tend to become more disordered as they become products. Thus, since $\Delta S = S_p - S_r$, then $\Delta S > 0$ for a spontaneous process. In other words, the entropy increases. (It is like the way any room in a house becomes messy spontaneously if you just let it alone. On the other hand, you can restore order if you do work on it.) In many cases, the change in entropy is very small compared with the change in free energy; and thus ΔS is often neglected. In some cases, however, like the melting of ice, the change in entropy is very important. Entropy changes must be calculated; they cannot be measured directly. The actual calculation of entropy is not significant for us here; however, we must realize that entropy is one of the two decisive factors in the spontaneity of a reaction.

Figure 7.7 If you were to drop 16 marbles into a box and look in from the top, it would be highly improbable that you would see case (a), which is a highly ordered state, having low entropy. It would be much more likely that you would see something like case (b), which is disordered with higher entropy. Case (b) represents one of the many possible disordered states.

(a)   (b)

Relation to Free Energy

Entropy and enthalpy changes for a reaction can be combined to give the free-energy change for a reaction, according to the equation

$$\Delta G_{\text{reaction}} = \Delta H_{\text{reaction}} - T\Delta S_{\text{reaction}}$$

where T is the temperature at which the reaction occurs. A combination of ΔH and ΔS that gives $\Delta G < 0$ brings about a spontaneous reaction. Usually, the effect of the entropy term $(-T\Delta S)$ on ΔG is very small, so for most reactions that take place over a wide temperature range, the free energy change can be written

$$\Delta G_{\text{reaction}} \approx \Delta H_{\text{reaction}}$$

Thus, a reaction that is exothermic is usually spontaneous. A reaction that is endothermic is usually not spontaneous. The study of free energy, enthalpy, and entropy are included in a field called **thermodynamics**. Using the principles of thermodynamics can help one predict the spontaneity of untried reactions.

7.7   Balanced Equations and Heat

Heat is measured in calories; thus the heat given off or absorbed during a reaction, the enthalpy change for that reaction, is measured in calories. The SI unit for heat is the joule; 4.184 joules = 1 calorie. Chemists most often measure heat in calories, but joules are becoming more popular. (Calories will be used throughout this textbook.)

To standardize the relative amount of heat produced or absorbed in a reaction, one reports the heat as that amount produced or absorbed by 1 mol of the reactant of interest. For example, if hydrogen is burned in air according to the equation $2H_2 + O_2 \rightarrow 2H_2O$, heat is given off, or $\Delta H < 0$. For every mole of hydrogen that burns, $\Delta H = -68,300$ cal/mol. From the equation, you can see that for every mole of hydrogen that burns, 0.5 mol of oxygen is consumed, and 1 mol of water is formed. (Remember that the equation has indicated $H_2 : O_2 : H_2O = 2:1:2$.) When 1 mol of hydrogen reacts or 0.5 mol of oxygen reacts, or 1 mol of water is formed, 68,300 cal of heat is evolved. It is also true that if twice as much hydrogen had been burned, twice as much heat, or 136,600 cal, would have been produced. Also, twice as much oxygen would have been used, and twice as much water would have formed.

Although many things are involved in picking fuels for heating systems, such as availability, cost, and pollution, it is easy to see that the heat given off per mole of fuel is very important. The more heat given off per mole, the more efficient the fuel.

Glossary

Chemical equation	A statement that represents a chemical reaction; symbols are used to show reactants and products.
Chemical reaction	A process in which bonds are formed or broken or both.
Coefficients in a chemical reaction	Numbers placed before formula units in a chemical reaction that indicate the ratio of formula units participating in a reaction.
Endothermic reaction	A reaction that requires heat energy to proceed.

Enthalpy change for a reaction	Heat that is given off or taken in during a reaction.
Entropy change	A function that is a measure of the change in the order in a system.
Exothermic reaction	A reaction that emits heat energy as it proceeds.
Free energy	A function used to determine whether a reaction proceeds spontaneously. If the change in free energy for a reaction is negative, the reaction is spontaneous.
Product	A new species that is formed when compounds or elements interact in a chemical reaction (the material produced).
Reactant	Element or compound that takes part in a chemical reaction (the starting material).
Spontaneous reaction	A reaction that once begun will proceed without added energy.
Thermodynamics	The study of the relation between heat and mechanical energy through such functions as entropy, enthalpy, and free energy.

Problems

1. Explain, using an example, what happens in a chemical reaction. Label the products and reactants in the equation.

2. State the following equations in terms of moles:
   (a) $HCl + NaOH \rightarrow NaCl + H_2O$
   (b) $BaCO_3 + 2HNO_3 \rightarrow H_2O + Ba(NO_3)_2 + CO_2$
   (c) $Ca + 2H_2O \rightarrow Ca(OH)_2 + H_2$
   (d) $2KClO_3 \rightarrow 2KCl + 3O_2$
   (e) $4FeS + 7O_2 \rightarrow 2Fe_2O_3 + 4SO_2$
   (f) $3H_2 + 2HNO_3 \rightarrow 2NO + 4H_2O$
   (g) $3CuS + 8HNO_3 \rightarrow 3Cu(NO_3)_2 + 3S + 2NO + 4H_2O$
   (h) $4HNO_3 + P_4O_{10} \rightarrow 2N_2O_5 + 4HPO_3$
   (metaphosphoric acid)
   (i) $2Pb(NO_3)_2 \rightarrow 2PbO + 4NO_2 + O_2$
   (j) $2Na + O_2 \rightarrow Na_2O_2$ (sodium peroxide)

3. State the equations of Problem 2 in terms of molecules, formula units, and atoms.

4. State the equations of Problem 2 in terms of grams of each compound or element.

5. Express the following chemical statements symbolically:
   (a) One mole of sodium chloride plus 1 mol of silver nitrate will react to produce 1 mol of silver chloride and 1 mol of sodium nitrate.
   (b) One molecule of sulfuric acid plus two molecules of ammonium hydroxide produces one molecule of ammonium sulfate and two molecules of water.
   (c) 6.02×10^{23} molecules of iron(III) chloride reacts with 18.06×10^{23} molecules of sodium hydroxide to produce 6.02×10^{23} molecules of iron(III) hydroxide and 18.06×10^{23} molecules of sodium chloride.
   (d) Twenty-eight grams of nitrogen gas reacts with 6 g of hydrogen gas to produce 34 g of ammonia. (Remember that hydrogen gas and nitrogen gas are diatomic.)
   (e) One hundred fifty-two grams of chromium(III) oxide reacts with 6 g of hydrogen to produce 104 g of chromium and 54 g of water.
   (f) Two moles of phosphoric acid reacts with 3 mol of calcium hydroxide to produce 1 mol of calcium phosphate and 6 mol of water.

6. Express each reaction symbolically and balance both sides for a proper equation.
   (a) Aluminum + hydrochloric acid → hydrogen + aluminum chloride
   (b) Sodium + water → hydrogen + sodium hydroxide
   (c) Calcium oxide + water → calcium hydroxide
   (d) Aluminum sulfide + water → aluminum hydroxide + hydrogen sulfide
   (e) Fluorine + sodium chloride → sodium fluoride + chlorine
   (f) Carbon disulfide + water → carbon dioxide + hydrogen sulfide
   (g) Carbon disulfide + oxygen → carbon monoxide + sulfur dioxide
   (h) Antimony sulfide + iron → antimony + iron(II) sulfide
   (i) Sodium arsenide + ammonium bromide → ammonium arsenide + sodium bromide
   (j) Selenium dioxide + selenium + hydrogen chloride → diselenium dichloride + water

7. Balance the following equations:
   (a) $Mg + N_2 → Mg_3N_2$
   (b) $KOH + K → K_2O + H_2$
   (c) $Ca(OH)_2 + Na_2CO_3 → NaOH + CaCO_3$
   (d) $Na_2O_2 + H_2O → H_2O_2 + NaOH$
   (e) $NH_4Cl + CaO → NH_3 + H_2O + CaCl_2$
   (f) $BaSO_4 + C → BaS + CO$
   (g) $MnO_2 + HCl → MnCl_2 + Cl_2 + H_2O$
   (h) $MgO + P_4O_{10} → Mg_3(PO_4)_2$
   (i) $Cu_2S + O_2 → Cu_2O + SO_2$
   (j) $FeS + O_2 → FeO + SO_2$
   (k) $HgO → Hg + O_2$

   (l) $Hg_2Cl_2 + NH_3 → Hg + Hg(NH_2)Cl + NH_4Cl$
   (m) $CuO + NH_3 → Cu + H_2O + N_2$
   (n) $SO_2 + O_2 → SO_3$
   (o) $H_2S + O_2 → SO_2 + H_2O$
   (p) $Cu_2O + O_2 → CuO$
   (q) $Al + O_2 → Al_2O_3$
   (r) $S_8 + O_2 → SO_2$
   (s) $P_4 + O_2 → P_4O_{10}$
   (t) $H_2SO_4 + NaOH → Na_2SO_4 + H_2O$
   (u) $AgNO_3 + MgCl_2 → AgCl + Mg(NO_3)_2$
   (v) $CaCO_3 + HCl → CaCl_2 + H_2O + CO_2$
   (w) $H_3PO_4 + KOH → K_3PO_4 + H_2O$
   (x) $SO_2 + O_2 → SO_3$
   (y) $K_2O + H_2O → KOH$
   (z) $P_4 + Cl_2 → PCl_5$

8. Which of the following reactions are endothermic and which are exothermic? Explain in words what your answers mean.
   (a) $2C_2H_6 + 7O_2 → 4CO_2 + 6H_2O$
   $\Delta H = -621.2$ kcal
   (b) $SO_2 → S + O_2$ $\Delta H = 70.96$ kcal
   (c) $4Al + 3O_2 → 2Al_2O_3$ $\Delta H = -798.18$ kcal
   (d) $H_2 + S → H_2S$ $\Delta H = -4.815$ kcal
   (e) $3Pb + 2Al_2O_3 → 4Al + 3PbO_2$
   $\Delta H = 599.82$ kcal

9. Explain what is meant by free energy. Include the terms used to find the free energy of a chemical reaction.

10. Explain the difference between **exothermic** and **endothermic**. Can an endothermic reaction be spontaneous?

"no" chapter 5

Learning Objectives for Chapter 8

Define **limiting reagent.**

Given a chemical equation and the quantity of one reactant or product present in moles or grams, calculate the quantity, in moles or grams, of any other reactant used or product produced.

Given quantities of reactants present, determine the limiting reagent and the quantities used in the reaction.

8 WORKING CHEMICAL PROBLEMS

Calculating quantities of reactants and products involved is the next step in our study of chemical reactions. There are several different kinds of calculations, and these are best presented through examples. Let us begin by looking at a familiar situation. How much unpopped corn must be added to a 4-qt popcorn pan to produce one pan of popped popcorn? The popping of popcorn can be represented by a statement that is like a chemical equation (Figure 8.2):

Unpopped corn + 4-qt pan + oil = popped corn + dirty 4-qt pan

To solve any chemical problem, the first step is writing the chemical equation.

When popping popcorn, it is undesirable for the pan to overflow; however, it is advantageous to pop as much popcorn at one time as possible. It is also

Figure 8.1 The success or failure of a rocket launch depends upon the precise calculation of reactants and products. (Photo courtesy of NASA)

Figure 8.2 It is necessary to have a balanced equation to determine exactly how much popcorn to put in the pot.

2 tablespoons oil $+$ 1 cup popcorn $+$ 1-4 quart pan $\longrightarrow$ 1 dirty 4 quart pan full of popped popcorn

important not to have either oily or burnt popcorn (from using too much or too little oil). To prepare the maximum amount of good popped corn without overflow, it is necessary to know some of the quantities in the popcorn equation written above. In other words, the next step in solving the problem is to balance the equation. The balanced popcorn equation is

1 c unpopped corn + 4-qt pan + 2 T oil →

4 qt popped corn + dirty 4-qt pan

The balanced equation indicates the quantities of materials needed to produce the desired product. If a person wanted to produce twice the amount of product, each coefficient in the balanced equation would have to be doubled. If one-half the product were desired, the coefficients would be halved. Thus, the balanced equation can be used to determine the quantity of reactants needed to produce any desired quantity of products.

8.1 Chemical Calculations

Problems dealing with chemical equations are solved in the same sequence.

Step 1   Write the reactants and products as they occur.
Step 2   Balance the chemical equation.

Zinc metal, for instance, reacts with hydrochloric acid to produce zinc chloride and hydrogen gas. How many grams of hydrogen can be produced if one begins with 300. g of Zn? According to step 1, reactants and products are written:

$$Zn + HCl \rightarrow ZnCl_2 + H_2$$

According to step 2, the sides must be balanced:

$$Zn + 2HCl \rightarrow ZnCl_2 + H_2$$

The equation is balanced. It indicates that 1 mol of zinc reacts with 2 mol of hydrochloric acid to produce 1 mol of zinc chloride and 1 mol of hydrogen. The balanced equation yields information about the ratios of moles of reactants and products used and produced.

This equation can be used to derive a set of unit factors that will be useful in solving problems. Several unit factors are implied by the balanced equation. Since the equation indicates that the ratio of moles of zinc, moles of hydrochloric acid, moles of hydrogen, and moles of zinc chloride is 1:2:1:1, the following equations can be written:

$$1 \text{ mol Zn} = 2 \text{ mol HCl}$$

$$1 \text{ mol Zn} = 1 \text{ mol ZnCl}_2$$

$$1 \text{ mol Zn} = 1 \text{ mol H}_2$$

$$2 \text{ mol HCl} = 1 \text{ mol ZnCl}_2$$

$$2 \text{ mol HCl} = 1 \text{ mol H}_2$$

$$1 \text{ mol ZnCl}_2 = 1 \text{ mol H}_2$$

The following unit factors are obtained:

$$\frac{1 \text{ mol Zn}}{2 \text{ mol HCl}} = 1 = \frac{2 \text{ mol HCl}}{1 \text{ mol Zn}}$$

$$\frac{1 \text{ mol Zn}}{1 \text{ mol ZnCl}_2} = 1 = \frac{1 \text{ mol ZnCl}_2}{1 \text{ mol Zn}}$$

$$\frac{1 \text{ mol Zn}}{1 \text{ mol H}_2} = 1 = \frac{1 \text{ mol H}_2}{1 \text{ mol Zn}}$$

$$\frac{2 \text{ mol HCl}}{1 \text{ mol ZnCl}_2} = 1 = \frac{1 \text{ mol ZnCl}_2}{2 \text{ mol HCl}}$$

$$\frac{2 \text{ mol HCl}}{1 \text{ mol H}_2} = 1 = \frac{1 \text{ mol H}_2}{2 \text{ mol HCl}}$$

$$\frac{1 \text{ mol ZnCl}_2}{1 \text{ mol H}_2} = 1 = \frac{1 \text{ mol H}_2}{1 \text{ mol ZnCl}_2}$$

It is now time to introduce step 3 in the calculation. Step 3 consists in converting grams of material (in this case grams of zinc) to moles (moles of zinc). By the unit factor 1 mol Zn/65.4 g Zn, grams of zinc are converted to moles of zinc in the following way:

$$300. \text{ g Zn} \times \frac{1 \text{ mol Zn}}{65.4 \text{ g Zn}} = 4.59 \text{ mol Zn}$$

Notice that grams cancel, leaving moles of zinc as units.

In step 4, moles of zinc are converted to moles of the product of interest, hydrogen. The balanced equation shows that 1 mol of zinc produces 1 mol of H_2. Since there is 4.59 mol zinc present, 4.59 mol hydrogen is produced. To show this mathematically, one uses the appropriate unit factor. Choosing this unit factor is part of step 4. The solution is

$$4.59 \text{ mol Zn} \times \frac{1 \text{ mol } H_2}{1 \text{ mol Zn}} = 4.59 \text{ mol } H_2$$

The unit factor was chosen from the six unit factors possible from the balanced equation. The unit factor was selected to give the units needed for the answer. In any balanced equation, a unit factor can be selected for converting one material to another, and the unit factors from other parts of the equation can be ignored.

Now that the number of moles of hydrogen produced is known, the weight of hydrogen produced can be found by multiplying the number of moles of hydrogen produced by the appropriate unit factor needed for converting to grams of hydrogen. This conversion can be considered step 5, the final step in the problem:

$$4.59 \text{ mol } H_2 \times \frac{2.00 \text{ g } H_2}{1 \text{ mol } H_2} = 9.18 \text{ g } H_2$$

In the last problem, the number of grams of hydrogen that could be produced from a specific weight of zinc was calculated. This was accomplished in five steps.

Step 1   Write the equation.

Step 2   Balance the equation.

Step 3   Convert known gram weight to moles.

Step 4   Convert to the desired material, selecting an appropriate unit factor from the balanced equation.

Step 5   Convert moles of unknown material to grams.

8.2   Application of Techniques

Additional examples of calculation follow. From this point on in this chapter, unit cancellation will not be shown. The units will, however, be present and the cancellations must be made in your mind.

Example 8.1

Oxygen can be produced from the decomposition of potassium chlorate ($KClO_3$). How many grams of oxygen are produced from 26.0 g potassium chlorate (Figure 8.3)?

Proceed by the steps outlined.

Step 1   Write the products and reactants in equation form.

$$KClO_3 \rightarrow KCl + O_2$$

Step 2   Balance the equation:

$$2KClO_3 \rightarrow 2KCl + 3O_2$$

Step 3   Convert grams of $KClO_3$ to moles of $KClO_3$.

$$26.0 \text{ g } KClO_3 \times \frac{1 \text{ mol } KClO_3}{122.5 \text{ g } KClO_3} = 0.212 \text{ mol } KClO_3$$

Step 4   Determine, using the appropriate unit factor, the number of moles of oxygen produced. The three possible unit factors from the equation are:

$$\frac{2 \text{ mol } KClO_3}{2 \text{ mol } KCl} = 1 = \frac{2 \text{ mol } KCl}{2 \text{ mol } KClO_3}$$

$$\frac{2 \text{ mol } KClO_3}{3 \text{ mol } O_2} = 1 = \frac{3 \text{ mol } O_2}{2 \text{ mol } KClO_3}$$

$$\frac{2 \text{ mol } KCl}{3 \text{ mol } O_2} = 1 = \frac{3 \text{ mol } O_2}{2 \text{ mol } KCl}$$

Figure 8.3 Apparatus for preparing oxygen. Manganese dioxide (MnO_2) is added to the potassium chlorate ($KClO_3$) because it helps the $KClO_3$ to decompose at a lower temperature. The MnO_2 is not changed in the reaction. A substance that changes the speed of the reaction but does not itself change is called a catalyst.

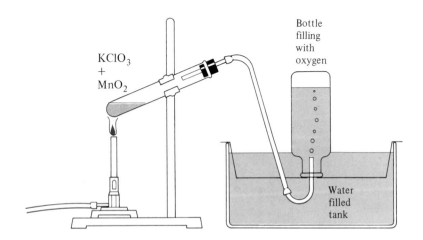

The second unit factor is used to determine the number of moles of O_2 produced.

$$0.212 \text{ mol KClO}_3 \times \frac{3 \text{ mol O}_2}{2 \text{ mol KClO}_3} = 0.318 \text{ mol O}_2$$

Step 5   Determine, using unit factors, the number of grams of oxygen produced.

$$0.318 \text{ mol O}_2 \times \frac{32.0 \text{ g O}_2}{1 \text{ mol O}_2} = 10.2 \text{ g O}_2$$

Another twist that can be added to reaction calculations is the following.

Example 8.2   Consider the reaction that occurs in a propane torch. Propane (C_3H_8) reacts with oxygen to produce water and carbon dioxide. How much oxygen (in grams) is needed to react with 20.0 g of propane gas (Figure 8.4)?

Step 1 $C_3H_8 + O_2 \rightarrow CO_2 + H_2O$
Step 2   Balance the equation:

$$C_3H_8 + 5O_2 \rightarrow 3CO_2 + 4H_2O$$

Step 3   Determine the number of moles of C_3H_8 present:

$$20.0 \text{ g C}_3H_8 \times \frac{1 \text{ mol C}_3H_8}{44.0 \text{ g C}_3H_8} = 0.454 \text{ mol C}_3H_8$$

Step 4   Find the number of moles of oxygen required. (All the possible unit factors involved in the equation are not listed. Mentally, concern yourself only with the materials of interest and write the correct unit factor. If you have difficulty at this point, write down the possible unit factors and select the unit factor appropriate to this problem.)

Figure 8.4 The reaction of propane with oxygen is very useful for heating homes and in propane torches. A propane torch is shown here.

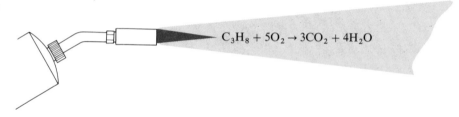

$$C_3H_8 + 5O_2 \rightarrow 3CO_2 + 4H_2O$$

$$0.454 \text{ mol } C_3H_8 \times \frac{5 \text{ mol } O_2}{1 \text{ mol } C_3H_8} = 2.27 \text{ mol } O_2$$

Step 5 $2.27 \text{ mol } O_2 \times \dfrac{32.0 \text{ g } O_2}{1 \text{ mol } O_2} = 72.6 \text{ g } O_2$

There is no concern for any unit factors relating to the right-hand side of the equation. These unit factors were not involved in the problem.

Example 8.3   Nitric acid can be produced from ammonia (NH_3) by burning ammonia on the surface of platinum. The balanced equation is $4NH_3 + 5O_2 \rightarrow 4NO + 6H_2O$. If 184 g of water were produced, how many grams of NO were produced?

Steps 1 and 2   The balanced equation is given.
Step 3   Converting to moles, we get

$$184 \text{ g } H_2O \times \frac{1 \text{ mol } H_2O}{18.0 \text{ g } H_2O} = 10.2 \text{ mol } H_2O$$

Step 4   From the equation,

$$10.2 \text{ mol } H_2O \times \frac{4 \text{ mol NO}}{6 \text{ mol } H_2O} = 6.80 \text{ mol NO}$$

Step 5   Converting back to grams of NO gives

$$6.80 \text{ mol NO} \times \frac{30.0 \text{ g NO}}{1 \text{ mol NO}} = 204 \text{ g NO}$$

Example 8.4   Aluminum chloride ($AlCl_3$) can be produced from its constituent elements. How many <u>moles</u> of $AlCl_3$ will 125 g of Cl_2 produce?

Step 1 $Al + Cl_2 \rightarrow AlCl_3$
Step 2 $2Al + 3Cl_2 \rightarrow 2AlCl_3$

Step 3 $125 \text{ g } Cl_2 \times \dfrac{1 \text{ mol } Cl_2}{71.0 \text{ g } Cl_2} = 1.76 \text{ mol } Cl_2$

Step 4 $1.76 \text{ mol } Cl_2 \times \dfrac{2 \text{ mol } AlCl_3}{3 \text{ mol } Cl_2} = 1.17 \text{ mol } AlCl_3$

Example 8.5   Carbon tetrachloride (CCl_4) was once used as a dry-cleaning solvent and as a fire extinguishing material. It became unpopular when it was discovered that if one breathed or touched carbon tetrachloride for too long a time, one's liver could be damaged. Carbon tetrachloride can be made by heating carbon disulfide with chlorine. This produces carbon tetrachloride and disulfur dichloride (S_2Cl_2). How much (in grams) chlorine is needed to make 1000.0 g of carbon tetrachloride (Figure 8.5)?

Figure 8.5 Carbon tetrachloride is prepared by heating chlorine with carbon disulfide.

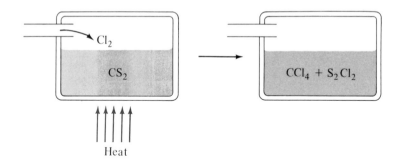

Step 1 $CS_2 + Cl_2 \rightarrow CCl_4 + S_2Cl_2$

Step 2 $CS_2 + 3Cl_2 \rightarrow CCl_4 + S_2Cl_2$

Step 3 $1000.0 \text{ g CCl}_4 \times \dfrac{1 \text{ mol CCl}_4}{153.8 \text{ g CCl}_4} = 6.502 \text{ mol CCl}_4$

Step 4 $6.502 \text{ mol CCl}_4 \times \dfrac{3 \text{ mol Cl}_2}{1 \text{ mol CCl}_4} = 19.51 \text{ mol Cl}_2$

Step 5 $19.51 \text{ mol Cl}_2 \times \dfrac{71.0 \text{ g Cl}_2}{1 \text{ mol Cl}_2} = 1380 \text{ g Cl}_2$

(Remember significant figures.)

Chemists can run into further complications in solving problems.

Example 8.6

In the reaction of carbon with sulfur dioxide to produce carbon disulfide and carbon monoxide, how much carbon disulfide could be produced if one started with 20.0 g of carbon and 30.0 g of sulfur dioxide? This problem is more complicated than the previous ones. The complication is introduced by the presence of known quantities of both reactants. The initial steps in solving this are identical to those in the previous problems.

Step 1   Write the equation:

$$C + SO_2 \rightarrow CS_2 + CO$$

Step 2   Balance the equation:

$$5C + 2SO_2 \rightarrow CS_2 + 4CO$$

Step 3   In this problem, both the number of moles of carbon present and the number of moles of SO_2 present must be calculated. The calculations are needed to determine which of the two materials is in excess. If one of the materials is in excess, all that material will not react; some of the material in excess is left untouched at the end of the reaction. This means that the amount of CS_2 produced will depend on the material that was not in excess, the material that was completely consumed in the reaction. The chemical that determines the amount of product is called the **limiting reagent** (Figure 8.6).

Reagent is just another word for chemical substance, or chemical material. To determine the limiting reagent, one more step is necessary. Step 3, conversion to moles, remains the same as in previous problems; the number of moles of each reactant present must be calculated:

$$20.0 \text{ g C} \times \frac{1 \text{ mol C}}{12.0 \text{ g C}} = 1.67 \text{ mol C}$$

$$30.0 \text{ g SO}_2 \times \frac{1 \text{ mol SO}_2}{64.0 \text{ g SO}_2} = 0.469 \text{ mol SO}_2$$

Step 4   Determining the limiting reagent is the new step 4. It must be done now. The equation says that 5 mol carbon reacts with 2 mol sulfur dioxide. There is only 1.67 mol carbon present. How many moles of sulfur dioxide are then needed?

Figure 8.6 The problem of finding the limiting reagent occurs when one has too much of one of the reactants. In this case, there is too much carbon, so sulfur dioxide is the limiting reagent that determines how much CS_2 is formed, and carbon is the reagent in excess.

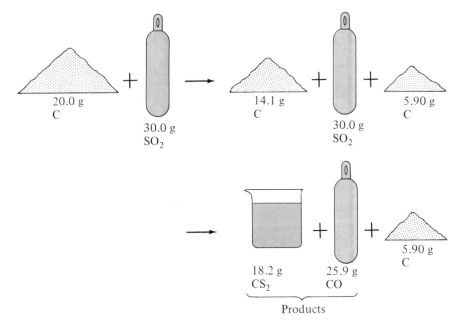

$$1.67 \text{ mol C} \times \frac{2 \text{ mol SO}_2}{5 \text{ mol C}} = 0.668 \text{ mol SO}_2$$

Since there are only 0.469 mol SO_2 available, the carbon is in excess. All of it will not react, since the required amount of sulfur dioxide is not present. The sulfur dioxide is the limiting reagent. Knowing the limiting reagent, we can calculate the quantity of CS_2 produced.

Step 5   Step 5 is the old step 4; convert moles of the limiting reagent to moles of the desired compound.

$$0.469 \text{ mol SO}_2 \times \frac{1 \text{ mol CS}_2}{2 \text{ mol SO}_2} = 0.234 \text{ mol CS}_2$$

Step 6   Step 6, the final step is the old step 5. Convert moles of the desired compound to grams of the desired compound.

$$0.234 \text{ mol CS}_2 \times \frac{76.0 \text{ g CS}_2}{1 \text{ mol CS}_2} = 17.8 \text{ g CS}_2$$

The quantity of unreacted carbon may also be of interest. It can be calculated by considering the number of moles of carbon that reacted and then subtracting that value from the total number of moles of carbon originally present.

Example 8.7   Boron and oxygen are mixed 10.0 mol to 5.00 mol in a reaction to form B_2O_3. Which is the limiting reagent, and how many grams of B_2O_3 are produced?

Step 1 $B + O_2 \rightarrow B_2O_3$
Step 2 $4B + 3O_2 \rightarrow 2B_2O_3$
Step 3   Convert to moles. This has already been done.
Step 4   Use unit factors to calculate number of moles produced by each mixture. For 5.00 mol of oxygen,

$$5.00 \text{ mol O}_2 \times \frac{4 \text{ mol B}}{3 \text{ mol O}_2} = 6.67 \text{ mol B}$$

$$10.0 \text{ mol B} \times \frac{3 \text{ mol O}_2}{4 \text{ mol B}} = 7.50 \text{ mol O}_2$$

The amount 7.50 mol O_2 is not present, so O_2 must be the limiting reagent.

Step 5 $$6.67 \text{ mol B} \times \frac{2 \text{ mol B}_2O_3}{4 \text{ mol B}} = 3.34 \text{ mol B}_2O_3$$

Step 6 $$3.34 \text{ mol B}_2O_3 \times \frac{69.6 \text{ g B}_2O_3}{1 \text{ mol B}_2O_3} = 232 \text{ g B}_2O_3$$

Another kind of problem involves determining the percentage of an element or compound in an impure sample. Example 8.8 shows this.

<table>
<tr><td>**Example 8.8**</td><td>A miner was able to find some mercury(II) oxide ore. He gave a sample of the ore to a chemist to determine the percentage of HgO in the ore. The chemist knew that the ore was partly pure HgO and partly other rock. The problem was attacked in the following manner: A 10.0-g sample of the ore was carefully weighed. The ore was then heated to convert the mercury(II) oxide to pure mercury, which was collected and weighed. This process produced 5.0 g of pure mercury. This information can be used to determine the percentage of HgO in the original ore.</td></tr>
</table>

The thought process involved is the following. Mercury(II) oxide decomposes when heated, forming mercury and oxygen. Measuring the amount of mercury produced allows the amount of mercury(II) oxide originally present to be calculated. The percentage of HgO in the original sample can then be determined by dividing the amount of HgO calculated by the total sample weight and multiplying the answer by 100. The problem is initiated by the familiar first three steps.

Step 1 $HgO \rightarrow Hg + O_2$

Step 2 $2HgO \rightarrow 2Hg + O_2$

Step 3 $5.0 \text{ g Hg} \times \dfrac{1 \text{ mol Hg}}{200.6 \text{ g Hg}} = 0.025 \text{ mol Hg}$

Step 4 Convert mol Hg to mol HgO:

$$0.025 \text{ mol Hg} \times \frac{2 \text{ mol HgO}}{2 \text{ mol Hg}} = 0.025 \text{ mol HgO}$$

Step 5 Convert moles of HgO to grams of HgO:

$$0.025 \text{ mol HgO} \times \frac{216.6 \text{ g HgO}}{1 \text{ mol HgO}} = 5.4 \text{ g HgO}$$

Step 6 Determine the percentage of HgO in the sample.

$$\frac{\text{g HgO}}{\text{total wt of ore sample}} \times 100 = \% \text{ HgO in ore}$$

$$\frac{5.4 \text{ g HgO}}{10 \text{ g sample}} \times 100 = 54\% \text{ HgO}$$

| Example 8.9 | A chemist was given a sample of muriatic acid that contained 65 percent by weight hydrochloric acid. How many grams of zinc will be dissolved by 200.0 g of this acid? |

Step 1 Write the equation:

$$HCl + Zn \rightarrow ZnCl_2 + H_2$$

Step 2 Balance the equation:

$$2HCl + Zn \rightarrow ZnCl_2 + H_2$$

Step 3 Calculate the amount of HCl present. This is done by taking 65% of the 200.0 g (200.0 g HCl × 0.65 = 130 g of HCl); thus 130 g of HCl is available to react with the zinc.

Step 4 Convert 130 g of HCl to moles of HCl:

$$130 \text{ g HCl} \times \frac{1 \text{ mol HCl}}{36.5 \text{ g HCl}} = 3.6 \text{ mol HCl}$$

Step 5 Find the number of moles of zinc that reacted.

$$3.6 \text{ mol HCl} \times \frac{1 \text{ mol Zn}}{2 \text{ mol HCl}} = 1.8 \text{ mol Zn}$$

Step 6 The weight of zinc dissolved is

$$1.8 \text{ mol Zn} \times \frac{65.4 \text{ g Zn}}{1 \text{ mol Zn}} = 120 \text{ g Zn}$$

(Remember significant figures.)

| Example 8.10 | What weight of MgO can be prepared by heating 100.0 g of material containing 90.0 percent $MgCO_3$? |

Step 1 Write the equation:

$$MgCO_3 + heat \rightarrow MgO + CO_2$$

Step 2 Balance the equation. In this case, it is already balanced.

Step 3 A 100.0-g sample of material that contains 90.0 percent $MgCO_3$ will contain

$$100.0 \text{ g} \times 0.900 = 90.0 \text{ g MgCO}_3$$

The number of molecular weights is

$$90.0 \text{ g MgCO}_3 \times \frac{1 \text{ mol MgCO}_3}{84.3 \text{ g MgCO}_3} = 1.07 \text{ mol MgCO}_3$$

Step 4 $1.07 \text{ mol MgCO}_3 \times \dfrac{1 \text{ mol MgO}}{1 \text{ mol MgCO}_3} = 1.07 \text{ mol MgO}$

Step 5 $1.07 \text{ mol MgO} \times \dfrac{40.3 \text{ g MgO}}{1 \text{ mol MgO}} = 43.1 \text{ g MgO}$

The best way to learn how to do problems is by doing many examples. It is necessary to become comfortable with the numbers as well as the words. Working these sorts of problems takes practice. There are numerous problems at the end of the chapter to help you understand the methods presented.

Glossary

Limiting reagent   The reactant that determines the maximum quantity of product that is obtainable in a chemical reaction.

Problems

1. The first step in the production of nitric acid from ammonia (NH_3) involves burning ammonia on the surface of a platinum catalyst. The balanced equation is

    $$4NH_3 + 5O_2 \rightarrow 4NO + 6H_2O$$

    (a) Write all the possible unit factors from this equation.
    (b) How many moles of oxygen are required to react with 4.00 mol of ammonia?
    (c) How many moles of oxygen are required to react with 1.00 mol of ammonia?
    (d) How many moles of water are produced for each mole of ammonia burned?
    (e) How many grams of NO are produced from burning 4.00 mol of ammonia?
    (f) How many grams of water are produced from 1.00 mol of oxygen?

    (g) How many grams of NO are produced from 8.50 g of NH_3?
    (h) How many grams of oxygen react with 10.0 g of NH_3?

2. Sulfur dioxide is a serious pollutant in the atmosphere. As much as 5.1 billion kilograms of SO_2 are dumped into the atmosphere from industrial plants each year. Much of this SO_2 comes from smelters, since many ores that are smelted are found in nature as sulfides. A typical example is copper metal production, which can be accomplished by roasting Cu_2S and thus producing SO_2. The unbalanced equation is

    $$Cu_2S + O_2 \rightarrow Cu + SO_2$$

    How many kilograms of SO_2 are produced from 100. kilograms of Cu_2S treated in this manner?

3. Another roasting process that is a step in a series of reactions for producing metals from ores is the following:

$$ZnS + 2O_2 \rightarrow ZnO + SO_2$$

For each 1.00 kilogram of ZnO produced, how many kilograms of SO_2 are released into the atmosphere?

4. Sulfur trioxide (SO_3) can be removed from the atmosphere by rain that reacts with the SO_3 to form sulfuric acid:

$$SO_3 + H_2O \rightarrow H_2SO_4$$

If 1 cubic meter of air contains 0.000100 g SO_3, how many m^3 of air are needed to form 1.00 g of H_2SO_4?

5. Nitric acid in the atmosphere may come from the following reaction:

$$3\ NO_2 + H_2O \rightarrow 2HNO_3 + NO$$

How much NO_2 is needed to form 55 g of HNO_3?

6. A possible problem a farmer might have in fertilizing his fields is losing nitrogen, owing to chemical reaction. This loss sometimes happens when nitrite ion in reaction with ammonium ion is converted to nitrogen:

$$NH_4Cl + NaNO_2 \rightarrow H_2O + N_2 + NaCl$$

If 100. g of nitrogen gas N_2 is produced, how many grams of sodium nitrite are destroyed?

7. Various phosphates are valuable fertilizers. Often the phosphate can be mined as calcium phosphate ($Ca_3(PO_4)_2$) by treatment with sulfuric acid:

$$Ca_3(PO_4)_2 + H_2SO_4 \rightarrow CaSO_4 + Ca(H_2PO_4)_2$$

If 750 g of impure $Ca_3(PO_4)_2$ containing 80 percent $Ca_3(PO_4)_2$ is treated with sulfuric acid, how much $Ca(H_2PO_4)_2$ (in grams) is produced?

8. If there is a short supply of oxygen present when carbon is burned, carbon monoxide is produced. How much oxygen (in grams) is needed to produce 18.6 g carbon monoxide?

9. Sodium carbonate reacts with calcium hydroxide to produce calcium carbonate, which precipitates, and sodium hydroxide. If a chemist starts with 23 g of sodium carbonate in solution and adds a solution containing 56 g of calcium hydroxide, how much calcium carbonate (in grams) is precipitated? (Remember to find the limiting reagent.)

10. Magnesium metal is very light, much lighter than aluminum. It was once thought that if you could build an airplane with magnesium, it would be much lighter than one of aluminum. The investigators found one problem. If the plane was flown through a rainstorm, the following reaction occurred,

$$Mg + 2H_2O \rightarrow Mg(OH)_2 + H_2$$

and the airplane fell apart. If an airplane weighed 1.00×10^3 kg and all the magnesium reacted, how many kilograms of H_2 would be produced?

11. Aluminum chloride can be made by passing dry chlorine gas over heated aluminum metal:

$$2Al + 3Cl_2 \rightarrow 2AlCl_3$$

If 36 g of chlorine gas are passed over 28 g of aluminum, how many grams of aluminum chloride are produced? How many grams of the excess element do not react?

12. Silicon carbide is very hard and is used as an abrasive on sand paper and in grinding tools. It is made by heating a mixture of carbon and sand in a special electric furnace:

$$SiO_2 + C \rightarrow SiC + CO$$

How many grams of impure SiO_2 (95 percent pure) react with 86 g of carbon? How many grams of CO are produced?

13. A possible use for SO_2 is in the conversion to CS_2, which can be used as a solvent in chemical laboratories. The equation is

$$5C + 2SO_2 \rightarrow CS_2 + 4CO$$

How much CS_2 can be prepared from 420 g of SO_2?

14. Iron(III) oxide can be converted to metallic iron by reducing the oxide with CO:

$$3CO + Fe_2O_3 \rightarrow 2Fe + 3CO_2$$

If 86.5 g of iron is produced, how much CO_2 (in grams) is produced?

15. Mercury metal will dissolve in nitric acid according to the equation

$$3Hg + 8HNO_3 \rightarrow 3Hg(NO_3)_2 + 2NO + 4H_2O$$

What weight of water is produced from 428 g of mercury metal?

16. Titanium tetrachloride has been used to make smoke screens, since there is a rapid reaction of the liquid $TiCl_4$ with water to form fine particles of TiO_2 and HCl gas:

$$TiCl_4 + H_2O \rightarrow TiO_2 + HCl$$

How many grams of water react with 486 g of $TiCl_4$?

17. Chlorine gas can be made by causing manganese dioxide to react with hydrochloric acid:

$$MnO_2 + 4HCl \rightarrow Cl_2 + MnCl_2 + 2H_2O$$

How many grams of chlorine can be produced from 76 g MnO_2 and 84 g HCl?

18. Hydrogen peroxide can decompose according to the reaction

$$2H_2O_2 \rightarrow 2H_2O + O_2$$

If 38 g of oxygen is produced, how much hydrogen peroxide (in grams) is decomposed?

19. Copper(II) oxide can be reduced by hydrogen gas:

$$CuO + H_2 \rightarrow Cu + H_2O$$

An impure sample of CuO weighed 4.3 g and produced 2.0 g of copper. What was the percentage of CuO in the original sample?

20. A compound containing carbon and hydrogen was burned in oxygen. It was found that 16 g of the compound produced 44 g of CO_2 and 36 g of water. What was the formula of the compound?

Learning Objectives for Chapter 9

Define **oxidation, reduction, oxidation-reduction reaction, oxidation number, oxidizing agent, reducing agent, combination reaction, decomposition reaction, single-replacement reaction, ionization, ionic equation, net ionic equation, activity series, double-replacement reaction, precipitation, precipitate, solubility rules, Arrhenius acid and base, Brønsted-Lowry acid and base, Lewis acid and base, weak acid, weak base, dynamic equilibrium, salt.**

Using a set of rules, determine oxidation numbers for elements combined in compounds.

In an oxidation-reduction reaction, identify the oxidized species, the reduced species, the oxidizing agent, and the reducing agent.

Explain how an activity series can be experimentally determined.

Using an activity series, predict whether a given single-replacement reaction will occur.

Using the solubility rules, predict whether a precipitation reaction will occur.

Given a compound, state whether it is an Arrhenius acid or base, a Brønsted-Lowry acid or base, or a Lewis acid or base.

Identify a given reaction by type.

Given a set of reactants, identify their potential reaction by type and predict whether a reaction will occur.

9 CLASSIFYING CHEMICAL REACTIONS

Understanding chemical reactions includes having some ability to predict whether there will be a reaction when substances are mixed. Part of developing this ability is learning to place reactions in categories. To do this, one does not have to memorize individual reactions. New and unfamiliar reactants can be classified according to type, and products can be predicted more easily.

Chemical reactions can be grouped in one or more of the following general categories:

1. Oxidation-reduction reactions
   (a) Combination reactions
   (b) Decomposition reactions
   (c) Single-replacement reactions
   (d) General redox reactions
2. Non-oxidation-reduction reactions
   (a) General double-replacement reactions
   (b) Acid-base reactions

9.1 Oxidation-Reduction (Redox) Reactions

Oxidation-reduction reactions involve the transfer of one or more electrons from one atom, ion, or molecule to another atom, ion, or molecule. This transfer occurs because some atoms, ions, and molecules, compared with others, have a greater affinity for electrons. Thus, in any oxidation-reduction reaction, one atom, ion, or molecule must lose electrons while another gains electrons. The term **oxidation** is associated with the loss of electrons, and the term **reduction** is associated with the gain of electrons.

Here is an example of an oxidation-reduction reaction. If copper metal is placed in a silver nitrate solution, there is a reaction as follows:

$$Cu + 2AgNO_3 \rightarrow Cu(NO_3)_2 + 2Ag$$

At the beginning of the reaction, the copper exists as atoms, and each atom has a zero charge. As the reaction proceeds, the copper atoms are converted to ions, and each ion has a +2 charge. When an ion with a positive charge is formed, that ion is often called a **cation**. If on the other hand, the ion formed has a negative charge, the ion may be referred to as an **anion**. When an atom of an element exists in the elemental state, that atom has the same number of protons as electrons; it has a zero charge or oxidation number.

The **oxidation number** (sometimes called **valence number**) is the charge assigned to an element either alone or in a compound.

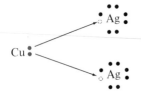

$$Cu^0 + 2Ag^+ \rightarrow$$
$$Cu^{2+} + 2Ag^0$$

Figure 9.1 In a redox reaction, electrons are transferred from one atom to another. Copper is oxidized from Cu^0 to Cu^{2+}. Silver is reduced from Ag^+ to Ag^0.

When an ion forms, the atom either gains or loses electrons. To change from zero charge to a +2 charge, each copper atom loses two electrons. Oxidation takes place. Copper atoms are oxidized. Whenever oxidation occurs, reduction must go on at the same time. There must be some place for those electrons to go. In this reaction, the electrons are absorbed by the silver ions (Figure 9.1). The silver ions, which originally had a +1 charge, become silver atoms with zero charge as the reaction proceeds. Each silver ion gains an electron. Reduction takes place. Silver ions are reduced.

There are other terms used in the language of oxidation-reduction reactions. One is **oxidizing agent**, which describes the species that causes oxidation and is thereby reduced. In the copper–silver nitrate reaction, the oxidizing agent is the ion Ag^+.

The **reducing agent** is the species that causes reduction and is thereby oxidized. Thus the reducing agent in the above reaction is the copper metal.

Reactant oxidized = reactant that loses electrons = reducing agent

Reactant reduced = reactant that gains electrons = oxidizing agent

Any redox reaction involves both a species oxidized and a species reduced.

9.2 Assignment of Oxidation Numbers

To understand oxidation-reduction reactions, one must be able to determine oxidation numbers in general. What, for example, is the oxidation number of the nitrogen in NO_3^-? A series of rules governs assigning oxidation numbers to participants in reactions. They are:

1. All free elements have a zero oxidation number whether they are monatomic, diatomic, or polyatomic (Al, H_2, N_2, S_8). The sum of all oxidation numbers in a compound equals zero. In a polyatomic ion the sum of all oxidation numbers equals the charge on the ion.

2. In compounds, group IA (except hydrogen) always has a $+1$ oxidation number and group IIA always has a $+2$.

3. In compounds, hydrogen atoms have a $+1$ oxidation number unless the hydrogen atoms are associated with a metal ion in a binary compound. These compounds are called metal hydrides. Lithium hydride (LiH) and sodium hydride (NaH) are examples. In these examples, hydrogen atoms are assigned an oxidation number of -1.

4. In compounds, fluorine atoms always have a -1 oxidation number.

5. In compounds, oxygen atoms are usually assigned a -2 oxidation number. Oxygen atoms can have a -1 oxidation number in peroxides like H_2O_2 and Na_2O_2.

6. Oxidation numbers for all other elements in compounds can be calculated using rules 1–5.

The next five examples show how to use these rules in assigning oxidation numbers to atoms in compounds.

7. *Oxidation numbers must add up to give you charge of whatever.*

Example 9.1

For the ion $NO_3{}^-$, find the oxidation number of nitrogen.

Step 1 Determine the oxidation numbers for known elements in the ion or compound and determine the contribution of each. The nitrate ion contains two different kinds of atoms, nitrogen and oxygen. Rule 5 assigns the oxygen atoms the oxidation number -2. Since three oxygen atoms are present, the total charge from the oxygen atoms is $3 \times (-2) = -6$.

Step 2 Use the overall charge on the ion or compound to determine the final answer. The charge on the nitrate ion is -1, so five of the six negative charges must have been canceled. Therefore, the oxidation number for the nitrogen atom must be $+5$:

$$+5 + (-6) = -1$$

This example does not mean to say that the nitrogen atom has an actual $+5$ charge. Oxidation numbers are only a way of making it easier to see how electrons are changing position in oxidation-reduction reactions; they are not meant to be real charges, even though some do exist on ions like Na^+, Mg^{2+} and Cl^-.

Example 9.2	For $HClO_4$, find the oxidation number of chlorine.

Step 1 From rule 3, hydrogen is $+1$. From rule 5, oxygen is -2; since there are four of them, the total contribution is $4 \times (-2) = -8$. The total contribution from hydrogen and oxygen is $-8 + 1 = -7$.

Step 2 $HClO_4$ has no charge, so the chlorine oxidation number must be $+7$:

$$+1 + (+7) + (-8) = 0$$

Example 9.3	For $KClO_3$, find the oxidation number of chlorine.

Step 1 From rule 2, potassium is $+1$. From rule 5, oxygen is -2; since there are three of them, the total contribution is $3 \times (-2) = -6$. The total contribution from potassium and oxygen is $-6 + 1 = -5$.

Step 2 $KClO_3$ has no charge so the chlorine oxidation number must be $+5$:

$$+1 + (+5) + (-6) = 0$$

Example 9.4	For $NaClO$, find the oxidation number of the chlorine.

Step 1 From rule 2, the sodium ion is $+1$. From rule 5, oxygen is -2. The total contribution from the oxygen and sodium ion is $-2 + 1 = -1$.

Step 2 The compound is neutral, so the oxidation number of the chlorine must be $+1$:

$$+1 + (+1) + (-2) = 0$$

Note that the oxidation number of chlorine is different in each of the three Examples.

Example 9.5	Find the oxidation number of the chromium in $Cr_2O_7{}^{2-}$.

Step 1 From rule 5, oxygen is -2; since there are seven of them, the total contribution must be $7 \times (-2) = -14$.

Step 2 The charge on the dichromate ion is -2; so the two chromiums must be contributing $+12$:

$$+12 + (-14) = -2$$

The oxidation number of each chromium must be $+12/2 = +6$.

Ch. 9   CLASSIFYING CHEMICAL REACTIONS

Knowing oxidation numbers makes it possible to find which are the oxidizing and which the reducing agents in redox reactions.

9.3 Combination Reactions

Combination reactions involve the combining of elements to form compounds. This kind of oxidation-reduction is usually not complicated, since in most reactions only two elements are involved. One example of this type of reaction already considered is the rusting of iron; iron (Fe) reacts with oxygen (O_2) to form iron(III) oxide (Fe_2O_3). (When a reaction involves oxygen in the atmosphere, it is molecular oxygen, O_2, and not atomic oxygen, O.) The reaction equation is

$$4Fe + 3O_2 \rightarrow 2Fe_2O_3$$

Two elements combine to form a compound. Iron is oxidized, losing three electrons per atom and changing from oxidation number 0 to oxidation number $+3$. Oxygen is reduced, gaining two electrons per atom and changing from an oxidation number of zero to an oxidation number of -2.

Iron, like the other transition elements, exists in more than one oxidation state, so other reactions are possible. The kind of reaction depends on the conditions. The following reaction is a possibility:

$$2Fe + O_2 \rightarrow 2FeO$$

In this reaction, iron is oxidized from a zero oxidation state to a $+2$. Again, oxygen is reduced to a -2 oxidation state. To determine which of the two possible reactions will take place, we must know whether the temperature is high or low, whether the pressure of the oxygen is high or low, and the other details of the reaction conditions.

In many elements that undergo combination reactions, only one oxidation number is possible for the element. For example, the elements in group IA easily lose one electron (Chapter 3). One expects them to react with oxygen.

Example 9.6

In the following reaction, determine which element is oxidized and which is reduced: $4Li + O_2 \rightarrow 2Li_2O$.

Oxidation: Lithium changes from 0 to $+1$.

Reduction: Oxygen changes from 0 to -2.

Example 9.7

In the following reaction, decide which element is oxidized and which is reduced: $2Na + Cl_2 \rightarrow 2NaCl$.

    Oxidation: Sodium changes from 0 to $+1$.

    Reduction: Chlorine changes from 0 to -1.

In each of these cases, the metal atoms are oxidized from a zero oxidation state to a $+1$. The nonmetallic elements have been reduced.

    The elements in Group IIA lose two electrons, and the following type of reaction results.

Example 9.8

In the reaction, $2Be + O_2 \rightarrow 2BeO$, identify the oxidized and the reduced elements.

    Oxidation: Beryllium changes from 0 to $+2$.

    Reduction: Oxygen changes from 0 to -2.

Example 9.9

In the reaction $Mg + F_2 \rightarrow MgF_2$, decide which element is oxidized and which is reduced.

    Oxidation: Magnesium changes from 0 to $+2$.

    Reduction: Fluorine changes from 0 to -1.

Oxidation of the metals to a $+2$ state occurs in conjunction with a reduction of the nonmetallic elements.

    Group IIIA elements undergo reactions like those in Examples 9.10 and 9.11.

Example 9.10

Identify the oxidized and reduced elements in

$$4Al + 3O_2 \rightarrow 2Al_2O_3$$

    Oxidation: Aluminum changes from 0 to $+3$.

    Reduction: Oxygen changes from 0 to -2.

Example 9.11

Point out the elements oxidized and reduced in the reaction

$$2Al + 3Br_2 \rightarrow 2AlBr_3$$

Oxidation: Aluminum changes from 0 to $+3$.

Reduction: Bromine changes from 0 to -1.

The metals are oxidized to a $+3$ state as the nonmetallic elements are reduced.

Compound formation is complicated for the remaining elements of the periodic chart because of the variety of oxidation states these elements show. Of the many complicated reactions possible, the formation of various air pollutants furnishes examples.

Example 9.12

One of the chief components of air pollution comes from the reaction at high pressures of nitrogen and oxygen in a car's cylinders. The reaction is $N_2 + O_2 \rightarrow 2NO$. Identify the elements oxidized and those reduced.

Oxidation: Nitrogen changes from 0 to $+2$.

Reduction: Oxygen changes from 0 to -2.

Example 9.13

When NO (nitric oxide) comes out of the car's tailpipe, it undergoes a further reaction, $2NO + O_2 \rightarrow 2NO_2$. This is also an oxidation-reduction reaction. Identify the oxidized and reduced reactants.

Oxidation: Nitrogen changes from $+2$ to $+4$.

Reduction: Oxygen changes from 0 to -2.

The compound NO_2, called nitrogen dioxide, is responsible for the brown color seen over many large cities. Nitrogen dioxide causes a burning irritation in the eyes, throat, and lungs, even from very small quantities. An increasing concentration of NO_2 in the air can cause death.

Example 9.14

Another air pollution problem caused by a complicated oxidation-reduction reaction is the presence of sulfur dioxide (SO_2) in the atmosphere. Some coal that is burned to produce electricity and heat contains concentrations of sulfur (S) as high as 3 percent. When the coal is burned, the sulfur present reacts with oxygen in the air to form sulfur dioxide. The equation for the reaction is $S + O_2 \rightarrow SO_2$. Show the elements oxidized and reduced.

Oxidation: Sulfur changes from 0 to $+4$.

Reduction: Oxygen changes from 0 to -2.

Sulfur dioxide has also been found to be damaging to health.

Finally, there is one oxide that is important to chemists because of the history surrounding it. Joseph Priestley studied mercuric oxide (HgO), or mercury(II) oxide, in the late 1700s. (See Figure 9.2.) This substance is formed in the following reaction:

$$2Hg + O_2 \rightarrow 2HgO$$

Oxidation: Mercury changes from 0 to $+2$.

Reduction: Oxygen changes from 0 to -2.

Mercury(II) oxide is a red powder and mercury is a metallic liquid. The interesting thing that Priestley found about mercury(II) oxide was that the reaction could be reversed by heating the red powder:

$$2HgO \rightarrow 2Hg + O_2$$

This reaction is classified as a decomposition. This part of Priestley's discovery was extremely important. Because he was clever enough to decide to weigh the HgO which he started with and then weigh the mercury formed after heating. He found that the product weighed less than the reactant. He thus decided that there must be some other element present. This decision was a significant link in the discovery of oxygen. Priestley is said to have discovered oxygen.

Figure 9.2 Joseph Priestley, 1733–1804. (Photo courtesy of Edgar Fahs Smith Memorial Collection, Van Pelt Library, University of Pennsylvania).

9.4   Decomposition of Compounds

Decomposition reactions involve breaking up compounds to form simpler compounds or elements. Decompositions can be oxidation-reduction reactions, as you can see by the following examples. The decomposition reaction that Priestley used in which he liberated oxygen was

$$2HgO \rightarrow 2Hg + O_2$$

Oxidation: $O^{2-} \rightarrow O^0$

Reduction: $Hg^{2+} \rightarrow Hg^0$

Some other metal oxides can be reconverted to the metallic element and oxygen by heating. Gold and silver oxides are two examples.

Example 9.15

Identify the oxidized and the reduced parts of the reactant in the equation

$$2Ag_2O \rightarrow 4Ag + O_2$$

Oxidation: Oxygen changes from -2 to 0.

Reduction: Silver changes from $+1$ to 0.

Example 9.16   In the decomposition of gold(III) oxide, identify the part of the reactant oxidized and the part reduced:

$$2Au_2O_3 \rightarrow 4Au + 3O_2$$

Oxidation: Oxygen changes from -2 to 0.

Reduction: Gold changes from $+3$ to 0.

Mercury(II) sulfide (HgS) is called cinnabar. Cinnabar is a mercury ore taken directly from mines. It is an interesting historical note that political prisoners during the Spanish Inquisition were sent to the cinnabar mines to mine ore for the state. This sentence was a form of execution, since most of the prisoners died from mercury poisoning. The decomposition reaction for cinnabar is

$$HgS \rightarrow Hg + S$$

Oxidation: $S^{2-} \rightarrow S^0$

Reduction: $Hg^{2+} \rightarrow Hg^0$

Most decomposition reactions occur when the reactants are heated. Heat energy is necessary to break the bonds holding the different atoms together.

Example 9.17   A convenient method of preparing oxygen is to heat potassium chlorate. Identify the subjects of oxidation and of reduction in the reaction:

$$2KClO_3 \rightarrow 2KCl + 3O_2$$

Oxidation: $O^{2-} \rightarrow O^0$

Reduction: $Cl^{5+} \rightarrow Cl^-$

On some occasions, there can be decomposition without oxidation and reduction. For example, when a bottle of soda pop is opened, bubbles fizz out very rapidly. As time passes, the rate of bubbling slows. This is the result of the decomposition of carbonic acid (H_2CO_3) to give CO_2 and water (Figure 9.3):

$$H_2CO_3 \rightarrow H_2O + CO_2$$

This is not an oxidation-reduction reaction and can be determined by calculating the oxidation numbers of the elements involved both before and

Figure 9.3 Decomposition of carbonic acid in soda pop.

after the reaction. Hydrogen has an oxidation number of $+1$ in H_2CO_3 and H_2O. Carbon has an oxidation number of $+4$ in H_2CO_3 and CO_2. Oxygen has an oxidation number of -2 in H_2CO_3, H_2O, and CO_2.

Carbonic acid exists only in water solution and is not a separable compound. Pumping CO_2 into the soda pop forces the reaction to go in the opposite direction and was initially used to carbonate the drink.

Another example of a decomposition that is not oxidation-reduction is **dehydration**, removal of water from certain compounds. Often when a solid compound forms, it contains water molecules trapped between its molecules or ions. Such compounds are called hydrates. An example of this is copper(II) sulfate; this substance can exist as a solid in which each unit of $CuSO_4$ has five molecules of water associated with it. The formula for the compound is $CuSO_4 \cdot 5H_2O$. The formula means that five water molecules are associated with each formula unit of $CuSO_4$; the 5 should not be confused with the coefficient prefixed to the whole formula unit.

When a hydrated compound is heated, the water is driven off,

$$CuSO_4 \cdot 5H_2O \rightarrow CuSO_4 + 5H_2O$$

and a decomposition occurs. Hydrated compounds, the compounds that contain water, are very important in everyday life. Plaster of Paris, $2CaSO_4 \cdot H_2O$, when it sets, becomes gypsum, $CaSO_4 \cdot 2H_2O$. The reaction is

$$2CaSO_4 \cdot H_2O + 3H_2O \rightarrow 2(CaSO_4 \cdot 2H_2O)$$

Plaster of Paris is often used to make casts for broken bones. This reaction is the reverse of the dehydration.

9.5 Single-Replacement Reactions

Another kind of oxidation-reduction is the **single-replacement reaction**. The reaction has this name since only one replacement is made—an atom replaces an ion from a compound in solution, the ion then becoming an atom. The products are a different compound and a different element. Whether this type of reaction occurs or not depends on the reactivity of an element. Reactivity depends on how difficult or easy it is for an element to gain or lose electrons. To understand this, it is easiest to look at an example.

Example 9.18

In the reaction

$$Cu + 2AgNO_3 \rightarrow 2Ag + Cu(NO_3)_2$$

or $Cu + 2Ag^+ + 2NO_3^- \rightarrow Cu^{2+} + 2NO_3^- + 2Ag,$

illustrated in Figure 9.4, identify the oxidized and reduced parts of the compounds.

$$\text{Oxidation:} \quad Cu^0 \rightarrow Cu^{2+}$$

$$\text{Reduction:} \quad Ag^+ \rightarrow Ag^0$$

Figure 9.4 Copper replaces silver in a solution of silver nitrate.

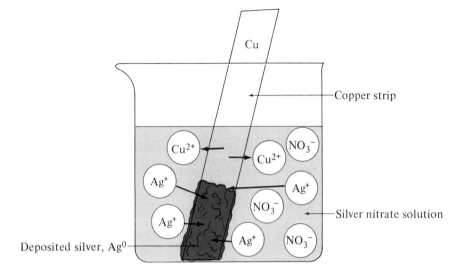

The second way the equation in Example 9.18 is written shows reactants and products separated into ions. It is called an **ionic equation**. The reaction begins when a piece of copper metal is placed in a solution of silver nitrate ($AgNO_3$) in water. (Our definition of the term *solution* is confined for the time being to "a solid dissolved in water.") In the solution, the silver nitrate has separated into the ions Ag^+ and NO_3^- in a process called **ionization**, or dissociation. Initially, the solution contains only the ions Ag^+ and NO_3^-. Toward the end of the reaction, the solution will contain mostly the ions Cu^{2+} and NO_3^-, and only a few Ag^+. The copper has released electrons to the silver ions, and thus the pure metal silver is formed. This can be seen in an equation in which only the reactants and products that were oxidized and reduced are shown. Such an equation is called a **net ionic equation**.

$$Cu + 2Ag^+ \rightarrow Cu^{2+} + 2Ag$$

Whether the reaction occurs or not depends on which ion attracts electrons most strongly, the Cu^{2+} or the Ag^+. In the reaction shown, the Ag^+ ions attract electrons strongly enough to remove them from copper; silver metal and Cu^{2+} are thus produced. Copper metal is oxidized and Ag^+ is reduced. If silver metal had been placed in a solution of copper ions, no reaction would have occurred.

The results of numerous experiments like this, in which a metal is put into a water solution containing the ion of another metal, have established an order of reactivity for a series of metals, the **activity series**. The metals that react are more active than the metals that do not. The data are analyzed by looking at which combinations of metals and ions react. For example, copper replaces Ag^+ in a solution of silver ions. Will mercury replace Ag^+ in the same way? Placing mercury metal into contact with a silver nitrate solution brings about the following reaction:

$$2Hg + 2Ag^+ + 2NO_3^- \rightarrow 2Ag + Hg_2^{2+} + 2NO_3^-$$

Mercury $+1$ exists as Hg_2^{2+}.

Figure 9.5 Three experiments must be done to find the relative reactivities of Cu, Hg, and Ag: (a) Copper replaces silver in a solution of silver ions; (b) Mercury replaces silver in a solution of silver ions; (c) Mercury does not replace copper in a solution of copper ions.

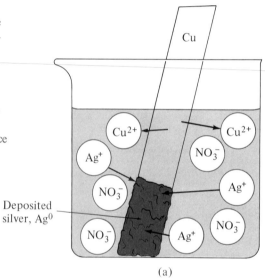

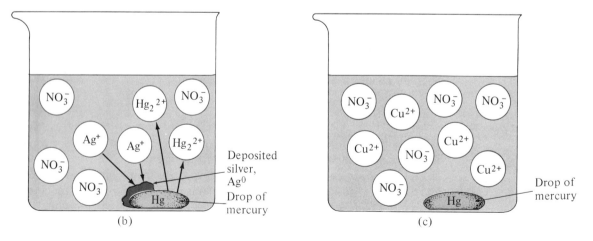

$$\text{Oxidation:} \quad 2Hg^0 \rightarrow Hg_2{}^{2+}$$

$$\text{Reduction:} \quad Ag^+ \rightarrow Ag^0$$

Mercury replaces the ions Ag^+ in solution.

Mercury metal in contact with a solution containing copper ions does not produce any reaction. The order of reactivity for these three elements, silver, copper, and mercury in their ionized state (Figure 9.5) is then:

Cu^{2+} ions attract electrons least strongly.

$Hg_2{}^{2+}$ ions attract electrons more strongly.

Ag^+ ions attract electrons most strongly.

If these statements about the ions are true, then the following statements can be made about the metals:

Copper metal releases electrons most easily to form Cu^{2+}.

Mercury metal releases electrons less easily to form $Hg_2{}^{2+}$.

Silver metal releases electrons least easily to form Ag^+.

This approach can be taken for a series of metals, and a table like Table 9.1 can be devised, in which metals are listed in relation to hydrogen.

Table 9.1 is useful for predicting single-replacement reactions. By this table, a metal replaces the ion of any metal below it in the table when the metals are in solution.

Table 9.1 The Activity Series of Some Metals

K	Most reactive—gives off electrons easily to form ions
Ca	
Na	
Mg	
Al	
Zn	
Fe	
Pb	
H	
Cu	
Hg	
Ag	Least reactive—does not give off electrons easily
Au	to form ions

Example 9.19

Predict the reaction if magnesium is placed in contact with a solution containing the ions Zn^{2+}.

Magnesium is above zinc in Table 9.1, so the reaction

$$Mg + Zn(NO_3)_2 \rightarrow Mg(NO_3)_2 + Zn$$

occurs, in which

$$Mg + Zn^{2+} + 2NO_3^- \rightarrow Zn + Mg^{2+} + 2NO_3^-$$

Oxidation: $Mg^0 \rightarrow Mg^{2+}$

Reduction: $Zn^{2+} \rightarrow Zn^0$

Example 9.20

Predict whether placing lead in contact with a solution containing Cu^{2+} causes a reaction.

Lead is above copper in Table 9.1, so the reaction

$$Pb + Cu(NO_3)_2 \rightarrow Cu + Pb(NO_3)_2$$

occurs, in which

$$Pb + Cu^{2+} + 2NO_3^- \rightarrow Cu + Pb^{2+} + 2NO_3^-$$

Oxidation: $Pb^0 \rightarrow Pb^{2+}$

Reduction: $Cu^{2+} \rightarrow Cu^0$

Metals above hydrogen in the table react with compounds having hydrogen as their positive ion, yielding the metal ion and hydrogen gas as products. The hydrogen-containing compounds are called acids.

Example 9.21

Predict whether the following reaction will occur:

$$Zn + H_2SO_4 \rightarrow ZnSO_4 + H_2$$

Zinc is above hydrogen in Table 9.1, so there is a reaction. The reaction can be shown as

$$Zn + 2H^+ + SO_4^{2-} \rightarrow Zn^{2+} + SO_4^{2-} + H_2$$

Oxidation: $Zn^0 \rightarrow Zn^{2+}$

Reduction: $2H^+ \rightarrow H_2^0$

Example 9.22   Does the following reaction take place?

$$Ca + 2HCl \rightarrow CaCl_2 + H_2$$

Calcium is above hydrogen in Table 9.1, so the reaction occurs. It can be shown as

$$Ca + 2H^+ + 2Cl^- \rightarrow Ca^{2+} + H_2 + 2Cl^-$$

$$\text{Oxidation:} \quad Ca \rightarrow Ca^{2+}$$

$$\text{Reduction:} \quad 2H^+ \rightarrow H_2{}^0$$

Some metals are so reactive, or lose electrons so easily, that they react with water. Hydrogen also acts as the positive ion in the compound H_2O. The reaction of sodium and water is

$$2Na + H_2O \rightarrow 2Na^+ + 2OH^- + H_2$$

Calcium acts similarly:

$$Ca + 2H_2O \rightarrow Ca^{2+} + 2OH^- + H_2$$

In every one of the examples used, the metals have a position in the table above the metals whose ions they replaced. The metals were oxidized and the ions reduced.

Some examples in which metals are introduced to substances and there is no reaction involve acid and the metals silver (Ag), gold (Au), and copper (Cu). These metals are below hydrogen in the table; therefore we expect that when pieces of these metals are placed in acid, there will be no reaction. This is exactly what happens—nothing. An interesting manifestation of this non-reaction is that gold coins in sunken ships are unaffected by the water, whereas most metal parts of the ships seem to have melted away by comparison.

9.6   General Oxidation-Reduction Reactions

It is important to realize that the category oxidation-reduction reactions is broad. Single-replacement reactions and combinations of elements are examples of oxidation-reduction reactions; and decomposition reactions are often oxidation-reduction reactions. All other oxidation-reduction reactions are grouped into the general category. The reactions are usually complex and often involve many compounds. An example of a general oxidation-reduction is

$$2HNO_3 + 3H_2S \rightarrow 2NO + 4H_2O + 3S$$

In this reaction, the nitrogen is reduced from $+5$ to $+2$, which means that it gains three electrons. Sulfur is oxidized from -2 to 0; it loses two electrons. (The special rules usually needed to balance these equations are given in Appendix A.)

9.7 Non-Oxidation-Reduction Reactions: Double Replacement

Non-oxidation-reduction reactions are reactions that do not involve the exchange of electrons between atoms and ions. In such reactions, oxidation numbers do not change. Non-oxidation-reduction reactions can be divided into two types: (1) double-replacement reactions, exclusive of acid-base reactions, and (2) acid-base reactions. Acid-base reactions can be thought of as a special case. Besides these two categories, we must remember to include among the non-oxidation-reduction reactions some decomposition reactions that do not involve oxidation and reduction. (These reactions were covered in Section 9.4.)

In **double-replacement reactions**, reactants exchange ion partners; the positive and negative ions interchange. It is impossible, however, to combine two positive ions with each other and two negative ions with each other. The reaction of aqueous solutions of silver nitrate ($AgNO_3$) and sodium chloride (NaCl) illustrates this concept. An aqueous solution is a mixture of the compound being studied and water.

$$AgNO_3 + NaCl \rightarrow AgCl + NaNO_3$$

A solution of silver nitrate ($AgNO_3$) is added to a solution of sodium chloride (NaCl) and the reaction occurs. Here the silver ion (Ag^+) present in the aqueous solution switched negative ion partners with the sodium ion (Na^+), also in aqueous solution. The ion Ag^+ and the ion Cl^- form a strong ionic bond and precipitate (fall) out of the water solution as solid AgCl. The ions Na^+ and NO_3^- remain in solution. Solid $NaNO_3$ forms only if the water is removed.

This reaction occurs because of the insolubility of silver chloride (AgCl) in water. When the solutions are mixed, silver ions and chloride ions come into contact, attract strongly, and appear as a white solid that falls to the bottom of the reaction flask. The equation for this reaction is

$$AgNO_3 + NaCl \rightarrow AgCl(s) + NaNO_3$$

Figure 9.6 Formation of a precipitate is one way in which a double-replacement reaction occurs.

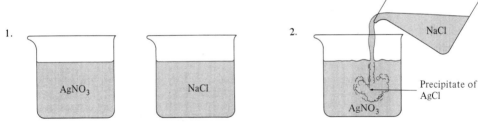

The **s** in parentheses stands for "solid," and shows that the AgCl dropped to the bottom of the flask as a solid. This phenomenon is called **precipitation**, and the silver chloride is the **precipitate** (Figure 9.6).

Another way of showing this reaction is to show the positive and negative ions separately. This is done because ionic compounds, when dissolved in water, are separated into ions. This reaction, written as an ionic equation, would be

$$Ag^+(aq) + NO_3^-(aq) + Na^+(aq) + Cl^-(aq) \rightarrow$$
$$AgCl(s) + Na^+(aq) + NO_3^-(aq)$$

The abbreviation *aq*, for *aqueous*, means "dissolved in water solution." The sodium nitrate ($NaNO_3$) is still dissolved, but the silver chloride (AgCl) is not.

How does one determine when compounds precipitate? Table 9.2 is a list of "**solubility rules**." This list contains information concerning whether

Table 9.2 Solubility Rules

assuming water was solvent

Number	Ion	Rule
1	NO_3^-	All nitrates are soluble.
2	$C_2H_3O_2^-$	All acetates are soluble.
3	Cl^-	All chlorides are soluble except AgCl, Hg_2Cl_2, and $PbCl_2$.
4	SO_4^{2-}	All sulfates are soluble except $BaSO_4$ and $PbSO_4$. The compounds $CaSO_4$, Hg_2SO_4, and Ag_2SO_4 are slightly soluble.
5	CO_3^{2-}	All carbonates are insoluble except Na_2CO_3, K_2CO_3, and $(NH_4)_2CO_3$.
6	PO_4^{3-}	All phosphates are insoluble except Na_3PO_4, K_3PO_4, and $(NH_4)_3PO_4$.
7	OH^-	All hydroxides are insoluble except NaOH, KOH, NH_4OH, and $Ba(OH)_2$.
8	S^{2-}	All sulfides are insoluble except Na_2S, K_2S, $(NH_4)_2S$, MgS, CaS, SrS, BaS, and H_2S.

9) all element in group 1 are soluble as a Compound form (Hydrogen dosn't count)

compounds will dissolve in water or remain separate. If all the possible ionic compounds that can be formed in a given reaction are soluble, there is no reaction.

Example 9.23

Is there any reaction when solutions of NaCl and KNO_3 are mixed?

Step 1 Write the possible products. The possible compounds are NaCl, KNO_3, $NaNO_3$, and KCl.

Step 2 Check the solubility rules. All the possible compounds are soluble; therefore no reaction occurs.

Example 9.24

Is there any reaction when solutions of barium nitrate and sodium sulfate are mixed?

Step 1 The possible products are $Ba(NO_3)_2$, Na_2SO_4, $BaSO_4$, $NaNO_3$.

Step 2 $BaSO_4$ is insoluble (Rule 4). In the reaction, $BaSO_4$ precipitates:

$$Ba(NO_3)_2 + Na_2SO_4 \rightarrow BaSO_4(s) + 2NaNO_3$$

Thus a reaction takes place.

Example 9.25

When solutions of lead(II) nitrate and sodium sulfide are mixed, is there a reaction?

Step 1 Possible products are $Pb(NO_3)_2$, NaS, PbS, $NaNO_3$.

Step 2 PbS is insoluble (Rule 8); hence a reaction:

$$Pb(NO_3)_2 + Na_2S \rightarrow PbS(s) + 2NaNO_3$$

The reaction occurs because PbS precipitates.

Another kind of double-replacement reaction is the following:

$$Na_2CO_3 + 2HCl \rightarrow 2NaCl + H_2CO_3$$

or

$$2Na^+ + CO_3{}^{2-} + 2H^+ + 2Cl^- \rightarrow 2Na^+ + 2Cl^- + H_2CO_3$$

Carbonic acid (H_2CO_3) decomposes in the following reaction (familiar from Section 9.4):

$$H_2CO_3 \rightarrow H_2O + CO_2(g)$$

The **g** means that CO_2 is a gas and bubbles off. The reaction involving Na_2CO_3 and HCl proceeds because the product, H_2CO_3, decomposes to form a gas, which bubbles from the solution. In this kind of double-replacement reaction, a gaseous product forms.

A third kind of double-replacement reaction is the following:

$$HCl + NaOH \rightarrow NaCl + H_2O$$

or

$$H^+ + Cl^- + Na^+ + OH^- \rightarrow Na^+ + Cl^- + H_2O$$

Nothing precipitates in this reaction; however, there has been a very significant change. Water, a compound containing covalent bonds, has been formed from previously ionic compounds. This type of double-replacement reaction involves the formation of a molecule that contains primarily covalent bonds and exists in solution as a molecule and not an ion. The reaction shown is an acid-base reaction, since an acid (HCl) reacts with a base ($NaOH$).

9.8 Acids and Bases

To study acid-base reactions, one must have a clear idea of what acids and bases are and how they react. Several different ways of defining acids and bases are possible. Most scientists use the definition that is the simplest one for the problem on which they are working. Three acid-base definitions or models will be covered in our study.

Arrhenius Definition

The first is the Arrhenius model.

> In the **Arrhenius** model, an **acid** is any compound that will produce hydrogen ions (H^+) when it is dissolved in water; any compound that produces hydroxide ions (OH^-) when it is dissolved in water is called a **base**.

When a compound from one of these classifications combines with one from the other, a reaction takes place and water is formed:

$$H^+ + OH^- \rightarrow H_2O$$

The driving force behind the reaction is the formation of the compound water which contains only covalent bonds. Other ions are present besides the H^+ and the OH^-, but of primary interest is the formation of water.

By the Arrhenius definition, compounds like nitric acid (HNO_3), sulfuric acid (H_2SO_4), and phosphoric acid (H_3PO_4) are acids because they donate hydrogen ions in chemical reactions. Equations like the following three show this:

$$HCl \rightarrow H^+ + Cl^-$$

$$HNO_3 \rightarrow H^+ + NO_3{}^-$$

$$H_2SO_4 \rightarrow 2H^+ + SO_4{}^{2-}$$

Also by this definition, compounds like potassium hydroxide (KOH), barium hydroxide ($Ba(OH)_2$), and aluminum hydroxide ($Al(OH)_3$) are bases. The reactions of these substances in solution are

$$KOH \rightarrow K^+ + OH^-$$

$$Ba(OH)_2 \rightarrow Ba^{2+} + 2OH^-$$

$$Al(OH)_3 \rightarrow Al^{3+} + 3OH^-$$

By the Arrhenius definition, acid-base reactions for any combination of hydrogen-ion donor (acid) and hydroxide-ion donor (base) can be written. For example,

$$2HBr + Ba(OH)_2 \rightarrow BaBr_2 + 2H_2O$$

When an Arrhenius acid and an Arrhenius base are combined, another product besides water is formed. This product is called a **salt**. Perhaps the most familiar salt is table salt, sodium chloride (NaCl). Sodium chloride can be produced by the reaction of aqueous solutions of hydrochloric acid (HCl) and sodium hydroxide (NaOH):

$$HCl + NaOH \rightarrow NaCl + H_2O$$

The sodium chloride remains in solution until the water is removed.

The reaction of hydrobromic acid (HBr) and calcium hydroxide ($Ca(OH)_2$) produces the water-soluble salt calcium bromide ($CaBr_2$) and water:

$$\underset{\text{(acid)}}{2HBr} + \underset{\text{(base)}}{Ba(OH)_2} \rightarrow \underset{\text{(salt)}}{CaBr_2} + \underset{\text{(water)}}{2H_2O}$$

The solubility rules do not usually apply to acid-base reactions so long as one of the reactants is soluble in water. For example, nitric acid (HNO_3), a water-soluble acid, will react readily with calcium hydroxide ($Ca(OH)_2$), a compound that is nearly insoluble in water, to produce water and the soluble salt calcium nitrate ($Ca(NO_3)_2$):

$$2HNO_3 + Ca(OH)_2 \rightarrow Ca(NO_3)_2 + 2H_2O$$

It is important to understand that the combination of an Arrhenius acid and an Arrhenius base will always produce a salt and water.

Brønsted-Lowry Definition

Another way of defining an acid and a base is the Brønsted-Lowry model. This model is like the Arrhenius model but covers more types of compounds.

According to the **Brønsted-Lowry** model, an **acid** is any compound that will donate a proton in a chemical reaction; and a **base** is any compound that will accept a proton (hydrogen ion) in a chemical reaction.

In this model, hydrochloric acid (HCl) is still an acid because it can donate a proton; sodium hydroxide (NaOH) is still a base because the hydroxide ion, OH^-, can accept a proton. The definition of a base now, however, extends to ammonia (NH_3). Ammonia can accept a proton to form the ammonium ion and thus is classified as a Brønsted-Lowry base. The reaction is illustrated by the equation

$$H^+ + NH_3 \rightarrow NH_4^+$$

This behavior can be predicted by analyzing the electronic structure of ammonia. The electron dot structure for ammonia is

$$\begin{array}{c} H \\ :\overset{\cdot\cdot}{\underset{\cdot\cdot}{N}}:H \\ H \end{array}$$

Ammonia has a pair of electrons on the nitrogen atom that are not shared with any other atom. The electron dot structure for H^+ is

$$H^+$$

The hydrogen ion has no electrons. The nitrogen in ammonia has two electrons available to form a coordinate covalent bond with a proton. The following equation shows how ammonia acts as a Brønsted-Lowry base:

$$H^+ + :\overset{H}{\underset{H}{\overset{\cdot\cdot}{N}}}:H \rightarrow H:\overset{H}{\underset{H}{\overset{\cdot\cdot}{N}}}:H^+$$

This is not a double-replacement reaction even though it is an acid-base reaction. It is a reaction that shows how the Brønsted-Lowry model works.

Lewis Definition

The third model allows even more compounds to be classified as acids and bases. Some compounds having no hydrogens can be called acids. The model is the **Lewis** model of **acids** and **bases**. G. N. Lewis defined an acid as any compound or ion that can accept an electron pair, and a base is defined as a compound or ion that can donate an electron pair. By this definition, the ion H^+ and the ion OH^- are still an acid and a base. The H^+ can accept an electron pair and the OH^- donates the electron pair:

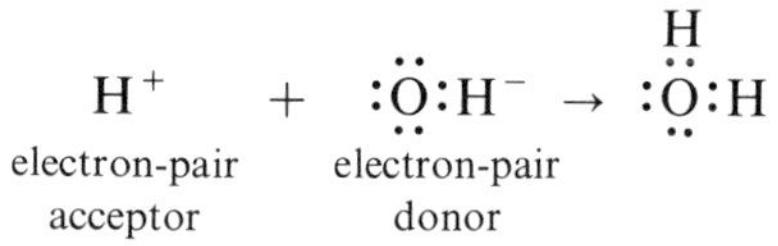

$$H^+ \quad + \quad :\overset{..}{\underset{..}{O}}:H^- \quad \rightarrow \quad :\overset{..}{\underset{..}{O}}:\overset{H}{H}$$

electron-pair   electron-pair
acceptor   donor

The following reaction is another example of a Lewis acid-base reaction:

$$BCl_3 + Cl^- \rightarrow BCl_4^-$$

In electron dot structures, this reaction is

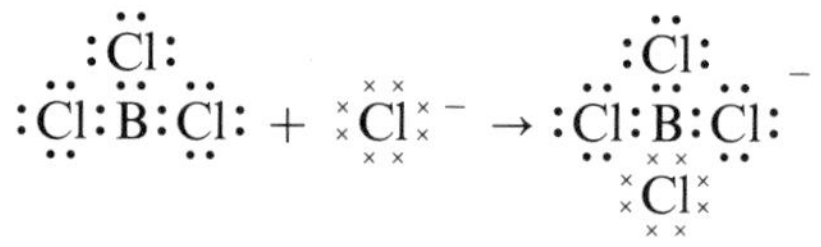

$$\begin{array}{ccc}
 & :\overset{..}{\underset{..}{Cl}}: & \\
 & \overset{..}{\underset{..}{Cl}}:B:\overset{..}{\underset{..}{Cl}}: & \\
\end{array}
+ \; {\overset{\times\times}{\underset{\times\times}{Cl}}}{}^{\times} \;^- \rightarrow
\begin{array}{c}
:\overset{..}{\underset{..}{Cl}}: \\
:\overset{..}{\underset{..}{Cl}}:B:\overset{..}{\underset{..}{Cl}}: \\
{\overset{\times\times}{\underset{\times\times}{Cl}}}{}^{\times}
\end{array}{}^-$$

The Cl^- (chloride ion) has donated the pair of electrons, so it is the base. The BCl_3 (boron trichloride) has accepted the pair of electrons, so it is the acid. Therefore, in the Lewis concept, it is possible to have an acid-base reaction without hydrogen ions or hydroxide ions.

9.9   More on Non-Oxidation-Reduction Reactions

Double-replacement reactions and acid-base reactions (considered as a separate category) are two kinds of non-oxidation-reduction reactions. A double-replacement reaction takes place when one of the following occurs:

1. A precipitate is formed from the initial ions.
2. A gas is formed from the initial ions.
3. A new compound is formed that does not exist as ions.

Consider the possibility of the formation of a gas in a reaction. Mixing a solution of sodium sulfite (Na_2SO_3) with hydrochloric acid (HCl) causes the gas sulfur dioxide (SO_2) to form:

$$Na_2SO_3 + 2HCl \rightarrow H_2SO_3 + 2NaCl$$

or

$$2Na^+ + SO_3^{2-} + 2H^+ + 2Cl^- \rightarrow H_2SO_3 + 2Na^+ + 2Cl$$

$$H_2SO_3 \rightarrow H_2O + SO_2(g)$$

Another example involves aqueous solutions of ammonium chloride (NH_4Cl) and sodium hydroxide (NaOH):

$$NH_4^+ + Cl^- + Na^+ + OH^- \rightarrow NH_4OH + Na^+ + Cl^-$$

$$NH_4OH \rightarrow H_2O + NH_3(g)$$

Ammonia is the gas that is evolved.

The third reason for double-replacement reaction is the formation of a compound containing primarily covalent bonds. Some compounds are bonded more covalently than ionically. When a covalently–bonded compound forms, a double–replacement reaction occurs. Most compounds of this type are weak acids or weak bases. An example of this kind of reaction is the addition of hydrochloric acid (HCl) to an aqueous solution of sodium acetate ($NaC_2H_3O_2$). The resulting product is the weak acid, acetic acid. (Acetic acid, in very dilute solution, is called vinegar.)

$$NaC_2H_3O_2 + HCl \rightarrow HC_2H_3O_2 + NaCl$$

or

$$Na^+ + C_2H_3O_2^- + H^+ + Cl^- \rightarrow HC_2H_3O_2 + Na^+ + Cl^-$$

A **weak acid** is an acid that produces few hydrogen ions when it is dissolved in water. This happens because the proton bond is primarily covalent. The more numerous the hydrogen ions produced from a given number of acid molecules placed in solution, the more ionically bonded the proton, and the stronger the acid. Thus nitric acid is very strong, since it is almost completely separated into the ions H^+ and NO_3^- in water solution (strongly ionized); and acetic acid is weak, since it is only slightly ionized (existing mostly as $HC_2H_3O_2$ in water solution).

When acetic acid ($HC_2H_3O_2$) is dissolved in water, water molecules surround the ions and the reaction is

$$HC_2H_3O_2 \rightarrow H^+ + C_2H_3O_2^-$$

This ionization is not complete. The ions in the solution are in constant motion, and the ions H^+ and $C_2H_3O_2^-$ often recombine to reform $HC_2H_3O_2$. A **dynamic equilibrium** exists; ions and molecules are constantly being re-formed and broken apart but the total concentration remains constant. However, in a 1-molar (1 M) solution of acetic acid, only about four out of every thousand $HC_2H_3O_2$ molecules are ionized at any one time, while the other 996 exist as molecules. The percentage of ionized molecules present at any time is 0.4%. What is happening is better shown by changing the chemical equation slightly. If the equation is represented with arrows as shown,

$$HC_2H_3O_2 \rightleftharpoons H^+ + C_2H_3O_2^-$$

a dynamic equilibrium is seen to exist, and both the left-to-right and right-to-left reactions are happening at the same time. The longer arrow indicates that the majority of the $HC_2H_3O_2$ molecules exist in the unionized state. The strength of any acid depends on the concentration of hydrogen ions in solution at a given molecular acid concentration, or the percentage of acid ionized.

The dissociation of acids containing one hydrogen ion is a one-step reaction:

$$HNO_3 \rightarrow H^+ + NO_3^-$$

The dissociation of acids with two hydrogens takes two steps, one for each hydrogen:

(1) $\quad H_2SO_4 \rightleftharpoons H^+ + HSO_4^-$

(2) $\quad HSO_4^- \rightleftharpoons H^+ + SO_4^{2-}$

The dissociation of acids with three ionizable hydrogens occurs in three steps:

(1) $\quad H_3PO_4 \rightleftharpoons H^+ + H_2PO_4^-$

(2) $\quad H_2PO_4^- \rightleftharpoons H^+ + HPO_4^{2-}$

(3) $\quad HPO_4^{2-} \rightleftharpoons H^+ + PO_4^{3-}$

One might think that more hydrogens on an acid would mean a stronger acid, but as each H^+ is removed from the molecule, it becomes increasingly difficult to remove the next H^+; therefore, the amount of ionization decreases sharply from one H^+ removal to another.

The acids that ionize least are weakest, since they produce the fewest hydrogen ions in solution; and those that ionize most are the strongest acids. Acetic acid ($HC_2H_3O_2$) and phosphoric acid (H_3PO_4) are weak and do not ionize much, whereas H_2SO_4, HCl, and HNO_3 are strong. They ionize extensively. This is determined by experiment.

Weak bases are those that produce relatively few hydroxide ions when they are dissolved in water. Most ionic bases like KOH, NaOH, and Ca(OH)$_2$ are strong bases that ionize 100 percent in water solution.

An example of a weak base is ammonia gas dissolved in water to form a solution called ammonium hydroxide. Some ammonia molecules will react with water molecules to form ammonium ions and hydroxide ions.

$$NH_3 + H_2O \rightleftharpoons NH_4^+ + OH^-$$

Glossary

Anion	A negatively charged ion.
Arrhenius acid	A species that can donate a hydrogen ion in a chemical reaction.
Arrhenius base	A species that can donate a hydroxide ion in a chemical reaction.
Brønsted-Lowry acid	A species that can donate a proton in a chemical reaction.
Brønsted-Lowry base	A species that can accept a proton in a chemical reaction.
Cation	A positively charged ion.
Combination-of-elements reaction	A reaction in which elements combine to form compounds.
Decomposition-of-compounds reaction	A reaction in which compounds break up to form simpler compounds or elements.
Dehydration reaction	A type of decomposition reaction in which one compound decomposes to form a simpler compound and water.
Double-replacement reaction	A reaction in which there is an exchange of anions associated with two different cations.
Ionization	The process in which formula units separate into ions when dissolved in solution. Also called dissociation.
Lewis acid	A species that can accept an electron pair in a chemical reaction.
Lewis base	A species that can donate an electron pair in a chemical reaction.
Oxidation	A loss of electrons in a chemical reaction.
Oxidation number or state	A charge assigned to an element in a compound.
Oxidation-reduction reaction (redox)	A reaction in which elements in compounds or in the pure state change oxidation numbers.
Oxidizing agent	A species reduced in a redox reaction.
Precipitation	A reaction in water solution during which an insoluble product forms.

Reducing agent	A species oxidized in a redox reaction.
Reduction	A gain of electrons in a chemical reaction.
Salt	The other product besides water that results from the reaction of an Arrhenius acid and base.
Single-replacement reaction	A type of oxidation-reduction consisting of an element displacing another, less active element from a compound.
Weak acid	An acid in which most of the substance does not ionize in water to form hydrogen ions.
Weak base	A base in which most of the substance does not ionize in water to produce hydroxide ions.

Problems

1. State in which of five categories you would place each of the following reactions: (I) combination of elements; (II) decomposition reaction; (III) replacement reaction; (IV) oxidation-reduction reaction; (V) acid-base reaction. In some cases, more than one category will be correct.
   (a) $2Al + 3Cl_2 \rightarrow 2AlCl_3$
   (b) $AgNO_3 + HCl \rightarrow AgCl + HNO_3$
   (c) $Mg + 2HNO_3 \rightarrow Mg(NO_3)_2 + H_2$
   (d) $CuCl_2 + H_2S \rightarrow CuS + 2HCl$
   (e) $Ba + 2H_2O \rightarrow Ba(OH)_2 + H_2$
   (f) $HCl + NH_3 \rightarrow NH_4Cl$
   (g) $4HCl + MnO_2 \rightarrow MnCl_2 + Cl_2 + 2H_2O$
   (h) $2Au_2O_3 + heat \rightarrow 4Au + 3O_2$
   (i) $2KNO_3 \rightarrow 2KNO_2 + O_2$
   (j) $2Al + 3H_2SO_4 \rightarrow 3H_2 + Al_2(SO_4)_3$
   (k) $2Al + 3CuSO_4 \rightarrow 3Cu + Al_2(SO_4)_3$
   (l) $2Ca + O_2 \rightarrow 2CaO$
   (m) $2C_2H_6 + 7O_2 \rightarrow 4CO_2 + 6H_2O$
   (n) $PbS + 2O_3 \rightarrow PbSO_4 + O_2$
   (o) $H_2SO_4 + Ba(OH)_2 \rightarrow 2H_2O + BaSO_4$

2. Predict whether each of the following reactions is a possibility or not and give probable products.
   (a) $Mg + AgNO_3 \rightarrow$
   (b) $Ca + HCl \rightarrow$
   (c) $Na + H_2O \rightarrow$
   (d) $Zn + steam \rightarrow$
   (e) $Fe + Al_2(SO_4)_3 \rightarrow$

   (f) $BaCl_2 + Na_2SO_4 \rightarrow$
   (g) $CuSO_4 + H_2S \rightarrow$
   (h) $Na_3PO_4 + MgCl_2 \rightarrow$
   (i) $Na_2CO_3 + CaCl_2 \rightarrow$
   (j) $NH_4Cl + AgNO_3 \rightarrow$
   (k) $Pb(NO_3)_2 + KCl \rightarrow$
   (l) $Na_2CO_3 + H_2SO_4 \rightarrow$
   (m) $Na_2SO_3 + HCl \rightarrow$
   (n) $NaCl + KNO_3 \rightarrow$
   (o) $(NH_4)_2CO_3 + Ca(C_2H_3O_2)_2 \rightarrow$
   (p) $K_2S + NaCl \rightarrow$
   (q) $H_2SO_4 + Ca(OH)_2 \rightarrow$
   (r) $Al(OH)_3 + H_3PO_4 \rightarrow$
   (s) $AgNO_3 + BaCl_2 \rightarrow$
   (t) $NH_4OH + H_2SO_4 \rightarrow$

3. Find the oxidation number of each element in the following compounds and ions.
   (a) HF
   (b) BF_3
   (c) SF_6
   (d) H_2O
   (e) MnO_4^-
   (f) H_2SO_4
   (g) H_2O_2
   (h) Cl_2
   (i) PO_4^{3-}
   (j) $Mg_3(PO_4)_2$
   (k) NH_4Cl
   (l) $AgNO_3$
   (m) N_2O_4
   (n) $Ba_3(PO_4)_2$
   (o) MgH_2
   (p) CO_3^{2-}
   (q) $FeCO_3$
   (r) $Fe_2(CO_3)_3$
   (s) $Cr_2O_7^{2-}$
   (t) $Al(ClO_3)_3$

4. Find the compound that is oxidized and the compound that is reduced in the following oxidation-reduction equations. Show oxidation number changes.

(a) $FeO + H_2 \rightarrow Fe + H_2O$

(b) $3H_2 + N_2 \rightarrow 2NH_3$

(c) $Al + 3AgNO_3 \rightarrow Al(NO_3)_3 + 3Ag$

(d) $MnO_2 + 4HCl \rightarrow MnCl_2 + Cl_2 + 2H_2O$

(e) $3Br_2 + 6KOH \rightarrow 5\,KBr + KBrO_3 + 3H_2O$

(f) $2Fe + 3Cl_2 \rightarrow 2FeCl_3$

(g) $2Al + 3CuSO_4 \rightarrow Al_2(SO_4)_3 + 3Cu$

(h) $As_4O_6 + 2H_2O + 8HNO_3 \rightarrow 4H_3AsO_4 + 8NO_2$

(i) $I_2 + 10HNO_3 \rightarrow 2HIO_3 + 10NO_2 + 4H_2O$

(j) $2FeCl_2 + H_2O_2 + 2HCl \rightarrow 2FeCl_3 + 2H_2$

5. Which of the following compounds are acids and which are bases? (By what definition?) For each compound, show an equation for reaction with HCl if it is a base and with NaOH if it is an acid. Balance all equations.

(a) $Fe(OH)_2$ (b) H_2SO_4 (c) KOH

(d) NH_3 (e) $Ca(OH)_2$ (f) BCl_3

(g) $NaHCO_3$ (h) NaH_2PO_4 (i) PH_3

(j) $HC_2H_3O_2$ (k) $AlBr_3$ (l) $HClO_3$

(m) HBr (n) $HClO$ (o) $Ba(OH)_2$

(p) PBr_3 (q) H_3PO_4 (r) HF

(s) HNO_3 (t) $Al(OH)_3$

6. Which of the compounds in Problem 5 are Brønsted-Lowry acids or bases?

7. For each description, give an example of a compound.

(a) A Brønsted-Lowry base but not an Arrhenius base.

(b) A Brønsted-Lowry acid and a Lewis acid.

(c) A Brønsted-Lowry acid and an Arrhenius acid.

(d) A Brønsted-Lowry base and an Arrhenius base.

Learning Objectives for Chapter 10

Define **gas, liquid, solid, pressure, manometer, atmospheric pressure, Boyles law, standard temperature, standard pressure, STP, ideal gas, crystal lattice, amorphous, allotrope, critical temperature, critical pressure, vapor pressure, surface tension, viscosity, metal, nonmetal, metalloid, heat of vaporization, heat of fusion, heat of sublimation.**

Explain how the phases of a single substance are related.

Describe, on a particle level, solids, liquids, and gases.

Explain several methods and units of pressure measurement.

Calculate gas properties using Boyle's law, Charles' law, the combined gas law, and the ideal-gas equation.

Explain an experimental development of Boyle's law and Charles' law.

Describe the molecular model for gases in terms of temperature, pressure, and volume effects.

Explain the effect of temperature and pressure on the vapor pressures of liquids.

Explain, on a molecular level, why surface tension exists.

10 STATES OF MATTER

All the elements and the compounds derived from those elements can be placed in endless categories. The choice of the category depends on what the person classifying the compound or elements wants to emphasize. Any classification dealing with physical properties places elements and compounds in categories such as metals, nonmetals, metalloids, solids, liquids, and gases. Many substances can be classified in more than one category.

10.1 States of Matter

The elements can be categorized by the state in which they exist. Thus we can classify a substance as a solid, a liquid, or a gas. The differences among these states can be easily defined if each is considered separately. First, consider the solid state. **Solids** have the following properties: (1) a definite shape; (2) a definite volume that they occupy. A chair is an example of a solid. The shape of a chair cannot be altered without destroying the chair, possibly by smashing it. Once the material was smashed, it would no longer be in the shape of a chair, but the individual pieces would together occupy the volume of the intact chair. In addition, each piece of the smashed chair would have a definite shape.

Liquids, on the other hand (1) have no definite shape, although they (2) occupy a definite volume. For an example, consider a glass of water. The number of milliliters of water in the glass will be the same whether the water is in a tall narrow glass or a short fat tumbler, but the shape of the water will be different.

Gases have the characteristics that they (1) have no definite shape, and (2) occupy no definite volume. A gas will fill the total container in which it is confined. In an example, we consider odorous gas that has been introduced into a room. In a short time, the gas can be detected throughout the room. The gas molecules are distributed throughout the whole room (Figure 10.1).

Figure 10.1 The solid block on the left has its own shape. The liquid in the container on the right takes on the shape of the container in which it is stored. The gas surrounding the solid and liquid occupies the whole space inside the box surrounding the block and the liquid container, and will try to escape if it can.

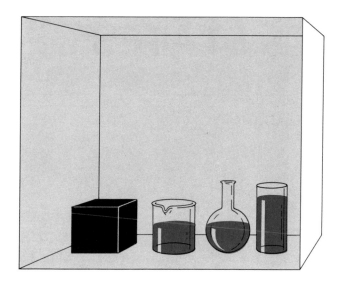

Scientists understand the interactions of molecules and atoms in solids and gases very well. Sophisticated mathematical equations have been developed to describe the behavior of these states of matter. Liquids, on the other hand, have structures that involve very complicated molecular interactions.

The three states of matter can be easily compared by considering a familiar substance, water. Water as a liquid is one of the most common substances on earth. Water is known as a solid in the form of snow and ice. Water in its gaseous state is known as vapor or steam. How does each of these three states differ from the others? First, from your experience you know that each different state exists over a different range of temperatures. Ice is cold and steam is hot. At sea level, water usually freezes at $0\,°C$ and boils at $100\,°C$:

$$\text{ice} \xrightarrow{\;0\,°C\;} \text{water} \xrightarrow{\;100\,°C\;} \text{steam}$$

Heating ice will cause it to be converted to water, and heating water will cause it to change to steam.

A sensible person would not dive into a swimming pool full of ice, since ice is known to be hard. By the same token, a person would not dive into a pool full of steam because he would crash to the bottom of the pool. Water, therefore, must have its molecules packed less tightly than ice but more tightly than steam. A person diving into water does not crash as he would with ice, nor does he pass right through, as with steam.

Finally, comparing the relative volumes of 1 g of water, 1 g of ice, and 1 g of steam, one finds that the water and ice samples have about the same volume, but steam occupies about 1000 times more volume than either of the other forms.

From this information about the different states of water, let us formulate a model to help understand the transitions.

It is known that 1 g of steam occupies a much larger volume than 1 g of water or 1 g of ice. This must mean that although there are equal amounts of water in the three samples, the molecules in steam are spaced much farther apart than they are in water and in ice. This idea is supported by the potentiality that exists for walking right through a cloud of steam, contrasted with the harder going in both water and ice. What about the difference between water and ice? One gram of each occupies about the same volume, but ice is hard and liquid water is not. The model can be expanded by saying that the water molecules in ice are held in a rigid structure, whereas the same molecules in liquid water would be freer to move around. The water molecules in steam have almost unrestricted freedom of motion.

These ideas are held true for all solids, liquids, and gases. In many solids, the particles are closely and regularly spaced in a rigid structure (called a **lattice**). In liquids, the particles are very nearly as closely spaced as in solids but not held in place so rigidly.

Although attraction exists between particles in a liquid, it is not nearly so strong as the attraction between particles in a solid. Hence, molecules, ions, or atoms are relatively free to move about in a liquid. In gases, the particles are spaced very far apart and are completely free to move in all directions. There is very little attraction between particles in the gaseous state.

What has this to do with temperature? The **temperature** of a substance is a measure of how vigorously the molecules of that substance are moving. High temperatures mean increased motion. As a solid is heated, the particles begin to vibrate in the rigid structure until at the melting point, they are vibrating vigorously enough to break out of the structure and become a liquid. Heating the liquid causes the particles to move about even more rapidly, until at a temperature known as the **boiling point**, they split from the liquid and spread out into the atmosphere as a vapor or gas. Heating this vapor will only cause the individual particles to move faster and faster.

This concept presents a reasonable model of the submicroscopic structures of solids, liquids, and gases. The model explains what is known about each state so far.

The periodic table is useful in remembering physical states of elements. It is found that at room temperature elements exist in solid, liquid, and gaseous states. Look at the periodic chart in Figure 10.2. The gaseous elements are indicated. Among them are the noble gases, the main gases of the atmosphere: oxygen and nitrogen, and several others—hydrogen, fluorine, and chlorine. There are five elements that are liquids at room temperature (if a warm room is assumed). They are mercury (Hg), bromine (Br), gallium (Ga), cesium (Cs), and francium (Fr). These elements are also shown in Figure 10.2. The rest of the elements are solids at room temperature.

We begin studying the states of matter by considering gases, since chemists know more about gases than liquids and solids. Many properties of gases can

I A																	VIII A
1 **H** 1.0080	II A		Gas Liquid Solid									III A	IV A	V A	VI A	VII A	2 **He** 4.003
3 **Li** 6.940	4 **Be** 9.013											5 **B** 10.82	6 **C** 12.011	7 **N** 14.008	8 **O** 16.000	9 **F** 19.00	10 **Ne** 20.183
11 **Na** 22.991	12 **Mg** 24.32	III B	IV B	V B	VI B	VII B	VIII B			I B	II B	13 **Al** 26.98	14 **Si** 28.09	15 **P** 30.975	16 **S** 32.066	17 **Cl** 35.457	18 **Ar** 39.944
19 **K** 39.100	20 **Ca** 40.08	21 **Sc** 44.96	22 **Ti** 47.90	23 **V** 50.95	24 **Cr** 52.01	25 **Mn** 54.94	26 **Fe** 55.85	27 **Co** 58.94	28 **Ni** 58.71	29 **Cu** 63.54	30 **Zn** 65.38	31 **Ga** 69.72	32 **Ge** 72.60	33 **As** 74.91	34 **Se** 78.96	35 **Br** 79.916	36 **Kr** 83.80
37 **Rb** 85.48	38 **Sr** 87.63	39 **Y** 88.92	40 **Zr** 91.22	41 **Nb** 92.91	42 **Mo** 95.95	43 **Tc** (99)	44 **Ru** 101.1	45 **Rh** 102.91	46 **Pd** 106.4	47 **Ag** 107.880	48 **Cd** 112.41	49 **In** 114.82	50 **Sn** 118.70	51 **Sb** 121.87	52 **Te** 127.61	53 **I** 126.91	54 **Xe** 131.30
55 **Cs** 132.91	56 **Ba** 137.36	57 *****La** 138.92	72 **Hf** 178.50	73 **Ta** 180.95	74 **W** 183.86	75 **Re** 186.22	76 **Os** 190.2	77 **Ir** 192.2	78 **Pt** 195.09	79 **Au** 197.0	80 **Hg** 200.61	81 **Tl** 204.39	82 **Pb** 207.21	83 **Bi** 209.00	84 **Po** (210)	85 **At** (210)	86 **Rn** (222)
87 **Fr** (223)	88 **Ra** (226)	89 †**Ac** (227)	104 **Ku** (261)	105 **Ha** (260)													

* Lanthanides	58 **Ce** 140.13	59 **Pr** 140.92	60 **Nd** 144.27	61 **Pm** (147)	62 **Sm** 150.35	63 **Eu** 152.0	64 **Gd** 157.26	65 **Tb** 158.93	66 **Dy** 162.51	67 **Ho** 164.94	68 **Er** 167.27	69 **Tm** 168.94	70 **Yb** 173.04	71 **Lu** 174.99
† Actinides	90 **Th** (232)	91 **Pa** (231)	92 **U** 238.07	93 **Np** (237)	94 **Pu** (242)	95 **Am** (243)	96 **Cm** (247)	97 **Bk** (249)	98 **Cf** (251)	99 **Es** (254)	100 **Fm** (253)	101 **Md** (256)	102 **No** (253)	103 **Lw** (257)

Figure 10.2 Chart showing the states of the elements: gas, liquid, or solid (see key at top).

be measured and described with numbers. Examples of these properties are pressure, volume, temperature, and mass. All gases exert pressure. **Pressure** is a force pushing on a given area. When an automobile tire is filled with air, it is filled to a certain air pressure. It would be difficult to get a filling-station attendant to put 10 g of air in a tire, since it is difficult to measure air and other gases by mass or weight.

10.2   How Is the Pressure of a Gas Measured?

You are already familiar with ways of measuring volume, mass, and temperature. To work with gases, one must also understand pressure measurements. One way of measuring a pressure is to define a standard term such as the amount of pressure the weight of the atmosphere exerts on the earth. At sea level, how much would a 1-in.^{2} column of air extending to the top of the atmosphere weigh? It would weigh 14.7 lb. Therefore, the pressure exerted by the atmosphere at sea level is 14.7 lb/in.^{2}. (This is an often-used **pressure** unit—force per unit area. In this case, it is pounds per square inch.) A 1-cm^2 column of air would weigh 1034 g. Thus, stating that the pressure is 14.7 lb/in.^{2} is equiv-

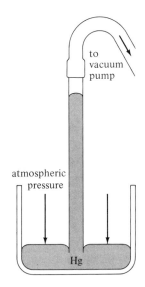

Figure 10.3 Even when almost all of the air is removed, the mercury can only rise as high as atmospheric pressure can cause it to rise.

alent to stating it as 1034 g/cm². Note that weight and mass have been used interchangeably again. These pressures are called "one atmosphere (1 atm)."

Pressure can also be measured by determining the height of a column of mercury lifted by this force of a gas pushing on a specific area, in this case, one square centimeter. This is done by using an instrument called a **manometer**. A manometer is a long tube that is dipped into a pool of mercury. Figure 10.3 shows one way of making a manometer; a vacuum pump is attached to the tube and as much air as possible is removed through the top. Another way of doing this would be to fill a tube sealed at one end while it was upside down and then invert it in a container of mercury. As the air at the top of the tube is removed by the vacuum pump, the pressure of the atmosphere pushing on the pool of mercury pushes the mercury up into the empty tube. When all the air is removed, the liquid mercury will stop rising. Why, if the vacuum pump continues to operate, does the mercury stop rising? The mercury stops rising because the air pushing down on the mercury in the dish can raise the mercury in the tube only until the pressure exerted by the column of mercury equals the pressure the air is exerting. The air can push only so hard. If the manometer is taken to a higher altitude such as that at the top of a mountain, there is less air above the instrument and the pressure pushing on the instrument must lessen. A column of mercury will not rise as high on a mountain top as it would at sea level.

Whenever the pressure the column of mercury exerts in the evacuated tube equals the pressure the air is exerting, the column will go no higher. The same principles apply to a tube of mercury that is inverted into a pool of mercury. Assuming that the tube is long enough, the mercury in the tube will fall until the pressure the column of mercury exerts in pushing down equals the pressure of the air pushing it up. When either of these experiments is performed at sea level, the column of mercury will be 76 cm, or 760 mm, high, no matter what the diameter of the tube is. (Air pressure changes with weather conditions. The accepted pressure at sea level in good weather is 760 mmHg.) In other words, the air pressure is pushing on the mercury pool with enough force per unit area to raise a mercury column of that unit cross-sectional area 76 cm. This is 1 atm of pressure. To see that this height of mercury is equivalent to the previous pressure measurements, consider the following calculation. The weight of a column of mercury can be calculated by multiplying the density of mercury, 13.60 g/cm³, by its height, 76.00 cm, to get 1034 g/cm²:

$$13.60 \text{ g/cm}^3 \times 76.00 \text{ cm} = 1034 \text{ g/cm}^2$$

Remember to cancel units as we have done in earlier calculations (Chapter 3). The value for the weight of the mercury column corresponds to the pressure value given at the beginning of the section.

At this point, it is interesting to consider how high a column of water can be lifted by drawing it up a tube with a vacuum pump. This calculation is very easy. All that is necessary is to multiply the unit factor by the pressure that air is exerting on 1 cm². The unit factor is the inverse of the density of water, that is, the inverse of 1 g/cm³, and the air pressure is 1034 g/cm².

$$\frac{1\ cm^3\ H_2O}{g\ H_2O} \times \frac{1034\ g}{cm^2} = 1034\ cm$$

By multiplying these two numbers, we find that (if a perfect vacuum could be created) a column of water could be raised 1034 cm, or about 32 ft. The height to which water can be raised by the atmosphere is another way of expressing pressure. Each centimeter of the water column is called a millibar. Thus **1-atm pressure** is 1034 millibars. Weather forecasters often use this pressure term. The knowledge has a very practical application when one is trying to siphon water from one container into another. Care must be taken to make sure that the height of the hump over which the water is to be lifted is well below this maximum number of 32 ft; otherwise siphoning is impossible.

Five different ways of expressing pressure have now been stated. It can be expressed in atmospheres (1 atm is equivalent to 76 cm of mercury), in centimeters of mercury (cmHg), in millimeters of mercury (mmHg), in pounds per square inch, and in millibars (centimeters of the water column). (The unit g/cm² does not really express pressure, since g is not a force unit.) One more unit is useful. One Torr is essentially equivalent to one millimeter of mercury (1 mmHg). The Torr was named for Evangelista Torricelli, who in the seventeenth century invented the mercury barometer, another pressure-measuring device. **Torr** is a more general term than **mmHg**; both terms will appear in this textbook.

10.3 ⚗Pressure and Boyle's Law

Since we can measure some of the properties of gases. It is possible now to study the behavior of gases. Gas behavior has been studied extensively and is summarized by gas laws. The first law to consider is called Boyle's law (Figure 10.4).

Robert Boyle carefully studied the compression of a gas. He performed an experiment similar to the one pictured in Figure 10.4, in which he put a sample of gas (1 L at 25 °C) in a glass tube and then added mercury to create a pressure on the gas. As he added more mercury, he found what was generally known—that the volume the gas occupied became smaller. His special discovery was the exact way in which it became smaller. Boyle made measurements and found that doubling the pressure of the gas by adding more mercury caused the gas to be contained in half the volume.

This can be stated more conveniently by equations and numbers. Let us say that one of Boyle's experiments gave the following information for a specific

Figure 10.4 As in Boyle's original experiment, the volume occupied by the trapped air becomes smaller as more mercury is added to create a higher pressure.

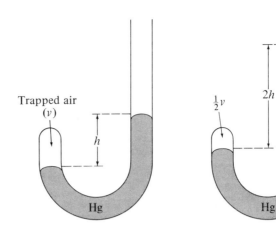

$$P \propto \frac{1}{V}$$

$$P = \frac{k}{V}$$

$$PV = k$$

amount of gas, where the temperature was held constant (Table 10.1). There is something very interesting about this set of data. When the pressure in atmospheres (atm), is multiplied by the volume in liters (L), the same answer is obtained in each case.

(1) 4 L × 1 atm = 4 L·atm
(2) 2 L × 2 atm = 4 L·atm
(3) 1 L × 4 atm = 4 L·atm
(4) 0.5 L × 8 atm = 4 L·atm

It can generally be said that for a sample of gas kept at a constant temperature, pressure times volume equals a constant, or

$$P \times V = k$$

where k is a constant number. If k always stays the same, then as P goes up, V must go down. As V goes up, P must go down. This is a mathematical statement of **Boyle's law**. A verbal statement is,

The pressure is inversely proportional to the volume.

Now look at experiments (1) and (2) in Table 10.1. If the amount 4 L in (1) is assigned the general value V_1, and the 1 atm is assigned the value P_1;

Table 10.1

Experiment Number	Volume of Trapped Air (L)	Pressure of Gas (atm)
1	4	1
2	2	2
3	1	4
4	0.5	8

then 4 L × 1 atm = 4 L·atm or $P_1V_1 = 4$ L·atm. In (2), with the same weight of gas, a new pressure, 2 atm (P_2), caused a new volume, 2 L = V_2. The product is still 4 L·atm ($P_2V_2 = 4$ L·atm). Since things equal to the same thing are equal to each other, a new form of Boyle's law can be written.

$$P_1V_1 = 4 \text{ L·atm}$$
$$P_2V_2 = 4 \text{ L·atm}$$

Therefore, at constant temperature,

$$P_1V_1 = P_2V_2$$

With this equation, a chemist can look at the pressure of a gas occupying a given volume and find out what its pressure is at some other volume if the temperature is kept constant. Only liters and atmospheres have been considered in this equation, but the equation could work with any units so long as the same units are used throughout.

The following example uses Boyle's law.

Example 10.1

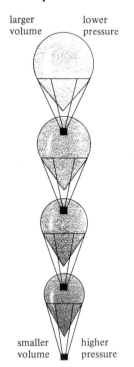

larger volume   lower pressure

smaller volume   higher pressure

Figure 10.5

Start with a helium-filled balloon that is at sea level. The baloon contains 10.0 L of helium. The pressure on the balloon would be 1.00 atm. Release the balloon and let it rise until the pressure pushing on it is only 0.500 atm. Assume that the temperature stays the same. What would be the balloon's volume?

Step 1   Identify P_1, V_1, P_2, V_2. Let P_1 be the first pressure of 1 atm and V_1 the first volume of 10.0 L: $P_1 = 1.00$ atm; $V_1 = 10.0$ L. Let P_2 be the final pressure of 0.500 atm and V_2 be the unknown volume: $P_2 = 0.500$ atm; $V_2 = ?$ Be sure that P_1 and P_2 have the same units and V_1 and V_2 have the same units.

Step 2   Use the Boyle's law equation. The following equation can now be written,

$$10.0 \text{ L} \times 1.00 \text{ atm} = 0.500 \text{ atm} \times V_2$$

in which numbers are substituted for P_1, V_1, and P_2. The values for P_1 and P_2 must be in the same units; and the same applies for V_1 and V_2. Otherwise the units will not cancel. If both sides of the equation are divided by 0.500 atm, the 0.500 atm on the right-hand side will cancel, and the equation will become

$$V_2 = \frac{1.00 \times 10.0 \text{ L}}{0.500} = 20.0 \text{ L}$$

The volume of the balloon is 20.0 L; it has expanded substantially. Changes like this must be considered in making weather surveys with balloons. The expansion of a balloon as it rises in the atmosphere is large (Figure 10.5) due

232

to the decrease in atmospheric pressure on the outside of the balloon, and if this expansion were not allowed for, the balloon could break before the desired measurements were made.

Example 10.2

If 10.0 L of a gas at 50.0 °C and 1.00 atm pressure were compressed to 5.00 L at the same temperature, what would be the pressure of the gas?

Step 1 V_1 equals 10.0 L, and P_1 equals 1.00 atm. The quantity P_2 is the unknown, and V_2 equals 5.00 L.

Step 2   10.0 L × 1.00 atm = 5.00 L × P_2. Divided on both sides by 5.00 L, the equation becomes:

$$P_2 = \frac{10.0 \text{ L} \times 1.00 \text{ atm}}{5.00 \text{ L}} = 2.00 \text{ atm}$$

The pressure increased as expected.

Example 10.3

As the outer reaches of the atmosphere are approached, pressure becomes very low, reaching the small value about 5.00×10^{-7} Torr. What volume would a balloon that occupied 1.00 L at sea level (1.00 atm) occupy in this outer region of space, if it is assumed that the temperature remains constant?

Step 1   We know that $V_1 = 1.00$ L and $P_1 = 760.$ Torr. These are the conditions at sea level. The quantity V_2 is the unknown, and P_2 is 5.00×10^{-7} Torr.

Step 2   1.00 L × 760. Torr = $V_2 \times 5.00 \times 10^{-7}$ Torr
Dividing both sides of the equation by 5.00×10^{-7} Torr gives

$$V_2 = \frac{1.00 \text{ L} \times 760. \text{ Torr}}{5.00 \times 10^{-7} \text{ Torr}} = 1.52 \times 10^9 \text{ L}$$

In fact, 10^9 L is about the size of the oil holds of two supertankers.

There is another way of looking at this kind of problem.

Example 10.4

Assume that a container initially holding 5.00 L oxygen gas at pressure 1.00 atm is compressed (at constant temperature) until the final pressure becomes 4.00 atm. Calculate the final volume. The final volume V_2 of the gas must equal the initial volume V_1 times a pressure factor.

$$V_2 = V_1 \times \text{pressure factor}$$

or

$$V_2 = 5.00 \text{ L} \times \text{pressure factor}$$

The pressure factor is a ratio of the initial and final pressures on the system. The final pressure is greater than the initial pressure, so the final volume must be smaller than the original volume. The pressure factor is 1.00 atm/4.00 atm:

$$V = 5.00 \text{ L} \times \frac{1.00 \text{ atm}}{4.00 \text{ atm}} = 1.25 \text{ L}$$

Multiplying by this ratio produces a smaller final volume, 1.25 L. If the reciprocal relation had been picked (4.00 atm/1.00 atm), a larger volume would have been generated. Such an answer is impossible, because the gas was compressed. This is a good way either to solve problems or to check the answer to see whether it is reasonable. The answer must always make sense with what is being done to the gas.

Similar logic can be applied to solving for a new pressure.

Example 10.5

If 2.00 L of a gas initially at 760.0 Torr pressure is expanded to 8.00 L, at constant temperature, what is the new pressure?

The new pressure can be expressed in terms of a volume factor.

$$P_2 = P_1 \times \text{volume factor}$$

or

$$P_2 = 760.0 \text{ Torr} \times \text{volume factor}$$

The volume factor is a ratio of the volumes so chosen that the resulting pressure will be smaller. This must be what we are looking for, since the volume expanded. The correct volume factor is 2.00 L/8.00 L. Therefore

$$P_2 = 760.0 \text{ Torr} \times \frac{2.00 \text{ L}}{8.00 \text{ L}} = 190. \text{ Torr}$$

10.4

Temperature and Charles' Law

Now that the effect of pressure on a gas is known, it is time to look at the effect of temperature on a gas. In this case, the pressure of the gas will be kept constant. The temperature and volume will be allowed to change. Experimenting with the effect of temperature on gases was done by Jacques Alexander Cesar Charles, and the equation he discovered is named **Charles' law**.

Figure 10.6 When a gas is heated, it expands.

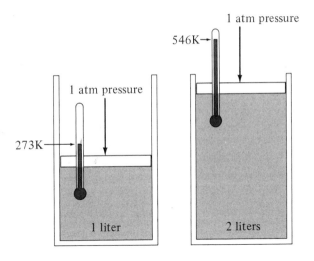

546K→

1 atm pressure

1 atm pressure

273K→

1 liter

2 liters

Charles found that when the pressure is kept constant, the volume of a gas sample is directly proportional to the absolute temperature or the temperature in degrees Kelvin. That is, as temperature goes up, volume goes up, and as temperature goes down, volume goes down.

In problems involving temperature and gases, the temperature is always expressed in degrees Kelvin; K = °C + 273. Charles found that if he raised the temperature of 1.00 L of gas at 1.00 atm pressure from 273 K (which equals 0 °C) to 546 K, the volume would double, to 2.00 L. When air is heated, it expands (Figure 10.6); and when air cools, it contracts (Figure 10.7). Charles' law states this fact. For a given quantity of gas at a set pressure, as the temperature rises, volume increases, and as temperature falls, volume decreases. Mathematically, this is

$$V = kT$$

where k equals some constant number. The temperature is expressed as the

Figure 10.7 According to Charles' law, the balloon in the hot water will be larger than the one in the ice water, even though they both contain the same amount of gas.

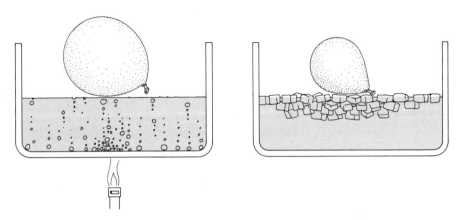

Table 10.2

Experiment Number	Volume of Gas (L)	Temperature of Gas (K)
1	1.000	273
2	1.098	300.
3	1.464	400.
4	2.000	546

absolute temperature, the temperature in degrees Kelvin. A kind of calculation like that done with Boyle's law can be done with the mathematical expression of Charles' law. If we solve for k, then $V/T = k$. That $V/T = k$ can be seen from the results of the following hypothetical experiments. Assume that a cylinder of gas is fitted with a piston. When the apparatus is heated, the piston will rise. This allows the pressure on the gas to remain constant while the volume of the gas increases. The experimental data might be shown as in Table 10.2. When the volume in liters is divided by the temperature in degrees Kelvin for each measurement, a constant is obtained (in this case 3.66×10^{-3} L/K).

$$(1) \quad \frac{1.000 \text{ L}}{273 \text{ K}} = 3.66 \times 10^{-3} \frac{\text{L}}{\text{K}}$$

$$(2) \quad \frac{1.098 \text{ L}}{300. \text{ K}} = 3.66 \times 10^{-3} \frac{\text{L}}{\text{K}}$$

$$(3) \quad \frac{1.464 \text{ L}}{400. \text{ K}} = 3.66 \times 10^{-3} \frac{\text{L}}{\text{K}}$$

$$(4) \quad \frac{2.000 \text{ L}}{546 \text{ K}} = 3.66 \times 10^{-3} \frac{\text{L}}{\text{K}}$$

Let us assign the general terms V_1 and T_1 to the volume and temperature in the first measurement and V_2 and T_2 for the second measurement. Then V_1/T_1 equals k, and V_2/T_2 equals k. Hence,

$$\frac{V_1}{T_1} = \frac{V_2}{T_2}$$

Example 10.6

A given quantity of oxygen gas occupies the volume 3.00 L at 20.0 °C. What would the volume of this oxygen be at 50.0 °C if the pressure remained constant?

Step 1 Convert the temperature to degrees Kelvin if necessary. Converting gives 20.0 °C = 293 K and 50.0 °C = 323 K.

Step 2 Identify V_1, T_1, V_2, T_2. Since we know that V_1 equals 3.00 L, T_1 equals 293 K, and T_2 equals 323 K, it is possible to solve for V_2.

Step 3   Using the Charles' law equation, we get the equation

$$\frac{3.00 \text{ L}}{293 \text{ K}} = \frac{V_2}{323 \text{ K}}$$

If both sides of the equation are multiplied by 323 K, the new volume can be expressed as

$$V_2 = \frac{3.00 \text{ L} \times 323}{293} = 3.31 \text{ L}$$

The quantity V_2 equals 3.31 L. The volume increases.

Example 10.7

For 1000.0 L of chlorine gas at 15.0 °C and 1.00 atm pressure, calculate the temperature at which the volume would equal 200.0 L. The pressure remains constant.

Step 1   Convert 15.0 °C to K. This is 273 + 15.0, or 288 K.
Step 2   Here V_1 is 1000.0 L, and T_1 is 288 K, and V_2 is 200.0 L.

Step 3
$$T_2 = \frac{200.0 \text{ L} \times 288 \text{ K}}{1000.0 \text{ L}} = 57.6 \text{ K}$$

Converting 57.6 K to degrees Celsius gives a temperature equal to -215 °C (57.6 − 273).

Charles found that the volume is directly proportional to the temperature expressed in Kelvin degrees. One has only to try to double the temperature of an object at 0 °C to realize that the Celsius scale does not work for these problems.

Logic like that used to solve pressure-volume problems can also be used to solve temperature-volume problems. For example, when nitrogen gas that has a volume of 15.0 L at 25.0 °C is heated to 50.0 °C at constant pressure, the new volume can be determined by applying a temperature factor. The final volume must equal the initial volume times a temperature factor:

$$V_2 = V_1 \times \text{temperature factor}$$

The temperature factor is a ratio of the temperatures, so chosen that the final volume will be greater than the initial volume. A gas expands on being heated. If the gas were being cooled, the temperature factor would have to produce a final volume smaller than the initial volume. A gas contracts on being cooled. In this case, the desired temperature factor is 323 K/298 K:

$$V_2 = 15.0 \text{ L} \times \frac{323 \text{ K}}{298 \text{ K}}$$

$$= 16.3 \text{ L}$$

The volume factor is also applicable in solving problems relating to temperature, as the following example shows.

Example 10.8

A 33.0-L container of helium gas initially at $0\,^\circ\text{C}$ was heated to expand to 66.0 L as the pressure was held constant. Calculate the new temperature in degrees Celsius.

The new temperature must equal the initial temperature times some volume factor:

$$T_2 = T_1 \times \text{volume factor}$$

Gases expand when they are heated, so T_2 must be larger than T_1. To get this relation, one must arrange the volumes in the volume factor in the ratio 66.0 L/33.0 L

$$T_2 = 273 \text{ K} \times \frac{66.0 \text{ L}}{33.0 \text{ L}}$$

$$= 546 \text{ K}$$

Expressing the answer in degrees Celsius, we get

$$^\circ\text{C} = 546 - 273 = -273\,^\circ\text{C}$$

10.5 Combined Gas Law

Charles' law and Boyle's law are the two important equations describing the behavior of gases. In many cases, however, the temperature pressure, and volume are all changing. There are three variables, P, V, and T. To work problems like this, one must combine the two laws, to yield the **combined gas law**. This law, expressed in symbols is

$$\frac{P_1 \times V_1}{T_1} = \frac{P_2 \times V_2}{T_2}$$

The equation allows taking a volume of gas at one temperature and pressure and finding the volume that the gas would occupy at some other temperature and pressure. For any sample of gas, if P_1, T_1, and V_1 are known, and also any two of P_2, T_2, and V_2, then the unknown value can be calculated. More generally, if five of the values are known, the sixth can be calculated. The following two examples illustrate this principle.

Example 10.9

If 1.00 L of nitrogen initially at 0 °C and 760.0 Torr pressure is heated to 50 °C with pressure increase to 1000.0 Torr, what will be the new volume of this gas?

Step 1   Convert °C to K. Zero degrees Celsius equals 273 K. Fifty degrees Celsius equals 323 K.

Step 2   Identify the factors to be used in the equation.

$$V_1 = 1.00 \text{ L} \qquad V_2 = ?$$
$$T_1 = 273 \text{ K} \qquad T_2 = 323 \text{ K}$$
$$P_1 = 760.0 \text{ Torr} \qquad P_2 = 1000.0 \text{ Torr}$$

Step 3   Solve the equation. Substituting the appropriate values into the combined gas law equation produces the following:

$$\frac{760.0 \text{ Torr} \times 1.00 \text{ L}}{273 \text{ K}} = \frac{1000.0 \text{ Torr} \times V_2}{323 \text{ K}}$$

This equation is solved for V_2:

$$V_2 = \frac{760.0 \times 1.00 \text{ L} \times 323}{273 \times 1000.0} = 0.899 \text{ L}$$

In connection with gas law problems, the abbreviation **STP** is often used. This stands for standard temperature and pressure. **Standard temperature** is 0 °C or 273 K. **Standard pressure** is 1.00 atm, or 760. Torr.

The concept of STP is used so that scientists can have a simple, widely known set of conditions by which they can refer to a gas.

Example 10.10

A container holds 3.00 L neon at STP. What volume will this neon occupy at 100 °C and 10.0-atm pressure? First convert °C to K.

Step 1   The temperature 0 °C equals 273 K, and 100 °C equals 373 K.

Step 2 $V_1 = 3.00 \text{ L} \qquad V_2 = ?$

                $P_1 = 1.00 \text{ atm} \qquad P_2 = 10.0 \text{ atm}$

                $T_1 = 273 \text{ K} \qquad T_2 = 373 \text{ K}$

Step 3 The equation becomes

$$\frac{1.00 \text{ atm} \times 3.00 \text{ L}}{273 \text{ K}} = \frac{10.0 \text{ atm} \times V_2}{373 \text{ K}}$$

Solving this equation yields

$$V_2 = \frac{1.00 \times 3.00 \text{ L} \times 373}{273 \times 10.0} = 0.410 \text{ L}$$

The problems involving changes in all three conditions of temperature, pressure, and volume can also be solved using the same kind of logic we used in the pressure-volume and temperature-volume examples. One only needs to treat the pressure, temperature, and volume factors independently and then multiply them all together. Here is how it works.

Example 10.11 A 50.0-L volume of argon initially at 27 °C and 2.00 atm is compressed to 5.00 atm. During the compression, the temperature increases to 45.0 °C. What is the new volume of the gas?

Applying the temperature factor and the pressure factor would give us an equation that looks like this:

$$V_2 = V_1 \times \text{temperature factor} \times \text{volume factor}$$

or

$$V_2 = 50.0 \text{ L} \times \text{temperature factor} \times \text{volume factor}$$

We temporarily ignore the volume factor and consider only the temperature factor. Conversion to Kelvin is first necessary:

$$27 \text{ °C} + 273 = 300. \text{ K}$$
$$45 \text{ °C} + 273 = 318 \text{ K}$$

The gas is being heated, so the temperature factor must effect an increase in the volume of gas. Thus, the temperature factor is 318 K/300. K. The equation now looks like this:

$$V_2 = 50.0 \text{ L} \times \frac{318 \text{ K}}{300. \text{ K}} \times \text{pressure factor}$$

Now consider the pressure factor. The pressure is being increased from 2.00 atm to 5.00 atm. This increase in pressure causes a reduction in volume. The pressure factor must therefore be 2.00 atm/5.00 atm. The equation now looks like this:

$$V_2 = 50.0 \text{ L} \times \frac{318 \text{ K}}{300. \text{ K}} \times \frac{2.00 \text{ atm}}{5.00 \text{ atm}} = 21.2 \text{ L}$$

Notice that the pressure change caused a much greater reduction in volume compared with the increase in volume from the temperature change. The net result was a smaller volume. Such is not always the case.

Example 10.12   A sample of air initially at 35 °C and 755 Torr pressure is contained in a 585-mL container. The container is heated to 105 °C while the pressure is increased to 760. Torr. What is the new volume?

Applying the temperature and pressure factors gives the equations

$$V_2 = V_1 \times \text{temperature factor} \times \text{pressure factor}$$

or

$$V_2 = 585 \text{ mL} \times \text{temperature factor} \times \text{pressure factor}$$

To determine the temperature factor, we consider that a heating of the gas produces an expansion. The temperature factor is 378 K/308 K.

To determine the pressure factor, we consider that the gas will contract under increased pressure, and we get the pressure factor 755 Torr/760. Torr.

The equation now is

$$V_2 = 585 \text{ mL} \times \frac{378 \text{ K}}{308 \text{ K}} \times \frac{755 \text{ Torr}}{760. \text{ Torr}} = 713 \text{ mL}$$

The volume increases. In this example, the temperature effect is much greater than the pressure effect.

10.6   Why Do the Gas Laws Work?

The gas laws present a mathematical picture of the behavior of gases. Chemists would like to explain this mathematical description of gases with a molecular model. In other words, what is happening to the gases on a molecular scale, when they expand and contract? In formulating such a model, it is necessary to review what is known about the behavior of gases. It is known that as temperature increases, either the volume or the pressure rises, or both rise, depending on the experiment. Temperature is a measure of how fast the particles are moving. The higher the temperature is raised, the faster the particles move. Pressure is a measure of the bombardment of particles on the walls of a container.

Imagine what happens when a ball is thrown against a wall. When the ball hits the wall, pressure is put on the wall for an instant. The amount of

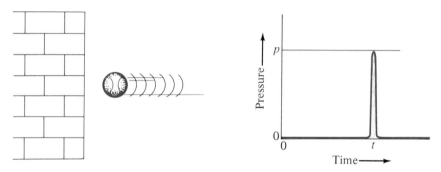

Figure 10.8 The ball exerts an instantaneous pressure, p, when it hits the wall at time t.

pressure exerted depends on how much the ball weighs and how hard it is thrown (that is, how fast it is going). The heavier the ball, the greater the pressure it exerts at a set speed. The faster it goes, the greater the pressure it exerts. Look at that pressure on a graph, as shown in Figure 10.8. Now imagine that the ball is in a box and that you give it a push. It will move back and forth in one direction forever.* As shown in Figure 10.9, the ball hits only two walls as it travels. A graph showing the pressure exerted on either wall is also given in Figure 10.9.

At this point only one ball and two walls have been used. Imagine further that the balls are atoms or molecules and that there are 10 of them, all moving at about the same speed. A graph like the one in Figure 10.10 could be prepared, containing 10 times as many "pressure" spikes as the graph in Figure 10.9.

Now try to imagine 10^{23} molecules in the box. You could not see each spike; there would be so many of them that a blur would be produced—an average value. This is what is actually seen when pressure is measured. The average of many hits of molecules on the pressure gauge produces the indicated pressure.

Consider now the gas laws in terms of the molecular model proposed. First, if the volume of the box is decreased, although the box encloses the same amount of gas, more particles will hit the wall during a given period. The

---

* It moves back and forth forever, because in this imaginary situation, the ball does not lose energy each time it hits either wall, nor is there air in the box to slow it down. In the real world, it would lose energy at each contact, eventually slowing down and stopping.

Figure 10.9 The ball is shown moving continuously in one dimension within a box, hitting the walls on either side. The graph shows the instantaneous pressure created each time the ball hits a wall.

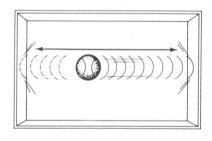
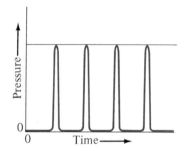

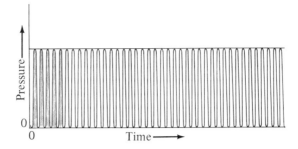

Figure 10.10 Graph of the instantaneous pressure created by ten balls bouncing off the walls of the box in Figure 10.9.

pressure will rise. This agrees with Boyle's experiments. If the temperature is raised, the particles will move faster and hit the wall more often, and once again the pressure will rise. If the walls of the container are movable, raising the temperature will cause the pressure to rise, and the walls may be pushed out so that the volume will rise.

Thus, a molecular model has been proposed that can explain some of the behavior of gases.

10.7 The Ideal-Gas Law

The molecular model for the behavior of gases proposed in Section 10.6 is the basis for an equation from which all of the earlier gas laws could have been derived. It is called the **ideal-gas equation**, and it relates the temperature, pressure, volume, and number of moles present in a single gas sample. An **ideal gas** is one that is described by this equation and the others given. The equation is

$$pV = nRT$$

where p = pressure of the gas expressed in atmospheres;
V = volume of the gas expressed in liters;
T = temperature of the gas expressed in K;
n = number of moles of gas present;
R = a constant number (called the gas constant), having the value

$$\frac{0.082\ L \times atm}{mol \times deg\ K}$$

(Note that R is expressed in units that can be canceled in the equation.)

The equation is consistent with Boyle's law, since at constant temperature, $pV = nRT$; thus $pV = k$, where k is a constant. It is also consistent with Charles' law, since at constant pressure, $V = (nR/p) \times T$; thus $V = kT$, where k is a constant. The equation is simple to use so long as one chooses the units properly.

Example 10.13   A 1.0-mol sample of gas occupies the volume 3.0 L at 50 °C. Calculate the pressure of the gas.

Step 1   Determine the values to be used in the equation.
$$V = 3.0 \text{ L} \qquad\qquad n = 1.0 \text{ mol}$$
$$T = 50. \text{ °C} = 323 \text{ K} \qquad p = ?$$

Step 2   Substitute values and solve the equation.

$$p = \frac{nRT}{V} = \frac{1.0 \text{ mol} \times 0.082 \dfrac{\text{L} \times \text{atm}}{\text{mol} \times \text{K}} \times 323 \text{ K}}{3.0 \text{ L}} = 8.8 \text{ atm}$$

Note the cancellation of units.

Example 10.14   A 5.7-mol sample of a gas occupies a 15-L container at 17 atm pressure. What is its Celsius temperature?

Step 1 $p = 17 \text{ atm} \qquad n = 5.7 \text{ mol}$

$V = 15 \text{ L} \qquad\qquad T = ?$

Step 2 $$T = \frac{pV}{nR} = \frac{17 \text{ atm} \times 15 \text{ L}}{5.7 \text{ moles} \times .082 \dfrac{\text{L} \times \text{atm}}{\text{mol} \times \text{K}}} = 550 \text{ K}$$

Step 3 $°C = 550 - 273 = 277 \text{ °C}$

10.8   Molar Volumes of Gases in Chemical Calculations

The ideal gas law leads to an important use of gas volumes in chemical calculations. Standard temperature and pressure (STP) is defined as 0 °C and 1.00 atm pressure. At STP, 1.00 mol of any ideal gas occupies 22.4 L. A simple calculation proves the statement:

$$V = \frac{nRT}{p} = \frac{1.00 \text{ mol} \times 0.082 \dfrac{\text{L} \cdot \text{atm}}{\text{mol} \cdot \text{K}} \times 273 \text{ K}}{1.00 \text{ atm}} = 22.4 \text{ L}$$

Thus, if ideal gas behavior is assumed, 32.0 g of O_2 or 2.0 g H_2 or 28.0 g N_2 or 16.0 g CH_4 or 27.0 g HCN occupies the volume 22.4 L at STP. Stated differently, one gram formula weight (gfw) of a gaseous substance occupies the volume 22.4 L at STP. This volume is often called the **molar volume** and has units of L/mol. Consider one example that uses this information and simplifies an ideal gas calculation.

Example 10.15

A sample of O_2 at STP occupies the volume 1.67 L. How many moles of O_2 are present?

If 1 mol O_2 occupies 22.4 L at STP, then fewer moles must occupy 1.67 L. The calculation proceeds—

$$1.67 \text{ L } O_2 \times \frac{1 \text{ mol } O_2}{22.4 \text{ L } O_2} = 7.46 \times 10^{-2} \text{ mol } O_2$$

Now consider how molar volumes can be applied to chemical calculations. In the reaction $2KClO_3 \rightarrow 2KCl + 3O_2(g)$, assume that 2.00 mol KCl are used and that the reaction is carried out at STP. The volume of oxygen resulting from the reaction is easily calculated.

Step 1 Calculate the number of moles of O_2 produced:

$$2.00 \text{ mol } KClO_3 \times \frac{3 \text{ mol } O_2}{2 \text{ mol } KClO_3} = 3.00 \text{ mol } O_2$$

Step 2 Using the molar volume, calculate the volume of O_2 produced:

$$3.00 \text{ mol } O_2 \times \frac{22.4 \text{ L } O_2}{1 \text{ mol } O_2} = 67.2 \text{ L } O_2$$

Example 10.16

In a reaction at STP, $N_2O_4(g) \rightarrow 2NO_2(g)$, there are 10.0 L of N_2O_4 consumed. How many liters of NO_2 are produced?

Step 1 Calculate the number of moles of NO_2 produced:

$$10.0 \text{ L } N_2O_4 \times \frac{1 \text{ mol } N_2O_4}{22.4 \text{ L } N_2O_4} = 0.446 \text{ mol } N_2O_4$$

$$0.446 \text{ mol } N_2O_4 \times \frac{2 \text{ mol } NO_2}{1 \text{ mol } N_2O_4} = 0.892 \text{ mol } NO_2$$

Step 2 Calculate the volume of NO_2 produced:

$$0.892 \text{ mol } NO_2 \times \frac{22.4 \text{ L } NO_2}{1 \text{ mol } NO_2} = 20.0 \text{ L } NO_2$$

This is an interesting answer, since the volume of NO_2 is exactly double the N_2O_4.

This answer leads to the statement that under any set of constant conditions of temperature and pressure, the coefficients in a balanced chemical equation relate the volumes of gases involved. Two final examples illustrate this.

Example 10.17

In producing ammonia, the reaction $3H_2 + N_2 \rightarrow 2NH_3$ occurs. At some high but constant temperature and pressure, 9 L of H_2 are consumed. How many liters of NH_3 form?

This problem is solved directly, using a unit factor from the equation:

$$9 \text{ L H}_2 \times \frac{2 \text{ L NH}_3}{3 \text{ L H}_2} = 6 \text{ L NH}_3$$

Example 10.18

What volume of oxygen (at STP) is needed to burn completely 3.00 mol of propane (C_3H_8)? The final products are water and carbon dioxide.

Step 1   Write a balanced equation:

$$3 \text{ mol} \quad 15 \text{ mol}$$
$$C_3H_8 + 5O_2 \rightarrow 3CO_2 + 4H_2O$$

Step 2   Calculate the number of moles of oxygen needed:

$$3.00 \text{ mol C}_3\text{H}_8 \times \frac{5 \text{ mol O}_2}{1 \text{ mol C}_3\text{H}_8} = 15.0 \text{ mol O}_2$$

Step 3   Calculate volume of O_2 at STP:

$$15.0 \text{ mol O}_2 \times \frac{22.4 \text{ L O}_2}{1 \text{ mol O}_2} = 336 \text{ L O}_2$$

10.9   Solids

Many of the equations dealing with gases are very simple compared with the equations that describe the solid state. Despite the complexity of the mathematical equations needed to describe solids, however, scientists know a great deal about this form of matter. Since the atoms, molecules, and ions in solids are held in a fairly small space, and since these particles cannot move at random, scientists can examine characteristics like the size of the atom and the different ways in which particles can be grouped. Scientists whose specialty involves solids are called crystallographers; and the science that concerns the arrangement of particles in crystals is **crystallography**. The study of crystallography is complex and often involves using X rays, directing them at specific crystals. The data collected from bouncing X rays off crystals are analyzed through complicated mathematical equations and computers. The study of crystallography alone can take many years and fill many books. Our consideration of solids will be limited to studying the structure of solids and some of the meaning of changes in the particle arrangement.

What is a solid? A true solid must have a crystalline structure. A **crystalline structure** is a pattern that repeats itself. That is, a true solid contains a few particles in a specific arrangement, the arrangement of particles indefinitely repeated until a visible size is reached.

All these groups of atoms arranged in a solid make up the **crystal lattice**.

The few atoms having the particular arrangement that is repeated in space belong to a unit called the **unit cell**.

A few interesting comparisons of solids show the importance of their crystal structures. First, compare diamond and graphite, the material in pencil lead. Both these materials are composed of pure carbon. The only difference between them is their crystal structure, as shown in Figure 10.11. Materials that are composed of the same elements but have different properties because of different crystalline structures are called allotropes. Thus diamond and graphite are **allotropes**. Another pair of allotropes is white phosphorus and red phosphorus. Both materials are of the same element, but there is a great difference in their behavior. Red phosphorus is fairly stable. It must be heated if burning is to begin. White phosphorus, on the other hand, is very dangerous. If white phosphorus is exposed to air, it will spontaneously begin burning. White phosphorus was using during World War II for fire bombs, and the people using it were responsible for much destruction.

Figure 10.11 Diagrams showing two different crystal structures. The dashed lines in the graphite structure indicate weak bonds between the layers of covalently bonded carbon atoms.

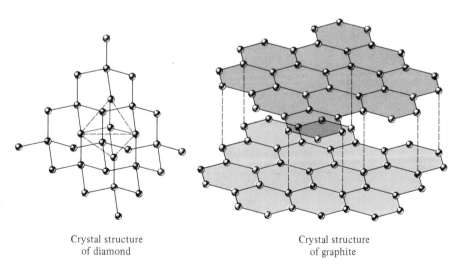

Crystal structure
of diamond

Crystal structure
of graphite

Some other materials appear to be solids but are really not.

These are **amorphous** substances, which are materials that seem to be solid but have no definite crystal structure.

Materials like glass, asphalt, and many plastics fall into this category.

Consider glass to see how it differs from other materials that are true solids. Ordinary glass is made from three crystalline materials—pure sand, or silicon dioxide (crystalline), sodium carbonate (crystalline), and calcium carbonate (crystalline). These three materials are placed in an oven and heated to about 1300 °C. A chemical reaction occurs between the carbonate compounds and the silicon dioxide, and silicates of calcium and sodium are formed. The result is a liquid that flows very slowly. This phenomenon can be compared with the cooling of molasses until it becomes so thick that it will no longer pour. It is still a liquid. Glass is like this, but even more rigid. In fact, glass in very old windows is slightly thicker at the bottom than at the top. This is because it has flowed downward over a long period. Scientists do not understand the nature of such liquids very well.

10.10   Liquids

The molecules in liquids, compared with molecules of the solid phase and of the gas phase, have a freedom of movement somewhere in-between. The molecules are closely spaced but not rigidly fixed. Although scientists do not know nearly as much about liquids as they do about solids and gases, they have distinguished some important properties of liquids.

Let us speculate how a liquid might form from a gas. Gases are composed of molecules in constant motion. Two gas molecules passing in close proximity are attracted to each other. After molecules or atoms pass one another, the attraction diminishes. If they pass too close to each other, they behave like two marbles colliding; they bounce apart.

The attraction can be thought of as attraction of the nucleus of one atom for the electrons of another. Such an attraction is expected to be weak, and indeed it is; molecules or atoms must be very close for it to have any significant effect. On the other hand, if the molecules or atoms get too close, the electron clouds repel each other. In liquids, the particles are separated by a distance that achieves at once the most attraction and the least repulsion.

Now think of the gas molecules in a cylinder with a piston that compresses the gas. As the gas is compressed, the molecules are forced to move in a smaller and smaller space; they spend more time closer to each other, and therefore there is increasing attraction for each other. When the space in which the molecules can move becomes so small that they cannot escape the attraction of other molecules, a liquid forms. Liquids can be formed by compressing gases. If the temperature is too high (which means that the molecules are moving very fast), the molecules can never be forced into a situation in which they are caught by the other molecules, and the gas will not liquefy. The temperature above which a gas cannot be liquefied by compression alone is called the **critical temperature**. The critical temperature varies from gas to gas.

10.11   Vaporization of Liquids

Molecules of a liquid are in constant motion. Some of the molecules move faster than other molecules; at a particular temperature, therefore, there is an average speed associated with the molecules in a liquid. (See Figure 10.12.) The very fast molecules can break away from the surface of the liquid and go into the air. This is **evaporation**, or vaporization, the change of a sample of liquid to gas. Evaporation, or vaporization, brings about cooling of the liquid sample. Climbing from a swimming pool, for example, can be chilling even on a hot day. Such cooling can be explained by the way liquids evaporate. If only the fastest molecules leave, the average speed of the molecules still in the liquid decreases, which means that the temperature goes down. (Since temperature and molecular speed are related).

If a lid is placed on a jar that contains a liquid, the liquid molecules that escape into the air cannot leave the vicinity of the liquid. If the molecules continue to move about the liquid, they eventually collide with the liquid and become part of the liquid again. When the number of molecules leaving the liquid equals the number of molecules returning to the liquid, a dynamic equilibrium is reached. This is shown diagramatically in Figure 10.13.

While the molecules are in the vapor state, they exert a pressure on the walls of a container just as any gas exerts pressure. This pressure is called the **vapor pressure** of the liquid. It can be very high for liquids that evaporate very fast, like ether or wood alcohol, or very low for liquids that evaporate very slowly, like oil or mercury.

Figure 10.12 Distribution of speeds of atoms or molecules in a liquid for two temperatures. The atoms or molecules are traveling at different speeds, but their average speed is the same at a given temperature.

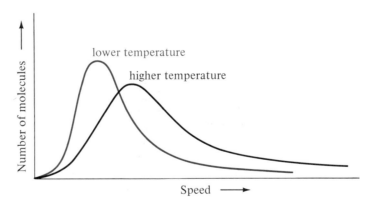

Figure 10.13 Molecules leaving and returning to the surface of a liquid in a closed container.

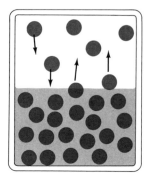

tors

normal boiling point →

Vap press = 1atm 760 tors

The vapor pressure of a liquid depends on the temperature of the liquid. The higher the temperature, the more numerous the molecules that escape into the air, and the higher the vapor pressure. As a liquid is heated, the vapor pressure increases, until a point is reached at which the vapor pressure of the liquid equals the atmospheric pressure against the liquid. This temperature is the **boiling point** of the liquid. If more heat is added to the liquid, the temperature is not increased; only the number of molecules escaping into the gaseous phase is changed. It is impossible to raise the temperature of a liquid higher than its boiling point without increasing the external pressure.

At sea level, where the atmospheric pressure is higher than it is in the Colorado mountains, say, it is necessary to raise the temperature of water to produce boiling. Since water boils at about 95 °C in Denver, a chef in Denver must boil an egg much longer for complete cooking than a chef in New York, where water boils at 100 °C. A lower temperature means slower cooking.

Another example of the effect of pressure on the boiling point of water is the pressure cooker. If the steam that is given off from boiling water is trapped, an increased pressure over the boiling water results, and the boiling point of the water rises. The hotter the water, the faster the cooking process. Hence, a pressure cooker helps people to cook things more quickly by raising the pressure above the water and thus the temperature.

10.12   Surface Tension

Water rising up a narrow tube by itself, raindrops, and blown soap bubbles are examples of surface tension. Some insects can skate on water because of surface tension. Surface tension is possible because there are molecules on the surface of a liquid that are not completely surrounded by other molecules of the liquid. If a molecule down deep inside the liquid could be observed, it would seem to be pulled by other molecules equally in all directions. The molecule on the

Figure 10.14 A molecule at the surface of a liquid is attracted by the molecules beneath it. This is the reason for surface tension. A molecule within the liquid is pulled by other molecules equally in all directions.

surface, however, is being pulled only from the molecules on either side and below it, as shown in Figure 10.14.

The result of such attraction is an inward pull, or uniform **surface tension**. There is extra force on surface molecules since there is no upward pull on them to cancel the downward pull. This is why raindrops are nearly round. If there is an equal pull on all the surface molecules of the drop, the drop will become a sphere, since this is the only shape that will allow that equal pull toward the center. (The lengthened sphere, or teardrop shape, forms when the molecule falls through the air and bumps air molecules, changing its shape.

The idea of surface tension has some practical value. Lead shot for shotgun pellets is made by pouring liquid lead through a screen at the top of a tower. As the lead falls, it forms round beads (owing to surface tension) that solidify as they hit a vat of water at the bottom of the tower.

When a liquid is placed in a tube with a small diameter (a capillary tube), it is possible to observe one of two different events (Figure 10.15). The liquid may be higher on the sides of the tube, rising above the main level of the liquid; or it may be lower on the side of the tube, falling below the surface of the main liquid. Water tends to rise above the level of the main liquid because the water molecules have more attraction for the glass than they do for themselves. Mercury atoms, on the other hand, follow the second trend, because the mercury

Figure 10.15 The two types of behavior of liquids in a capillary tube. On the left, the liquid molecules have more attraction for themselves than for the glass. On the right, the liquid molecules have more attraction for the glass than for themselves.

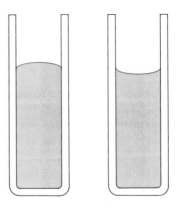

atoms have more attraction for themselves than they do for the glass. The height to which a liquid will rise or the depth to which it will fall in a capillary tube is a measure of the liquid's surface tension.

10.13 Viscosity

Slow-pouring liquids like cold motor oil are said to be very viscous. **Vicosity** is the resistance of a liquid to flowing; it depends on several things. The attraction of molecules for each other is very important. The greater the attraction of molecules for each other, the more viscous the liquid. The shapes of the molecules are also important. If the molecules of a liquid are long and gangly and can get tangled up with other molecules, it will be more difficult to pour the liquid. The size of the molecules directly affects the viscosity; and temperature also has a direct effect. If the molecules are moving faster, the attraction between them, will be less effective, and pouring the liquid will be easier.

Ease of pouring is represented by a viscosity value; a very thick liquid has a high viscosity value. The manufacturers of automobiles and the people who produce motor oil are much concerned about viscosity. The oil that lubricates an engine must be able to flow to rubbing parts and remain where needed. If the viscosity of the oil is too high, starting the car in the winter will be hard; and without proper lubrication, some parts will experience excessive wear. If the viscosity of the oil is too low, the oil will not remain on the parts that need lubrication, and they will wear. Since the viscosity of liquids goes down as the temperature goes up, an oil that has the proper viscosity to start a cold car may not have the proper viscosity for the hot engine 20 minutes later. Oil companies have tried to overcome this problem with multiweight motor oils. These oils have the proper viscosity at many temperatures.

10.14 Getting the Phases Together

All three phases—gas, liquid, and solid—interact. Water is a good example of phase interaction. When pressure is plotted against temperature for water, the graph in Figure 10.16 is obtained. This called a *phase diagram* and shows the relation of the three phases of water with each other. For a given temperature and pressure in the areas labeled solid, liquid, or vapor, only one phase can exist. For a temperature and a pressure value that are chosen so that they coincide on one of the lines, two phases are in dynamic equilibrium. A point on line *TB*, for example would contain vapor and liquid in dynamic equilibrium.

Figure 10.16 The phase diagram for water.

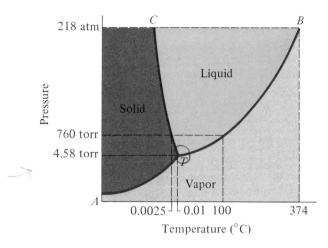

Along line *TC*, the liquid and solid phases are in dynamic equilibrium; and along line *AT*, the solid and vapor phases are in dynamic equilibrium.

At the point of intersection of the three lines, point *T*, all three phases are in dynamic equilibrium. This point is called the **triple point**. The triple point for a liquid exists at a very precise temperature and pressure. For water, the temperature is 0.01 °C and the pressure is 4.58 Torr. Triple points are very useful in calibrating thermometers because they indicate temperature precisely.

Concerning the transformation from one phase to another, if the starting material is a solid, say ice, energy is needed for the conversion. It takes energy to convert that ice to liquid water; heat must be added—79.7 cal are required to convert 1 g of ice to 1 g of water. It is also necessary to remove the same amount of heat, 79.7 cal, from 1 g of water to form 1 g of ice. This amount of heat is called the **heat of fusion**. There is also a **heat of vaporization**. For water, 540 cal are required to convert 1 g of water to 1 g of steam. The same amount of heat is released, 540 calories, when 1 g of steam is converted to water.

There is one other possibility for phase interaction; see Figure 10.16. That is the conversion of a solid directly to a vapor without the liquid state. This kind of change is called **sublimation**. The heat of sublimation for water at 0 °C is 675.1 cal/g. This value approximates the sum of the heat of fusion of water, 79.7 cal/g at 0 °C, and the heat of vaporization of water, 540 cal/g at 100 °C. The difference in values—between 619.7 cal/g, the theoretically calculated value, and 675.1 cal/g, the actual value—can be understood by realizing that more heat is needed to vaporize water if the process is started at 0 °C instead of 100 °C. At 0 °C, 595.4 cal of heat energy must be added to convert 1 g of water to 1 g of vapor. Thus, to go from ice to vapor requires that 595.4 cal/g, plus the 79.7 cal/g that is the amount of energy ordinarily called for to change water to vapor; these added equal 675.1 cal/g. This is the heat of sublimation for water.

A familiar example of sublimation is seen when clothes are hung outside to dry in the winter. The clothes may freeze solid, but they dry anyway. The

Figure 10.17 Heating curve for a substance. When a pure solid substance is heated continuously, it will usually melt and then boil. The temperature will remain constant while the substance is melting and while it's boiling even though more heat is being added.

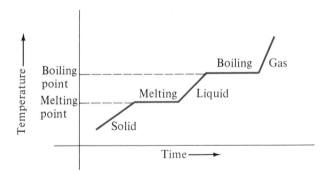

water goes directly from the solid to the vapor state. Another familiar example is seen with Dry Ice (solid carbon dioxide). Dry Ice disappears with time, leaving no liquid. The solid is passing directly to the vapor state without ever becoming a liquid.

It is important to realize that when a substance changes from one state to another, the temperature of the mixture will remain constant until all of the first phase is gone. If ice and water are stirred, the water will remain at 0 °C until all the ice has melted; then the water will warm up. The same thing happens when water boils. The temperature of water does not rise after the water starts to boil. The temperature will remain constant until all the water is converted to steam. Figure 10.17 shows what happens if temperature is plotted against time. Notice the plateaus that occur at the melting point of ice and the boiling point of water.

10.15   Metals, Nonmetals, and Metalloids

In addition to the classification of the elements as solids, liquids, and gases, another method of classification is useful. Elements may be classified as metals, nonmetals, and metalloids. The periodic chart is very useful for making this classification. For example, everything on the left-hand side of the chart except hydrogen is classified as a metal. **Metals** have the following properties:

1.   They form positive ions in solution.
2.   They are ductile; that is, they can be pulled into a wire.
3.   They are malleable; that is, they can be pounded or rolled into a sheet.
4.   They readily transport heat and electric current.
5.   They have a physical appearance that is more or less bright and shiny.

On the right-hand side of the chart are nonmetals. **Nonmetals** are those elements that do not have the properties of metals. In addition, they generally form negative ions in solution. The zigzag line separating metals and nonmetals is shown in Figure 10.2. It begins at boron. Those elements to the right of this zigzag line are called nonmetals. All the elements to the left, and also the lanthanides and the actinides, are called metals. The elements that lie right on the line, boron, aluminum, silicon, germanium, arsenic, antimony, tellurium, and polonium, are called **metalloids**. These elements display both metallic and nonmetallic properties. For example, germantum conducts electricity very poorly compared with copper, but much better than a nonmetal such as sulfur. This property is a factor in the manufacture of transistors.

Glossary

Allotropes	Substances that are composed of the same atoms but have different properties because of their different forms.
Amorphous	Having no definite crystalline structure.
Atmospheric pressure	The force of the earth's atmosphere pushing on a unit area of the earth. Atmospheric pressure can be expressed in many ways.
Boiling point	The temperature at which the vapor pressure of a liquid equals the external pressure on the liquid.
Boyle's law	At constant temperature, the volume that a fixed quantity of gas occupies is inversely proportional to the pressure the gas exerts.
Charles' law	At constant pressure, the volume that a fixed quantity of gas occupies is directly proportional to the Kelvin temperature of that gas.
Combined gas law	A combination of Boyle's and Charles' laws, which relates the volume, temperature, and pressure of a fixed quantity of gas under one set of conditions to the volume, temperature, and pressure of that gas under another set of conditions.
Critical pressure, critical volume	The pressure and volume of a given quantity of a gas at the critical temperature.
Critical temperature	The temperature above which a gas cannot be liquefied regardless of pressure applied to it.
Crystal	A solid in which the atoms, ions, or molecules composing it are arranged in definite, repeating structures.
Crystallography	The study of the arrangement of atoms, ions, and molecules in crystals.
Dynamic equilibrium	A phenomenon that exists when the number of atoms, molecules, or ions leaving all states of the system exactly equals the number returning to those states.

Evaporation	A phenomenon manifested as atoms, molecules, or clusters of ions move from the liquid state to the gaseous state.
Gas	A state of matter in which atoms, molecules, or clusters of ions move freely, unrestricted by cohesive forces. A gas has neither definite shape nor volume.
Heat of fusion	The amount of energy (usually measured in calories) needed to convert a specified quantity of solid to a liquid at a given temperature and pressure.
Heat of sublimation	The amount of energy (usually measured in calories) needed to convert a specified quantity of solid directly to a gas at a given temperature and pressure.
Heat of vaporization	The amount of energy (usually measured in calories) needed to convert a specified quantity of liquid to a gas at a given temperature and pressure.
Ideal gas	A gas whose properties obey the combined gas law and the ideal-gas law.
Kinetic energy	Energy possessed by atoms, ions, or molecules by virtue of their motion.
Lattice	The arrangement of atoms, ions, or molecules in a crystalline solid.
Liquid	State of matter in which the atoms, molecules, or ions are relatively free to change their positions but restricted by cohesive forces so the substance maintains a fixed volume. Liquids have definite volume but no definite shape.
Manometer	A device used to measure the pressure of gases.
Metallic elements	Those elements that are malleable, ductile, conduct electricity and heat, and form positive ions.
Metalloids	Elements that have properties of both metals and nonmetals.
Millibar	A unit of pressure defined in terms of the height in centimeters a column of water can be raised by a force. One millibar is equal to one cm of water.
Nonmetallic elements	Elements that are not malleable and ductile and have low conductivity. All elements that are not metals or metalloids.
Phase diagram	A graph on which pressure is plotted against temperature, showing the relations among the various phases for a substance.
Pressure	Force per unit area.
Solid	State of matter in which atoms, molecules, or clusters of ions cannot move freely relative to each other, since they are almost completely restricted by cohesive forces. Solids have definite shape and definite volume.
Standard temperature and pressure (STP)	A standard, widely known set of conditions to which scientists can refer. Standard temperature is $0\,°C$ or $273\,K$. Standard pressure is 1 atm or 760 mmHg or 760 torr.
Surface tension	A force exerted on the surface of a liquid that is the result of attraction of atoms, ions, or molecules below the surface of the liquid for atoms, ions, or molecules on the surface of that liquid.

Temperature	A measure of the average kinetic energy of the atoms, ions, or molecules of a substance.
Torr	A unit of pressure defined in terms of the height in millimeters a column of mercury can be raised by a force. One Torr is equal to one mm of mercury.
Triple point	The temperature and pressure at which the solid, liquid, and gaseous phases of a substance all exist in equilibrium.
Unit cell	The simplest arrangement of atoms, ions, or molecules in a crystal. This arrangement is repeated in space, and each unit cell must be outlined by atoms, ions, or molecules of the same kind.
Vapor pressure	Pressure exerted by those atoms, molecules, or clusters of ions of a liquid that are in the vapor state.
Viscosity	The resistance of a fluid to flow.

Problems

1. Most aerosol cans have written on them a warning against throwing them into incinerators. Why is this?

2. Convert:
   (a) 760 mmHg = _____ cmHg
   (b) 0.25 atm = _____ mmHg
   (c) 3.5 atm = _____ cmHg
   (d) 200 mmHg = _____ atm
   (e) 28 lb/in.^{2} = _____ atm
   (f) 730 mmHg = _____ Torr
   (g) 620 Torr = _____ cmHg
   (h) 10. atm = _____ Torr
   (i) 1.3 Torr = _____ atm
   (j) 2.0 × 10^3 Torr = _____ atm

3. A bicycle tire usually holds about 75 lb/in.^{2} pressure. How many atmospheres is this?

4. A glass filled with cola and ice was left on a table in a restaurant. Its temperature was 0 °C. Later, when the table was cleared off, all the ice had melted, but the temperature was still 0 °C. What happened?

5. Convert:
   (a) 25 °C = _____ K   (b) −40 °C = _____ K
   (c) −40 °F = _____ K   (d) 72 °F = _____ K
   (e) 300 °C = _____ K

6. Using $P_1 V_1/T_1 = P_2 V_2/T_2$, work the following problems:

	P_1	V_1	T_1	P_2	V_2	T_2
(a)	1 atm	3 L	273 K	5 atm	?	273 K
(b)	2.3 atm	4.1 L	50 °C	2.3 atm	7.0 L	? °C
(c)	760 mmHg	300 mL	250 K	?	960 mL	450 K
(d)	20. cmHg	25 mL	30 °C	36 cmHg	?	80 °C
(e)	1.5 atm	7.5 L	20 °F	?	7.5 L	100 °F

7. Define the following terms:
   (a) Gas   (b) Vapor
   (c) Liquid   (d) Solid
   (e) Vapor pressure   (f) Vaporization
   (g) Fusion   (h) Sublimation
   (i) Crystal lattice   (j) Pressure
   (k) Critical temperature (l) Amorphous
   (m) Triple point
   (n) Standard condition for a gas

8. What do you think would happen to the volume of a balloon if you doubled the weight of gas in it but kept the pressure and temperature the same?

9. A balloon is filled with gas and occupies 3.5 L at 25 °C and 3 atm. What volume will it occupy at STP?

10. The density of pure drinking alcohol is 0.789 g/cm^3. Vodka that is 100 proof is half alcohol and half water. How long would a vodka manometer have to be to work properly? (Assume that densities can be averaged.)

11. Explain why standard conditions for gases were adopted. Could some other set of standard conditions be adopted, such as standard pressure = 650 torr and standard temperature = 25 °C?

12. The temperature on Venus is reported to be 700. K with an atmospheric pressure of 100. atm. A 5.0-L sample of Earth air at 25 °C and 1.0-atm pressure is taken to Venus and allowed to equilibrate on Venus. What is the volume of the gas on Venus?

13. Explain the factors that determine whether a certain substance exists as a solid, a liquid, or a gas.

14. Gases are known to exert pressure on the walls of a container. Explain this according to the kinetic molecular theory.

15. A sample of gas is initially at a temperature of 60 °C and occupies a volume of 700 mL at 600 Torr. What volume would it occupy at 400 Torr and a temperature of 30 °C?

16. Explain what happens to the volume of a gas sample at constant temperature when the pressure is increased or decreased.

17. Draw a phase diagram for water. Indicate the triple point and the gas, liquid, and solid phases.

18. A jet aircraft engine must take in air to get oxygen for burning its fuel. At an altitude of 10,000 m, a jet engine requires about six times the volume of the air it needs for equal power on the ground. Explain.

19. A sample of gas is confined to a cylinder. Under a pressure of 1.3 atm, it occupies a volume of 2.5 L. When the piston is lowered, the pressure is increased to 3.0 atm. If the temperature is held constant, what volume will the gas occupy at this new pressure?

20. Consider an aerosol spray can that will burst when the internal pressure reaches 1400. mmHg. If the can has a pressure of 900. mmHg at 25 °C, how much must the temperature be increased before the can will burst?

21. Atmospheric pressure is lower in the mountains than at sea level. Explain this phenomenon. Why is physical exertion more strenuous in the mountains than at sea level?

22. Calculate the final volume of a sample of gas that is initially at 3.0-atm pressure and a volume of 500. mL if it is allowed to expand until a final pressure of 1.6 atm is reached. Assume that the temperature remains constant.

23. What volume of hydrogen at STP can be produced if one allows 1.3 mol of zinc to react with excess hydrochloric acid? The relevant equation is
$$Zn + 2HCl \rightarrow H_2(g) + ZnCl_2$$

24. Given the equation $2CO(g) + O_2(g) \rightarrow 2CO_2(g)$, determine the answers to these questions:
   (a) How many moles of O_2 must react to produce 5.0 mol CO_2?
   (b) How many moles of CO must react to produce 5.0 mol CO_2?
   (c) How many liters of CO and O_2 must react to produce 5.0 L CO_2?
   (d) How many liters of CO_2 are formed when 1.0 L CO and 1.0 L O_2 react?

25. Given the equation $4P + 5O_2(g) \rightarrow 2P_2O_5$, determine the answers to these questions:
   (a) How many liters of O_2 at STP will react with 1.00 g P?
   (b) How many grams of P_2O_5 will be produced from 1.00 L O_2 at STP?

#23

$$Zn + 2n\ CL \rightarrow Zn\ Cl_2 + H_2$$

1.3 mol

$$V = \frac{22.4\ L}{1.3\ mol} \times 1.3\ mol$$

Learning Objectives for Chapter 11

Define **solution, solute, solvent, solvation, saturation, supersaturation, dynamic equilibrium, colloid, Tyndall effect, concentration of a solution, weight-weight percentage, weight-volume percentage, molarity, titration, normality, equivalents.**

Explain, on a molecular level, how solutions form.

Explain how temperature, pressure, and physical form of the solute affect solution formation.

Compare and contrast colloids and solutions.

Given appropriate data, calculate weight-weight percentage of a solution.

Given appropriate data, calculate weight-volume percentage of a solution.

Given appropriate data, calculate molarity of a solution.

Explain how given concentrations of solutions can be prepared: weight-weight, weight-volume, molar concentration.

Calculate the final concentration of a solution after dilution.

Calculate the final concentration of a solution resulting from the mixture of two or more other solutions.

For reactions, calculate the quantities of solutions necessary for exact neutralization.

Calculate unknown concentrations using data from titration experiments.

Calculate reaction quantities using normality as the concentration unit.

11 SOLUTIONS

Until now, we have given only passing mention to the most important setting in which chemical reactions occur and the most common part of our environment—the solution. Many substances (even the air we breathe, whether or not it is polluted) are solutions; almost all the chemical reactions in our bodies occur in solution.

Exactly what is a solution?

A **solution** is a homogeneous mixture of two or more components.

In this case, **homogeneous** means that on a molecular or an ionic level, the solution is uniform in structure and composition. For example, a sample removed from any other part of the solution. Even using the most powerful optical micro-

Figure 11.1 A common example of a solution is the one formed when antacid tablets are added to water. (Photo courtesy of Miles Laboratories, Inc.)

Figure 11.2 When sodium chloride dissolves in water, it separates into individual sodium ions (Na$^+$) and chloride ions (Cl$^-$). Sand (SiO$_2$) remains as larger particles containing many SiO$_2$ molecules, and thus it does not dissolve. Sugar dissolves in water, with the sugar breaking into individual sugar molecules.

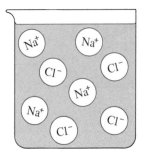
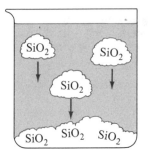
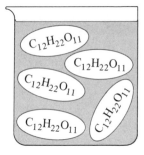

scope available, individual particles in the solution cannot be distinguished.

There is a definite difference between a solution (a homogeneous mixture) and a mixture of suspended particles, called a **heterogeneous** mixture (non-uniform, on a molecular or ionic level.) In a homogeneous mixture, or a solution, individual ions or molecule-sized particles are suspended in solution. In a heterogeneous mixture, the suspended particles are clusters of atoms, molecules, or ions that are large compared with the individual particles. Optical examination of heterogeneous mixtures (with microscope or the unaided eye, depending on the situation) would reveal individual clusters of particles suspended in the medium.

In one example shown in Figure 11.2, the salt is separated into individual ions (Na$^+$ and Cl$^-$) by the action of the water on the crystalline salt. As the individual ions are formed, each ion is surrounded by many water molecules which are attracted to the ions. This phenomenon is called **solvation**. Thus the salt dissolves; a solution forms. Sand is not separated so finely by the water; it remains as individual grains composed of groups of many formula units, no matter how vigorously it is stirred. Because sand does not dissolve, a heterogeneous mixture is formed. Sugar dissolves in water, and the solution looks like the NaCl solution; but individual sugar molecules are solvated and thus are separated from the sugar's crystal lattice. Hence, in solutions, the particles of the substance that dissolves can be individual atoms, molecules, or ions. Clusters of such particles constitute the suspended particles in a heterogeneous mixture. The definition of solutions, therefore, is actually a statement about particle size. The "homogeneous" part of the definition really means that the particles dissolved are reduced to the size of atoms, molecules, or ions; if the situation were otherwise, a true solution would not exist.

Two other terms are important and relevant to solutions.

The substance dissolved is called the **solute**, and the substance that dissolves the solute is called the **solvent**.

The solute dissolves in the solvent. Although these words are most often used in referring to liquid solutions, they can also be applied to other kinds of solutions. When both the solute and the solvent are liquids, the substance present in greater quantity is usually referred to as the solvent.

11.1

Saturation

In the solutions considered thus far, a solid solute has been added to a liquid solvent to form the solution. Can any quantity of solid be added to a solution? In an experiment in which a solid is slowly being dissolved in a liquid, continuing to add the solid to the solution will cause a point to be reached eventually at which no more solid seems to dissolve. When this happens, any additional solid begins to accumulate on the bottom of the container. Once the solid material starts to collect on the bottom, the solution can hold no more solute, no matter how much is added.

When this point is reached, the solution is said to be **saturated**. This does not mean that the solid settled on the bottom does not continue to dissolve. It means that individual particles are continually returning to the solid material as fast as they are leaving. This phenomenon is another example of **dynamic equilbrium**. No additional solid dissolves, but particles of the solid are continually changing places with the particles in the solution, as shown in Figure 11.3.

It is sometimes possible to cause more solute to dissolve in a solvent than what would normally dissolve. This condition is called **supersaturation**, and it is shown in the following example. Sodium acetate ($NaC_2H_3O_2$) is dissolved in water at room temperature (25 °C) until the water is saturated with sodium acetate. The solution is then heated to 50 °C. At the higher temperature, more sodium acetate can dissolve. More solid sodium acetate is added to form a saturated solution at 50 °C. Now the solution is allowed to cool very slowly, undisturbed, to room temperature. No solid forms. The solution, containing more sodium acetate than it originally did at 25 °C, is supersaturated. This is a very unstable situation, but a precipitate does not form because there is nothing present for the solid particles to begin forming around. As soon as a crystal of sodium acetate is dropped into the solution or even a particle of

Figure 11.3 Dynamic equilibrium and saturation. When the solution becomes saturated, sodium ions and chloride ions are returning to the solid as fast as sodium and chloride ions are leaving the solid and going into solution. This definition is true for any substance in a saturated solution, whether it ionizes or remains as molecules.

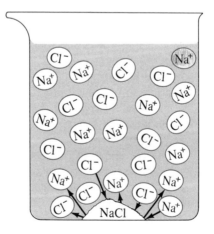

Figure 11.4 The slightest change (in this case, the addition of a particle) will cause a supersaturated solution to begin to precipitate solute.

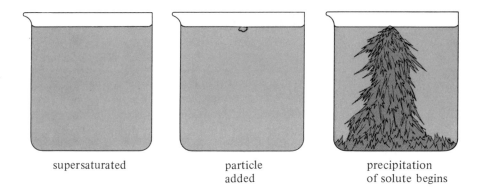

supersaturated   particle added   precipitation of solute begins

dust, or if the container is shaken, all the excess sodium acetate precipitates from the solution (Figure 11.4).

11.2 Solubility and the Factors Affecting It

Several conditions affect the solubility of a solute in a solvent.

Solubility means that amount of a solute that will dissolve in a given quantity of solvent.

One criterion for solubility is the **nature of the solvent and the solute.** Polar solvents (like water) tend to dissolve solutes that are also polar (like ionic solutes). (The discussion of polarity is in Section 4.7). Sodium chloride, for example, an ionic compound, dissolves in water; sugar, a polar but nonionic compound, also dissolves in water. Similarly, nonpolar solutes dissolve in nonpolar solvents. Naphthalene (mothballs) dissolves in benzene. However, naphthalene (nonpolar) does not dissolve in water (polar); and sodium chloride (polar) does not dissolve in benzene (nonpolar). This effect might be called the polarity factor. It is often referred to as the rule "Like dissolves like."

Besides the polarity factor, the **temperature of the solution** has an important effect on how much solute dissolves in a solvent. The amount of solid that generally dissolves in a solvent increases as the temperature is increased. For a gas dissolved in a liquid, however, the solubility decreases as the temperature is increased. Dissolved gas, for example, leaves a water solution as bubbles when a pan of water is heated. The bubbles are bubbles of dissolved air that are forced out of the water as the solubility of the air in water decreases with increased temperature.

Another factor that can affect the solubility of a substance is **pressure** on the solution. Pressure has very little effect on solids dissolving in liquids, but it has a large effect on gases dissolving in liquids. As the pressure of a gas over a liquid is increased, more gas dissolves. If a bottle of soda pop is

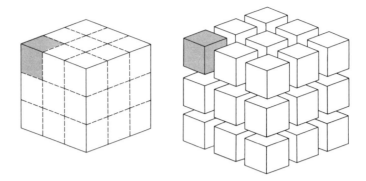

Figure 11.5 As shown in this schematic, one large crystal of sodium chloride will dissolve much more slowly than many small crystals because less surface area and thus, fewer ions, are exposed to water.

opened and the pressure inside the bottle is relieved, the gas bubbles out of the liquid.

There are also numerous factors that affect the rate at which a solute dissolves in a solvent. These factors include the **size** of the particles of the solute, **stirring** of the solute and solvent, the **temperature** of the solvent, and the **concentration** of solute already in solution.

Relative to particle size, you may have noticed that big particles of rock salt dissolve much more slowly than small particles of table salt. The reason is that a solid ground into fine particles has a greatly increased surface area that it can present if exposed to a liquid. The greater the surface area exposed, the faster the dissolution of a given solid (Figure 11.5).

During stirring, when an ion or a molecule is pulled away from the surface of a solid by solvent action, it moves from that site very slowly; sometimes it even returns to the solid. Thus, a volume of liquid right around the solid can become saturated with solute even though the whole solution isn't saturated. As the concentration of the dissolved solute increases, the rate of dissolving decreases because of the returning solute particles. If the solution is stirred, the degree of saturation in the vicinity of the solid is reduced, and the solid dissolves faster (Figure 11.6). Finally, if the temperature is increased, the energy

Figure 11.6 Stirring solutions increases the speed with which a solute dissolves.

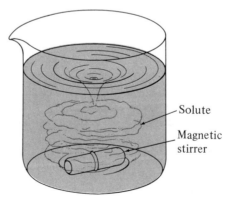

Solute

Magnetic stirrer

of the solvent and the solute molecules increases. When this happens, new solvent molecules come in contact with the solid much more frequently, and the rate of solution is increased.

<h2>11.3   Types of Solutions</h2>

Solutions are not limited to solid and gaseous solutes dissolved in liquid solvents. Other kinds of solutions can exist. Table 11.1 lists the kinds of solutions that are possible.

Three possible kinds of solutions have been omitted from Table 11.1. They are gas in solid, solid in gas, and liquid in gas. They have been omitted because it is difficult to define or demonstrate them. In the case of solutions of liquids and solids in gases, gas particles are too far apart and too energetic to solvate individual solid or liquid atoms, ions, or molecules. For solutions of gases in solids, gas molecules lose their freedom of motion if dissolved in solids and cannot be easily defined as gases. Also, the gas molecules or atoms often form compounds with the solid molecules or atoms.

Table 11.1 Types of Solutions

Type of Solution	Solvent	Solute
Solid in liquid	Water (H_2O)	Sodium chloride (NaCl)
Gas in liquid	Water (H_2O)	Carbon dioxide (CO_2)
Liquid in liquid	Isopropyl alcohol (C_3H_7OH)	Water (H_2O)
Gas in gas	Nitrogen (N_2)	Oxygen (O_2)
Liquid in solid	Silver (Ag)	Mercury (Hg)
Solid in solid	Titanium (Ti)	Niobium (Nb)

<h2>11.4   Colloids</h2>

In some mixtures, particles are spread throughout a solvent and never settle out of the solvent, yet they are not really dissolved. These particles are called **colloidal particles**, and the mixture is called a **colloid**. Colloidal particles are groups of molecules, ions, or atoms that bunch together. There are never enough particles in a cluster, however, to become heavy enough to settle. Milk is a good example of colloidal particles in a liquid. The reason milk is white instead of clear is that it contains millions of very tiny globules of fat

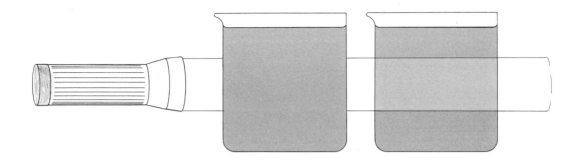

Figure 11.7 The Tyndall effect. The figure shows a side view of two beakers through which a beam of light is being passed. The beaker on the right contains a colloidal dispersion of starch in water, and the beaker on the left contains a pure solution. Note that as a result of the Tyndall light-scattering effect, the beam of light can be seen passing through the colloidal dispersion and cannot be seen passing through the pure solution.

that are not dissolved, yet don't settle out. To get an idea of the size of colloidal particles, recall that atoms and molecules range from about 5×10^{-9} to 3×10^{-8} cm in diameter. Colloidal particles are about 1×10^{-7} to 1×10^{-5} cm in diameter. If the particles are larger than 10^{-7} cm, they cannot be thought of as truly dissolved.

One reason the colloidal particles do not settle out is that the molecules of the liquid are in constant motion and are constantly hitting the colloidal particles. If the particles are light enough, they are held in suspension by these collisions. As the particles get heavier, collisions with solvent molecules cannot hold them up, and they settle out. Another reason the particles may not settle is that they are charged, and even though they are large, they may be solvated by the solvent.

Sometimes colloidal particles in a liquid are so small that the mixture appears to be a solution. One way of determining whether a mixture is a true solution or not is by shining an intense beam of light through the liquid. If a colloid is present, the tiny particles reflect the light, and the beam of light can be seen in the liquid. This phenomenon is called the **Tyndall effect** (Figure 11.7). If a true solution is present, the beam will pass right through the liquid, the light is unscattered, and the beam is invisible.

Many different types of colloids are present in every day life. Table 11.2 lists some of them, and Figure 11.8 shows some examples.

Table 11.2 Types of Colloids

Colloid	Name	Example
Solid in liquid	Sol	Milk
Solid in gas	Aerosol	Smoke, dust
Liquid in liquid	Emulsion	Mayonnaise
Liquid in gas	Aerosol	Clouds
Liquid in solid[a]	Gel	Jello

$Fe(OH)_3$

[a] This is a special type of colloid, in which the solid and the liquid form a continuous medium that seems solid; it is different from a sol like milk.

(a)

(b)

(c)

(d)

Figure 11.8 Several types of colloids: clouds, whipped cream, jello, and smoke. (Photos courtesy of (a) Ezra Stoller © Esto, (b) Friendly Ice Cream Corporation, (c) Ronni Linowitz, and (d) Naval Photographic Center).

11.5

The Importance
of Solutions in Chemistry

Many chemical reactions take place in solution. Reactions that might be slow under ordinary circumstances may become very rapid if a solvent is present. For example, relative to the reaction

$$HCl(aq) + NaOH(aq) \rightarrow NaCl + H_2O$$

it would be inefficient to mix HCl gas and solid sodium hydroxide to make water and NaCl. The reaction would be slow because the reactants would not be well mixed. Dissolving HCl in water and NaOH in water, however, allows the ions H^+, Cl^-, Na^+, and OH^- to form. These ions are now free to move about rapidly. When the two solutions are combined, this movement allows the hydrogen ions to colloide with the hydroxide ions; and these rapidly combine to form water. Pouring these solutions together mixes the reactants intimately.

How do chemists know that one reactant will get close enough to another to react? How do they know that the water will not just smother the reaction as it smothers fires? How can chemists be sure that they are mixing the proper amounts of two reactants in solutions?

We have already examined why reactions occur (Chapter 9). A partial list of possible reactions includes the formation of an insoluble compound, the formation of compounds that decompose to form gases, and the formation of nonionized compounds. Regardless of the reasons for forming, the initial starting material contained ions or molecules in solution. These were the particles that reacted.

Water aids in such reactions by separating atoms, molecules, or ions that originally were in a solid crystal lattice. The atoms, molecules, and ions, once solvated, become free to move around. As they move about, they can interact with other reactant atoms, molecules, or ions, and a reaction occurs. This movement is very rapid, so reactions in solutions often take only a very short time. In these ways, dissolution makes the most use of the surface area of a solid and also of the ability of its particles to interact. Of course, there are other solvents besides water, but our interest lies primarily with water solutions, since they are the most predominant.

The final question, which concerns how it is possible to ascertain exactly how much of each reactant is present when two solutions are poured together, leads to the definition of the term **concentration**.

11.6   Concentration Terms

The **concentration of a solution** defines the relative amounts of solute and solvent present in solution. There are several ways of stating concentrations. From the solute's point of view, these are:

1. **Weight-weight percentage** (weight of solute to weight of solvent plus solute).
2. **Weight-volume percentage** (weight of solute in grams to total volume of solution in milliliters).
3. **Molar concentration**, or **molarity** (moles of solute to 1 L of solution).
4. **Normal concentration**, or **normality** (equivalents of solute to 1 L of solution).
5. **Volume-volume percentage** (volume of solute in milliliters to total volume of solution in milliliters).
6. **Parts per thousand, parts per million** (weight of solute to thousand or million weights of solvent plus solute).
7. **Mole fraction** (moles of solute to total number of moles of solute plus moles solvent).
8. **Molal concentration**, or **molality** (moles of solute to 1 kg of solvent).

Each of these units of concentration has its use, but only the first four are important at this level of chemistry. The first three will be defined now, using examples. The fourth, normality, will be defined later.

1. **Weight-weight percentage:** weight-weight percentage, or percentage by weight, is defined as

$$\frac{wt\ of\ solute}{wt\ of\ solute + wt.\ of\ solvent} \times 100 \qquad wt\text{-}wt\ \% = \frac{wt\ solute}{wt\ solution} \times 100$$

Example 11.1

Calculate the weight-weight percentage concentration of a solution made by dissolving 10.0 g of sodium chloride (NaCl) in 100.0 g of water.

Step 1   Determine the weight of solute and weight of solution in similar units. There are 10.0 g of NaCl and 100.0 g of water present. The total solution weight is 110.0 g.

Step 2   Substitute in the equation and solve:

$$\%\ NaCl = \frac{10.0\ g\ NaCl}{110.0\ g\ solution} \times 100$$

$$= 9.09\%\ NaCl\ by\ wt\ in\ the\ solution$$

Example 11.2   Vanillin, a compound responsible for the aroma of vanilla beans, is dissolved in alcohol to make a test solution for determining the presence of marijuana. If 0.30 g of vanillin is dissolved in enough alcohol to make 16 g of solution, what is the weight-weight percentage of the solution?

Step 1   0.30 g vanillin; 16 g solution

Step 2 $\%$ vanillin $= \dfrac{0.30 \text{ g vanillin}}{16 \text{ g solution}} \times 100 = 1.9\%$

2. **Weight-volume percentage:**   the weight-volume percentage is a common way of expressing the percentage concentration of a liquid solution. It is an important concentration unit since it is easier to measure the volume of a liquid (particularly a large volume) than to measure the weight of a liquid. In addition, in using weight-weight percentage, it is necessary to weigh the components of the solution or know the density of the solution to determine how much solute is being removed when a portion of the solution is transferred to another container.

To find the **weight-volume percentage** of a solution, use the equation

$$\text{wt-vol } \% = \frac{\text{wt solute (g)}}{\text{vol solution (mL)}} \times 100$$

Remember that the solution is a mixture of the solute and solvent.

Example 11.3   In hospitals, sodium chloride solutions having 1.0 g NaCl dissolved in enough water to make 50.0 mL of solution are often used both externally and internally. Calculate the weight-volume percentage of such a solution.

Step 1   State the quantities of solute and solution in appropriate units: 1 g NaCl, 50.0 mL solution.

Step 2   Substitute in the equation and solve:

$$\frac{1.0 \text{ g NaCl}}{50.0 \text{ mL solution}} \times 100 = 2.0\% \text{ NaCl by wt-vol}$$

Example 11.4   Boric acid and tannic acid are often mixed in water-alcohol solutions and are used to kill fungus infections. Calculate the weight-volume percentage of each component of a solution made by dissolving 5.8 g of boric acid and 15.0 g of tannic acid in enough alcohol-water mixture to make 200. mL of solution.

Step 1   15.0 g tannic acid, 5.8 g boric acid, 200. mL solution.

Step 2 $\dfrac{15.0 \text{ g tannic acid}}{200. \text{ mL solution}} \times 100 = 7.50\%$ tannic acid (wt-vol)

$\dfrac{5.8 \text{ g boric acid}}{200. \text{ mL solution}} \times 100 = 2.9\%$ boric acid (wt-vol)

While volume-volume percentage is not an important concentration unit in this textbook, it is commonly used when two liquids are combined. In this case, it is much easier to measure the volume of the liquids involved than to weigh the liquids. This concentration unit leads to an interesting comparison.

The different ways of defining the percentage of solute in a solvent are often used by industry to gain an economic or a marketing advantage. Consider the labeling of alcoholic beverages by the liquor industry. Wineries monitor the formation of alcohol during fermentation by measuring the density of the wine mixture as it is formed. Thus, it is common for a wine to be produced that is approximately 9.47 wt-vol % ethyl alcohol. When the wine is marketed, the label on the bottle will often read 12% vol-vol. The winery is not lying to the public. A conversion has simply been made from one set of units to another. A 100.-mL sample of the wine contains 9.47 g of ethyl alcohol. The volume of this weight of alcohol can be found by dividing the weight of the alcohol, 9.47 g, by the density of pure ethyl alcohol, 0.7893/mL.

$$\frac{9.47 \text{ g}}{0.7893 \text{ g/mL}} = 12.0 \text{ mL}$$

Thus, the 9.47 wt-vol % is 12 vol-vol %.

3.   **Molar concentration (Molarity):**   molar concentration, or molarity, is by far the most common and important concentration term used in chemistry. It is defined as the number of moles of solute per liter of solution; or mathematically expressed,

$$M = \frac{\text{mol solute}}{\text{L solution}}$$

(Capital M is the symbol for molar concentration.) The following are examples of how molar concentration can be calculated. (Soln is the abbreviation for solution.)

Example 11.5   What is the molar concentration of 0.1 L of a solution containing 0.005 mol H_2SO_4?

Step 1   State, or convert to, appropriate units for solute and solvent: 0.005 mol H_2SO_4; 0.1 L solution.

272

Step 2   Substitute in defining equation:

$$M = \frac{0.005 \text{ mol } H_2SO_4}{0.1 \text{ L solution}} = \frac{0.05 \text{ mol } H_2SO_4}{\text{L solution}} = 0.05M \text{ } H_2SO_4$$

Example 11.6   What is the molar concentration of a solution that contains 0.75 mol silver nitrate ($AgNO_3$) in 250 mL of solution?

Step 1   Convert to appropriate units. Converting milliters to liters, we get

$$250 \text{ mL } \times \frac{1 \text{ L}}{1000 \text{ mL}} = 0.25 \text{ L}$$

Step 2   Substitute in the defining equation:

$$M = \frac{0.75 \text{ mol } AgNO_3}{0.25 \text{ L soln}} = \frac{3.0 \text{ mol } AgNO_3}{\text{L soln}} = 3.0M \text{ } AgNO_3$$

Because compounds must be weighed to determine the number of moles present, problems like the following often appear.

Example 11.7   What is the molar concentration of exactly 500. ml of a solution that contains 26 g of calcium chloride ($CaCl_2$)?

Step 1   Calculate the number of moles of $CaCl_2$ present:

$$26 \text{ g } CaCl_2 \times \frac{1 \text{ mol } CaCl_2}{110.9 \text{ g } CaCl_2} = 0.23 \text{ mol } CaCl_2$$

Convert volume to liters:

$$500. \text{ mL } \times \frac{1 \text{ L}}{1000 \text{ mL}} = 0.500 \text{ L}$$

Step 2   The molar concentration is

$$\frac{0.23 \text{ mol } CaCl_2}{0.500 \text{ L soln}} = \frac{0.46 \text{ mol } CaCl_2}{\text{L soln}} = 0.46M$$

Example 11.8 is slightly more difficult.

Example 11.8   What is the molar concentration of a solution prepared by dissolving 10.0 g of sodium chloride in exactly 100. g of water? The density of the solution is 1.089 g/mL at 25 °C.

Step 1   Convert to solution volume. When 10.0 g of NaCl is dissolved in 100. g of water, the volume of the solution is unknown. To find this volume one must either physically measure the volume of the solution with a graduated cylinder (or other measuring device) or find the density of the solution. Usually the density of the solution is the most accurately determined quantity. By measurement, the density of the sodium chloride solution was found to be 1.089 g/mL. Multiplying the weight of the solution by this density gives the volume of the solution:

$$110. \text{ g} \times \frac{1 \text{ mL}}{1.089 \text{ g}} = 101 \text{ mL of solution}$$

Calculate number of moles of solute present. The number of moles of NaCl present can be found by multiplying 10.0 g by the unit factor 1 mol NaCl/58.4 g NaCl:

$$10.0 \text{ g} \times \frac{1 \text{ mol NaCl}}{58.4 \text{ g NaCl}} = 0.171 \text{ mol NaCl}$$

Step 2   The molarity is then found by dividing the number of moles of NaCl by the total volume, found to be 101 mL.

$$M = \frac{0.171 \text{ mol NaCl}}{0.101 \text{ L soln}} = \frac{1.69 \text{ mol NaCl}}{\text{L soln}} = 1.69 M$$

11.7   Preparation

The importance of allowing chemical reactions to occur in solution has been stressed (Section 11.5). How then can we produce the desired concentration? The methods of preparing solutions are demonstrated here in examples.

1.   Weight-weight percentage

Example 11.9

Suppose a solution that is 1 percent by weight NaOH (sodium hydroxide) in water is needed. Explain how it can be prepared.

One percent NaOH means that in every 100. g of solution, 99 g is H_2O and 1 g is NaOH (Figure 11.9).

To prepare 100. g of this solution, a balance is used to weigh out 1 g of sodium hydroxide. The sodium hydroxide is transferred to another container designed to contain the final solution. Following this, 99 g of water is weighed on the balance and then added to the solid NaOH.

Figure 11.9 Making a 1% solution (by weight) of NaOH in water.

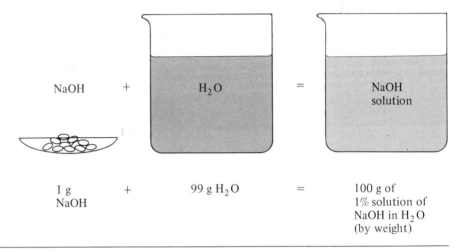

NaOH   + H_2O =   NaOH solution

1 g NaOH   +   99 g H_2O =   100 g of 1% solution of NaOH in H_2O (by weight)

It is important in preparing this solution, as it is with all solutions, to mix it thoroughly. This involves either vigorously stirring it or thoroughly shaking it in a sealed container.

Any desired amount of this solution can be made, but it is important to maintain the proper proportions.

2.   Weight-volume percentage

Example 11.10

Suppose a hospital needs to prepare 100 mL of a 10 percent weight-volume solution of NaCl. How can it be prepared?

The solution contains 10 g NaCl in each 100 mL of solution. This solution is prepared by weighing out 10 g NaCl in an appropriate container, usually a beaker. A small quantity of water is added to the beaker to dissolve the NaCl. The NaCl solution is then transferred to an appropriate measuring container, usually a volumetric flask.

The beaker is rinsed with water to remove any traces of solution that may be left, and additional water is added to produce a total volume of 100 mL. Thorough mixing is critical.

An example of the measurement container described in Example 11.10 is the volumetric flask. A **volumetric flask** is a special container designed to hold a specific amount of liquid. A line circles the neck of the flask. When liquid is added to the container just to this line, the desired volume is obtained (see Figure 11.10).

3. Molarity

The volume of solution is also important in molar concentration calculations. To make up solutions whose concentrations are expressed in molarity, one must weigh the solute and then add enough solvent to get a specific volume of solution. Volumetric flasks are used here also.

Example 11.11

Describe how a one-molar ($1M$) solution of NaOH can be prepared.

Since 1 mol NaOH weighs 40.0 g, weighing out 40.0 g of NaOH is necessary. The sodium hydroxide can then be placed in a 1000-mL volumetric flask. Water is added to dissolve the NaOH, and the solution is diluted with water to the mark. This process give 1 mol of NaOH in a liter of solution, in other words, a one-molar solution. Any one of the following combinations or any other correct ratio also gives a $1\ M$ solution.

$$0.50 \text{ mol NaOH in } 500. \text{ mL solution because } \frac{0.50 \text{ mol}}{0.500 \text{ L}} = 1.0\, \frac{\text{mol}}{\text{L}}$$

$$0.25 \text{ mol NaOH in } 250. \text{ mL solution because } \frac{0.25 \text{ mol}}{0.250 \text{ L}} = 1.0\, \frac{\text{mol}}{\text{L}}$$

Figure 11.10 Making a 1-molar solution of NaOH. Remember that the definition of molarity is moles/liter of **solution**. (1) Add 1 mol of NaOH to a 1 liter volumetric; (2) add enough water to dissolve the NaOH; (3) fill volumetric to mark with water.

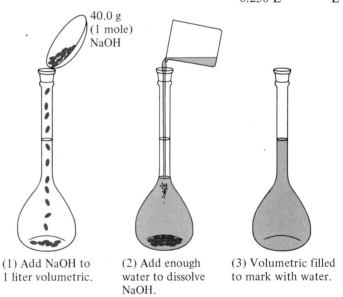

40.0 g
(1 mole)
NaOH

(1) Add NaOH to 1 liter volumetric.

(2) Add enough water to dissolve NaOH.

(3) Volumetric filled to mark with water.

$$0.10 \text{ mol NaOH in } 100. \text{ mL solution because } \frac{0.10 \text{ mol}}{0.100 \text{ L}} = 1.0 \frac{\text{mol}}{\text{L}}$$

$$0.010 \text{ mol NaOH in } 10. \text{ mL solution because } \frac{0.10 \text{ mol}}{0.010 \text{ L}} = 1.0 \frac{\text{mol}}{\text{L}}$$

Thus, the chemist is not limited to using only 1000-mL flasks but can make any concentration using any size flask.

Figure 11.10 illustrates the procedure for making a 1-molar solution.

Example 11.12

A 0.30-molar (0.30M) solution of NaCl is needed. The chemist preparing the solution has only a 200.-mL volumetric flask available. Explain how the solution can be prepared.

Since 200. mL of solution can be made, one must calculate how many moles of NaCl are present in 200. mL of 0.30 M solution:

$$\frac{0.30 \text{ mol NaCl}}{\text{L soln}} \times 0.200 \text{ L soln} = 0.060 \text{ mol NaCl}$$

Since 0.060 mol NaCl is present, the weight of NaCl present is

$$0.060 \text{ mol NaCl} \times \frac{58.4 \text{ g NaCl}}{\text{mol NaCl}} = 3.50 \text{ g NaCl}$$

Thus, the chemist must weigh out 3.50 g NaCl, place it in the volumetric flask, and add water to the mark on the flask.

Molar concentration is different from most other concentration units because it uses weights and volumes instead of just weights. Chemists rely chiefly on molar concentration as their primary concentration unit for measuring.

Very often, acids found in chemistry laboratories are already in solution. If the stock sample of acid is already in solution, how can different solution concentrations of acid be prepared from the stock solution? New solutions cannot be made more concentrated than the stock solution, but they can be made more dilute by adding water. This process is called **dilution**.

When one is diluting to a new, lower concentration by adding solvent, the quantity of solute present stays the same; since the amount of solvent increases, however, the concentration of the solution goes down. This is seen in Example 11.13.

Example 11.13   If 100 mL of a 0.10M HCl in water solution is added to 100 ml of water, what is the new concentration?

Offhand, you can see that the volume of solution is doubled. Since the amount of HCl is unchanged, and since molar concentration is moles of solvent per liter of solution, the concentration has been cut in half as the volume has doubled. The new concentration is 0.05M (Figure 11.11).

Using a mathematical approach, molar concentration is defined as moles of solute per liter of solution.

Step 1   Calculate the number of moles of solute present. In 100 mL of 0.10M HCl, there exists

$$\frac{0.10 \text{ mol HCl}}{\text{L soln}} \times 0.1 \text{ L soln} = 0.01 \text{ mol HCl}$$

(The number of moles of solute present is the molar concentration times the volume of solution. The units cancel.)

Step 2   Calculate the new concentration using the new volume. When 100 mL of water is added to this solution, the amount of HCl remains constant, 0.01 mol, but the volume is now 200 mL (100 mL solution + 100 mL water). The concentration is now

$$\frac{0.01 \text{ mol HCl}}{0.2 \text{ L soln}} = 0.05M \text{ HCl}$$

This is exactly the concentration previously calculated, using common sense instead of mathematics.

Figure 11.11   Dilution: if the volume of the solution is doubled by adding solvent, the concentration is cut in half.

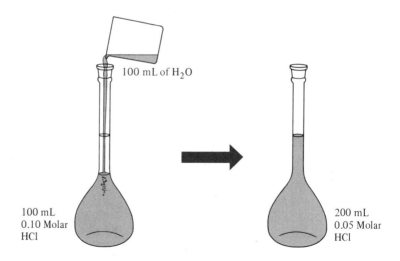

100 mL of H$_2$O

100 mL
0.10 Molar
HCl

200 mL
0.05 Molar
HCl

The problem could also be solved using the formula

$$M_1 V_1 = M_2 V_2$$

where M_1 is the molarity of the original solution and V_1 is the volume of the original solution. The value M_2 is the molarity of the final, diluted solution and V_2 is the volume of that final solution.

Step 1   State the known and unknown values in the equation:

$$M_1 = 0.10M$$
$$V_1 = 100 \text{ mL}$$
$$M_2 = ?$$
$$V_2 = 200 \text{ mL}$$

Step 2   Use the equation, to find a value for M_2. We write according to the equation:

$$M_2 = \frac{M_1 V_1}{V_2} = \frac{0.10M \times 100 \text{ mL}}{200 \text{ mL}} = 0.05M$$

The equation is a simplification of the mathematical method shown in the first half of the example and works because the moles of solute in solution before and after dilution do not change.

Another example of a practical problem involves calculating how much solvent must be added to the stock solution to dilute to desired concentration.

Example 11.14   A chemist may want to produce a 1.0M solution of HCl from 200. mL of 6.0M HCl. How can this be done?

Step 1   Calculate the quantity of solute present:

$$0.200 \text{ L soln} \times \frac{6.0 \text{ mol HCl}}{\text{L soln}} = 1.2 \text{ mol HCl}$$

Step 2   Calculate the volume of solution needed to get the desired concentration from the old solution. Molar concentrations can also be used as unit factors. In this case, a 1M solution is desired.

$$\frac{1.0 \text{ mol HCl}}{1.0 \text{ L soln}} = 1 = \frac{1.0 \text{ L soln}}{1.0 \text{ mol HCl}}$$

There are 1.2 mol HCl that must be diluted to give a $1M$ solution. Using the unit factor to cancel units gives

$$1.2 \text{ mol HCl} \times \frac{1.0 \text{ L soln}}{1.0 \text{ mol HCl}} = 1.2 \text{ L soln}$$

To produce the desired concentration, one must add water until a volume of 1.2 L is reached.

The formula can also be used in this calculation:

Step 1 $M_1 = 6.0M$ $M_2 = 1.0M$
$V_1 = 0.200 \text{ L}$ $V_2 = ?$

Step 2 $V_2 = \dfrac{M_1 V_1}{M_2} = \dfrac{6.0M \times 0.200 \text{ L}}{1.0M} = 1.2 \text{ L}$

The total volume is 1.2 L; therefore $1.2 \text{ L} - 0.200 = 1.0 \text{ L}$ water must be added.

Example 11.15

If a chemist wanted to prepare 250 mL of $0.30M$ sodium carbonate (Na_2CO_3) and had on hand a bottle of sodium carbonate solution that was $1.0M$, how much of the original solution would be needed to prepare a $0.30M$ solution?

Step 1   Calculate how many moles of Na_2CO_3 are contained in the final solution:

$$0.25 \text{ L soln} \times 0.30 \frac{\text{mol } Na_2CO_3}{\text{L soln}} = 0.075 \text{ mol } Na_2CO_3$$

Step 2   Calculate the volume of original solution needed to get the number of moles calculated in step 1. To get 0.075 mol of Na_2CO_3 from the $1.0M$ solution requires

$$0.075 \text{ mol } Na_2CO_3 \times \frac{1.0 \text{ L soln}}{1.0 \text{ mol } Na_2CO_3} = 0.075 \text{ L soln}$$

To prepare the final solution, place 75 mL of the $1.0M$ Na_2CO_3 solution in a 250-mL volumetric flask and add water up the 250-mL mark on the flask.

The formula can be used in this calculation.

Step 1 $M_1 = 1.0M$
$V_1 = ?$
$M_2 = 0.30M$
$V_2 = 0.25 \text{ L}$

Step 2 $$V_1 = \frac{M_2 V_2}{M_1} = \frac{0.30M \times 0.25 \text{ L}}{1.0M} = 0.075 \text{ L}$$

Thus, 75 mL of the $1.0M$ Na_2CO_3 must be used.

In the last kind of dilution problem we consider, two solutions of different concentrations are mixed and the final concentration is determined.

Example 11.16

Exactly 300. mL of a $0.25M$ NaCl solution is mixed with exactly 150. mL of a $0.80M$ solution of NaCl. What is the final concentration?

Step 1 Calculate the total number of moles of solute present after mixing. In the first solution, there is

$$\frac{0.25 \text{ mol NaCl}}{\text{L soln}} \times 0.30 \text{ L soln} = 0.075 \text{ mol NaCl}$$

In the second solution, there is

$$\frac{0.80 \text{ mol NaCl}}{\text{L soln}} \times 0.15 \text{ L soln} = 0.12 \text{ mol NaCl}$$

The total NaCl present is, in number of moles,

$$\begin{array}{r} 0.075 \\ +0.12 \\ \hline 0.195 \text{ mol of NaCl} = 0.20 \text{ mol NaCl} \end{array}$$

Step 2 Calculate the total volume of solution present after mixing. The total number of milliliters of solution present is

$$\begin{array}{r} 300. \\ +150. \\ \hline 450. \text{ mL of soln} = 0.450 \text{ soln} \end{array}$$

Step 3 Calculate the final concentration:

$$\frac{0.20 \text{ mol NaCl}}{0.450 \text{ L soln}} = 0.44M$$

It is logical to expect the new concentration to be between the two former concentrations.

The formula cannot be easily used in this kind of problem.

Solutions and Reactions

The knowledge we have been accumulating about solutions will be the basis for examining how solutions are used in reactions and how concentration affects this use. In all chemical reactions, the quantities of materials involved are calculated by using the mole relations of the balanced equation. Molar concentration is defined as moles of solute per liter of solution. This suggests that if concentrations are known, it is possible to mix given volumes of reactant solutions to determine exact quantities of reactants present.

The reaction of hydrochloric acid with sodium hydroxide illustrates this process:

$$HCl + NaOH \rightarrow NaCl + H_2O$$

This reaction is usually carried out in solution. The appropriate quantities of HCl and NaOH used in the reaction can be calculated merely from the concentrations of the reactant solutions. The simplest way to determine these quantities is to start with solutions that have the same concentrations of NaOH and HCl. For example, mixing equal volumes of $1M$ NaOH and $1M$ HCl assures that all reactants are used up. This is illustrated in Table 11.3, which contains examples for $1M$ solutions.

According to the balanced equation, the number of moles of HCl and NaOH present must be equal. Table 11.3 shows that so long as equal volumes of solution of equal concentrations are mixed, all reactants are consumed.

Table 11.3 Comparing Solutions with Equal Moles of NaOH and HCl

Volume of Liquid (mL)	Moles of HCl in 1M Solution	Moles of NaOH in 1M Solution
50	0.05	0.05
100	0.1	0.1
500	0.5	0.5
1000	1.0	1.0

It is very rare to have solutions of equal concentrations, and the problem of having reacting solutions with different concentrations must be solved. Consider the following example.

Example 11.17

How many milliliters of $0.50M$ NaOH must be mixed with exactly 100. mL of $0.15M$ HCl for a reaction in which there is no excess reactant?

Step 1 Write the balanced chemical equation:

$$NaOH + HCl \rightarrow NaCl + H_2O$$

The equation shows that equal numbers of moles of each reactant are needed.

Step 2   Calculate the number of moles present in the known volume of reactant solution:

$$\frac{0.15 \text{ mol HCl}}{\text{L soln}} \times 0.100 \text{ L soln} = 0.015 \text{ mol HCl}$$

Step 3   Using the balanced equation, determine the number of moles of the second reactant needed. The balanced equation indicates that 0.015 mol of HCl requires 0.015 mol of NaOH for complete reaction.

Step 4   Calculate the volume of solution needed to contain that number of moles:

$$\frac{1 \text{ L soln}}{0.50 \text{ mol NaOH}} \times 0.015 \text{ mol NaOH} = 0.030 \text{ L soln}$$

The answer is logical, since it should take less volume of the more concentrated NaOH to neutralize 100. mL of the less concentrated acid (Figure 11.12).

Figure 11.12 Sometimes it is not necessary to add equal volumes of acid and base for neutralization. Neutralization occurs when no excess acid or base is present after reaction. Because the concentration of the NaOH is greater than the concentration of the HCl, less is needed to achieve neutralization.

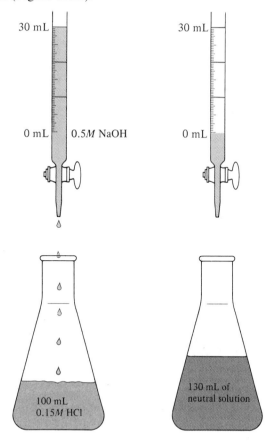

Since moles of each reactant must be equal according to the balanced equation, a formula can be used here also:

Moles HCl = moles NaOH

Molarity HCl × volume HCl = molarity NaOH × volume NaOH

$$M_{HCl} \times V_{HCl} = M_{NaOH} \times V_{NaOH}$$

$$V_{NaOH} = \frac{M_{HCl} \times V_{HCl}}{V_{NaOH}} = \frac{0.15M \times 0.100 \text{ L}}{0.50M} = 0.030 \text{ L NaOH}$$

There is another twist to this kind of problem that is worth considering. It is common in chemical analysis to want to know the concentration of acids or bases. This is usually found by titrating the unknown acid or base with a base or acid of known concentration.

Titrating means adding just enough reactant of known concentration, a **standard solution**, to exactly neutralize a reactant of unknown concentration. In the laboratory, a known volume of the unknown solution is drawn into a pipet, from which it is expelled into a flask. A dye, called an **indicator**, that changes color when the reaction is complete is often added if the reaction itself does not cause a color change. The solution of known concentration is slowly added until the color of the mixture changes. The volume used is recorded. This process is illustrated in Figure 11.13. Titration is a process that can be used to determine concentrations in many kinds of reactions. The technique is useful in acid-base reaction, oxidation-reduction, precipitation, or almost any reaction in which the reactants can be mixed slowly and the final step of the reaction can be monitored. Consider the titration of HCl with NaOH.

Example 11.18

A chemist has a solution of HCl of unknown concentration. He has an NaOH solution that is $0.91M$. He pipets exactly 25 mL of acid into a flask, adds some indicator, and begins adding the base. The indicator changes color after he has added 35.30 mL of NaOH. What is the acid concentration?

Step 1   NaOH + HCl → NaCl + H_2O

From the reaction equation, the chemist knows that he needs equal numbers of moles of acid and base.

Step 2 $\dfrac{0.91 \text{ mol NaOH}}{\text{L soln}} \times 0.0353 \text{ L soln} = 0.032 \text{ mol NaOH}$

Figure 11.13 Titration: knowing the volume and concentration of Reactant 1 and the volume of Reactant 2, the concentration of Reactant 2 can be calculated.

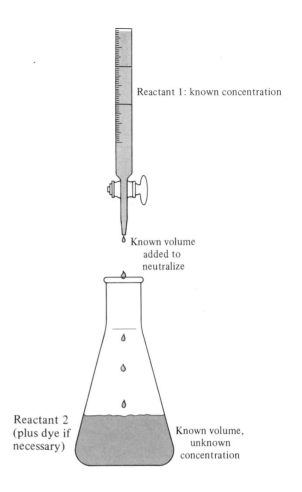

Reactant 1: known concentration

Known volume added to neutralize

Reactant 2 (plus dye if necessary)

Known volume, unknown concentration

Step 3   The balanced equation shows that 0.032 mol of HCl must be in the 25 mL of acid solution that the chemist used.

Step 4   Calculate the concentration of the unknown solution:

$$\frac{0.032 \text{ mol HCl}}{0.025 \text{ L soln}} = 1.3M$$

This answer is logical, since it took a larger volume of NaOH than HCl. The HCl solution must have been more concentrated.

In another solution, this problem could have been set up in one step, using unit factors. Since 1 mol NaOH = 1 mol HCl, a unit factor is defined:

$$\frac{1 \text{ mol NaOH}}{1 \text{ mol HCl}} = 1 = \frac{1 \text{ mol HCl}}{1 \text{ mol NaOH}}$$

By this unit factor,

$$\frac{0.91 \text{ mol NaOH}}{\text{L NaOH soln}} \times 0.0353 \text{ L NaOH soln}$$

$$\times \frac{1 \text{ mol HCl}}{1 \text{ mol NaOH}} \times \frac{1}{0.025 \text{ L HCl soln}}$$

$$= \frac{1.3 \text{ mol HCl}}{\text{L HCl soln}} = 1.3M$$

The problem could also be solved by setting as an equality the numbers of moles necessary in the reaction:

Moles HCl = moles NaOH

Molarity HCl × volume of HCl = molarity NaOH × volume of NaOH

$$\text{Molarity HCl} = \frac{\text{molarity NaOH} \times \text{volume of NaOH}}{\text{volume HCl}} = \frac{0.91 \times 35.30}{25}$$

$$= 1.3M$$

These problems are relatively easy because the ratio of moles of reactants was 1:1. The calculations become more complicated when the mole relations are not 1:1. An example of this new situation is the reaction of barium hydroxide with hydrochloric acid:

$$Ba(OH)_2 + 2HCl \rightarrow BaCl_2 + 2H_2O$$

In this case, two moles of HCl are needed for each mole of $Ba(OH)_2$. Table 11.4 shows the equivalent amounts of reactants necessary for the combination of $0.05M$ $Ba(OH)_2$ and $0.05M$ HCl. In each case, neutralization requires a mole relation of HCl to $Ba(OH)_2$ of 2:1. Thus, the volumes of HCl to $Ba(OH)_2$ are also in the ratio 2:1. If the concentrations are not equal, the calculation is more complicated.

Table 11.4   Comparing Solutions with Equivalent Moles of HCl and $Ba(OH)_2$

Volume of Liquid (mL)	Moles of HCl in 0.0500M Solution	Moles of Ba(OH)₂ in 0.0500M Solution
50.0	0.00250	0.00125
100.	0.00500	0.00250
500.	0.0250	0.0125
1000.	0.0500	0.0250

Example 11.19

How many milliliters of 0.030M Ba(OH)$_2$ are needed to neutralize exactly 100. mL of 0.015M HCl?

Step 1
$$Ba(OH)_2 + 2HCl \rightarrow BaCl_2 + 2H_2O$$

Step 2 100. mL of 0.015M HCl contains

$$\frac{0.015 \text{ mol HCl}}{\text{L soln}} \times 0.100 \text{ L soln} = 0.0015 \text{ mol HCl}$$

Step 3 According to the chemical equation, only half as many moles of Ba(OH)$_2$, compared with HCl, are needed; thus 0.00075 mol of Ba(OH)$_2$ should be added.

Step 4
$$\frac{1 \text{ L soln}}{0.030 \text{ mol Ba(OH)}_2} \times 0.00075 \text{ mol Ba(OH)}_2 = 0.025 \text{ L soln}$$

In another solution this problem could have been done in one step. Since, from the equation, 2 mol HCl = 1 mol Ba(OH)$_2$, the unit factor is

$$\frac{2 \text{ mol HCl}}{1 \text{ mol Ba(OH)}_2} = 1 = \frac{1 \text{ mol Ba(OH)}_2}{2 \text{ mol HCl}}$$

The problem could have been solved thus:

$$\frac{0.015 \text{ mol HCl}}{\text{L HCl soln}} \times 0.100 \text{ L HCl soln}$$

$$\times \frac{1 \text{ L Ba(OH)}_2 \text{ soln}}{0.030 \text{ mol Ba(OH)}_2} \times \frac{1 \text{ mol Ba(OH)}_2}{2 \text{ mol HCl}}$$

$$= 0.025 \text{ L Ba(OH)}_2 \text{ soln}$$

The formula approach does not work easily when the unit factors are not 1. Note that the changes in the reaction equation have caused changes only in the unit factor. No matter how complicated the reaction equation becomes, the equation unit factor will be the only one to change.

The limiting reagent concept is also pertinent with solutions.

Example 11.20

A chemist wants to calculate the number of grams of silver chloride produced when 75 mL of 0.10M calcium chloride is mixed with 85 mL of 0.20M silver nitrate. How can this be done?

Step 1
$$CaCl_2 + 2AgNO_3 \rightarrow 2AgCl + Ca(NO_3)_2$$

Step 2 The number of moles of each of the reactants involved must now be found.

For $CaCl_2$: $(0.10M)(0.075 \text{ L}) = 0.0075 \text{ mol } CaCl_2$
For $AgNO_3$: $(0.20M)(0.085 \text{ L}) = 0.017 \text{ mol } AgNO_3$

Step 3 The balanced equation can now be used to convert moles of $CaCl_2$ to moles of $AgNO_3$. This is done to determine the limiting reagent.

$$(0.0075 \text{ mol } CaCl_2)\left(\frac{2 \text{ mol } AgNO_3}{1 \text{ mol } CaCl_2}\right) = 0.015 \text{ mol } AgNO_3$$

The starting material contains 0.017 mol of $AgNO_3$. Since 0.0075 mol of $CaCl_2$ requires only 0.015 mol $AgNO_3$ for complete reaction, the $AgNO_3$ solution is in excess. Thus $CaCl_2$ is the limiting reagent.

Step 4 From this information, the problem can be completed. Convert moles of $CaCl_2$ to moles of $AgCl$; then convert to grams of $AgCl$

$$(0.0075 \text{ mol } CaCl_2)\left(\frac{2 \text{ mol } AgCl}{1 \text{ mol } CaCl_2}\right)\left(\frac{143.3 \text{ g } AgCl}{1 \text{ mol } AgCl}\right) = 2.1 \text{ g } AgCl$$

Thus 2.1 g AgCl was produced in the reaction.

An interesting follow-up calculation is in Example 11.21.

Example 11.21 Calculate the molarity of the excess reagent remaining in the final solution in Example 11.20.

Step 1 Find the number of moles of the excess reagent, $AgNO_3$, remaining at the end of the reaction. Subtract the number of moles of $AgNO_3$ used from the number of moles of $AgNO_3$ present:

$$0.017 \text{ mol } AgNO_3 \text{ present} - 0.015 \text{ mol } AgNO_3 \text{ used}$$
$$= 0.002 \text{ mol excess } AgNO_3$$

Step 2 Calculate the total volume of solution present after mixing. The total volume of the solution must equal the sum of the volumes of the $CaCl_2$ solution and the $AgNO_3$ solution.

$$\text{Total volume} = 0.075 \text{ L } CaCl_2 \text{ soln} + 0.085 \text{ L } AgNO_3 \text{ soln}$$
$$= 0.16 \text{ L final soln}$$

Step 3 Calculate the final concentration. The molarity of the $AgNO_3$ in the final solution is thus

$$\frac{0.002 \text{ mol AgNO}_3}{0.16 \text{ L soln}} = 0.01 M \text{ AgNO}_3$$

11.9

Normality:
Another Concentration Unit

In some areas of chemistry, particularly analytical chemistry, a specialized concentration term called normality is widely used. Normality is a convenient term that makes solving some chemical problems easier. To discuss normality, it is necessary to define a new term, equivalent weight.

Equivalent weight is related to formula weight. The equivalent weight can be found from the formula weight by applying a few simple rules. The **equivalent weight of a base** is the weight of that base that can produce 1 mol of hydroxide ions when the base is dissolved in water. In general,

$$\text{Equivalent weight of a base} = \frac{\text{formula weight of base}}{\text{number of reacting hydroxides in a formula unit of base}}$$

Example bases are shown in Table 11.5.

Table 11.5 Equivalents of Some Common Bases

Base	Formula Weight	Equivalent Weight[a]	Number of Moles	Number of Equivalents
$Ba(OH)_2$	171.4	85.7	1	2
$Na(OH)$	40.0	40.0	1	1
$Ca(OH)_2$	74.1	37.0	1	2
KOH	56.1	56.1	1	1
$Al(OH)_3$	78.0	26.0	1	3

[a] It is assumed that all hydroxide ions react.

The **equivalent weight of an acid** is the weight of the acid that can produce 1 mole of hydrogen ions when the acid is dissolved in water. The equivalent weight of an acid is defined as

$$\text{Equivalent weight of an acid} = \frac{\text{formula weight of acid}}{\text{number of reacting hydrogens in a formula unit of acid}}$$

Sample acids are shown in Table 11.6.

Table 11.6 Equivalents of Some Common Acids

Acid	Molecular Weight	Equivalent Weight[a]	Number of Moles	Number of Equivalents
HCl	36.4	36.4	1	1
HNO_3	63.0	63.0	1	1
$HC_2H_3O_2$[b]	60.0	60.0	1	1
H_2SO_4	98.1	49.0	1	2
H_2S	34.1	17.0	1	2
H_3PO_4	98.0	32.7	1	3

[a] It is assumed that all hydrogen ions react.
[b] Note that acetic acid has four hydrogen atoms but when it ionizes, it gives off only one hydrogen ion. The other three hydrogen atoms are covalently bonded to carbon atoms and are not easily removed.

Normality is the number of equivalent weights of a compound per liter of solution. For a base like $Ba(OH)_2$, a 1-normal ($1N$) solution consists of 0.5 mol or 85.6 g of $Ba(OH)_2$ dissolved in enough water to make 1 L of solution. The following relation is also true:

$$2 \times \text{molar concentration of } Ba(OH)_2 = \text{normality of } Ba(OH)_2$$

Using Table 11.5, you can see that:

A $1M$ solution of NaOH is $1N$
A $1M$ solution of $Ca(OH)_2$ is $2N$
A $1M$ solution of $Al(OH)_3$ is $3N$

It all depends on the number of hydroxides in each formula unit. We are not saying that it is possible to dissolve these quantities of $Ba(OH)_2$, $Ca(OH)_2$, or $Al(OH)_3$ in a liter of water; we are only using these compounds as examples.

Normality can be determined for acids just as it is for bases. Using Table 11.6, you can see that:

A $1M$ solution of HCl is $1N$
A $1M$ solution of H_2SO_4 is $2N$
A $1M$ solution of H_3PO_4 is $3N$

The important thing about normality is that the chemical equation has already been taken into account. Since by definition in any reaction

$$\text{Equivalents of acid} = \text{equivalents of base}$$

a new unit factor has been defined:

$$\frac{1 \text{ eq acid}}{1 \text{ eq base}} = 1 = \frac{1 \text{ eq base}}{1 \text{ eq acid}}$$

This unit factor is used in Example 11.22.

Example 11.22   A chemist needs to know the concentration of a sulfuric acid solution (H_2SO_4). She has a 0.20N NaOH solution with which to titrate the unknown H_2SO_4. The titration of 25.00 mL of the unknown acid requires a total of 37.05 mL of the base. Calculate the sulfuric acid concentration.

To get the original acid concentration, the chemist uses a unit factor method. The unit factor based on the definition of equivalents is

$$\frac{1 \text{ eq } H_2SO_4}{1 \text{ eq NaOH}} = 1 = \frac{1 \text{ eq NaOH}}{1 \text{ eq } H_2SO_4}$$

For this problem, the solution is

$$\frac{0.20 \text{ eq NaOH}}{\text{L NaOH soln}} \times 0.03705 \text{ L NaOH soln}$$

$$\times \frac{1}{0.025 \text{ L } H_2SO_4 \text{ soln}} \times \frac{1 \text{ eq } H_2SO_4}{1 \text{ eq NaOH}}$$

$$= \frac{0.30 \text{ eq } H_2SO_4}{\text{L } H_2SO_4 \text{ soln}}$$

The problem is simplified since the units cancel to give the desired units. The concentration of H_2SO_4 is 0.30N or 0.15M.

In any reaction, the number of equivalents for each reactant is equal— that is why they're called equivalents. In the acid-base reaction just shown,

Equivalents of NaOH = equivalents of H_2SO_4

Volume of acid × normality of acid = volume of base × normality of base

$$V_a \times N_a = V_b \times N_b$$

This equation can be used to solve acid-base problems like Example 11.23.

Example 11.23   Calculate what the concentration of H_2SO_4 will be if 37.05 mL of 0.20N NaOH exactly neutralizes 25.00 mL of the acid.

$$\text{Normality of acid} = \frac{\text{volume of base} \times \text{normality of base}}{\text{volume of acid}}$$

$$= \frac{0.20 \times 0.03705}{0.025} = 0.30N$$

There is always a 1:1 ratio when one is using equivalents, so the balanced chemical equation is unnecessary in the calculation (Figure 11.14).

Figure 11.14   The equality of equivalents.

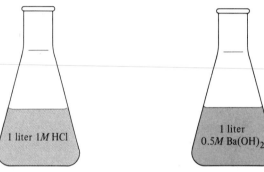

1 liter 1M HCl

1 liter 0.5M Ba(OH)$_2$

1 liter 1M HCl contributes 1 mole H$^+$ ions
1 equivalent of HCl contributes 1 mole H$^+$ ions
1 liter 1M HCl contains 1 equivalent of HCl
. 1M HCl is the same as 1N HCl

1 liter 0.5M Ba(OH)$_2$ contributes 1 mole OH$^-$ ions
1 equivalent of Ba(OH)$_2$ contributes 1 mole OH$^-$ ions
1 liter of 0.5M Ba(OH)$_2$ contains 1 equivalent Ba(OH)$_2$
0.5M Ba(OH)$_2$ is the same as 1N HCl

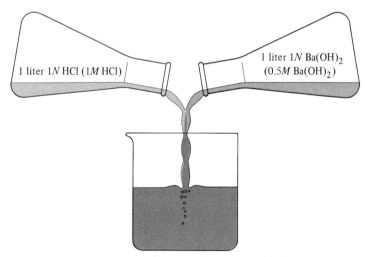

1 liter 1N HCl (1M HCl)

1 liter 1N Ba(OH)$_2$
(0.5M Ba(OH)$_2$)

1 liter 1N HCl completely neutralizes 1 liter 1N Ba(OH)$_2$

Glossary

Colloid	A heterogeneous mixture that is not a true solution; it contains suspended particles 10^{-7} to 10^{-5} cm in diameter.
Dilution	Reducing the concentration of solute in a solution by adding solvent.
Equivalent weight	For a base, the formula weight of the base divided by the number of hydroxide ions that one formula unit of the base in solution can release. For an acid, the formula weight of the acid divided by the number of hydrogen ions that one formula unit of the acid in solution can release.
Heterogeneous	Not uniform in structure and composition throughout.
Homogeneous	Uniform in structure and composition throughout.
Indicator	A dye that indicates the completion of a reaction by changing color.
Molal concentration, or molality	Concentration term; moles of solute per kilogram of solvent.
Molar concentration, or molarity	Concentration term; moles of solute per liter of solution.
Mole fraction	Concentration term; moles of one solution constituent divided by the total number of moles of all constituents in the solution.
Normality	Concentration term; equivalents of solute per liter of solution.
Parts per thousand (ppt) or parts per million (ppm)	Concentration term; weight or volume of solute per thousand or million weights or volumes of solute plus solvent.
Saturated solution	At a specific temperature, solution in which no additional solvent can dissolve.
Solubility	The amount of solute that will dissolve in a given quantity of solvent.
Solute	The dissolved substance in a solution.
Solution	A homogeneous mixture of two or more components.
Solvation	A phenomenon resulting from the attraction of solvent atoms, molecules, or ions to atoms, molecules, or ions of solute.
Solvent	The medium in which solute is dissolved in a solution.
Standard solution	Any solution whose concentration is accurately known.
Supersaturation	A situation in which a solution contains more solute than what is contained in the corresponding saturated solution at a specific temperature.
Titration	The quantitative addition of a standard solution of some reagent to a solution of unknown concentration of some chemical with which it reacts quantitatively.

Tyndall effect	The scattering of light by a colloid.
Volumetric flask	A flask used to measure precisely specific volumes of liquid.
Weight-volume percentage	A concentration term; weight of solute (grams) divided by total volume of solution (milliliters) times 100; or number of grams of solute in 100 mL of solution.
Weight-weight percentage	A concentration term; weight of solute divided by total weight of solution; or number of grams of solute in 100 g of solution.

Problems

1. A 15-g sample of potassium chloride is dissolved in 100 g of water. What is the percentage of potassium chloride in the solution?

2. A beaker contains 150 g of a 23 percent (by weight) aluminum nitrate solution. How many grams of aluminum nitrate are present?

3. Hospitals often give 5.0 percent (by weight) glucose solution to patients intravenously, following an operation. How many grams of glucose are contained in 5.0×10^2 g of this solution?

4. How many grams of sodium bicarbonate are needed to prepare 25 g of a 1.5 percent (by weight) solution of sodium bicarbonate in water?

5. A storage battery contains 38 percent by weight of sulfuric acid. How many grams of water are contained in 250 g of the sulfuric acid solution?

6. A solution of nitric acid in water contained 2.00 mol of nitric acid in 10.0 mol of water. What was the percentage by weight of nitric acid in the solution?

7. Calculate the percentage by weight of potassium perchlorate $(KClO_4)$ in a solution that contains 10. g of $KClO_4$ and 58 g of water.

8. A solution is reported to have 6.0 percent NH_3 by weight in water. The solution contains 4.0 mol of NH_3. How many moles of water does the solution contain?

9. If you want to prepare a solution that has a weight percentage of NaOH of 1.5, how many moles of sodium hydroxide will you need if you start with 5.0 mol of H_2O?

10. It has been found that a 6-hr exposure of an apple tree to air containing 4.8×10^{-7} grams of SO_2 in 1.0 g air causes a 50 percent decrease in the amount of fruit. What is this concentration percentage by weight?

11. If 1.0 mol of silver nitrate is dissolved in enough water to make 3500 mL of solution, what is the molarity of the solution?

12. The storage battery solution in Problem 5 that contains 38 percent sulfuric acid (by weight) has a density of 1.29 g/mL. What is the molarity of the solution?

13. A $0.45M$ solution of iron(III) chloride $(FeCl_3)$ contains how many moles of iron(III) chloride in 5.0×10^2 mL of solution?

14. A solution contains 20 g of $MgCl_2$ in 1000 mL of solution. What is the molarity of the solution?

15. A volume of 250 mL of $6.0M$ HCl contains how many grams of HCl?

16. What volume of a $0.50M$ solution of glucose $(C_6H_{12}O_6)$ would contain 25 g of glucose?

17. If you dissolve 30 g of table sugar $(C_{12}H_{22}O_{11})$ in 500 g of water, what will be the percentage by weight of the solution?

18. One hundred milliliters of a $0.50M$ solution of $K_2Cr_2O_7$ was poured into a 250-mL volumetric flask. Water was then added to the flask to make 250 mL. What is the new concentration of the solution?

19. If a student were to get a bottle of HCl from the shelf, he would find its concentration to be $12M$. If he wished to prepare 500 mL of $6M$ HCl solution, how many milliliters of the concentrated acid should he start with?

20. Concentrated sulfuric acid is $18M$. If 10. mL of this solution were diluted to 500. mL, what would be the concentration of the new solution?

21. What volume of $0.01M$ HCl will react with 0.5 mol of NaOH?

22. How many moles of aluminum chloride will react with 50. mL of $0.10M$ NaOH?

$$AlCl_3 + 3NaOH \rightarrow Al(OH)_3 + 3NaCl$$

23. What volume of $0.0550M$ H_2SO_4 exactly neutralizes 38.50 mL of $0.0450M$ $Ba(OH)_2$?

24. What is the weight of calcium carbonate produced when 50. mL of $0.10M$ Na_2CO_3 reacts with 100. mL of $0.10M$ $Ca(NO_3)_2$?

$$Na_2CO_3 + Ca(NO_3)_2 \rightarrow CaCO_3 + 2NaNO_3$$

25. What weight of aluminum sulfide is produced when 95 mL of $0.20M$ aluminum nitrate reacts with 85 mL of $0.10M$ hydrosulfuric acid?

$$2Al(NO_3)_3 + 3H_2S \rightarrow Al_2S_3 + 6HNO_3$$

26. (a) What is the molarity of sodium phosphate produced when 50. mL of $0.50M$ phosphoric acid reacts with 100. mL of $0.60M$ sodium hydroxide?

$$H_3PO_4 + 3NaOH \rightarrow Na_3PO_4 + 3H_2O$$

(b) What is the concentration of the excess reagent left unreacted?

27. What is the gram equivalent weight of the following acids and bases? Assume that all H^+ or OH^- react.
(a) HCl   (b) H_2SO_4
(c) NaOH   (d) $Ca(OH)_2$
(e) $Al(OH)_3$ (f) H_3PO_4
(g) $H_2C_2O_4$ (h) $HC_2H_3O_2$

28. Calculate the gram equivalent weight of the acid and the base in each of the following:
(a) $NaOH + HCl \rightarrow NaCl + H_2O$
(b) $H_2CO_3 + 2NaOH \rightarrow Na_2CO_3 + 2H_2O$
(c) $H_2CO_3 + NaOH \rightarrow NaHCO_3 + H_2O$
(d) $Ca(OH)_2 + H_2SO_4 \rightarrow CaSO_4 + 2H_2O$

29. What is the normality of the following solutions? (Assume a completed acid-base reaction.)
(a) $0.1M$ H_2SO_4
(b) $5M$ HBr
(c) $2 \times 10^{-10}M$ $Al(OH)_3$
(d) $7.5M$ H_3PO_4

30. Fifty milliliters of a solution of $0.075N$ $Ba(OH)_2$ is neutralized by what volume of $1.0N$ HCl?

31. What weight of hydrogen gas is produced by 35 mL of $2M$ H_2SO_4 reacting with 1.0 g of zinc metal? Remember to find the limiting reagent.

$$H_2SO_4 + Zn \rightarrow ZnSO_4 + H_2$$

32. A $CrCl_3$ solution contained 2 mol $CrCl_3$ per liter of solution. How many milliliters of this solution will react with 24 g of KOH?

$$CrCl_3 + 3KOH \rightarrow Cr(OH)_3 + 3KCl$$

33. What is the molarity of the following solutions? Assume complete reactions.
(a) $12N$ H_3PO_4 (b) $1N$ NaOH
(c) $0.050N$ $Ca(OH)_2$ (d) $2N$ $H_2C_2O_4$

Learning Objectives for Chapter 12

Define **colligative property, Raoult's law, boiling-point elevation, freezing-point depression, osmosis, acidity, alkalinity, pH, buffer.**

Explain why the vapor pressure of a solution is lower than the vapor pressure of a pure solvent.

Explain the relation of vapor pressure to solution concentration.

Explain why the boiling point is higher for a solution than for a pure solvent.

Explain the relation of boiling point to solution concentration.

Explain why the freezing point of a solution is lower than the freezing point of a pure solvent.

Explain the relation of freezing point to solution concentration.

Explain osmosis and why it occurs.

Given hydrogen-ion or hydroxide-ion concentration in solution, calculate pH.

Given pH, state whether a solution is acidic, basic, or neutral.

Explain how buffer solutions function, showing examples.

12 PHYSICAL PROPERTIES OF SOLUTIONS

12.1   Properties of Solutions

The difference between chemical and physical properties must be thoroughly understood before a detailed analysis of physical properties of solutions can be made. Much has been said thus far about how elements and compounds act when they get together. Whether elements or compounds will react or not depends on their **chemical properties**. The chemical properties depend on the electronic configurations of the elements or compounds.

Other important aspects of substances in the environment must be considered—the physical properties. **Physical properties** are those properties whose measurements relate to how substances appear instead of how they react. (Physical and chemical properties were mentioned briefly in Chapter 1.) Examples of physical properties are hardness, color, freezing point, boiling

Figure 12.1 Since salt lowers the freezing point of water, the spreading of salt on icy roads causes the ice to melt, even though the air temperature may be below 0°C. (Photo Courtesy of Massachusetts Department of Public Works).

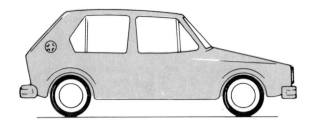

Figure 12.2 Physical properties vs. chemical properties.

How the car looks ("physical" properties)	How the car runs ("chemical" properties)
Color: Red	Engine: Runs smoothly
Length: 12′6″	Heater: Doesn't work
Height: 4′10″	Radio: Only works on one
Tires: Whitewalls	station
Doors: Two	Transmission: No reverse gear
	Doors: Passenger side doesn't
	work

point, crystalline form, size, and weight. The difference between physical and chemical properties is much like the difference between how a car looks and how it runs (Figure 12.2). Both are important. Physical properties are comparable to the car's appearance. Chemical properties (how a substance will react) are comparable to how the car runs.

Consideration of the physical properties of solutions raises certain questions.

1. Does adding a solute to a solvent change the vapor pressure of the solvent?
2. Does adding a solute to a solvent change the boiling point of the solvent?
3. Does adding a solute to a solvent change the freezing point of the solvent?
4. What other effects of the solute on the solution can be measured?

The properties listed in the questions are called **colligative properties**. They are physical properties that depend on the concentration of particles of all solutes dissolved in the solution. Colligative properties do not depend on the nature of the solute.

12.2   Vapor-Pressure Lowering

Consider solutions on the molecular level. Remember that a solute dissolves because the solute atoms, ions, or molecules and the solvent atoms or molecules have more attraction for each other than they do for their own kinds. Figure 12.3 shows a diagram of a solution. In the figure, light circles represent solvent

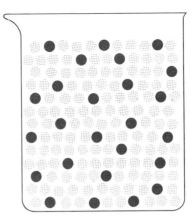

Figure 12.3 Light circles indicate the solvent, while the color circles indicate the solute in a solution.

particles and the color circles represent solute particles. What is happening at the surface of the pure solvent and the surface of a solution is shown in Figures 12.4 and 12.5. The concentration of solvent particles in the solution (Figure 12.5; light circles at the liquid surface) is lower than the concentration of solvent particles at the surface of the pure solvent (Figure 12.4). If the concentration of solvent particles at the surface is decreased, the probability that a particle will escape is lowered. Thus, there are fewer solvent molecules in the vapor phase above the solution, and the solution has a lower vapor pressure than the pure solvent. This has been experimentally verified.

Dissolving a solid in a liquid generally causes the liquid's vapor pressure to be lowered. It must also be true that the more concentrated the solution, the lower the vapor pressure. This is true to the point at which the concentration of solute particles becomes so great that an appreciable interaction exists between the solute molecules or the ions themselves.

Vapor-pressure lowering can be expressed numerically.

It is found experimentally that the vapor pressure of a solution depends on the vapor pressure of the pure solvent and the concentration of the solute in the solution. This holds strictly true only if the solute is a solid and has no vapor pressure.

The statement is called **Raoult's law**, after the original discoverer.

Figure 12.4 Pure solvent surface.

Surface

Figure 12.5 Solution surface. Light circles represent solvent; color circles represent solute.

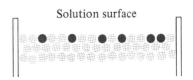
Solution surface

Figure 12.6 Graph of vapor pressure versus mole fraction of solvent for a solution of nonvolatile solute and a volatile solvent. This is an ideal solution, where p° equals vapor pressure of pure solvent. At the right vertical axis, only pure solvent is present.

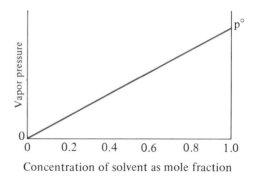

Concentration of solvent as mole fraction

It helps to represent ideas like this on graphs. Figure 12.6 shows a plot of concentration of solvent on the horizontal axis and vapor pressure of the solution on the vertical axis. It can be seen that the graph starts at zero for concentration of solvent equal to zero and ends at p°, the vapor pressure of the pure solvent when only solvent is present.

12.3 Boiling-Point Elevation

Looking back to the definition of boiling point, remember that the normal boiling point of any liquid is the temperature at which the vapor pressure of the liquid equals atmospheric pressure. The vapor pressure is lower for the solution than for the solvent alone, and the boiling point is higher. The effect is called **boiling-point elevation**.

> In general, one can say that when a solid solute is dissolved in a liquid solvent, the vapor pressure of the solvent is lowered, and the boiling point is raised.

This can be expressed mathematically. The number of degrees that the boiling point is raised depends on two factors: (1) the identity of the solvent; and (2) the concentration of the solute particles. For example, 1 mol of sugar dissolved in 1 kg of water makes a solution whose boiling point is 100.51 °C, a rise of 0.51 °C. One mole of sugar dissolved in 1 kg of ethyl alcohol (drinking alcohol) makes a solution whose boiling point is 79.72 °C, a rise of 1.22 °C.

The number of solute particles present determines the boiling-point elevation. If sugar is a solute, 1 mol of sugar produces 1 mol of individual sugar molecules in solution. If 1 mol of potassium chloride (KCl) is dissolved in water, the potassium chloride will be completely ionized, and there will be 1 mol of potassium ions, K^+, and 1 mol of chloride ions, Cl^-, in the solution. The effect is that of having 2 mol of particles in solution. The number of particles present in solution, not just the number of moles of solute, determines the boiling point. It is the particles that count.

Figure 12.7 Phase diagram for a solvent. The dotted lines are for solution. The melting point of the solution, T'_m, is lower than the one for the pure solvent, T_m. The boiling point is higher for the solution than for the pure solvent.

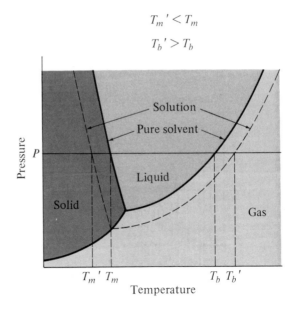

As examples, in water solution, NaCl ionizes to give two particles (one Na^+ and one Cl^-). Calcium chloride ($CaCl_2$) ionizes to give three (one Ca^{2+} and two Cl^-), and potassium phosphate (K_3PO_4) ionizes to give four particles (three K^+ and one PO_4^{3-}).

It is interesting that the boiling-point elevation can be seen on the phase diagram shown in Figure 12.7 (see also Chapter 10). You will remember that the line between solid and liquid shows the temperature at which the substance melts at various pressures. The line between liquid and gas shows the temperature at which the substance boils at various pressures. When the solute is added, the diagram changes as shown in Figure 12.7.

The boiling point has been raised from T_b for the pure solvent to T'_b for the solution. But look on the left side of the diagram. The freezing point T_m has been lowered to T'_m. This means that the freezing point of a solution is lower than the freezing point of the pure solvent.

12.4 Freezing-Point Depression

It may be more difficult to understand the lowering of the freezing point than the elevation of the boiling point. Our knowledge of crystal lattices will be relevant. Solids have definite, carefully arranged crystal structures. When a pure substance is cooled to its freezing point, the molecules or ions fall into this pattern. The same thing happens when a solution is cooled, since what freezes out is the pure solvent. The only difference is that solute molecules get in the way of the solvent's falling into the pattern. Therefore the solution must be cooled even further to overcome the interference and allow the solvent to freeze. It is important to note that pure solvent freezes from a solution. This concept is quite common in actual practice. Clear ice purchased from the store is formed by running water over a cold network of plates. As the ice was formed, the impurities that would otherwise make the ice cubes cloudy were carried away by the water. When a tray of ice cubes is frozen in a freezer, there is no place for impurities to go, so they are trapped in the ice and cause the ice cubes to be cloudy. A solution no longer exists. Another application of this phenomenon could be used if an Eskimo were stranded on an iceberg in the middle of the ocean. The water freezes pure from the ocean, so by melting some of the iceberg, the Eskimo could get drinking water. Some scientists have looked at this method for reclaiming polluted water for drinking. It is feasible on a small scale but it would be very expensive to purify water for a whole city this way.

The degree to which a solution's freezing point is depressed depends on (1) the identity of the solvent and (2) the concentration of solute particles. This is like the elevation of the boiling point. A solution of 1 mol of sugar in 1 kg of water has a freezing point of $-1.86\,°C$, a depression of $1.86\,°C$. A solution with a similar concentration of sugar in benzene results in a solution freezing point of $0.48\,°C$, which is $5.12\,°C$ lower than for pure benzene. The effect on freezing point depends on the number of particles of solute present, which is true for the boiling point.

12.5   Osmosis

The final colligative property we study is osmosis, a very important activity in biological systems. **Osmosis** is defined as the passage of a solvent through a semipermeable membrane from an area of low concentration of solute to an area of high concentration of solute. Let us elaborate on this definition.

The concept of osmosis is based on the semipermeable membrane. A semipermeable membrane is a barrier through which some molecules can pass but not others. A membrane exists, for example, that will allow water molecules to move through the barrier but not ions like Na^+, K^+, Ca^{2+}, Cl^-, Br^-, or NO_3^-, or molecules like sugar. This barrier will allow the phenomenon of osmosis. To induce osmosis, pure water could be placed on one side of a semipermeable membrane and a solution of sugar in water on the other side. Since the molecules of a liquid are in constant motion, molecules are constantly hitting the membrane from both sides.

This situation is much like two men standing on opposite sides of a wall and throwing balls at the wall (Figure 12.8). The man on the left has both tennis

Figure 12.8

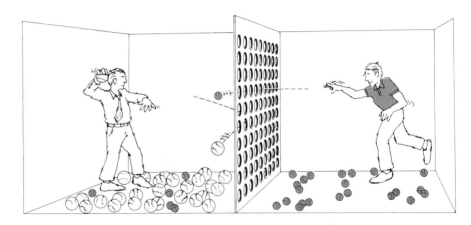

Figure 12.9

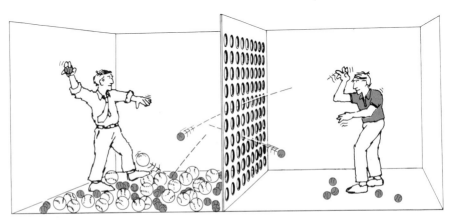

balls and softballs while the man on the right has only tennis balls. The wall has holes in it of such a size that tennis balls can pass through but softballs can't. Both men throw balls at exactly the same rate not caring which kind of of ball they throw. The man on the right will throw balls through the wall faster than the man on the left, because every ball he picks up has a chance of getting through. Eventually, the man on the left will have many more tennis balls on his side than he started with (Figure 12.9). In fact, he has so many tennis balls on his side that he very seldom grabs a softball. When that happens, the number of tennis balls passing both ways is equal, and a dynamic equilibrium has been attained.

The softballs and tennis balls of the example are like sugar and water molecules; the wall is the semipermeable membrane, and the tennis balls are like pure water. A similar thing happens with the sugar solution. The molecules are in constant motion. Since sugar and water hit the membrane from the left and only water hits it from the right, more water molecules pass from right to left, and the level of the solution on the left rises while the level on the right lowers (Figure 12.10).

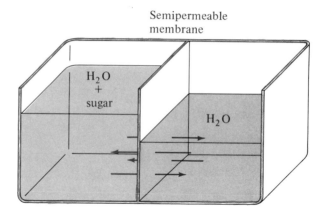

The change in levels continues until the pressure pushing back from the left slows down the passage of water from the right. When the rising stops, a dynamic equilibrium has been reached. There are equal numbers of water molecules passing in both directions. The pressure built up by the head of water on the left is called the **osmotic pressure**.

In a real laboratory experiment, the osmotic pressure is measured by pushing on the solution side of the semipermeable membrane with a piston. The pressure needed to keep the liquid from passing through the membrane is recorded as the osmotic pressure. In such a measuring device, hydrostatic (water) pressure is measured as the water height in a tube.

The osmotic pressure depends on the molality of sugar in the solution on the left. The higher the concentration of sugar, the greater the amount of water that must pass from right to left before equilibrium is reached. The higher the level on the left, the higher the osmotic pressure.

Semipermeable membranes are very common in biological systems. All cells have semipermeable membranes—semipermeable not just to water but also to small ions.

Red blood cells travel in veins and arteries in a liquid called plasma. The concentration of salts in the plasma and inside the blood cells is identical. The cell membrane is semipermeable. If the red cells are separated from the plasma and put into less concentrated salt solutions, water flows in by osmosis; and if the osmotic pressure builds up high enough, the cells burst, or **hemolyze**. This is a good way of testing both the concentration of salts inside the cell and the strength of the cell membrane.

The opposite effect exists if the cells are placed in a solution that is more concentrated than their interior makeup. Water flows out, and the cell becomes shriveled, or **crenated**.

All body cells can be affected like this, and doctors must take care in treating patients not to use solutions that are higher in concentration of salts than the body fluids (hypertonic) or lower in concentration of salts than the body fluids (hypotonic). Solutions put into the body must have concentrations

Figure 12.11 Osmosis: In whole blood, or isotonic solution, the red cells are discs. In hypotonic solutions, or in plasma in which the salt concentration has been reduced, water enters the cells and distends them so that they appear rounded. In very dilute solutions (water or diluted plasma) the cell envelope ruptures and the contents escape. In concentrated salt solution (hypertonic), water passes out of the cells and they become shriveled.

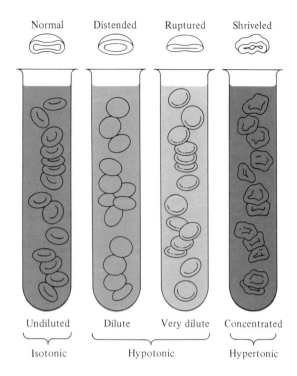

identical to solutions in the body; in other words, they must be isotonic (Figure 12.11).

A fish lives in a hostile environment. If the fish lives in fresh water, the body fluids contain more dissolved particles than the surroundings do. Water passes from the lake or stream into the body of the fish by osmosis. The result is that the fish needs to drink little water but to urinate often. The saltwater fish, on the other hand, finds itself in an environment in which the surrounding water has a higher concentration of dissolved particles than what exists in its body fluids. Osmosis now tends to take water from the fish and return it to the ocean; thus, the saltwater fish must drink large amounts of water, and it seldom urinates. This is one reason few fish can make the adjustment from salt water to fresh water or fresh water to salt water.

12.6 Acidity, Alkalinity, Buffers

Another important aspect of solutions is the measurement of acidity, commonly expressed by pH. The term pH has been used extensively in toothpaste and shampoo commercials, and also for many other products. Some products are advertised as alkaline, acidic, or neutral. All these terms are based on the hydrogen-ion (H^+) concentration of a solution relative to the H^+ concentration in pure water*. Pure water is neither acidic nor basic—it is neutral. To a small extent, however, the following reaction occurs:

$$H_2O \rightarrow H^+ + OH^-$$

The ions H^+ and OH^- are in dynamic equilibrium with water molecules. Water dissociates (water molecules separate into the ions H^+ and OH^-) to such a small degree that the process can be shown as

$$H_2O \rightleftharpoons H^+ + OH^-$$

This indicates that the left side is favored in the reaction.

In 1 L of pure water at 25 °C, 1×10^{-7} mol of water dissociates to form 1×10^{-7} mol of hydrogen ions and 1×10^{-7} mol of hydroxide ions. What fraction of the total water molecules have ionized? To solve this problem, one must find the number of moles of water in 1 L. Since 1 L water weighs 1000. g at 20 °C, the total number of moles of water is

$$1000. \text{ g } H_2O \times \frac{1 \text{ mol } H_2O}{18.0 \text{ g } H_2O} = 55.6 \text{ mol } H_2O$$

Since 1×10^{-7} mol of water has dissociated, the fraction dissociated is

$$\frac{1 \times 10^{-7} \text{ mol}}{55.6 \text{ mol}} = 1.8 \times 10^{-9}$$

a very small fraction.

In pure water, the concentration of hydrogen ions is equal to 1×10^{-7} mol per liter. Pure water, neither acidic nor basic, has equal numbers of moles of hydrogen ions (which are a measure of the acidity) and hydroxide ions (which are a measure of the alkalinity, or "nonacidity")

If there are more H^+ than OH^-, the solution is **acidic**. If there are more OH^- than H^+, the solution is basic, or **alkaline**. Pure water, having equal concentrations of the ions H^+ and OH^-, is **neutral**.

Any water solution at 25 °C can be described by the following equation:

Concentration of ions H^+ × concentration of ions $OH^- = 1 \times 10^{-14}$

---

* In water, many kinds of ions exist. Bare protons do not exist separately in water solution, since they are solvated by one or more water molecules to form H_3O^+, $H_5O_2^+$, $H_7O_3^+$, etc. The presence of all these species (H_3O^+ is the most commonly discussed) will be ignored and only the term H^+ will be used.

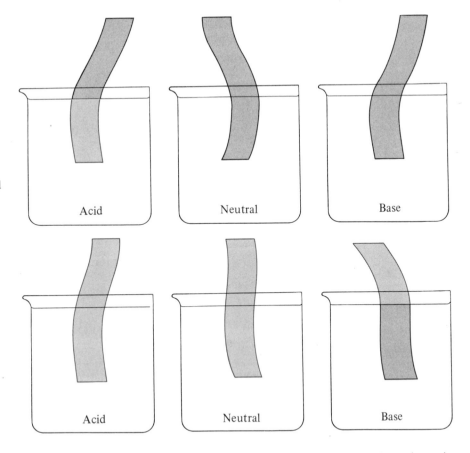

Figure 12.12 Litmus paper is a common way of determining if a solution is acidic or basic. In acid, blue litmus paper (shown here in gray) turns red, but in a base it does not change. In a base, red litmus paper turns blue (shown here as gray), but it remains unchanged in an acid. In a neutral solution, neither paper changes.

Acid   Neutral   Base

Acid   Neutral   Base

Concentrations here are expressed as moles per liter. By tradition, the units on the product are ignored in calculations. The equation above can be expressed mathematically as

$$[H^+][OH^-] = 1 \times 10^{-14}$$

The [ ] is used as a shortcut for writing "concentration in moles per liter." The equation reads, H^+ concentration in moles per liter times OH^- concentration in moles per liter $= 1 \times 10^{-14}$.

If an acid is added to pure water, the concentration of hydrogen ions increases, the concentration of hydroxide ions decreases, and the solution is acidic. The concentration of OH^- goes down because more H^+ are added. The reaction

$$H^+ + OH^- \rightarrow H_2O$$

is forced, and added ions H^+ plus the original OH^- are taken out of solution to form water (Figure 12.12).

The hydrogen-ion concentration of a neutral solution is 10^{-7} mol/L. The pH of the water is 7.

The term **pH** is defined as the negative of the power to which 10 is raised in expressing the hydrogen-ion concentration.

This is also called the negative logarithm of the hydrogen-ion concentration.

Example 12.1	If $[H^+] = 1 \times 10^{-7}$ mol/L, what is the pH?

Step 1   Write the concentration as 1 multiplied by an exponential.

$$[H^+] = 1 \times 10^{-7} \text{ mol/L}$$

Step 2   State pH as the negative of the power to which 10 is raised.

$$pH = -(-7) = 7$$

Example 12.2	If $[H^+] = 1 \times 10^{-6}$ mol/L, what is the pH?

Step 1 $[H^+] = 1 \times 10^{-6}$ mol/L
Step 2 $pH = -(-6) = 6$

This solution is acidic. Notice that the pH is less than 7. Any solution with a pH less than 7 is acidic.

Example 12.3	Calculate the pH of a solution in which the concentration of hydrogen ions is 1×10^{-8} mol/L.

Step 1 $[H^+] = 1 \times 10^{-8}$ mol/L
Step 2 $pH = -(-8) = 8$

This solution is basic. When the pH is greater than 7, hydroxide ions predominate.

A pH need not be a whole number. A solution could have, for example, a pH of 6.5. This means that $[H^+] = 1 \times 10^{-6.5}$. A calculation or table of logarithms shows

$$10^{-6.5} = 1 \times 10^{0.5} \times 1 \times 10^{-7} = \sqrt{10} \times 10^{-7} = 3.16 \times 10^{-7} = [H^+]$$

The explanation of this calculation is left to a mathematics course or a higher-level chemistry course. The hydrogen-ion concentration can be expressed numerically by using the concept of pH. It is enough that you realize that a pH of 6.5 is between 6 and 7 and that $[H^+]$ is therefore between 1×10^{-6} and 1×10^{-7}.

Remembering that an acidic solution has a pH less than 7 and a basic solution has a pH greater than 7 will help in solving examples.

Example 12.4
Find the pH of a solution that has a hydrogen-ion concentration of 10^{-9} mol/L. Also, find the $[OH^-]$ of the solution.

Step 1 $[H^+] = 1 \times 10^{-9}$
Step 2 $pH = -(-9) = 9$

The solution is basic.

Step 3   Substitute in the defining equation for $[H^+]$ and $[OH^-]$ in water solution.

$$[H^+][OH^-] = 1 \times 10^{-14}$$
$$10^{-9}[OH^-] = 1 \times 10^{-14}$$
$$[OH^-] = 1 \times 10^{-14} \times 1 \times 10^9$$
$$= 1 \times 10^{-14+9}$$
$$= 1 \times 10^{-5}$$

This also shows that the solution is basic, since $[OH^-] > [H^+]$.

Example 12.5
Find the pH of a solution for which $[OH^-] = 1 \times 10^{-12}$.

Step 1   Calculate $[H^+]$ using the defining equation for water.

$$[H^+][OH^-] = 1 \times 10^{-14}$$
$$[H^+] \times 1 \times 10^{-12} = 1 \times 10^{-14}$$
$$[H^+] = 1 \times 10^{-14} \times 1 \times 10^{12}$$
$$= 1 \times 10^{-14+12}$$
$$= 1 \times 10^{-2}$$

Step 2   Calculate pH.
$$pH = -(-2) = 2$$

This is an acidic solution.

Hydrochloric acid dissociates completely in water to produce hydrogen ions and chloride ions. A $1M$ solution of hydrochloric solution contains 1 mol/L hydrogen ions. Since $[H^+] = 1 \times 10^0$, the pH of the solution is

$$pH = -(0) = 0$$

The pH of the $1M$ HCl solution is 0.

Example 12.6   What is the pH of a $1M$ solution of acetic acid?

Step 1   Acetic acid is about 0.4 percent ionized in a $1M$ solution. If this is true, then $0.4\% \times 1M = 4 \times 10^{-3}$ mol H^+, or

$$[H^+] = 4 \times 10^{-3}$$

Step 2   This value lies between 1×10^{-2} and 1×10^{-3}, and the pH is between 2 and 3. (From a table of logarithms, the pH is found to be 2.4)

According to the above calculations, **weak acids** like acetic acid give fewer ions H^+ in solution for equal concentrations of acid than **strong** acids do. Similarly, **weak bases** give lower $[OH^-]$ than **strong bases** for equal concentrations. Table 12.1 illustrates some relative acid and base strengths.

Table 12.1   pH of Various Acid and Base Solutions At the Same Concentration

Acid or Base	Molar Concentration	pH	Strength
HCl	0.1	1	Strong
HNO_3	0.1	1	Strong
$HC_2H_3O_2$	0.1	2.87	Weak
NH_4OH	0.1	11.12	Weak
KOH	0.1	13.00	Strong

Measurements of pH are important in almost every field of chemistry. They are especially important in the workings of the human body. For example, how acidic is the stomach? When food is being digested, the stomach wall secretes juices that have a pH of about 1. At other times, the stomach fluids have a pH of 5 to 6. Ordinarily, the stomach fluids act as a buffer.

A **buffer solution** is a solution that resists changes in pH.

A buffer solution can be made by mixing a weak acid and the salt of a weak acid (for example, $HC_2H_3O_2$ and $NaC_2H_3O_2$) or a weak base and the salt of a weak base (for example NH_3 and NH_4Cl).

Look at the first example more closely. If base is added to this acetic acid–acetate solution, many of the ions OH^- undergo the reaction

$$OH^- + HC_2H_3O_2 \rightarrow H_2O + C_2H_3O_2^-$$

and there is little change in pH due to the added OH^-. If ions H^+ are added, they take part in the reaction:

$$H^+ + C_2H_3O_2^- \rightarrow HC_2H_3O_2$$

and there is little change in pH due to the added H^+.

For the basic buffer, adding acid or base causes the following reactions:

$$H^+ + NH_3 \rightarrow NH_4^+$$

$$OH^- + NH_4^+ \rightarrow NH_3 + H_2O$$

and again there is little change in the pH of the solution. If too much acid or base is added to the buffer, all one ion or the other will be consumed.

The human body contains a complex network of buffer mixtures. The pH of body fluids must be carefully regulated, or disease and death occur. One interesting buffer in the body is the carbonate buffer—H_2CO_3, HCO_3^-. Carbonic acid (H_2CO_3) decomposes and is formed according to the following equation

$$H_2CO_3 \rightleftarrows H_2O + CO_2$$

During respiration, the body eliminates CO_2 and brings in O_2. The amount of CO_2 in the body is regulated during breathing. More CO_2 retained by the body means more H_2CO_3 present. The buffer works in the following way. If there is too much OH^- present, it is removed by

$$OH^- + H_2CO_3 \rightarrow H_2O + HCO_3^-$$

If there is too much H^+ present, it is eliminated by

$$H^+ + HCO_3^- \rightarrow H_2CO_3$$

Too much acid can be handled by eliminating more CO_2 because this allows the reaction

$$\underset{\substack{\text{extra} \\ \text{acid}}}{H^+} + HCO_3^- \rightarrow H_2CO_3 \rightarrow H_2O + CO_2$$

Too much base can be handled by retaining more CO_2, allowing the reaction

$$CO_2 + H_2O \rightarrow H_2CO_3 + \underset{\substack{\text{extra} \\ \text{base}}}{OH^-} \rightarrow HCO_3^- + H_2O$$

This is one of the many buffer systems the body uses to maintain its pH.

Glossary

Acidic solution   A solution with pH lower than 7.

Alkaline solution   A solution with pH greater than 7.

Buffer solution   A solution that resists changes in pH.

Chemical properties   Properties that are associated with the ability of a substance to undergo chemical change.

Colligative properties   Physical properties of a solution that depend on the concentration of solute particles in solution and not the kind of solute.

Crenation   The shriveling of cells in hypertonic solutions.

Hemolysis   The bursting of cells in hypotonic solutions.

Neutral solution   A solution with pH equal to 7.

Osmosis   The passage of solvent through a semipermeable membrane from an area of low concentration of solute to an area of high concentration of solute.

Osmotic pressure   The pressure exerted as a result of osmosis.

pH   The negative of the logarithm of the hydrogen-ion concentration in a solution.

Physical properties   Properties associated with the appearance of a substance rather than its ability to undergo chemical reaction.

Raoult's law   The vapor pressure of an ideal solution equals the vapor pressure of the pure solvent multiplied by the mole fraction of that solvent.

Semipermeable membrane   A barrier through which some molecules can pass but others cannot.

Strong acid   An acid that is highly dissociated in aqueous solution.

Strong base   A base that is highly dissociated in aqueous solution.

Weak acid   An acid that is only slightly dissociated in aqueous solution.

Weak base   A base that is only slightly dissociated in aqueous solution.

Problems

1. Compare the vapor pressure of a pure solvent with the vapor pressure of a solution of that solvent and a nonvolatile solute. Use your own words.

2. Explain why salt is spread on icy sidewalks to melt the ice.

3. Blocks of ice bought from commercial producers are clear. Explain why.

4. A chef discovers that vegetables cooked in salted water cook faster than the same vegetables cooked in unsalted water. Explain.

5. Maple syrup evaporates more slowly than pure water. Explain.

6. State the pH of the following solutions:
   (a) $[H^+] = 1.0 \times 10^{-10}$
   (b) $[H^+] = 1.0 \times 10^{-3}$
   (c) $[H^+] = 1.0 \times 10^{-7}$
   (d) $[H^+] = 1.0 \times 10^{-4}$
   (e) $[H^+] = 1.0 \times 10^{-12}$

7. Calculate the $[H^+]$ and pH of the following solutions:
   (a) $[OH^-] = 1 \times 10^{-12}$
   (b) $[OH^-] = 1 \times 10^{-4}$
   (c) $[OH^-] = 1 \times 10^{-7}$
   (d) $[OH^-] = 1 \times 10^{-1}$
   (e) $[OH^-] = 1 \times 10^{-10}$

8. Calculate the $[H^+]$ in the following solutions:
   (a) pH = 5
   (b) pH = 10
   (c) pH = 12
   (d) pH = 7
   (e) pH = 2

9. State whether the solutions in Problem 8 are acidic, basic, or neutral.

10. Calculate the $[OH^-]$ in the following solutions:
    (a) pH = 2
    (b) pH = 7
    (c) pH = 11
    (d) pH = 3
    (e) pH = 8

11. State whether the solutions in Problem 7 are acidic, basic, or neutral.

Learning Objectives for Chapter 13

Define **chemical kinetics, rate law, activation energy, catalyst, equilibrium, spectator ion, equilibrium constant, solubility product constant, Le Châtelier's principle.**

Explain possible methods and units for measuring speed of reaction.

Explain the role of molecular collisions and ionic collisions in chemical reactions.

Explain the effect of catalysis on the speed of chemical reactions.

Explain the effect of temperature on the speed of chemical reactions.

Explain the effect of concentration on the speed of chemical reactions.

Explain the relation between rate of reaction and equilibrium.

Given a chemical equation, write the equilibrium-constant expression.

Given the numerical value of the equilibrium constant, determine whether reactants or products are favored, and to what extent qualitatively they are favored.

Use Le Châtelier's principle to predict how changes in conditions will affect reactions.

Discuss, in general, why equilibrium constants might have large or small values.

13 KINETICS AND EQUILIBRIUM

The aspects of chemical reactions we have examined thus far include determining the likelihood of reactions, the products formed, and the energy produced or consumed during the reaction. The rate, or speed, of reaction is also a relevant consideration. When the forward rate of a reaction is equivalent to the reverse rate, an **equilibrium** exists.

A stick of dynamite explodes almost instantaneously, the reaction taking less than 1 sec. A piece of magnesium dissolves in a beaker of hydrochloric acid according to the equation

$$Mg + 2HCl \rightarrow MgCl_2 + H_2$$

This is a slower reaction. The formation of iron oxide in air according to the equation

$$4Fe + 3O_2 \rightarrow 2Fe_2O_3$$

may take place in minutes, hours, or even years, depending on the conditions attending the reaction. Chemical reactions important in geology, like the formation of diamonds or oil, may require several million years.

Chemical kinetics is the study of the speed of chemical reactions and of the individual steps through which reactions proceed.

Through kinetics, chemists try to explain the differences in speeds of different reactions, differences like those in the reactions just mentioned. In studying chemical kinetics, chemists look for answers to questions like:

1. How can the speed of reactions be measured?
2. How do chemical reactions proceed? Or stated another way, what is happening to individual formula units during reactions?
3. How do temperature, reactant concentration, and other factors affect the speed of reactions?

Measuring the Speed of Chemical Reactions

The speed of a chemical reaction is an experimentally measured quantity. It is determined by measuring how fast a reactant disappears or how fast a product appears. For magnesium dissolving in hydrochloric acid at constant temperature, the equation is

$$Mg + 2HCl \rightarrow MgCl_2 + H_2$$

The speed of the reaction can be measured by determining one of four quantities: rate of disappearance of magnesium metal, rate of disappearance of hydrochloric acid, rate of formation of magnesium chloride, or rate of formation of hydrogen gas. The easiest approach would be to measure the rate of formation of hydrogen gas by monitoring the total pressure of the system, as shown in Figure 13.1. The rate of a reaction can be measured in a variety

Figure 13.1 The easiest method used to follow the rate of a reaction involves measuring the pressure of an evolved gas. In this case, the pressure of hydrogen gas increases as the reaction proceeds according to the equation $Mg + 2HCl \rightarrow MgCl_2 + H_2$.

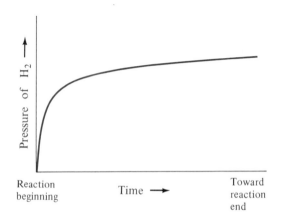

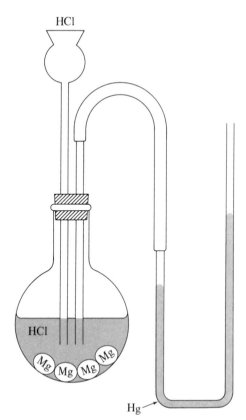

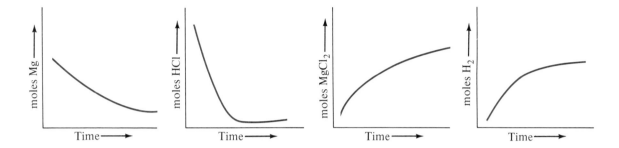

Figure 13.2 The concentration of various reactants and products is plotted against time for the reaction Mg + 2HCl → MgCl$_2$ + H$_2$. Notice that MgCl$_2$ and H$_2$ increase at the same rate Mg decreases. HCl, however, decreases at a rate twice that of the other three.

of units such as moles per second, grams per second, liters per second, or any other unit the chemist making the measurement determines convenient or appropriate. The results of these measurements can be shown on graphs, as in Figure 13.2. Notice from the graphs that the number of moles of HCl present decreases twice as fast as the number of moles of magnesium. The reason is that two molecules of HCl react with one atom of magnesium simultaneously. Also notice that MgCl$_2$ and H$_2$ appear at the same rate as that at which the Mg disappears. This could be stated in equationlike form as

$$\text{Rate of reaction} = \text{rate of disappearance of Mg}$$

$$= \tfrac{1}{2} \text{ rate of disappearance of HCl}$$

$$= \text{rate of appearance of MgCl}_2$$

$$= \text{rate of appearance of H}_2$$

The graphs in Figure 13.2 also indicate that after the reaction has proceeded for some time, it slows down considerably, and reactants disappear and products appear much more slowly. This slowing down indicates that the speed of a reaction depends on the quantity or concentration of reactants present.

The simple observations that have been made on the Mg + HCl reaction just described typify the experimental measurements carried out in kinetic studies. The actual experiments, however, might be extremely complicated. The measuring instruments might measure the absorption of light by a single chemical in solution, the electrical conductance of a solution caused by a single product or reactant in the solution, the change in the pH of a solution as acid is either produced or consumed, or numerous other possible properties. In each case, either the production of product or the consumption of reactant is measured.

Using kinetics is exemplified in the reaction in which hydrogen bromide (HBr) forms from its constituent elements. The equation is

$$\text{H}_2 + \text{Br}_2 = 2\text{HBr}$$

It was found experimentally that the rate of disappearance of H$_2$ equaled the rate of disappearance of Br$_2$, which equaled half the rate of formation of HBr.

The rate of the reaction can be stated as

$$\text{Rate of reaction} = \text{rate of disappearance of } H_2$$
$$= \text{rate of disappearance of } Br_2$$
$$= \tfrac{1}{2} \text{ rate of appearance of HBr}$$

The rate of the reaction could also be stated differently:

$$\text{Rate of reaction} = \text{rate of appearance of HBr}$$
$$= 2 \times \text{rate of disappearance of } H_2$$
$$= 2 \times \text{rate of disappearance of } Br_2$$

The relative speeds are the same. The overall rate depends on how this rate is initially defined, that is, which reactant or product is being monitored to determine the reaction rate.

13.2 Individual Steps in Chemical Reactions; Activation Energy

Scientists believe that on a molecular level, reactions occur when individual particles collide. Most reactions are so complicated, however, that there must be many collisions before the actual product is formed; not every collision is effective. In the reaction, for example, in which HBr is formed from its constituent elements, the complete reaction is

$$H_2 + Br_2 \rightarrow 2HBr$$

The individual steps, or the collisions during the reaction, are thought to be

Step 1 $Br_2 + \text{anything} \rightarrow 2Br + \text{anything}$

Anything may be the wall of the container or any molecule present.

Step 2 $Br + H_2 \rightarrow HBr + H$

Step 3 $H + Br_2 \rightarrow HBr + Br$

Also see Figure 13.3. Other possibilities could be proposed for the individual steps of the reaction of Br_2 and H_2. The steps are developed using experimental

Figure 13.3 Often reactions occur in a series of steps. The reaction described here is initiated when Br_2 molecules collide with the container walls to form activated Br atoms (a). These activated atoms react with H_2 molecules (b) to form HBr and activated H atoms (c). In turn, the activated H atom reacts with a Br_2 molecule (d) to form more HBr and more activated Br atoms (e).

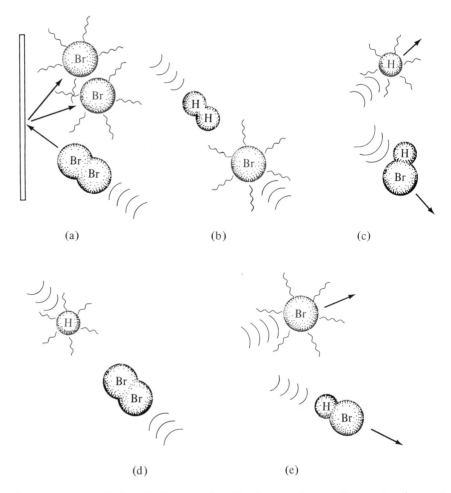

(a)　　　　　(b)　　　　　(c)

(d)　　　　　(e)

data and general chemical knowledge. In the reaction, a Br_2 molecule must collide with the wall or another molecule and break into two Br atoms. After this, a Br atom must collide with an H_2 molecule to form a product HBr molecule and an H atom. The H atom can then collide with a Br_2 molecule to form a product HBr molecule and another Br atom. The reaction continues as steps 2 and 3 are repeated. The concentration of the reactants is very important in determining the speed of this reaction. As more product forms, fewer and fewer H_2 and Br_2 molecules are present. This means that as the reaction continues, it becomes increasingly difficult for an H atom to collide with a Br_2 molecule or a Br atom to collide with an H_2 molecule, simply because there are fewer molecules. Thus, the reaction slows down as it proceeds.

Combining a knowledge of direct experiments and also other, general chemical knowledge, one might guess at a first step:

$$H_2 + \text{anything} \rightarrow 2H + \text{anything}$$

Figure 13.4(a) Not all collisions result in the formation of products.

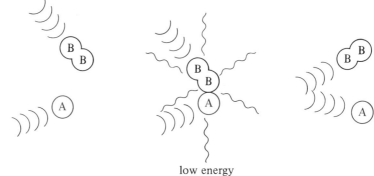

low energy

Figure 13.4(b) The collision must be of sufficient energy to overcome the tendency for molecules to remain in their original state.

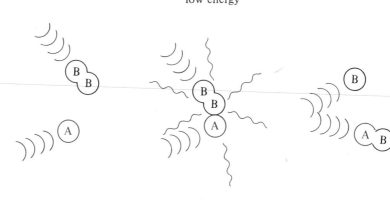

high energy

Chemists know that the bond between H atoms in H_2 is very strong compared with the bond between Br atoms in Br_2; it is therefore more likely for a Br_2 molecule to break apart as a result of a collision than for an H_2 molecule to break apart. This is also true of the HBr molecule. The HBr bond is stronger than the Br_2 bond and is therefore less likely to break apart as the result of a collision. Thus, the formation of HBr is favored, and it is not necessary to consider reaction steps like

$$HBr + anything \rightarrow H + Br + anything$$

Not every collision causes a new species to form. The molecules or atoms must collide with enough energy to cause something to happen. The minimum energy that must be available in a collision if that collision is to cause the colliding molecules to convert to a product or products is called the **activation energy**. Figures 13.4(a) and 13.4(b) show what happens for different energy conditions. All compounds have associated with them a specific amount of energy. If a reaction is exothermic, the energy associated with the products is lower than what is associated with the reactants. As the reaction proceeds, the extra energy is released. When molecules collide, they must do so with enough energy to overcome the energy barrier: the activation energy. Think

Figure 13.5 In a spontaneous reaction, the reactants contain more energy than the products. Once enough energy is supplied to the reactants to overcome the activation energy, the energy given off by the formation of the products will sustain the reaction.

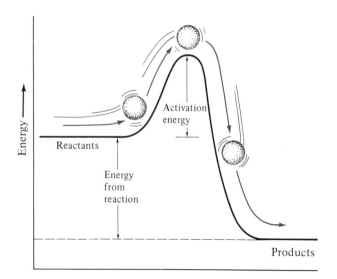

of a ball rolling along the curve in Figure 13.5 from the reactant side to the product side. If the ball is pushed up the curve with enough energy to reach the top, it will roll down to the product side. If too little energy is supplied, the ball will roll back to its starting position. The analogy can be carried over to molecular collision. If enough energy is supplied by the collision to reach the top of the energy curve, products will be formed. If too little energy is involved in the collision, the molecules will revert to their original states. The difference between the energy of the reactants and the top of the energy curve is the activation energy. In the example shown, the energy received from the fall from the top of the energy curve to the products is much greater than the energy needed to raise the reactants to the top of the energy curve. The excess energy is often used by other molecules or atoms of the reactants to help them over the energy barrier. Thus, such a reaction, once started, usually continues. Burning a piece of wood is a good example of this. The wood does not burn until it is heated to a high temperature. (The oxygen molecules must collide with the wood with enough energy to reach the top of the energy barrier.) Once the wood begins to burn, it will continue to burn, using the energy difference between the products and the reactants to push more collisions over the energy barrier.

If the reaction is not spontaneous, the curve illustrated in Figure 13.6 is obtained. Here the energy of the products is higher than the energy of the reactants. Energy must be continually added to sustain the reaction. An example of this kind of reaction is using electricity to convert water to hydrogen and oxygen:

$$2H_2O \xrightarrow{\text{electricity}} 2H_2 + O_2$$

Electrical energy must be continually supplied to cause the reaction. If the

Figure 13.6 In a reaction which is not spontaneous, energy must be continuously supplied to keep the reaction going.

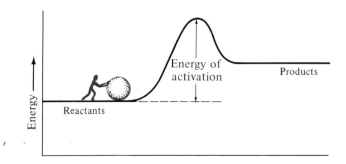

electricity is turned off, the reaction immediately stops. The activation energy is, once more, the difference between the energy of the reactants and the top of the energy curve.

Whatever the reaction involved, the set of steps is a chemist's best guess at exactly what is happening during a reaction. It shows the detailed path leading from reactants to products. This path consists of individual collisions and shifts of atoms. The simple steps proposed will evolve from experimentation and other knowledge of chemical reactions. Each step represents a single collision, usually between two formula units, or a shift of atoms within a formula unit.

13.3 Effect of Temperature, Catalysts, and Concentration on Speed of Chemical Reactions

The speed, or rate, of any chemical reaction depends on the conditions attending the reaction. Reaction conditions can be separated into several individual factors, three of which are important to us. These are temperature, catalysis, and concentration.

Temperature

Experiments show that increasing the temperature for a chemical reaction increases the speed of the reaction. Generally for every ten degrees the temperature is raised, the rate of the reaction increases two to three times. This phenomenon can be observed at home when a pressure cooker is used to prepare food. A pressure cooker increases the cooking temperature several degrees, thus increasing the cooking rate. Scientists believe that the mechanism of chemical reactions is that individual reactant particles collide, break apart, and form bonds producing product particles. Increasing temperature causes particles to travel faster, thus producing more numerous and harder collisions and forming products more quickly. The idea that reactions occur when particles collide is an accepted theory, and the explanation given above fits the observation that increasing temperature increases reaction speed.

Catalysts

Catalysts also affect the speed of chemical reactions. A **catalyst** is a substance that by its presence during a reaction causes the speed of the reaction to be changed. The catalyst itself remains unchanged in the reaction. It does its work by lowering the energy of activation or the force with which the molecules must collide for the successful formation of products. This is shown in Figure 13.7. An example is the reaction in which potassium chlorate decomposes. The equation is

$$2KClO_3 \rightarrow 2KCl + 3O_2$$

If pure $KClO_3$ is heated in a test tube to 350 °C, a reaction takes place, but only very slowly, and it is many hours before a significant amount of oxygen is produced. If manganese dioxide (MnO_2) is mixed with the $KClO_3$, however, and the mixture heated to 350 °C, bubbling is observed immediately, and the reaction proceeds rapidly. The chemical equation for this reaction can be written

$$2KClO_3 + MnO_2 \xrightarrow{\text{heat}} 2KCl + 3O_2 + MnO_2$$

Most often, catalysts are written into the equations shown for MnO_2 in the following manner:

$$2KClO_3 \xrightarrow[\text{MnO}_2]{\text{heat}} 2KCl + 3O_2$$

The MnO_2 whoewho causes the $KClO_3$ to decompose faster than it does as a pure substance. However, the MnO_2 can be recovered unchanged after the reaction is completed. The manganese dioxide is a catalyst. Because of its

Figure 13.7 A catalyst has the effect of lowering the activation energy of a reaction as illustrated by the dotted line. This does not affect the quantity of materials which are produced in a reaction. The catalyst affects only the rate of reaction.

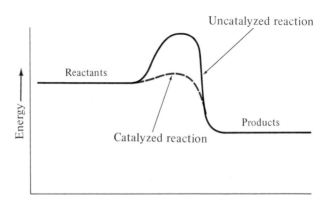

presence, the speed of reaction has been increased but the MnO_2 itself does not change as a result of the reaction.

Catalysts act in various ways to affect the speed of chemical reactions. When formula units collide, not all collisions bring about reactions.

Often the formula units do not collide with the right orientation for a reaction to occur.

Some catalysts act to hold reactant molecules in the correct orientations for effective collisions. Other catalysts help to form intermediates with reactants that are especially unstable and tend to break apart into products. Such is the case with MnO_2 in the $KClO_3$ decomposition. The MnO_2 molecule forms an intermediate with the ion ClO_3^-, which looks something like

$$O-Cl \begin{array}{c} O \\ \\ O \end{array} Mn \begin{array}{c} O^- \\ \\ O \end{array}$$

This intermediate can now decompose easily to form oxygen gas.

The enzymes in the human body are among the most important natural catalysts. Enzymes are biological catalysts that control the rate of chemical processes in plants and animal. These chemical processes control digestion, muscle movement, and all other physiological processes.

Concentration

The concentration of reactants also affects reaction speed. In many reactions, increasing the amount of any reactant increases the speed of the reaction. The theory that reactions result from collisions between particles fits this experimental result, since the presence of more reactant particles means that there are more collisions per unit time at a given temperature. More collisions per second mean a faster reaction. (See Figure 13.8.)

Figure 13.8 Higher concentrations of molecules cause more collisions, speeding up the reaction. For the same reaction (a) occurs more slowly than (b).

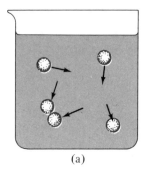

(a)

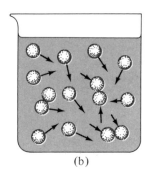

(b)

All these factors—temperature, concentration, and catalysis—are taken into account in a mathematical statement of reaction rates called the **rate law**. A rate law states the dependence of reaction rate on the concentration of reactants at a given temperature. It is an experimentally determined statement. For the reaction $2NO + 2H_2 \rightarrow N_2 + 2H_2O$, the rate law is

$$\text{Rate} = k \times (\text{concentration of NO})^2 \times \text{concentration of } H_2$$

This rate law shows the effect of concentration of reactants on the rate of the reaction. It also accounts for the effect of temperature and the presence of catalysts through k. Different reactions have differing k values. The larger the k values, the faster the reaction. Both k and the exponents on the concentration values are experimentally determined quantities. The exponents may or may not relate to the coefficients in the balanced equations. The rate law can be determined only from experiments; it cannot be deduced from a balanced equation. The rate law is a mathematical way of stating how fast a reaction proceeds and of indicating the factors affecting its speed.

If we look more closely at the rate law for the reaction of nitric oxide with hydrogen gas, we can see exactly how concentration changes affect the rate of reaction. If the reaction is allowed to proceed under the conditions shown in Experiment (a) of Table 13.1, the rate of the reaction is k:

$$\text{Rate} = (k)(1)(1)^2 = k$$

Doubling the concentration of H_2 while the concentration of NO is kept constant causes the reaction rate to double:

$$\text{Rate} = (k)(2)(1)^2 = 2k$$

These are the conditions shown in Experiment (b) of Table 13.1. Experiments (a), (b), and (c) in Table 13.1 indicate that increasing the concentration of H_2 causes the rate of the reaction to increase by a similar amount.

In Experiment (d) of Table 13.1, the concentration of NO is doubled, while the concentration of H_2 is held constant. In this case, the rate increases by the factor 4.

Table 13.1 Initial Concentration Conditions for H_2 and NO Reaction

Experiment	H_2 (mol/L)	NO (mol/L)	Rate (k)
(a)	1	1	1
(b)	2	1	2
(c)	4	1	4
(d)	1	2	4
(e)	1	4	16

$$\text{Rate} = k \times 1 \times 2^2 = 4k$$

Experiments (a), (d), and (e) indicate that the rate of the reaction changes with the square of the concentration of NO.

13.4 Chemical Equilibrium

The concept of dynamic equilibrium has been defined earlier. It had application for osmotic pressure, where passage of formula units through a semipermeable membrane constitutes an equilibrium. In osmosis, equilibrium is reached when equal numbers of formula units pass through the membrane in both directions.

The concept of dynamic equilibrium also is relevant to the vapor pressure of liquids, the conversion of solids to liquids, sublimation, solubility, and the dissociation of water into hydrogen and hydroxide ions. Equilibrium can also exist in chemical reactions. The existence of any chemical reaction implies the existence of a second reaction, the reaction in the opposite direction. If, for example, hydrogen and chlorine can react according to the equation

$$H_2 + Cl_2 \rightarrow 2HCl$$

the decomposition reaction is also possible,

$$2HCl \rightarrow H_2 + Cl_2$$

If hydrogen and chlorine are mixed in an open container, they can react, and the product, HCl, will spread out into the atmosphere (Figure 13.9). There is little chance that any of these product HCl molecules will ever encounter one another again. Another possibility for the reaction is in a closed container

Figure 13.9 If H_2 and Cl_2 are mixed in an open container, there is little chance that the product HCl molecules will ever encounter each other again.

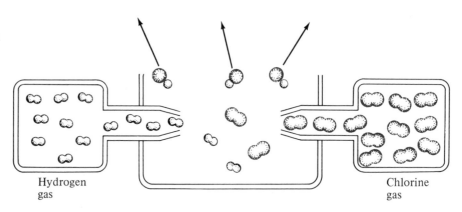

Hydrogen gas

Chlorine gas

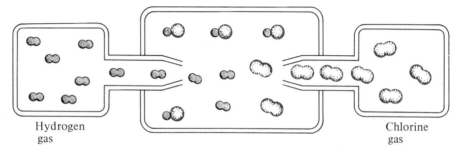

Hydrogen gas

Chlorine gas

(Figure 13.10). In this case, the HCl molecules form and remain in the reaction vessel. As more and more HCl forms, it becomes more probable that HCl molecules will be involved in collisions. Some of these collisions will cause HCl molecules to break apart and the original reactants might reappear as a result. Eventually, enough HCl is present and enough H_2 and Cl_2 have disappeared to cause HCl to form and disappear at the same rate. This is the definition of chemical equilibrium. If the formation of HCl is called the "forward reaction" and the decomposition of HCl the "reverse reaction," then chemical equilibrium is defined as the situation for which

Rate of forward reaction = rate of reverse reaction.

Thus, when equilibrium is reached, HCl is forming and decomposing at the same rate and there is no change in the general HCl concentration. This is another example of a dynamic equilibrium. The reaction can be shown as

$$H_2(g) + Cl_2(g) \rightleftarrows 2HCl(g)$$

The double arrow means that the reaction can go either way, and eventually reaches equilibrium. The "left to right" reaction is considered the forward reaction, and the right to left reaction the reverse reaction.

Another example of a reaction that reaches equilibrium in a sealed container is the reaction of NO_2 molecules with each other to form N_2O_4 molecules. It is expressed

$$2NO_2(g) \rightleftarrows N_2O_4(g)$$

When equilibrium is attained, N_2O_4 is forming and decomposing at the same rate, so that there is no net change in the amount of either NO_2 or N_2O_4 present. (See Figure 13.11.) Each of the two last-mentioned reactions is a gas-phase reaction—both reactants and products are gases. The reactions must be carried on in sealed containers, so that, with neither reactant nor product escaping, equilibrium can be attained.

Chemical equilibrium can also be reached in reactions in solution. Often in a reaction in a solution, all products and reactants remain in solution and the solution acts like a sealed container. Even when a precipitate forms or a

Figure 13.11 When equilibrium is reached, N_2O_4 is forming and decomposing at the same rate. At this time, the pressure on the system remains constant.

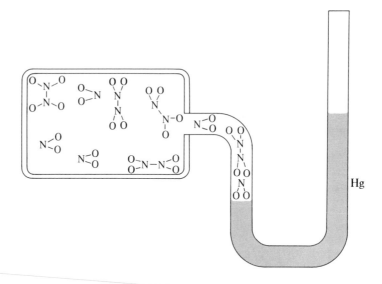

gas bubbles off, the product can remain in contact with the solution and enter an equilibrium.

First, consider an example of precipitation. When solutions of silver nitrate and sodium chloride are mixed, silver chloride precipitates according to the equation

$$Ag^+(aq) + NO_3^-(aq) + Na^+(aq) + Cl^-(aq) \rightleftarrows AgCl + Na^+(aq) + NO_3^-(aq)$$

Notice that the ions Na^+ and NO_3^- remain in solution, unchanged throughout the reaction. They are called **spectator ions**; they do not participate in the reaction. This equation is written as an equilibrium expression because the silver chloride remains in contact with the solution and some (if only a few) silver ions and chloride ions remain in solution. (See Figure 13.12.) An equi-

Figure 13.12 In the case of AgCl precipitation, the equilibrium lies far to the right of the equation $Ag^+ + Cl^- \rightleftarrows$ AgCl(s). Very few Ag^+ and Cl^- are left in solution.

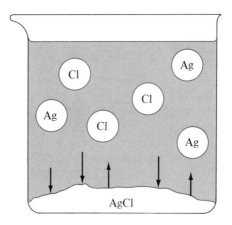

librium exists; ions are constantly leaving and entering the solution, and there is no net concentration change.

Next, consider an acid-base reaction. When hydrochloric acid and sodium hydroxide are allowed to react in solution, the reaction can be written

$$Na^+(aq) + OH^-(aq) + H^+(aq) + Cl^-(aq) \rightleftarrows Na^+(aq) + Cl^-(aq) + H_2O$$

All the ions and the water molecules remain in solution and continue to encounter each other. The equilibrium that is established involves only the water. This equilibrium can be written

$$H^+ + OH^- \rightleftarrows H_2O$$

omitting the spectator ions, $Na^+(aq)$ and $Cl^-(aq)$.

Whenever water is present, the ions H^+ and OH^- are present. The ions Na^+ and Cl^- are not involved in the equilibrium since they are always totally surrounded by water molecules (solvation) and do not form the ion pair Na^+Cl^- in solution. (See Figure 13.13.)

Chemical equilibrium can also exist in a reaction in which a gas is evolved. One such reaction involves adding an acid (HCl) to a solution of sodium carbonate (Na_2CO_3). In this reaction, H_2CO_3 forms, subsequently decomposing according to the reactions represented by the equation

$$2Na^+(aq) + CO_3{}^{2-}(aq) + H^+(aq) + Cl^-(aq) \rightleftarrows$$
$$HCO_3{}^-(aq) + 2Na^+(aq) + Cl^-(aq)$$

The Na^+ and the Cl^- are spectator ions and not involved in the equilibrium. The formation of the ion $HCO_3{}^-$ is followed by its reaction with another H^+ to produce the equilibrium:

$$HCO_3{}^-(aq) + H^+(aq) \rightleftarrows H_2CO_3(aq)$$

The H_2CO_3 formed can now decompose to form the gas CO_2, and one could

Figure 13.13 Ions in solution are completely surrounded by water molecules. The molecules are held to the ions by weak electrostatic forces.

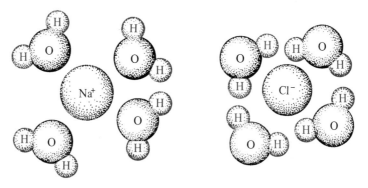

observe in a closed container the equilibrium

$$H_2CO_3(aq) \rightleftarrows H_2O + CO_2(g)$$

Trapping CO_2 above the solution eventually produces an equilibrium involving all six reactions (three forward and three reverse). These reactions are simultaneous, and there is no net change in concentration.

The equilibrium between carbon dioxide (CO_2) and water is commonly seen in an ordinary bottle of soda. When the top is removed from a bottle of soda, the conditions conducive to an equilibrium are destroyed as the trapped CO_2 is released from the bottle, and the CO_2 bubbles from the solution. The reaction equation is

$$H_2CO_3(aq) \rightleftarrows CO_2(g) + H_2O$$

The equilibrium can be described in terms of collisions—CO_2 bombards the water surface and combines with H_2O molecules to form H_2CO_3.

Finally, consider an oxidation-reduction reaction, represented by the equation

$$2Ag^+(aq) + 2NO_3{}^-(aq) + Zn(s) \rightleftarrows Zn^{2+}(aq) + 2NO_3{}^-(aq) + 2Ag(s)$$

When the reaction begins, $Zn(s)$ becomes Zn^{2+}, and silver ions, Ag^+, begin to precipitate from solution as silver metal. Eventually, the concentration of the ions Zn^{2+} and Ag^+ in solution becomes such that an equilibrium exists, and there is no net change in concentration of ions present. The explanation why this reaction reaches equilibrium is not a simple physical one; it can be stated in thermodynamic terms. While the complete explanation of this equilibrium will not concern us here, it is important to realize that even oxidation-reduction reactions reach an equilibrium, like all reactions in which products and reactants are confined together.

13.5

How Is the Existence of Equilibrium Confirmed?

Dynamic equilibrium as it exists for reactions can be proved in various ways. A simple experiment that indicates the existence of dynamic equilibrium is one involving iodine. Iodine atoms exist as several isotopes. Two of these are iodine-126, a stable isotope, and iodine-131, an unstable isotope, whose radioactivity can be measured (Chapter 17). Both isotopes of iodine act exactly the same chemically, but only iodine-131 emits radiation. With this information, consider a solution saturated with potassium iodide (KI) that contains only iodine-126. The solution emits no radiation. If a sample of solid KI containing some iodine-131 is placed in contact with the solution, an equilibrium exists, in which solid KI is constantly dissolving and the ions K^+ and I^- are combining to precipitate. In a true equilibrium, the iodine-131 will eventually be distributed between the solid and the solution, and the solution will become radioactive. This phenomenon has been experimentally observed; iodine-131 does become distributed throughout the solution, while the total quantity of solid at the bottom of the beaker and the total concentration of KI in solution remains the same. These results indicate a dynamic equilibrium.

13.6   The Equilibrium Constant

When reactions reach equilibrium, concentration of products and reactants remains constant, since forward and reverse reactions continue at equal rates. Under the same conditions of temperature and pressure, a specific reaction will always reach the same relative concentrations of reactants and products at equilibrium. Chemists use this knowledge to define the equilibrium constant for a reaction. The **equilibrium constant** K is a number that indicates whether the formation of products or of reactants dominates in a reaction. In the decomposition reaction

$$N_2O_4(g) \rightleftarrows 2NO_2(g)$$

for example, both the reactants and the products are gases. The equilibrium constant for this reaction is defined as

$$K = \frac{P_{NO_2}}{P_{N_2O_4}}$$

where P_{NO_2} equals the pressure exerted by NO_2 expressed in atmospheres and $P_{N_2O_4}$ equals the pressure exerted by N_2O_4 expressed in atmospheres.

> The constant K is a fraction, whose numerator consists of the pressures of the products at equilibrium raised to powers equal to their stoichiometric coefficients and whose denominator consists of the pressures of the reactants at equilibrium raised to their stoichiometric coefficients.

If the gas-phase reaction were $aA + bB \rightleftarrows cC + dD$, the equilibrium constant would be

$$K = \frac{P_C{}^c P_D{}^d}{P_A{}^a P_B{}^b}$$

Notice that each reactant is raised to the power of its coefficient in the balanced equation. You can see that K is definitely a constant at equilibrium, since at equilibrium, the pressures of reactants and products do not change. Expressing the equilibrium constant in pressures is correct for reactions that do not occur in solution.

The concept of an equilibrium constant can be expressed in more general terms for reactions in solution. If the reaction is a solution reaction, the equilibrium constant is formed by using concentrations of reactants and products. When acetic acid dissociates in water solution, the chemical equation is

$$HC_2H_3O_2(aq) \rightleftarrows H^+(aq) + C_2H_3O_2^-(aq)$$

and the equilibrium constant is

$$K = \frac{[C_2H_3O_2^-][H^+]}{[HC_2H_3O_2]}$$

Here, the quantities are molar concentrations (signified by the brackets). The equilibrium constant for this reaction is called an **acid dissociation constant**; it is often written K_a.

The equilibrium constant for the reaction

$$NH_3(aq) + H_2O \rightleftarrows NH_4^+(aq) + OH^-(aq)$$

is

$$K = \frac{[NH_4^+][OH^-]}{[NH_3]}$$

Notice that H_2O is missing. It has been omitted because $[H_2O]$ is constant and is simply absorbed into the value of K. A constant concentration does not affect the equilibrium. To prove this, we could write the equilibrium constant as

$$K' = \frac{[NH_4^+][OH^-]}{[NH_3][H_2O]}; \qquad \text{then} \qquad K'[H_2O] = \frac{[NH_4^+][OH^-]}{[NH_3]}$$

Since $[H_2O]$ is always the same, approximately $55M$, we can let $K = K'[H_2O]$. The concentration of any solid and any solvent is always included within the equilibrium constant.

A further example of this behavior can be seen by considering an equilibrium involving a material in a saturated solution. When mercuric chloride dissolves in water, the chemical equation can be written

$$HgCl_2(s) \rightleftarrows Hg^{+2}(aq) + 2Cl^-(aq)$$

The equilibrium constant for this reaction is written

$$K = [Hg^{2+}][Cl^-]^2$$

The $HgCl_2$ concentration is omitted from the equilibrium constant expression because $HgCl_2$ is a solid and has a constant concentration. For a reaction like this, the equilibrium constant is called a **solubility product constant**; it is written K_{sp}.

A final example of writing equilibrium constants will be the decomposition reaction that does not take place in solution:

$$CaCO_3(s) \rightleftarrows CaO(s) + CO_2(g)$$

Here, the $CaCO_3$ and CaO are omitted from the equilibrium-constant expression, and the equation produced is

$$K = P_{CO_2}$$

The numerical value of an equilibrium constant indicates whether reactants or products will be in excess at equilibrium. If the value of K is greater than 1, the right-hand side of the reaction is favored, and the products will be in excess at equilibrium.

Example 13.1

In the reaction $H_2(g) + S(s) \rightleftarrows H_2S(g)$, the equilibrium constant can be written

$$K = \frac{P_{H_2S}}{P_{H_2}}$$

Sulfur, a solid, has a negligible, almost constant vapor pressure, which is included in K. Experimentally, the value of K is found to be 6.3×10^5 at 298 K. Are reactants or products favored?

Since $P_{H_2S}/P_{H_2} = 6.3 \times 10^5$, there is 630,000 times as much H_2S present as H_2. If $H_2(g)$ and $S(s)$ are mixed in equal amounts, and the reaction is allowed to proceed to equilibrium, H_2S will form and there will be 630,000 molecules of H_2S for each S or H_2 molecule present. Products are favored.

Example 13.2

In the reaction $PCl_5(g) \rightleftarrows PCl_3(g) + Cl_2(g)$, the equilibrium constant expression is

$$K = \frac{P_{PCl_3}P_{Cl_2}}{P_{PCl_5}}$$

At 600 K, the constant $K = 26.3$. Are products or reactants favored?

The value of K means that the product pressure $P_{PCl_3}P_{Cl_2}$ is 26.3 times P_{PCl_5}. If this reaction were allowed to go to equilibrium, there would be about 5 molecules of PCl_3 and 5 molecules of Cl_2 present for each molecule of PCl_5. Products are favored.

Example 13.3

In the reaction $AgCl(s) \xrightarrow{H_2O} Ag^+(aq) + Cl^-(aq)$, for which the equilibrium constant is

$$K = [Ag^+][Cl^-]$$

at 298 K, the value $K = 1.7 \times 10^{-10}$. Are products or reactants favored?

If the concentrations of Ag^+ and Cl^- are equal in a solution, then

$$[Ag^+] = [Cl^-] = 1.3 \times 10^{-5} \, mol/L$$

and very little AgCl dissolves. Reactant, solid AgCl, predominates. This means that since 1 L of water contains about 55 mol water, there would need to be about 4.2 million moles of water present to dissolve 1 mol AgCl $[55/(1.3 \times 10^{-5}) = 4.2 \times 10^6]$.

Another example of using the equilibrium constant to predict status of reactants and products at equilibrium is the dissociation of acetic acid in water solution.

Example 13.4

For the reaction

$$HC_2H_3O_2(aq) \rightleftarrows H^+(aq) + C_2H_3O_2^-(aq)$$

$K = 1.8 \times 10^{-5}$ at 298 K. Write the equilibrium constant and decide whether reactants or products are favored.

The equilibrium constant is

$$K = \frac{[H^+][C_2H_3O_2^-]}{[HC_2H_3O_2]}$$

At 298 K, the value $K = 1.8 \times 10^{-5}$. This means that the ratio of numerator to denominator is 1.8×10^{-5}.

Since K has a value less than 1, reactant is favored.

Example 13.5

In the dissociation of water according to the equation $H_2O \rightleftarrows H^+ + OH^-$, where the equilibrium constant is defined as

$$K = [H^+][OH^-]$$

$K = 1 \times 10^{-14}$ at 298 K. Is reactant or product favored?

If H^+ and OH^- are present in equal amounts at equilibrium, approximately 5×10^8 water molecules are present for each H^+ or OH^- present. The reactant is clearly favored.

13.7 Le Châtelier's Principle

Whenever a chemical reaction reaches equilibrium, it does so under a specific set of conditions of temperature, pressure, and concentration of reactants and products. If these conditions are changed, the reactant and product concentrations will readjust until a new equilibrium is established. **Le Châtelier's principle** explains this readjustment and can be used to predict the results of changing reaction conditions. The principle states that if a chemical system at equilibrium is subjected to a stress (change in conditions) the concentrations of reactants and products will shift to relieve the effects of that stress.

Le Châtelier's principle can be applied to any reaction at equilibrium. Consider the reaction

$$H_2(g) + Br_2(g) \rightleftarrows 2HBr(g)$$

Since equilibrium is defined as the point at which the rate of the forward reaction equals the rate of the reverse reaction, the rate of the forward reaction here depends on how much H_2 and Br_2 are present. The rate of the reverse reaction depends on how much HBr is present. Let us examine the resulting shifts in equilibrium following certain stresses applied.

1. If more H_2 or more Br_2 is added, more HBr is formed, since the rate of the forward reaction increases; there is a larger reactant concentration. As more HBr is formed, the rate of the reverse reaction increases until the rate of the forward reaction equals the rate of the reverse reaction; a new equilibrium position is established. The reaction has relieved the stress of added reactant by forming more product from the added reactant.

2. If more HBr is added at equilibrium, more H_2 and Br_2 are formed, since the rate of the reverse reaction has been increased over the forward reaction. As more H_2 and Br_2 are formed, the rate of the forward reaction increases until the rates of the forward and reverse reactions are equal. A new equilibrium has now been established. The reaction has relieved the stress of added product by forming more reactant from the added product.

Figure 13.14 The original equilibrium (a) is disturbed with the addition of more reactant (R), shown in (b). This reaction produces more product (P), but in order to maintain the same equilibrium as in (a), more reactant is also present (c).

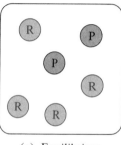

(a) Equilibrium (4R and 2P)

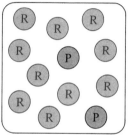

(b) Addition of reactant: equilibrium not yet established

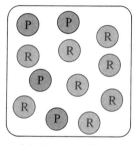

(c) New equilibrium established, with more product present (8R and 4P)

In general, Le Châtelier's principle means that adding reactant assures more product in the new equilibrium. Adding product assures more reactant in the new equilibrium. (See Figure 13.14.)

Example 13.6

If a stress is placed on the reaction

$$PCl_5(g) \rightleftarrows PCl_3(g) + Cl_2(g)$$

by decreasing container size, all pressures increase. Which way does the equilibrium shift?

If the container is made smaller, the probability for PCl_3 collisions with Cl_2 is higher. The PCl_5 decomposition rate does not increase so much; thus the rate of the reverse reaction increases. This continues until enough PCl_5 forms to equalize the forward and reverse rates. The result is a shift in equilibrium to form more PCl_5 (Figure 13.15). The left side of the reaction is favored.

Figure 13.15 Reducing the volume of the container means an overall increase in the pressure. This will cause reaction

$$PCl_5(g) \rightleftarrows PCl_3(g) + Cl_2(g)$$

to shift toward the reactant side.

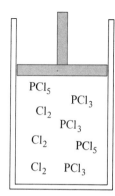
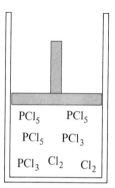

In general, Le Châtelier's principle states that if the pressure is increased on a reaction involving gases, the side favored is the one on which fewer moles of gas are formed. The reason is that the stress of pressure increase is relieved when the equilibrium shifts toward the side with fewer gas molecules.

Example 13.7

In the reaction

$$CaCO_3(s) \rightleftarrows CaO(s) + CO_2(g)$$

how does increasing pressure affect the equilibrium?

The left, or reactant, side is favored because fewer moles of gas are present.

Example 13.8

In the reaction

$$2NO_2(g) \rightleftarrows N_2O_4(g)$$

does decreasing pressure favor reactants or products?

Decreasing pressure favors the reactant side, because more moles of gas are present on the left side of the equation. In an attempt to regain the original pressure, N_2O_4 will dissociate to form NO_2, and create more molecules which lead to a higher pressure.

13.8

Why Products Are Favored in Some Reactions and Reactants in Others

The equilibrium constant, we have found, is a factor in determining the favored side of the equation for chemical reactions at equilibrium. The equilibrium constant is an experimentally determined number. At equilibrium, concentration or pressure, or both, of reactants and products is measured and an equilibrium constant is calculated from these. Why do equilibrium constants have the values that they have?

Consider the following three reactions at 298 K, along with their equilibrium constants:

$$H_2(g) + F_2(g) \rightleftarrows 2HF(g) \qquad k = 2.51 \times 10^{47}$$

$$H_2(g) + Cl_2(g) \rightleftarrows 2HCl(g) \qquad k = 4.90 \times 10^{16}$$

$$H_2(g) + Br_2(l) \rightleftarrows 2HBr(g) \qquad k = 2.12 \times 10^{9}$$

In all three reactions, the products are highly favored. However, HF is more favored than HCl, which is more favored than HBr, if we compare the sizes of the equilibrium constants. Physically, the most important difference among these products is the bond strength. The H–F bond is stronger than the H–Cl bond, which is stronger than the H–Br bond. Remember that equilibrium is defined as the point at which the rates of the forward and reverse reactions are equal. The forward reaction consists of the formation of HF, HCl, or HBr. These substances form at approximately the same rate. The reverse reaction consists of the decomposition of HF, HCl or HBr. Once a product forms, the collisions that cause it to decompose must be of high enough energy to cause the product molecule to break apart. The product having the strongest bond will decompose least easily, so its formation is the most favored. In a comparison of HF with HCl and HBr, fewer collisions at a single temperature will be effective in causing HF to break up. Thus, the HF decomposition will be slower than the HCl, which will be slower than the HBr. This idea fits well with the relative sizes of the k's. Hydrogen fluoride has the largest k value, HCl has the next, and HBr has the smallest. This consideration has neglected to consider the effect of the differences in the F–F, Cl–Cl, and Br–Br bond strengths on the relative rates of the forward reactions, because they have only small effects on the equilibrium constants.

This kind of argument works well in explaining the relative sizes of k values in most reactions, which are determined by the relative stabilities of reactants and products.

Glossary

Activation Energy
The minimum energy that must be available in a collision if that collision is to cause reactants to convert to products.

Catalyst
A substance that increases the rate of a chemical reaction but undergoes no change itself.

Chemical equilibrium
A condition involving two opposite reactions that have the same rate. There is no net change in the amount of reactants and products present.

Chemical kinetics
The study of speed of chemical reactions and also the individual steps through which a reaction proceeds.

Dissociation constant
The equilibrium constant for molecules or ions that dissociate or break into smaller fragments.

Equilibrium constant
The product of the concentration or pressures of the individual products in a chemical reaction raised to the power of the coefficients of the balanced equa-

tion divided by the concentration or pressures of the individual reactants raised to the power of the coefficients of the balanced equation.

Le Châtelier's principle   If a stress is applied to a system in equilibrium, the equilibrium will shift to reduce the applied stress.

Rate law   A mathematical statement that relates the reaction rate and the concentration of the reactants or of the products.

Solubility product constant   The equilibrium constant for a solid material in equilibrium with a saturated solution of that material.

Problems

1. Explain the difference between chemical kinetics and thermodynamics.

2. A 3-min egg (a raw egg cooked in boiling water for 3 min) prepared in San Francisco is considered by many people to be a delight to the palate. A 3-min egg served in Denver, Colorado (the mile-high city), would probably be returned to the kitchen for more cooking. How is kinetics related to this problem?

3. In 1910 there were very few collisions between automobiles. Today during rush-hour traffic in big cities, police are continually busy investigating automobile accidents. If you were to consider this a rate problem (number of accidents per day), to what would you attribute the increase in the rate of automobile accidents? Are there any similarities between your explanation and the collision of molecules in a chemical reaction?

4. It became almost impossible to travel a road between two small northern towns during snow-storms last winter because of a large hill situated halfway between the two towns. The traffic was often reduced to only a few cars an hour because of the hill. The county used a large bulldozer to build a new road by cutting a channel through the hill, thus reducing the climb. The number of cars an hour navigating the road increased tre-mendously. By a kinetics analogy, what function

did the bulldozer serve? Could there be any other factors involved in the number of cars per hour on the road?

5. A study was made of the number of students leaving a college dormitory per hour. Data were collected as shown in the accompanying table. Propose a rate equation to fit the data.

	No. Students Leaving per Hour	No. Calls from Professors	No. Open Doors	No. Calls from Girl Friends
Hour 1	4	1	1	1
Hour 2	8	1	2	1
Hour 3	4	5	1	1
Hour 4	16	1	1	2

6. What effect do temperature, concentration of reactants, and catalysts have on the speed of a reaction?

7. For the hypothetical reaction $A + B \rightarrow C$, the following information was obtained. When the concentration of A was doubled (B held constant), the rate formation of C was doubled. When the concentration of B was doubled, with A held constant, the rate of formation of C was doubled. Propose a rate equation.

8. For the hypothetical reaction A + B → C, data were obtained as shown in the accompanying table. Initial concentrations are given for the A + B reaction. Propose a rate equation.

Experiment	A (mol/L)	B (mol/L)	Rate (k)
(a)	1	1	1
(b)	2	1	2
(c)	4	1	4
(d)	1	2	4
(e)	1	4	16

9. Write the chemical equilibrium expressions for the following reactions.
(a) $2NO(g) + O_2(g) \rightleftarrows 2NO_2(g)$
(b) $N_2(g) + O_2(g) \rightleftarrows 2NO(g)$
(c) $C(s) + H_2O(g) \rightleftarrows CO(g) + H_2(g)$
(d) $AgF(aq) + KCl(aq) \rightleftarrows AgCl(s) + KF(aq)$
(e) $HCl(g) + Na_2S(s) \rightleftarrows H_2S(g) + 2NaCl(s)$

10. Write the chemical equilibrium expressions for the following reactions.
(a) $H_2CO_3(aq) \rightleftarrows H_2O(l) + CO_2(g)$

(b) $SO_2Cl_2(g) \rightleftarrows SO_2(g) + Cl_2(g)$
(c) $H_2(g) + Br_2(g) \rightleftarrows 2HBr(g)$
(d) $Pb(s) + PbO_2(s) + 2H_2SO_4(g) \rightleftarrows 2PbSO_4(s) + 2H_2O(g)$

11. In the reaction $2NOBr(g) \rightleftarrows 2NO(g) + Br_2(g)$, in which direction will the equilibrium be shifted by the following changes?
(a) Increasing the concentration of NOBr
(b) Increasing the concentration of Br_2
(c) Decreasing the pressure of NO
(d) Increasing the total pressure on the system
(e) Increasing the pressure of NOBr

12. In the reaction

$$HC_2H_3O_2(aq) \rightleftarrows H^+(aq) + C_2H_3O_2^-(aq),$$

in which direction will the equilibrium be shifted by the following changes?
(a) Increasing the concentration of $HC_2H_3O_2$
(b) Increasing the concentration of H^+
(c) Decreasing the concentration of $C_2H_3O_2^-$
(d) Decreasing the total amount of water present
(e) Increasing the pressure on the system

Learning Objectives for Chapter 14

Define **electricity, electrochemistry, current, resistance, electrolyte, strong electrolyte, weak electrolyte, nonelectrolyte, electrode, anode, cathode, electrolytic cell, electrolysis, voltaic cell, half-cell, salt bridge, standard hydrogen electrode, standard half-cell.**

Explain the model for electrical conductance.

Explain how solutions conduct electricity.

Explain the effect of ionic size on solution conductance.

Given the components, predict the reaction that will take place in an electrolytic cell.

Explain how a voltaic cell might be made.

Given a voltaic cell reaction, predict which reactant will be the anode and which the cathode.

Given cell components, calculate the voltage of the cell. write the cell reaction, and predict which component will be the anode and which the cathode.

Explain how batteries function.

14 ELECTROCHEMISTRY

Electrical energy is probably the most common form of energy in the present-day, highly technological society. Electricity is used to run motors, to provide the necessary energy for radio, television, and practically all communications, to weld metals, to manufacture chemicals, and to heat homes. Electrical energy is clean, easily transportable over large distances, and able to be produced easily and also stored.

> **Electricity** can be thought of as streams of electrons, the same electrons found in atoms.

Electricity is often produced by the chemical interaction of various substances, and it can be used to produce and purify elements and compounds. **Electrochemistry**, then, is the study of the relation between chemistry and electricity. Many of the basic particles of which matter is composed are electrical. Electrons are negatively charged, protons are positively charged, and ions, having charges resulting from an imbalance in numbers of protons and electrons present, can be either positively or negatively charged. The presence of these charged particles in matter can cause an object to have a net charge, to conduct electricity, or to be useful as part of a battery that produces electricity. Thus, electricity and the particles composing matter are closely related.

14.1 Electrical Terms

Electric current results from the movement of charge. The basic unit of electric current, the **ampere** (abbreviated A), is defined as quantity of charge that passes a point per unit time. Scientists believe that electrons are the primary charge

Figure 14.1 A copper wire can be thought of as containing a sea of electrons. Electrons move along the wire, creating a measurable current.

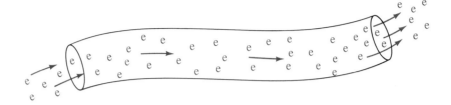

carriers in most substances. Thus, the flow of electricity along a wire can be thought of as the flow of electrons along that wire. (See Figure 14.1.)

These electrons are "pushed" along the wire by **electrical potential**.

Electrons flow from a point of high potential energy to a point of low potential energy, much as a river flows from high ground to low ground. The steeper the grade, the faster movement of the water. Differences in potential energy along a wire can be caused by making one end of the wire more negative than the other end. The negative electrons then are pushed from the more negative end toward the less negative end. Such a difference in potential energy can be caused by connecting a battery to a wire (Figure 14.2) and completing a circuit. The battery, made as it is of two different electrodes, each containing a different substance, creates a difference in potential; different substances have unequal capacities for retaining electrons. Thus, if electrons are transferred through an external circuit, a wire, from one substance to another, current flows. The greater the difference between the substances ability to retain electrons, the greater the potential energy for pushing the electrons along the wire. Electrical potential is measured in units called **volts** (abbreviated V).

Resistance is another important electrical property. Different substances have different abilities to resist the flow of electricity (or electrons). The concept can be likened to the river that moves from high to low ground. The steeper the grade, the faster the flow of the water. But what happens if a series of dams are placed between the high ground and the low ground? The water will be slowed. In other words, a high potential does not necessarily mean a high current flow, just as a steep hill does not necessarily mean that water will rush down its slopes. The current and the rate of water flow also depend on the situation between the points at which measurements are made. Metals, for

Figure 14.2 Electricity passes through a wire because of potential energy differences, as in this example of a car battery connected to a motor.

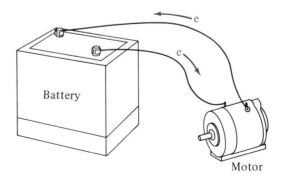

example, conduct electricity easily, whereas nonmetals do not. Many nonmetals are insulators and do not conduct electricity at all. Nonmetals have a high resistance to current flow and metals have a low resistance to current flow. Resistance is measured in units called **ohms**. (The ohm is abbreviated Ω, the Greek capital **omega**.)

The final electrical unit that it is important to define is the watt (abbreviated W). The **watt** is a measure of power used to rate light bulbs. A 100-W light bulb emits more light than a 25-W light bulb. It is more powerful.

14.2   Conductance

Metals and Nonmetals

Substances can be classified according to their ability to conduct electricity. Among the elements, metals generally conduct electricity well, whereas non-metals are very poor conductors of electricity. Substances that conduct electricity poorly are called **insulators**. Stated another way, metals have low resistances (they allow electrons to flow easily), and nonmetals have high resistances (they resist the flow of electrons). Table 14.1 shows that samples of metals have much lower resistances than comparable samples of nonmetals and therefore conduct electricity much more easily. **Conductance** of electricity can be defined by movement of electrons. Thus metals, which have mobile, easily lost electrons in the outer shells of their atoms, are better conductors than nonmetals, which tend to gain rather than lose electrons. Nonmetals are such poor conductors that they are used to insulate metal wires that carry electrical current (thereby keeping the electricity confined to the wire).

Table 14.1   Resistance Values of Elements

Element[a]	Symbol	Metal or Nonmetal	Resistance (ohms)
Aluminum	Al	M	2.65×10^{-6}
Copper	Cu	M	1.67×10^{-6}
Gold	Au	M	2.35×10^{-6}
Lead	Pb	M	2.07×10^{-5}
Platinum	Pt	M	1.06×10^{-5}
Silver	Ag	M	1.59×10^{-6}
Carbon	C	N	1.375×10^{-3}
Iodine	I	N	1.3×10^{9}
Phosphorus	P	N	1×10^{12}
Sulfur	S	N	2×10^{17}

[a] Sample consists of a cube, 1 cm on each side.

Solutions

Water solutions can also be classified by their ability to conduct electricity. Pure water does not conduct electricity, even though water molecules are polar. An applied voltage causes the water molecules to turn until their negative ends point toward the positive contact and the positive ends point toward the negative contact. Since each end of the molecule is attracted in the opposite direction, no net motion of charged particles results, and no current flows (Figure 14.3).

If a substance that produces ions in solution is dissolved, the situation is entirely different. Positive ions (cations) are attracted by the negatively charged electrode and migrate in that direction. Negative ions (anions) are attracted to the positively charged electrode and migrate toward it. This migration of charged particles causes a flow of current. Such a flow of current through a solution is called **electrolytic conduction**. It results from the movement of ions (Figure 14.4). If the solution of a compound in water conducts electricity, that compound is called an **electrolyte**. Ionic compounds are electrolytes to whatever extent they dissolve in water.

The higher the concentration of ions in the solution, the larger the current flow (or equivalently, the lower the resistance). Thus, a solution that contains 0.1 mol NaCl per liter, which dissociates completely into ions, will conduct electricity more efficiently than a solution of 0.01 mol NaCl per liter. Ionic

Figure 14.3 In pure water, the H_2O molecules orient themselves toward the respective electrodes. No current flows.

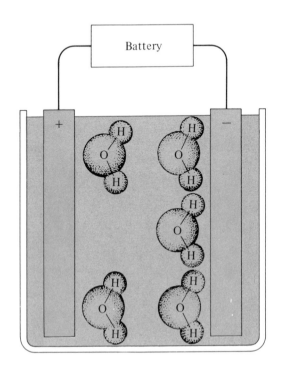

Figure 14.4 If ions are present, positive ions migrate toward the electron-rich electrode, where they are reduced; negative ions migrate toward the electron-poor electrode, where they are oxidized; hence the current flows.

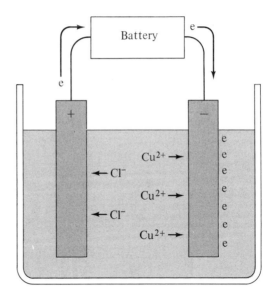

compounds that are essentially 100 percent dissociated in water are called **strong electrolytes**.

If 0.1 mol of acetic acid is dissolved to make 1 L of solution, there will be an equilibrium:

$$HC_2H_3O_2 \rightleftharpoons H^+(aq) + C_2H_3O_2{}^-(aq)$$

Since the equilibrium constant for this reaction is small (1.8×10^{-5}), the reactant, undissociated acetic acid, is favored. Therefore, there are relatively few ions present, and the acetic acid solution will not conduct nearly so much electricity as a sodium chloride solution of equal concentration. Substances that ionize only partially in water solution are called **weak electrolytes**. They conduct electricity only marginally.

Compounds like sugar dissolve in water and do not ionize at all. Such compounds are **nonelectrolytes**, and their solutions do not conduct electricity at all.

One other factor, aside from the number of ions in solution, determines how well the solution of an electrolyte will conduct electricity. This factor is the effective size of the ion. Large ions will be held back by the water molecules more than small ions, and they will move more slowly. For the same electrical potential, a solution that contains 0.1 mol of CsI per liter will conduct less electricity than a solution that contains 0.1 mol NaCl per liter. The number of ions in the two solutions is the same, but the cesium ions are larger than the sodium ions, and the iodide ions are larger than the chloride ions, respectively, and thus the cesium and iodide ions move more slowly. The slower the movement of the ions, the lower the conductance of the solution.

14.3

Electrolysis

Consider, now, a detailed description of what is happening when current is passed through a liquid (Figure 14.5). Two electrical contacts called **electrodes** are placed in the liquid. When the switch is closed and the circuit completed, electrons flow in one direction.

The electrons in the external circuit flow toward the **cathode**, the electrode that is negatively charged, and away from the **anode**, the other electrode, which is positively charged. Electrons are emitted at the cathode and absorbed at the anode.

If two such electrodes are placed in a molten sample of potassium chloride, a reaction takes place. Current begins to flow, potassium ions move toward the cathode, and chloride ions move toward the anode. At the cathode, electrons are emitted and a reduction is the result:

$$K^+ + e^- \rightarrow K$$

Reduction occurs at the cathode.

At the anode, electrons are absorbed and oxidation is the result:

$$Cl^- \rightarrow \tfrac{1}{2}Cl_2 + e^-$$

Oxidation occurs at the anode.

Electrons as such are not bodily moved across the container; their source is the ions, which are picking them up at the cathode and giving them off at

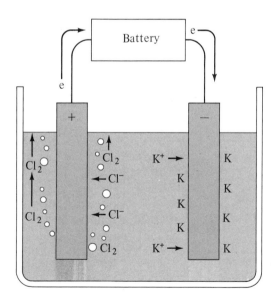

Figure 14.5 Positive potassium ions pick up an electron to become potassium metal at the cathode. Chloride ions lose an electron and then combine to form Cl_2 at the anode.

the anode. The process is called **electrolysis** and the apparatus is called an **electrolytic cell**. In an electrolytic cell, chemical changes occur when electrical energy is supplied from outside the cell.

Electrolysis is possible with any molten, ionic compound. The compound must be in liquid form so that the ions are mobile and electrical conductance is possible. The voltage necessary to cause electrolysis in a cell depends on the difficulty in causing the oxidation or reduction. According to the activity series (Chapter 9), it is more difficult to reduce lithium than to reduce potassium, and it is more difficult to reduce potassium than sodium. Thus, if LiCl, KCl, and NaCl were electrolyzed in separate experiments, the reactions would be the following:

$$\text{Cathode:} \quad \begin{cases} Li^+ + e^- \rightarrow Li \\ K^+ + e^- \rightarrow K \\ Na^+ + e^- \rightarrow Na \end{cases}$$

$$\text{Anode:} \quad Cl^- \rightarrow \tfrac{1}{2}Cl_2 + e^-$$

The voltage needed for electrolyzing LiCl is larger than what is necessary to electrolyze KCl; and that voltage is larger than what is necessary to electrolyze NaCl. These kinds of electrolytic processes are often used commercially to produce pure elements.

Electrolysis can also go on in water solutions. For the mixture of a solute dissolved in water, however, the oxidation-reduction that would be the reaction if the solute were pure must compete with the oxidation of water at the anode and its reduction at the cathode. These competing reactions are:

$$\text{Anode:} \quad 2H_2O \rightarrow 4H^+ + O_2 + 4e^- \qquad \text{(oxidation)}$$

$$\text{Cathode:} \quad 2H_2O + 2e^- \rightarrow H_2 + 2OH^- \qquad \text{(reduction)}$$

The likelihood of these reactions depends on the composition of the cathode, the anode, and the solute. The rules for determining the particular reactions are these:

1. If the cathode is a metal far down on the activity series, like platinum or gold, the character of the solute determines which reactions occur.

   (a) When the positive ion in solution is above the cathode reaction for water on the activity series (see Table 14.2 p. 357), water is reduced at the cathode; the solution is assumed neutral. If the positive ion in solution is lower, the metal ion itself is reduced.

   (b) When it is difficult to oxidize the negative ion in the solute (F^-, Cl^-, Br^-, NO_3^-, SO_4^{2-}), that is, when the negative ion is below the anode reaction for water, water is oxidized at the anode. If the negative ion is more easily oxidized (I^-), the ion itself will be oxidized; again a neutral aqueous solution is assumed.

2. When the anode material is a metal lower on the activity series than the cathode reaction for water, the anode itself will be oxidized.

Example 14.1

A current is passed through a water solution of potassium iodide at sufficient potential to oxidize or reduce any species present. The anode and cathode are made of platinum. Write equations for the anode and cathode reactions.

Cathode. Potassium is higher on the activity series than the cathode reaction for water. The reduction at the cathode therefore is

$$2H_2O + 2e^- \rightarrow H_2 + 2OH^-$$

and H_2 bubbles off.

Anode. Iodide is an easily oxidized anion. It is above the anode reaction for water. The oxidation at the anode therefore is

$$2I^- \rightarrow I_2 + 2e^-$$

Example 14.2

An electrolytic cell consists of platinum electrodes immersed in a solution of nickel nitrate $(Ni(NO_3)_2)$. Write equations for anode and cathode reactions. Both electrodes are platinum.

Cathode. Nickel is lower than the cathode reaction for water on the activity series. The reduction at the cathode is

$$Ni^{2+} + 2e^- \rightarrow Ni$$

Anode. Nitrate is a negative ion that it is difficult to oxidize. It lies below the anode reaction for water; therefore the anode oxidation is

$$2H_2O \rightarrow 4H^+ + O_2 + 4e^-$$

In any electrolytic cell, there must be both an oxidation and a reduction. The total number of electrons gained and lost must balance. Any depiction of the total reaction, oxidation and reduction combined, would show no electrons.

14.4   Useful Aspects of Electrolysis

Electrolysis is a process used extensively in many industries. Many metals are purified from their ores in two steps. The first step involves extracting a metal salt from the ore. The second step consists in electrolyzing the molten salt to

Figure 14.6 The preparation of aluminum metal by electrolysis of aluminum hydroxide. Aluminum ore (bauxite) is purified by addition of NaOH. The resulting aluminum hydroxide is mixed with Na_3AlF_6, CaF_2, and NaF. That mixture is melted and then electrolyzed, producing pure molten aluminum.

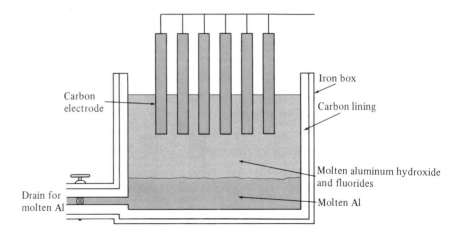

get the pure metal at the cathode. Preparing aluminum is a good example of metal purification. Aluminum exists naturally as bauxite ore, impure Al_2O_3. This aluminum oxide is chemically purified, melted with Na_3AlF_6, CaF_2, and NaF, and then placed in an electrolytic cell that has carbon anodes. The reactions are

$$\text{Cathode:} \quad Al^{3+} + 3e^- \rightarrow Al$$

$$\text{Anode:} \quad C + 2O^{2-} \rightarrow CO_2 + 4e^-$$

The complete reaction is

$$2Al_2O_3 + 3C \xrightarrow{\text{electrolysis}} 4Al + 3CO_2$$

Thus, pure aluminum is produced at the cathode, and harmless CO_2 bubbles off at the anode. Notice that the anode takes part in the reaction, providing the carbon for CO_2. This cell is shown in Figure 14.6.

Metals can also be purified in electrolytic cells. If impure metal plates, made of the metal to be purified, are used as anodes, and pure metal plates of the same metal are used as cathodes, an electrolysis using a solution of the metal's salts will cause the impure anode material to oxidize and enter the solution. Meanwhile, pure metal is being plated out on the cathode and can be removed. An example of this process, known as electrorefining, is shown in Figure 14.7.

Electroplating is an electrolytic process in which a thin coating of metal is deposited on an object. The object to be plated is used as the cathode so that the metal is plated onto it. Common examples of the result of this process are silverplated cutlery and serving dishes, which have become popular as solid sterling silver objects have become increasingly expensive.

Electroforming consists in allowing a thick coat of metal to be deposited on a mold that is used as the cathode. This thick coat of metal is then peeled

Figure 14.7 Impure metal plates are used as anodes; pure metal plates are used as cathodes. Pure Cu moves from the impure electrode and is plated out on the pure Cu electrode. The purification process is called electrorefining.

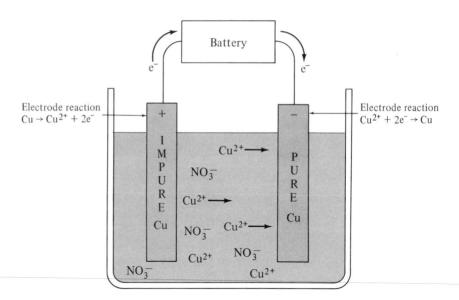

Electrode reaction
$Cu \rightarrow Cu^{2+} + 2e^-$

Electrode reaction
$Cu^{2+} + 2e^- \rightarrow Cu$

from the mold and used. Electroforming is used in the record industry to produce master molds, from which individual records are made. A recording is made on plastic that is cut with a needle. Nickel is then electroformed onto the original plastic. The nickel master is then peeled off and used as the mold for the records, which are stamped into it from large plastic sheets.

Finally, many industrially important chemical compounds are produced electrolytically. Such compounds include $NaOH$, $NaClO_3$, MnO_2, $KMnO_4$, and H_2O_2. Electrolytic processes are used because they are cheaper than chemical processes and the resulting products are pure.

14.5   Voltaic Cells

In a **voltaic cell**, chemical reactions occur that produce electricity.

Voltaic cells are essentially the opposite of electrolytic cells. The first such cell, in crude form, was discovered by Louis Galvani in the late 1700s, when he noticed that newly severed frogs' legs twitched when suspended from copper hooks hanging from an iron bar. Galvani thought that the small current that caused the legs to twitch came from the frogs' legs themselves. Alessandro Volta (1745–1827) eventually correctly theorized that the junction between the copper and iron caused the electric current to exist, hence the cell's name.

To see how the copper-iron junction is responsible for production of current, consider a more common voltaic cell. The Daniell cell is shown in Figure 14.8. The cell consists of two half-cells. Each **half-cell** consists of an electrode and an electrolyte solution. The electrodes are connected by wires through a current-measuring device (ammeter) or a potential-difference-measuring device (voltmeter). The circuit is completed when the electrolytes are connected through a salt bridge (see Figure 14.9, page 355).

A **salt bridge** is a gel containing ions, in this case the ions K^+ and Cl^-, which can migrate from the salt bridge but are not oxidized or reduced during cell functioning. The salt bridge provides an electrical connection between the two electrolyte solutions and prevents mixing.

The electrolyte solutions are $CuSO_4$ and $ZnSO_4$. The electrodes are copper metal and zinc metal.

Copper and zinc have unequal abilities to retain electrons. Zinc loses electrons more easily than copper. Thus, zinc is more easily oxidized to Zn^{2+} than copper to Cu^{2+}. A statement that is also true is that Cu^{2+} is more easily reduced to copper metal than Zn^{2+} is reduced to zinc metal.

When copper, zinc, and the ions Cu^{2+} and Zn^{2+} are placed in a voltaic cell, several things happen.

1. A zinc atom leaves two electrons on the electrode and enters the solution as an ion, Zn^{2+}.

2. Two chloride ions, Cl^-, enter the left beaker from the salt bridge to cancel the two extra positive ions present from the Zn^{2+}

3. The two electrons left on the zinc metal electrode cause an excess of two electrons in the wire. For this condition to become righted, two electrons are removed from the wire at the electrode in the right beaker as a Cu^{2+} is reduced to a copper atom.

Figure 14.8 Schematic diagram of a Daniell cell. Electrons flow from the zinc electrode through the external circuit to the copper electrode.

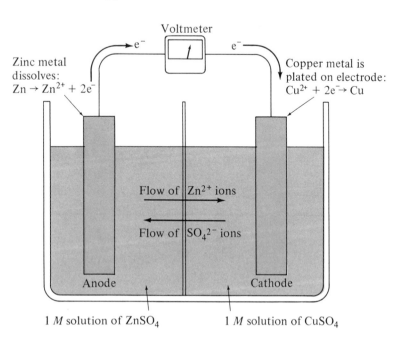

VOLTAIC CELLS   Sec. 14.5

353

4. The loss of two positive charges in the solution in the right beaker is canceled as two potassium ions, K^+, move into the solution from the salt bridge.

Each of these steps is repeated many times as many formula units are oxidized and reduced.

Each side of the voltaic cell is called a half-cell. The reactions that go on in each half-cell are:

$$\text{Cathode:} \quad Cu^{2+} + 2e^- \rightarrow Cu$$

$$\text{Anode:} \quad Zn \rightarrow Zn^{2+} + 2e^-$$

The complete reaction in the cell is

$$Cu^{2+} + Zn \rightarrow Zn^{2+} + Cu$$

Notice several details about what is happening in this cell. Electrons are flowing through the wire from the zinc electrode to the copper electrode.

Since the copper electrode is the site of the reduction, it is the cathode.
Since the zinc electrode is the site of the oxidation, it is the anode.

As the reaction proceeds, the zinc electrode begins to disappear as the zinc is oxidized to the ion Zn^{2+}. Similarly, copper metal plates out on the copper electrode as the Cu^{2+} is reduced. Eventually, the zinc electrode will disappear or all the copper ions will be removed from solution, and the reaction will cease. If an ammeter is hooked into this circuit, a current is measured. If a voltmeter is hooked into the circuit, a voltage is measured. The cell is a **battery**, a chemical device for producing electricity.

The cell produces electricity because there is a difference in potential for oxidation of the metals involved. The voltage of the cell depends on the metals involved, the temperature, the concentration of the ions in the electrolyte solutions, and the anions associated with the cations in solution. Many other cells are possible; the kind depends on the metals involved.

Consider a voltaic cell having cadmium and tin electrodes (Figure 14.9). It is possible to figure out which metal acts as the cathode and which as the anode by using the activity series for the metals. The metal that is the most easily oxidized, cadmium, is the anode, the electrode that disappears. Tin is the most easily reduced, so it is plated out on the cathode. The half-cell reactions are:

$$\text{Cathode:} \quad Sn^{2+} + 2e^- \rightarrow Sn \quad \text{(reduction)}$$

$$\text{Anode:} \quad Cd \rightarrow Cd^{2+} + 2e^- \quad \text{(oxidation)}$$

Figure 14.9 Electrons flow through the external circuit of a voltaic cell from the cadmium electrode to the tin electrode. At the Cd electrode, $Cd \rightarrow Cd^{2+} + 2e^-$. At the Sn electrode, $Sn^{2+} + 2e^- \rightarrow Sn$.

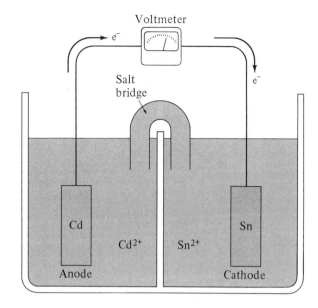

The complete cell reaction is

$$Sn^{2+} + Cd \rightarrow Cd^{2+} + Sn$$

The voltage of the cell depends on the factors already mentioned.

Half-cells need not be metallic. The **standard hydrogen electrode** is an example of a nonmetallic half-cell. It is shown in Figure 14.10. In the standard

Figure 14.10 To create a standard hydrogen electrode, shown here, hydrogen gas at a pressure of one atmosphere and a temperature of 25 °C must be bubbled over a platinum black electrode. The solution must be 1 molar in hydrogen ions.

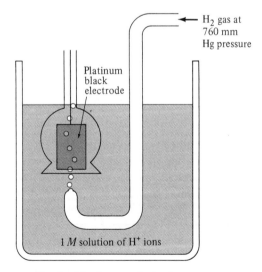

Standard hydrogen electrode

hydrogen electrode (abbreviated SHE), the reaction if the SHE is the anode is

$$H_2 \rightarrow 2H^+ + 2e^-$$

If the SHE is the cathode, then reduction occurs:

$$2H^+ + 2e^- \rightarrow H_2$$

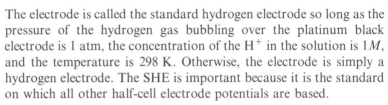

The electrode is called the standard hydrogen electrode so long as the pressure of the hydrogen gas bubbling over the platinum black electrode is 1 atm, the concentration of the H^+ in the solution is $1M$, and the temperature is 298 K. Otherwise, the electrode is simply a hydrogen electrode. The SHE is important because it is the standard on which all other half-cell electrode potentials are based.

It is arbitrarily assigned a value of zero volts, and all other half-cell potentials are either positive or negative, depending on whether the electrode acts as the cathode or the anode. A list of common half-cell potentials is shown in Table 14.2, along with the related activity series. Just as specific conditions exist for the standard hydrogen electrode, specific conditions can be stated for all half-cells. When these conditions are met, a **standard half-cell** potential is defined. These standard conditions include the presence of $1M$ solutions of all ions, a temperature of 298 K, and a pressure of 1 atm for all gases.

A metal atom is more easily oxidized than hydrogen if its standard electrode potential is positive. It is less easily reduced than hydrogen if its electrode potential is negative.

All reactions shown here are written as oxidations, because that is how the activity series has been presented (Chapter 9).

The voltage generated by any pair of standard half-cells at 298 K can be calculated by subtracting the potential for the reduction from the potential for the oxidation.

Potential for complete cell = oxidation half-cell potential
− reduction half-cell potential

If the cell potential is negative, the oxidation and reduction reactions have been mixed up, and the electrons flow in the opposite direction. If the cell potential is positive, then the cell generates current as written, and the reaction shown is spontaneous.

Example 14.3 Consider the zinc-copper cell. Find the cell potential and identify the anode and the cathode:

$$Zn + Cu^{2+} \rightarrow Zn^{2+} + Cu$$

Table 14.2 Standard Electrode Potentials (V)

$Li \rightarrow Li^+ + e^-$	3.095
$K \rightarrow K^+ + e^-$	2.925
$Ba \rightarrow Ba^{2+} + 2e^-$	2.90
$Sr \rightarrow Sr^{2+} + 2e^-$	2.89
$Ca \rightarrow Ca^{2+} + 2e^-$	2.87
$Na \rightarrow Na^+ + e^-$	2.714
$Mg \rightarrow Mg^{2+} + 2e^-$	2.37
$Al \rightarrow Al^{3+} + 3e^-$	1.66
$Mn \rightarrow Mn^{2+} + 2e^-$	1.18
$Zn \rightarrow Zn^{2+} + 2e^-$	_anode_ 0.763
$Cr \rightarrow Cr^{3+} + 3e^-$	0.74
$Fe \rightarrow Fe^{2+} + 2e^-$	0.440
$H_2 + 2OH^- (10^{-7}M) \rightarrow 2H_2O + 2e^-$	0.415
$Cd \rightarrow Cd^{2+} + 2e^-$	0.403
$Tl \rightarrow Tl^+ + e^-$	0.336
$Co \rightarrow Co^{2+} + 2e^-$	0.277
$Ni \rightarrow Ni^{2+} + 2e^-$	0.250
$Sn \rightarrow Sn^{2+} + 2e^-$	0.136
$Pb \rightarrow Pb^{2+} + 2e^-$	0.126 _cathode_
$H_2 \rightarrow 2H^+ + 2e^-$	0
$Cu \rightarrow Cu^{2+} + 2e^-$	-0.337
$Cu \rightarrow Cu^+ + e^-$	-0.521
$2I^- \rightarrow I_2 + 2e^-$	-0.5355
$Fe^{2+} \rightarrow Fe^{3+} + e^-$	-0.771
$2Hg \rightarrow Hg_2^{2+} + 2e^-$	-0.789
$Ag \rightarrow Ag^+ + e^-$	-0.80
$2H_2O \rightarrow O_2 + 4H^+ (10^{-7}M) + 4e^-$	-0.816
$Hg_2^{2+} \rightarrow 2Hg^{2+} + 2e^-$	-0.920
$NO + 2H_2O \rightarrow NO_3^- + 4H^+ + 3e^-$	-0.96
$Pd \rightarrow Pd^{2+} + 2e^-$	-0.987
$2Br^- \rightarrow Br_2 + 2e^-$	-1.066
$Pt \rightarrow Pt^{2+} + 2e^-$	-1.20
$2Cl^- \rightarrow Cl_2 + 2e^-$	-1.36
$Au \rightarrow Au^{3+} + 3e^-$	-1.50
$2SO_4^{2-} \rightarrow S_2O_8 + 2e^-$	-2.00
$2F^- \rightarrow F_2 + 2e^-$	-2.85

ACTIVITY SERIES

Step 1   Using Table 14.2, determine the half-cell potentials. Table 14.2 shows that the copper and zinc potentials are:

$$Zn \rightarrow Zn^{2+} + 2e^- \qquad 0.76 \text{ V}$$

$$Cu \rightarrow Cu^{2+} + 2e^- \qquad -0.34 \text{ V}$$

Step 2   Identify the oxidation half-cell and the reduction half-cell. In this voltaic cell, zinc metal is oxidized and the ions Cu^{2+} are reduced, since Zn is more easily oxidized than Cu.

Step 3   Subtract cell potentials according to the equation given.

Cell potential = oxidation cell potential − reduction cell potential

$$= \text{Zn cell potential} - \text{Cu cell potential}$$

$$= 0.76 \text{ V} - (-0.34 \text{ V}) = 1.10 \text{ V}$$

Step 4   Determine reaction direction and electrode identities. If the concentrations in the cell are all $1M$, the reaction will proceed as written and will generate a potential of 1.10 V. Reduction occurs at the cathode: copper. Oxidation occurs at the anode: zinc.

Example 14.4   If a cell were made using silver and gold as the electrodes, which would be the oxidation half-cell and which the reduction? What potential difference would exist if all solutions were $1M$?

Step 1   According to Table 14.2, the half-cell potentials are:

$$Ag \rightarrow Ag^+ + e^- \qquad -0.80 \text{ V}$$

$$Au \rightarrow Au^{3+} + 3e^- \qquad -1.50 \text{ V}$$

Step 2   Silver is more easily oxidized than gold, so choose it for the oxidation.

Step 3   Cell potential = Ag cell potential − Au cell potential

$$= -0.80 \text{ V} - (-1.50 \text{ V}) = 0.70 \text{ V}$$

The reaction proceeds as

$$3Ag + Au^{3+} \rightarrow 3Ag^+ + Au$$

and generates a potential of 0.70 V when all solutions are $1M$. The anode is silver (oxidation) and the cathode is gold (reduction).

14.6

Batteries

Batteries are chemical devices that produce electricity. There are two common kinds, primary cells and storage cells. **Primary cells** are batteries like the common dry cell. Figure 14.11 is a diagram of a dry cell. In this dry cell, the anode is the zinc container, and it is in electrical contact with the carbon rod cathode through a paste of NH_4Cl, $ZnCl_2$, C, and MnO_2. The reactions that occur are:

$$\text{Anode:} \quad Zn \rightarrow Zn^{2+} + 2e^-$$

$$\text{Cathode:} \quad 2MnO_2 + 2NH_4^+ + 2e^- \rightarrow 2MnO(OH) + 2NH_3$$

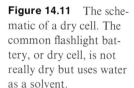

Figure 14.11 The schematic of a dry cell. The common flashlight battery, or dry cell, is not really dry but uses water as a solvent.

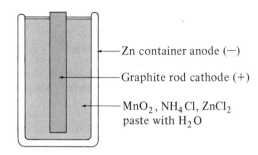

Zn container anode (−)

Graphite rod cathode (+)

MnO_2, NH_4Cl, $ZnCl_2$ paste with H_2O

Schematic of a dry cell

The most important aspect of primary cells is that they are designed not to be recharged. Connecting a more powerful source of electricity across the cell causes other reactions besides the reverse of those shown above. **Storage cells**, on the other hand, can be recharged. The automobile battery is the most common example of a storage cell. A diagram of one cell of such a lead-acid storage battery is shown in Figure 14.12. The anode consists of porous lead;

Figure 14.12 The lead storage battery commonly used in automobiles can be recharged many times simply by applying a potential to reverse the cathode and anode reactions. Anode reaction: $Pb + SO_4^{2-} \rightarrow PbSO_4 + 2e^-$ Cathode reaction: $PbO_2 + SO_4^{2-} + 4H^+ + 2e^- \rightarrow PbSO_4 + 2H_2O$

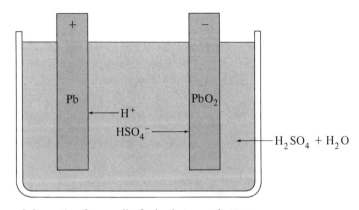

Pb

PbO_2

H^+

HSO_4^-

$H_2SO_4 + H_2O$

Schematic of one cell of a lead storage battery

the cathode consists of lead covered with lead oxide (PbO_2). The electrolyte between the electrodes is sulfuric acid (H_2SO_4). The reactions are:

$$\text{Anode:} \quad Pb + SO_4{}^{2-} \rightarrow PbSO_4 + 2e^-$$

$$\text{Cathode:} \quad PbO_2 + SO_4{}^{2-} + 4H^+ + 2e^- \rightarrow PbSO_4 + 2H_2O$$

Several of these anode-cathode combinations are placed in a single storage battery to produce enough current to start a car. The lead storage battery can be recharged by connecting a more powerful source of electricity backwards across the electrodes. This causes the reactions to run in reverse, regenerating the starting materials and rejuvenating the battery. Such recharging is done continually by the car's alternator or generator as the car is running. When the battery drops too far below useful amperage for starting the car, it must be recharged by the powerful charging machines available at many garages.

Glossary

Ampere	The basic unit of electric current; the quantity of charge that passes a given point per unit time.
Anode	The electrode that is the site of oxidation in a system.
Battery	A chemical device used to produce electricity; it consists of two half-cells that can be connected so that electrons flow through an external circuit.
Cathode	The electrode that is the site of reduction in a system.
Conductance	A measure of the ease of flow of electrons.
Electrical potential	A measure of the driving force on electrons between two points; it is measured in volts.
Electrochemistry	The study of the relation between chemistry and electricity.
Electrode	The substance through which electric current goes into or out of a liquid or gas.
Electroforming	Depositing a thick coat of metal on a mold that is used as the cathode.
Electrolysis	The motion of electric current through a liquid or a solution by which ions migrate to opposite electrodes.
Electrolyte	Ions in solution capable of migrating toward appropriate electrodes, thus causing electrons to flow through a circuit.
Electrolytic cell	A vessel in which electrolysis takes place.
Electroplating	Depositing a metal coating on an object by electrolysis.
Half-cell	The ions and electrodes composing half of a voltaic cell.
Insulator	Substances that conduct electrons poorly and thus are used to contain electrons.

Ohm	A measure of the resistance of electrical flow.
Primary cells	Batteries that cannot be recharged.
Salt bridge	A device containing ions in a medium that allows the ions to migrate from the salt bridge to different electrolytic solutions. It provides an electrical connection between two electrolytic solutions.
Standard half-cell	A half cell in which all ions are present at $1M$ concentration, at the temperature 298 K, with the pressure of all gases involved at 1 atm.
Standard hydrogen electrode	An electrode composed of platinum black over which is bubbled hydrogen gas at a pressure of 1 atmosphere and at a temperature of 25 °C. The electrode is immersed in a solution containing 1 molar hydrogen ion. The standard hydrogen electrode is arbitrarily assigned a value of 0 volts.
Storage cells	Batteries that can be recharged.
Volt	A measure of the electrical potential per unit charge.
Voltaic cell	A system that produces electricity through chemical reactions; in essence, a battery.
Watt	A measure of electrical power.

Problems

1. List several uses for electrochemistry that might affect you personally, for example, flashlight batteries, chrome automobile bumpers, and gold-plated rings.

2. Diagram a container with two platinum electrodes connected to an electron source. Show how, if the container is filled with an aqueous copper chloride solution, the ions migrate to complete the circuit and cause the electrons to flow.

3. Predict the products at anode and cathode from the following materials subjected to electrolysis:
   (a) Molten NaCl   (b) Aqueous NaCl
   (c) Aqueous $CuSO_4$ (d) Aqueous $ZnSO_4$
   (e) Sulfuric acid

4. An electric current was passed into aqueous solutions of the following compounds. What element will be produced at the cathode in each case?
   (a) $Al(NO_3)_3$ (b) $NiCl_2$
   (c) KBr   (d) HCl
   (e) $Ca(NO_3)_2$

5. Diagram the lead storage battery and indicate the reactions at the anode and the cathode.

6. Compute the voltage that would result if the following half-cells were combined. State which reaction is the oxidation and which the reduction. Identify the anode and the cathode.
   (a) $Cr \rightarrow Cr^{3+} + 3e^-$ (b) $Fe \rightarrow Fe^{2+} + 2e^-$
   $Ni \rightarrow Ni^{2+} + 2e^-$ $H_2 \rightarrow 2H^+ + 2e^-$
   (c) $Li \rightarrow Li^+ + e^-$ (d) $H_2 \rightarrow 2H^+ + 2e^-$
   $2F^- \rightarrow F_2 + 2e^-$ $2I^- \rightarrow I_2 + 2e^-$
   (e) $Pd \rightarrow Pd^{2+} + 2e^-$
   $2Cl^- \rightarrow Cl_2 + 2e^-$

7. Arrange the following metals in order of increasing ease of reduction:
   (a) Gold, silver, platinum, copper, palladium, mercury.
   (b) Lithium, sodium, potassium.

8. Choose two metals from Table 14.2 and explain how you would use them in designing a battery. Calculate the potential of the simplest battery made from these metals.

Learning Objectives for Chapter 15

Define **isomerism, homologous series, aromatic compounds.**

Draw possible isomers for simple hydrocarbons.

Name and draw structures for simple organic compounds.

Explain how crude oil is refined.

Explain how petroleum is cracked and why the process is important.

Illustrate the proportion of halogenated hydrocarbons.

Predict the products from the addition of halogen and acid halides to double and triple bonds.

Show how an alcohol is prepared.

Show two methods for preparing ethers.

Identify aldehydes and ketones.

Identify organic acids and esters.

Identify amines and amides.

Explain the difference between thermoplastic polymers and thermosetting polymers.

15 ORGANIC CHEMISTRY

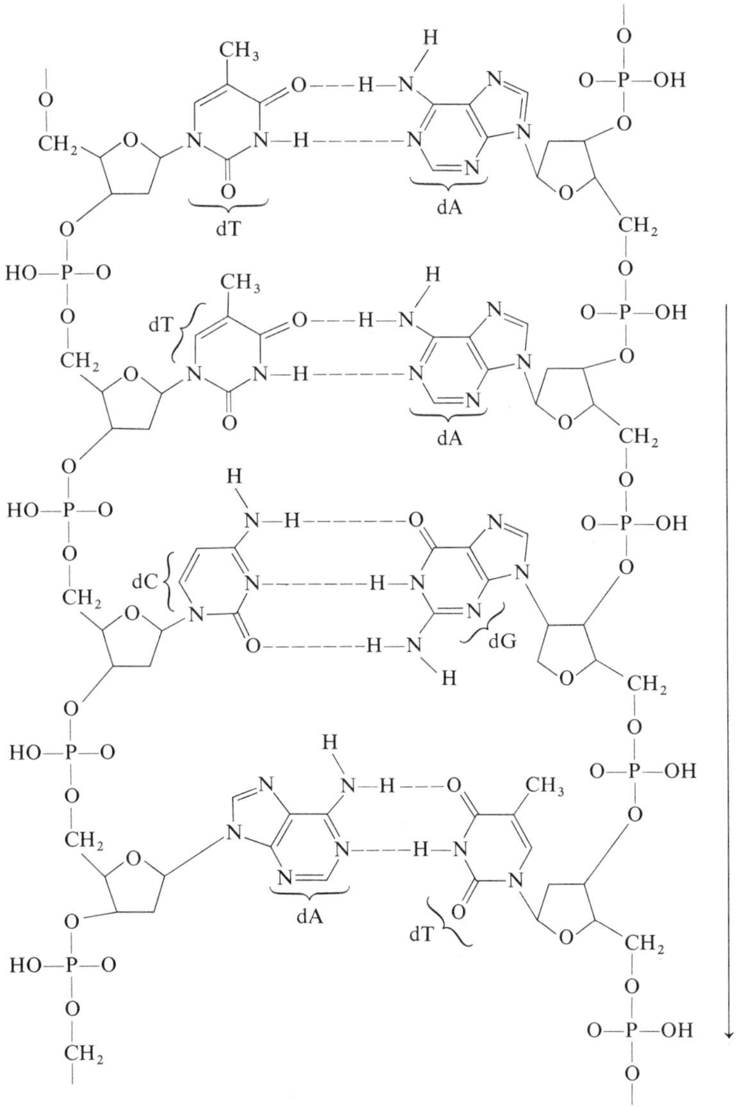

Figure 15.1 DNA, the cornerstone of genetics, is an organic molecule containing hundreds of thousands of individual atoms.

Approximately 6 million chemical compounds are known, and others are being discovered every day. Interestingly enough, 95 percent of these compounds contain the element carbon. The model used to describe the 5.5 million known organic compounds is very orderly and logical. Because of this, it is convenient to place the study of compounds containing carbon in a subsection of chemistry, called **organic chemistry**.

Until the early nineteenth century, chemists believed that compounds containing carbon could be found only in living organisms. They also believed that these compounds contained a special "vital force" and that the vital force could exist in a molecule only if the molecule were synthesized within a living system. Thus, chemists theorized, organic compounds (*organic* because they came from living organisms) could not be made simply by combining their constituent elements.

In 1828, Friedrich Wöhler succeeded in synthesizing an organic compound, urea (Figure 15.2), from compounds that had not come from living organisms. Thus, the vital force theory was overthrown, but the name **organic chemistry** for the study of compounds containing carbon was retained.

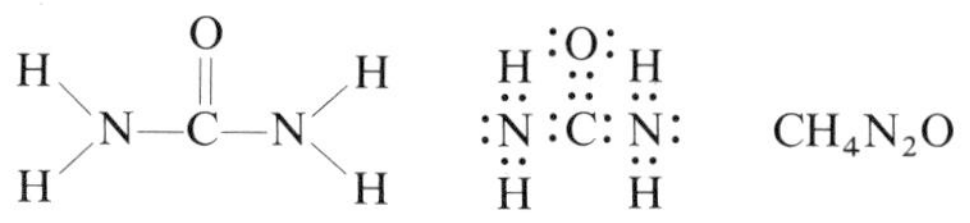

Figure 15.2 Three equivalent ways of showing the compound urea, synthesized by Friedrich Wöhler.

$$\begin{array}{ccc} \text{H} & \text{O} & \text{H} \\ \diagdown & \parallel & \diagup \\ & \text{N}-\text{C}-\text{N} & \end{array} \qquad \begin{array}{c} \text{H} \quad :\!\overset{..}{\underset{..}{\text{O}}}\!: \quad \text{H} \\ :\!\overset{..}{\text{N}}\!:\!\text{C}\!:\!\overset{..}{\text{N}}\!: \\ \text{H} \qquad \text{H} \end{array} \qquad CH_4N_2O$$

The percentage of the known compounds that contain carbon is almost incredible. Carbon is just one of 106 elements, yet carbon-containing compounds constitute 95 percent of all known compounds. How is carbon so different from the other elements that it can form such a vast range of compounds?

15.1   Carbon—The Tetrahedral Atom

If you review the concepts of electronic structure and bonding (Chapters 3 and 4), you will remember that an isolated carbon atom has the electronic structure $1s^2 2s^2 2p^2$ and has the ability to form four single bonds, one double bond and two single bonds, one triple bond and one single bond, and two double bonds. When four single bonds are formed, the tetrahedral configuration shown in Figure 15.3 is produced. The carbon tetrachloride molecule shown in Figure 15.4 is an example of the tetrahedral arrangement.

When one double bond and two single bonds are formed, the trigonal planar configuration shown in Figure 15.5 is produced. Figure 15.6 shows the formaldehyde molecule, which contains one double bond and two single bonds.

Figure 15.3 The tetrahedral arrangement of sp^3 orbitals.

Figure 15.4 Carbon tetrachloride: a tetrahedral molecule.

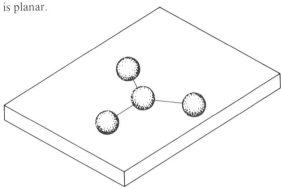

Figure 15.5 The trigonal arrangement is planar.

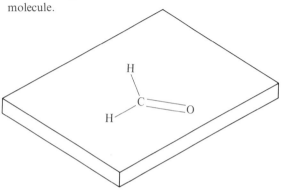

Figure 15.6 Formaldehyde: a trigonal molecule.

The formation of one triple bond and one single bond produces a linear arrangement, illustrated by the hydrogen cyanide molecule shown in Figure 15.7. The formation of two double bonds also produces a linear configuration. This possibility is represented by the carbon dioxide molecule, shown in Figure 15.8.

Figure 15.7 Hydrogen cyanide: a linear molecule.

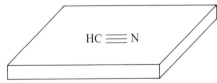

Figure 15.8 Carbon dioxide: a linear molecule.

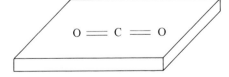

The ability of carbon atoms to form three different types of bonds (single, double, and triple) begins to explain the large number of carbon-containing compounds possible. The most important reason for the existence of so many different compounds containing carbon, however, involves the ability of a carbon atom to bond to other carbon atoms when forming molecules. Thus, carbon-containing molecules can contain rings of carbon atoms, chains of

Figure 15.9 Examples
of carbon chain and
ring compounds.

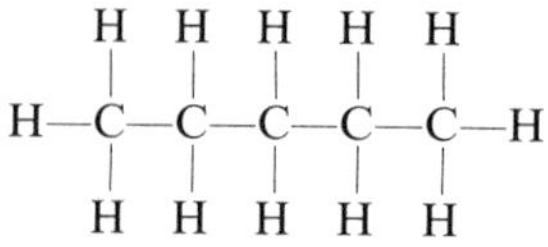

Pentane: a carbon chain compound 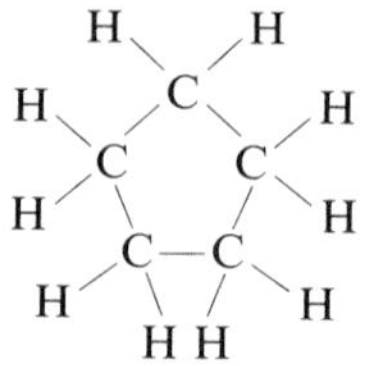   Cyclopentane: a carbon ring compound

carbon atoms, or some combination of rings and chains. Figure 15.9 shows examples of such compounds.

Finally, carbon has an electronegativity of 2.5, which is close to that of several other elements:

N	3.0	Cl	3.0
O	3.5	Br	2.8
P	2.1	Se	2.4
S	2.5	H	2.1

These elements all form covalent bonds with carbon by sharing electrons to obtain an outer octet.

Thus the vast numbers of organic molecules are possible because the length of carbon chain can be varied, the size of the carbon ring can be varied, atoms taking part in bonding can be varied, and types of bonds present can be varied.

Alterations made to the simple compound methane illustrate the variety of compounds possible. The formula for methane is CH_4, and its electron dot formula is

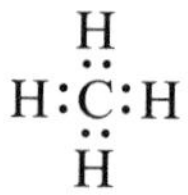

$$H:\overset{\displaystyle H}{\underset{\displaystyle H}{\overset{..}{\underset{..}{C}}}}:H$$

The hydrogens in this basic structure can be replaced with other elements to form different compounds. Replacing one hydrogen atom with a chlorine atom makes the structure for a compound called chloromethane:

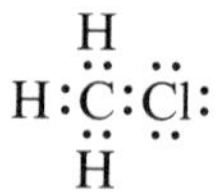

$$H:\overset{\displaystyle H}{\underset{\displaystyle H}{\overset{..}{\underset{..}{C}}}}:\overset{..}{\underset{..}{Cl}}:$$

Replacing two hydrogen atoms with two chlorine atoms makes the structure for a compound called dichloromethane:

$$H:\overset{\displaystyle :\overset{..}{Cl}:}{\underset{\displaystyle H}{\overset{..}{\underset{..}{C}}}}:\overset{..}{\underset{..}{Cl}}:$$

If three hydrogen atoms are replaced with three chlorine atoms, chloroform ($CHCl_3$) is formed:

$$\overset{\displaystyle H}{\underset{\displaystyle :\ddot{C}l:}{:\ddot{C}l:C:\ddot{C}l:}}$$

Finally, if all four hydrogens are replaced with chlorine, carbon tetrachloride is the compound formed:

$$\overset{\displaystyle :\ddot{C}l:}{\underset{\displaystyle :\ddot{C}l:}{:\ddot{C}l:C:\ddot{C}l:}}$$

The hydrogens could have been replaced with two chlorine atoms and two fluorine atoms to yield CCl_2F_2, Freon-12, which can be used in refrigerator cooling coils:

$$\overset{\displaystyle :\ddot{F}:}{\underset{\displaystyle :\ddot{C}l:}{:\ddot{F}:C:\ddot{C}l:}}$$

All bonds in these compounds are covalent. Notice that each atom (except H) has eight electrons around it.

The hydrogen atoms in methane can even be replaced with carbon atoms, to which other atoms must be bonded:

$$\overset{\displaystyle C}{\underset{\displaystyle C}{C:C:C}}$$

Each of the four outer carbons can now bond to three other atoms. These atoms could be from one of several elements. If the atoms are hydrogen, the compound neopentane is formed:

$$\begin{array}{c} H \\ H \therefore H \\ H\,\ddot{C}\,H \\ H:\ddot{C}:\ddot{C}:\ddot{C}:H \\ H\,\ddot{C}\,H \\ H \because H \\ H \end{array}$$

The possible combinations seem almost endless, and they are extended even further by the possibilities that multiple bond and ring compounds present.

15.2 The Structure of Organic Compounds

There are several compounds formed from only carbon and hydrogen—the **hydrocarbons**. If one of the hydrogens of methane is replaced by a carbon atom and three more hydrogen atoms, ethane (C_2H_6) is formed. The electron dot formula for ethane is

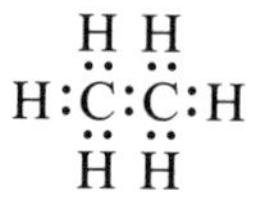

$$
\begin{array}{c}
\text{H H} \\
\text{H:C:C:H} \\
\text{H H}
\end{array}
$$

Organic chemists very rapidly tire of drawing dots for bonds, and they usually represent the covalent electron pair with a single line. This representation may be called the structural formula for the compound. The structural formula shows the arrangement of atoms in a molecule. The representation of ethane thus appears as

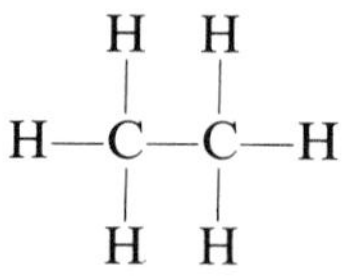

$$
\begin{array}{c}
\text{H H} \\
| \quad | \\
\text{H—C—C—H} \\
| \quad | \\
\text{H H}
\end{array}
$$

Replacing a hydrogen in ethane by a carbon atom and three hydrogen atoms yields propane (Figure 15.10). The carbons are not in a straight line since the

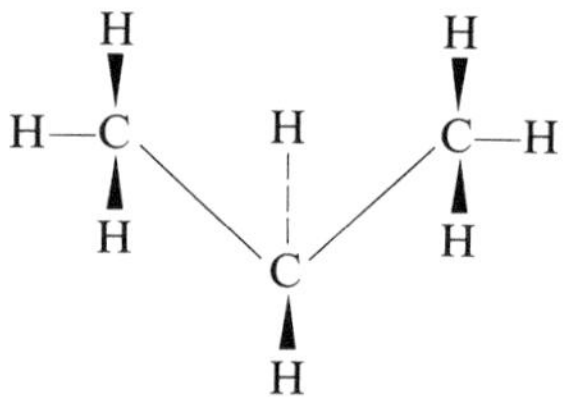

Figure 15.10 Propane.

angle between tetrahedral bonds is about 109°, an arrangement that makes a zigzag chain. Organic chemists simplify this structure by compressing it into two dimensions and putting the carbons in a straight line, like this:

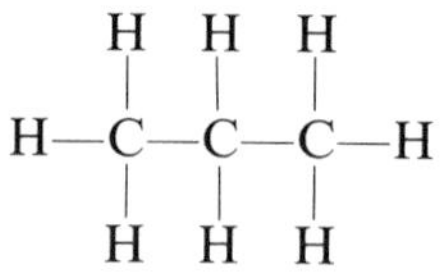

$$
\begin{array}{c}
\text{H H H} \\
| \quad | \quad | \\
\text{H—C—C—C—H} \\
| \quad | \quad | \\
\text{H H H}
\end{array}
$$

The structure is really zigzag, portrayed in a straight line for convenience only.

Often the bond between carbon and hydrogen is left out, and the structural formula becomes

```
    H   H   H
HC— C — CH
    H   H   H
```

or even shorter, $CH_3CH_2CH_3$. Chemists, like everyone else, try to keep the writing to a minimum, but it is important to remember what the symbols mean.

If one more carbon atom and three more hydrogen atoms replace an end hydrogen on propane, butane is formed:

```
    H   H   H   H
HC— C — C — CH
    H   H   H   H
```

Propane and butane are gases that are compressed and sold in tanks as bottled gas. They are often used as fuel for heating or cooking.

The possibilities of compound formation that exist for hydrocarbons having four carbons or more are interesting. More than one way is possible for combining the 4 carbon and 10 hydrogen atoms. They could be combined as in isobutane:

```
          H
        HCH
    H    |    H
HC— C — CH
    H   H   H
```

Isobutane has different properties from butane. Straight-chained (or normal) butane freezes at $-138\,°C$, whereas isobutane freezes at $-159.5\,°C$. Both compounds have the same molecular formula, C_4H_{10}, but different structural arrangements. Such a condition is called **isomerism**. Each individual structure is called an isomer. Chemists must be careful to show, in some way, which particular compound is being discussed. To understand isomers better, consider the molecular formula C_6H_{14} (hexane). Five isomers are possible for hexane. Their structural formulas are:

$$CH_3CH_2CH_2CH_2CH_2CH_3$$

$$\begin{array}{c} CH_3 \\ | \\ CH_3CHCH_2CH_2CH_3 \end{array}$$

$$\begin{array}{c} CH_3 \\ | \\ CH_3CH_2CHCH_2CH_3 \end{array}$$

$$\begin{array}{c} CH_3 \ CH_3 \\ | \ \ / \\ CH_3CHCHCH_3 \end{array}$$

$$\begin{array}{c} CH_3 \\ | \\ CH_3C—CH_2CH_3 \\ | \\ CH_3 \end{array}$$

The number of isomers possible for the molecular formula $C_{20}H_{42}$ includes 366,319 different structures.

Carbon also combines with itself and other elements in other ways. It can form double or triple bonds. The molecular formula C_2H_4, for instance, indicates the presence of a double bond. The compound is called ethene, and its structural formula is

$$\begin{matrix} H & H \\ HC & = CH \end{matrix}$$

The molecular formula C_2H_2 indicates the presence of a triple bond. The compound is called ethyne or acetylene, $HC \equiv CH$.

Longer carbon chains having one or more of these kinds of bonds are also possible. For the compound C_4H_8, the possible structures are

$$\begin{matrix} H & H & H & H \\ HC & = C & - C & - CH \\ & & H & H \end{matrix} \qquad \begin{matrix} H & H & H & H \\ HC & - C & = C & - CH \\ & H & & H \end{matrix} \qquad \begin{matrix} & & H \\ & HCH \\ & | & H \\ HC & = C & - CH \\ & H & H \end{matrix}$$

Thus, isomerism also includes double or triple bonds in various positions. For C_4H_6, possible structures are

$$\begin{matrix} H & H \\ HC \equiv C & - C & - CH \\ & H & H \end{matrix} \qquad \begin{matrix} H & & H \\ HC & - C \equiv C & - CH \\ H & & H \end{matrix}$$

or even

$$\begin{matrix} H & H & H & H \\ HC & = C & - C & = CH \end{matrix}$$

The formation of carbon rings also produces isomerism. The structure of the compound C_3H_6 may be a ring,

$$\begin{matrix} & CH_2 \\ & \diagup \diagdown \\ H_2C & - CH_2 \end{matrix}$$

called cyclopropane, or the structure may contain a double bond $C=C-C$ and be called propene. The formula C_6H_{12} represents many isomers, one of which is the ring compound cyclohexane:

CH$_2$
H$_2$C   CH$_2$
H$_2$C   CH$_2$
CH$_2$

The great number of organic molecules means that the different types of compounds have to be named and classified. This process reduces the amount of memorization needed for understanding organic chemistry. For example, all compounds that contain only carbon and hydrogen with no double bonds behave in chemically similar ways. Compounds that contain carbon, hydrogen, and double bonds are in another category, and so on. We shall examine several types of organic compounds, analyzing their chemical and physical properties.

15.3   Hydrocarbons

The term **hydrocarbon** refers to all compounds containing only carbon and hydrogen. Because this is such a large group of compounds, it is subdivided into several smaller groups. The primary subdivisions are alkanes, alkenes, alkynes, and aromatic hydrocarbons. Alkanes, alkenes, and alkynes form a homologous series. A **homologous series** of compounds has members that differ from each other in a consistent, regular way; they can differ, for example, by one —CH$_2$— group. Beginning with ethane, CH$_3$—CH$_3$, a —CH$_2$— group can be inserted to give CH$_3$—CH$_2$—CH$_3$, propane. Another —CH$_2$— group can be inserted to give CH$_3$—CH$_2$—CH$_2$—CH$_3$, butane. This is the beginning of a homologous series. Each successive compound differs by the addition of a —CH$_2$— group.

All the names in organic chemistry are based on a few roots. Chemists from all over the world meet periodically to decide how to name compounds. The organization they belong to is called the International Union of Pure and Applied Chemistry (IUPAC). These people have developed a naming system for organic compounds that has some simple rules. Naming compounds has been complicated by long-established common names. These names were given to compounds before the IUPAC system was initiated. Common names will be given here only when that name is the most often used name for a particular compound.

The simplest group of the hydrocarbons is the alkanes. Alkanes are called **saturated hydrocarbons** because they have no double or triple bonds. The term *saturated* means that the carbon atoms are bonded to as many hydrogen atoms as possible. **Unsaturated compounds** contain double or triple bonds, or both kinds. The distinction between saturated and unsaturated fats rests on this definition.

Alkanes are hydrocarbons that contain only single bonds. The name of each compound ends in -*ane*. The simplest alkane is called methane, CH_4. The replacement of one hydrogen with a —CH_3 group produces ethane, CH_3—CH_3. The next compound is formed by inserting a —CH_2— group to form propane, CH_3—CH_2—CH_3; the next, butane, CH_3—CH_2—CH_2—CH_3; and so on. Table 15.1 gives names and formulas of the first ten members of the series. Much organic nomenclature is based on the names of the saturated homologous series of alkanes. You should therefore memorize this series.

All the compounds in Table 15.1 are "straight-chain," or normal alkanes. All can be stretched out in the zigzag line. The nomenclature of isomers like

$$CH_3-\overset{\displaystyle |}{\underset{\displaystyle CH_3}{CH}}-CH_3$$

is based on the longest carbon chain, which in this case is three carbons long. The compound is named as a propane. Any group, one or more, attached to this chain is named, and the group's location on the chain is indicated. The group attached in this case is CH_3, and it is called methyl. Its name comes from the corresponding alkane in Table 15.1 and the -*ane* has been changed to -*yl*. These derived names are shown in Table 15.2. The compound

$$\overset{\displaystyle CH_3}{\underset{\displaystyle |}{}}$$
$$CH_3-CH-CH_3$$

is called 2-methylpropane. The 2 indicates that the methyl is attached to the second carbon in the main carbon chain of the compound. If more than one

Table 15.1 Series of Normal Alkanes

Name	Structural Formula
Methane	CH_4
Ethane	CH_3—CH_3
Propane	CH_3—CH_2—CH_3
Butane	CH_3—CH_2—CH_2—CH_3
Pentane	CH_3—$(CH_2)_3$—CH_3
Hexane	CH_3—$(CH_2)_4$—CH_3
Heptane	CH_3—$(CH_2)_5$—CH_3
Octane	CH_3—$(CH_2)_6$—CH_3
Nonane	CH_3—$(CH_2)_7$—CH_3
Decane	CH_3—$(CH_2)_8$—CH_3

Table 15.2 Common Alkyl Carbon Groups

	Carbon Group	Name
	$-CH_3$	Methyl
	$-CH_2CH_3$	Ethyl
	$-CH_2CH_2CH_3$	Propyl
	$-CH \diagup^{CH_3}_{\diagdown CH_3}$	Isopropyl

group of one kind is attached to the same carbon atom or basic carbon chain, prefixes (*di* for "two," *tri* for "three," and so on), are used in naming.

Example 15.1

Name the following compound:

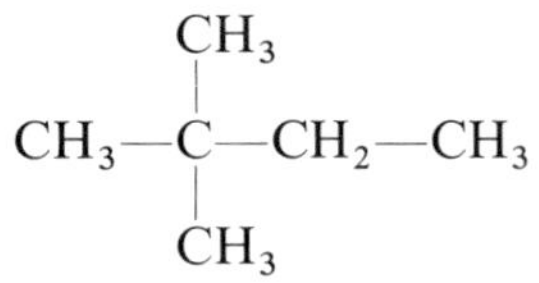

$$CH_3-\underset{\underset{CH_3}{|}}{\overset{\overset{CH_3}{|}}{C}}-CH_2-CH_3$$

Step 1 Identify and name the longest carbon chain: butane.

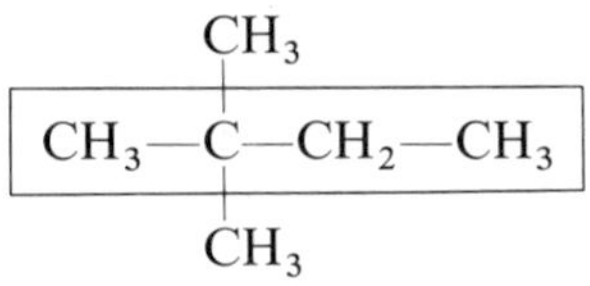

$$\overset{CH_3}{\underset{\underset{CH_3}{|}}{\boxed{CH_3-C-CH_2-CH_3}}}$$

Step 2 Number the carbon atoms in the longest chain, proceeding from the end nearest the specified group or groups:

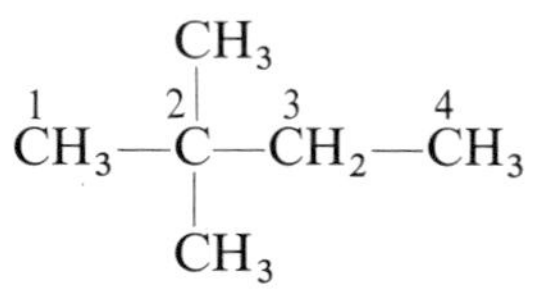

$$\overset{CH_3}{\underset{\underset{CH_3}{|}}{\overset{|}{\underset{1}{CH_3}-\underset{2}{C}-\underset{3}{CH_2}-\underset{4}{CH_3}}}}$$

Step 3 Name the groups and the location on the chain. Numbers are separated by commas, numbers and letters are separated by dashes: 2,2-dimethylbutane.

Example 15.2   Name the compound:

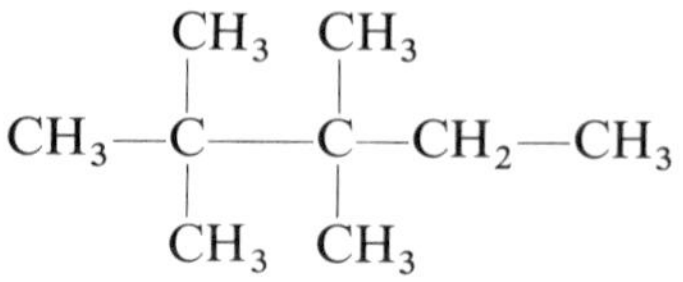

$$CH_3-\underset{\underset{CH_3}{|}}{\overset{\overset{CH_3}{|}}{C}}-\underset{\underset{CH_3}{|}}{\overset{\overset{CH_3}{|}}{C}}-CH_2-CH_3$$

Step 1   Pentane.

Step 2 $\overset{1}{C}H_3-\overset{2}{\underset{\underset{CH_3}{|}}{\overset{\overset{CH_3}{|}}{C}}}-\overset{3}{\underset{\underset{CH_3}{|}}{\overset{\overset{CH_3}{|}}{C}}}-\overset{4}{C}H_2-\overset{5}{C}H_3$

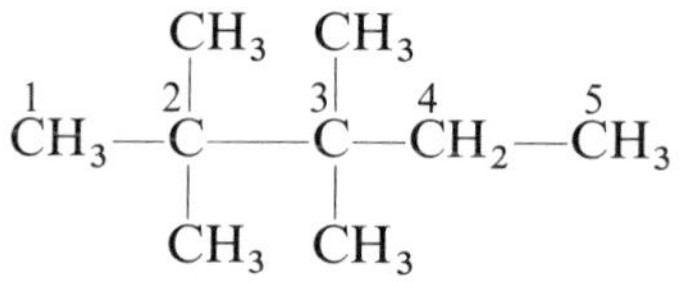

Step 3   2,2,3,3-tetramethylpentane.

Example 15.3   Name the compound:

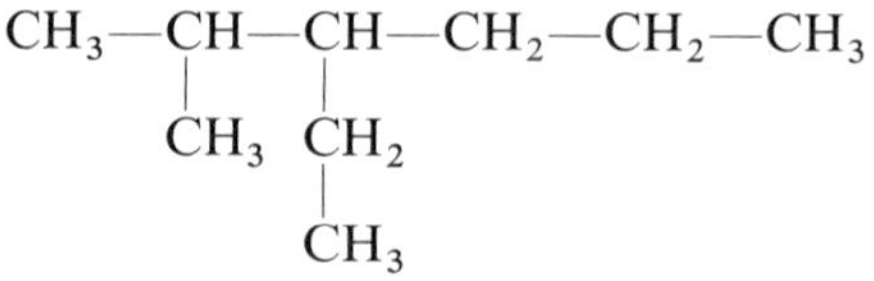

$$CH_3-\underset{\underset{CH_3}{|}}{CH}-\underset{\underset{\underset{\underset{CH_3}{|}}{CH_2}}{|}}{CH}-CH_2-CH_2-CH_3$$

Step 1   Hexane.

Step 2 $\overset{1}{C}H_3-\overset{2}{\underset{\underset{CH_3}{|}}{CH}}-\overset{3}{\underset{\underset{\underset{\underset{CH_3}{|}}{CH_2}}{|}}{CH}}-\overset{4}{C}H_2-\overset{5}{C}H_2-\overset{6}{C}H_3$

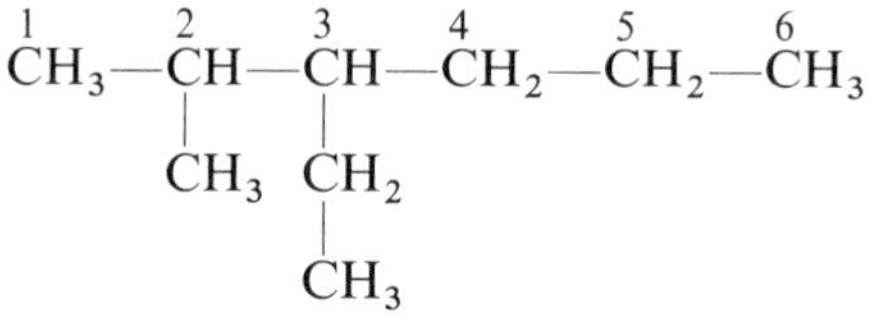

Step 3   3-ethyl-2-methylhexane.

Ethyl precedes *methyl* because groups are named alphabetically.

Example 15.4   Name the compound:

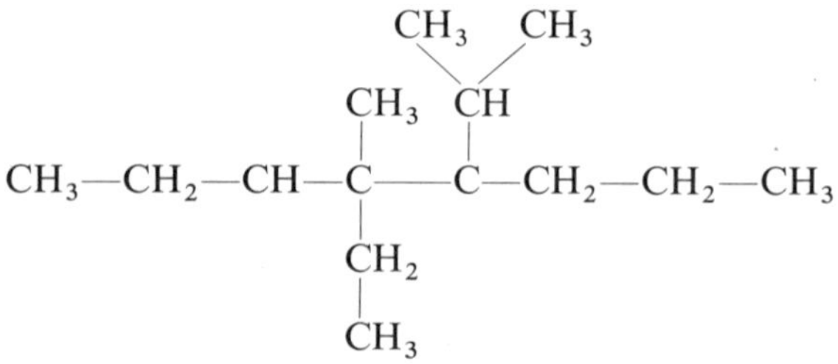

$$CH_3-CH_2-CH-\underset{\underset{\underset{CH_3}{|}}{CH_2}}{\overset{\overset{CH_3\ \ CH}{}}{C}}-\underset{}{C}-CH_2-CH_2-CH_3$$

Step 1   Octane.

Step 2

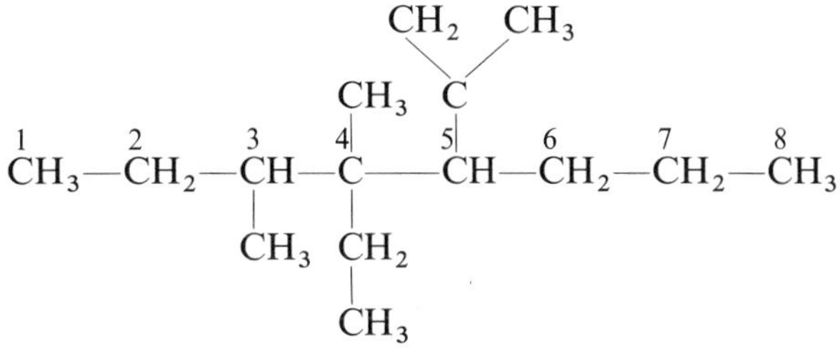

$$CH_3—CH_2—CH—C———CH—CH_2—CH_2—CH_3$$

with substituents:

$$\overset{1}{C}H_3—\overset{2}{C}H_2—\overset{3}{C}H—\overset{4}{C}———\overset{5}{C}H—\overset{6}{C}H_2—\overset{7}{C}H_2—\overset{8}{C}H_3$$

where carbon 4 bears CH_3 and C (with CH_2—CH_3 above and CH_3 to the side), and CH_2—CH_3 below; carbon 3 bears CH_3.

Step 3   4-ethyl-5-isopropyl-3,4-dimethyloctane.

This method of naming compounds can be expanded to include other groups. If a halogen is attached to a carbon chain, the *-ine* ending of the halogen atom is changed to -o, and the compound is named as before.

Example 15.5   Name the compound: $CH_3—CH_2—CH_2—Cl$

Step 1   Propane.

Step 2 $\overset{3}{C}H_3—\overset{2}{C}H_2—\overset{1}{C}H_2—Cl$

Step 3   1-chloropropane.

Example 15.6   Name the compound:

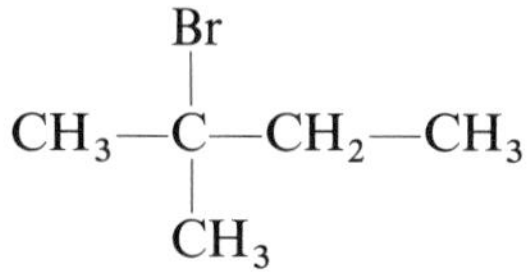

$$CH_3—\underset{\underset{CH_3}{|}}{\overset{\overset{Br}{|}}{C}}—CH_2—CH_3$$

Step 1   Butane.

Step 2 $\overset{1}{C}H_3—\underset{\underset{CH_3}{|}}{\overset{\overset{Br}{|}}{\overset{2}{C}}}—\overset{3}{C}H_2—\overset{4}{C}H_3$

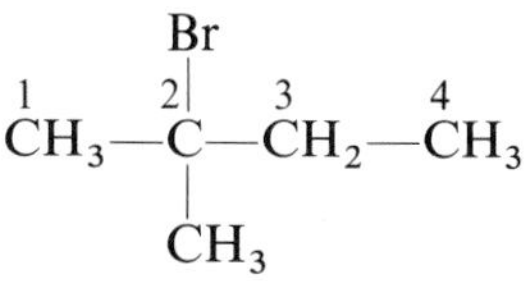

Step 3   2-bromo-2-methylbutane.

Always remember to state the location of each group on the chain, use the lowest numbers possible, and name substituents alphabetically. A substituent group is any group connected to the main chain or ring.

Example 15.7

Name the compound:

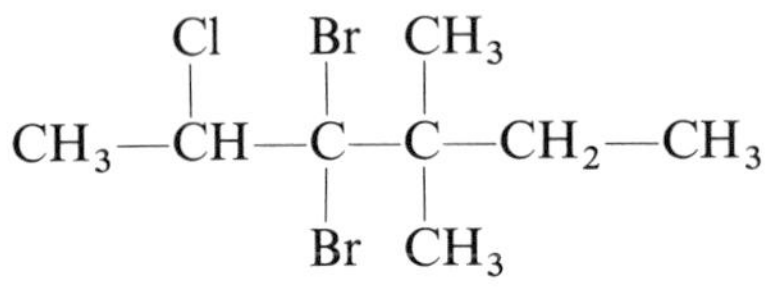

$$CH_3-\underset{}{CH}-\underset{\underset{Br}{|}}{\overset{\overset{Cl}{|}}{C}}-\underset{\underset{CH_3}{|}}{\overset{\overset{Br}{|}}{C}}-CH_2-CH_3 \quad (CH_3)$$

Cl   Br CH₃

CH₃—CH—C—C—CH₂—CH₃

Br CH₃

Step 1   Hexane.

Step 2

            Cl   Br CH₃
       1   2| 3| 4| 5   6
       CH₃—CH—C—C—CH₂—CH₃
                 | |
                 Br   CH₃

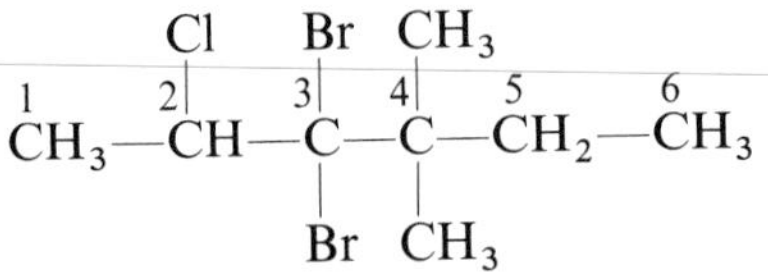

Step 3   3,3-dibromo-2-chloro-4,4-dimethylhexane.

It is also useful to be able to draw the structure of a compound if you are given its name.

Example 15.8

Draw the structure of 2-methyl-3-propylnonane.

Step 1   Draw and number the longest chain of carbons—nonane.

       1   2   3   4   5   6   7   8   9
       C—C—C—C—C—C—C—C—C

Step 2   Add the substituent groups:

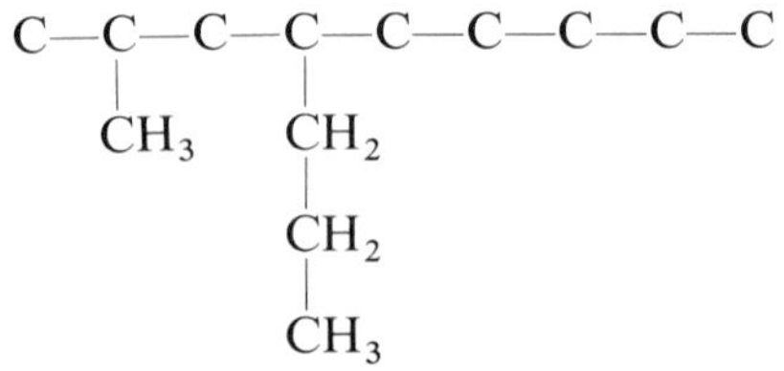

       C—C—C—C—C—C—C—C—C
             | |
             CH₃ CH₂
                  |
                  CH₂
                  |
                  CH₃

Step 3 Add the required hydrogen atoms, thus giving each carbon the required four bonds:

$$CH_3-CH-CH_2-CH-CH_2-CH_2-CH_2-CH_2-CH_3$$
$$\underset{\displaystyle CH_3}{|} \qquad \underset{\displaystyle CH_2}{|}$$
$$\underset{\displaystyle CH_2}{|}$$
$$\underset{\displaystyle CH_3}{|}$$

Hydrocarbons that contain one or more double bonds are called **alkenes**. Notice that the *-ane* ending is changed to *-ene*. The position of the double bond is indicated by writing the number of the first carbon to which the double bond is attached. (This is always chosen to be the lowest number possible.)

Table 15.3 shows several normal alkenes. Notice that beginning with butene, more than one isomer of each compound exists, depending on how the double bond is placed. Substituted alkenes are named like the alkanes; however, the position of the double bond must be specified.

Table 15.3 Series of Normal Alkenes

Name	Structural Formula
Ethene	$CH_2=CH_2$
Propene	$CH_2=CH-CH_3$
1-Butene	$CH_2=CH-CH_2-CH_3$
2-Butene	$CH_3-CH=CH-CH_3$
1-Pentene	$CH_2=CH-CH_2-CH_2-CH_3$
2-Pentene	$CH_3-CH=CH-CH_2-CH_3$
1-Hexene	$CH_2=CH-CH_2-CH_2-CH_2-CH_3$
2-Hexene	$CH_3-CH=CH-CH_2-CH_2-CH_3$
3-Hexene	$CH_3-CH_2-CH=CH-CH_2-CH_3$

Following are some examples.

Example 15.9 Name the compound:

$$CH_2=CH-CH-CH_3$$
$$\underset{\displaystyle CH_3}{|}$$

Step 1 Identify and name the longest carbon chain and change the ending to *-ene*— $\boxed{\text{butene}}$.

Step 2   Number the carbon atoms in the longest chain, starting with the end closest to the double bond:

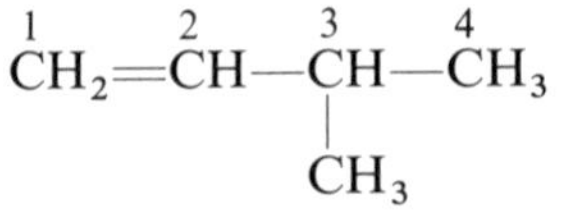

$$\overset{1}{CH_2}=\overset{2}{CH}-\overset{3}{CH}-\overset{4}{CH_3}$$
$$|$$
$$CH_3$$

Step 3   Name the group and the location on the chain and follow these with the location of the double bond: 3-methyl-l-butene.

Example 15.10   Name the compound:

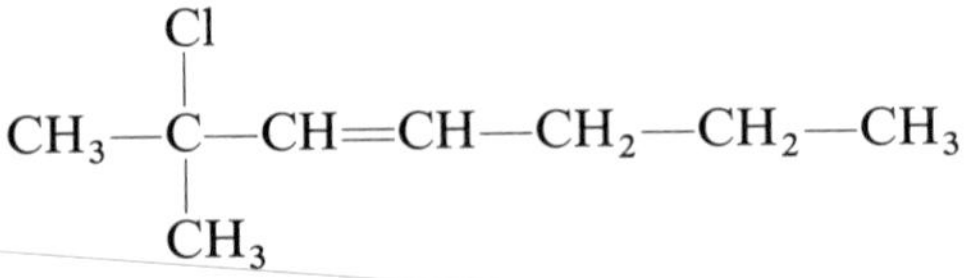

$$CH_3-\overset{\overset{\displaystyle Cl}{|}}{\underset{\underset{\displaystyle CH_3}{|}}{C}}-CH=CH-CH_2-CH_2-CH_3$$

Step 1   Heptene.

Step 2 $\overset{1}{CH_3}-\overset{\overset{\displaystyle Cl}{|}}{\underset{\underset{\displaystyle CH_3}{|}}{\overset{2}{C}}}-\overset{3}{CH}=\overset{4}{CH}-\overset{5}{CH_2}-\overset{6}{CH_2}-\overset{7}{CH_3}$

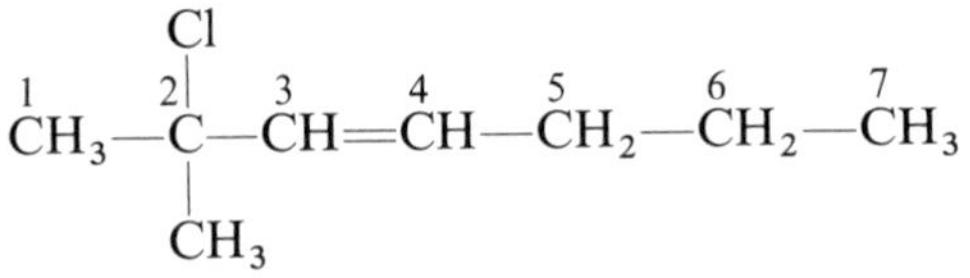

Step 3   2-chloro-2-methyl-3-heptene. Again the alphabetical naming of substituents is followed.

More than one double bond is possible in a single compound. Such compounds are called dienes, trienes, and so on, showing two, three, or more double bonds.

Example 15.11   Name the compound: $CH_2=CH-CH=CH_2$

Step 1   Butadiene.

Step 2 $\overset{1}{CH_2}=\overset{2}{CH}-\overset{3}{CH}=\overset{4}{CH_2}$

Step 3   1,3-butadiene

Table 15.4 Series of Normal Alkynes

Name	Structural Formula
Ethyne (Acetylene)	$HC{\equiv}H$
Propyne	$HC{\equiv}C{-}CH_3$
1-Butyne	$HC{\equiv}C{-}CH_2{-}CH_3$
2-Butyne	$H_3C{-}C{\equiv}C{-}CH_3$
1-Pentyne	$HC{\equiv}C{-}CH_2{-}CH_2{-}CH_3$
2-Pentyne	$H_3C{-}C{\equiv}C{-}CH_2{-}CH_3$
1-Hexyne	$HC{\equiv}C{-}CH_2{-}CH_2{-}CH_2{-}CH_3$
2-Hexyne	$H_3C{-}C{\equiv}C{-}CH_2{-}CH_2{-}CH_3$
3-Hexyne	$H_3C{-}CH_2{-}C{\equiv}C{-}CH_2{-}CH_3$

If the molecules of a hydrocarbon contain one or more carbon-to-carbon triple bonds, the compound is referred to as an alkyne. The *-ane* ending of alkane is changed to *-yne*. Table 15.4 shows several normal alkynes. The alkynes are named like the alkenes. The carbon chain is numbered to locate the triple bond in the lowest-numbered position.

Example 15.12	Name the compound:

$$CH_3{-}C{\equiv}C{-}CH{-}CH_3$$
$$|$$
$$CH_3$$

Step 1 Identify and name the longest carbon chain and change the ending to *-yne*: pentyne.

Step 2 Number the carbon atoms in the longest chain, starting with the end closest to the triple bond:

$$\overset{1}{C}H_3{-}\overset{2}{C}{\equiv}\overset{3}{C}{-}\overset{4}{C}H{-}\overset{5}{C}H_3$$
$$|$$
$$CH_3$$

Step 3 Name the group and the location on the chain, following with the location of the triple bond: 4-methyl-2-pentyne.

Hydrogen ring compounds are named according to Table 15.5.

In such compounds, the prefix cyclo- is attached to the hydrocarbon name. Naming more complex ring compounds requires numbering the carbon atoms around the ring. The numbering sequence is chosen to keep the substituent numbers at the lowest possible values.

Table 15.5 Series of Ring Hydrocarbons

Name	Structural Formula
Cyclopropane	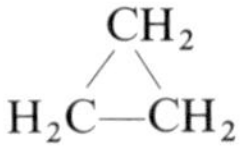 CH_2 H_2C-CH_2
Cyclobutane	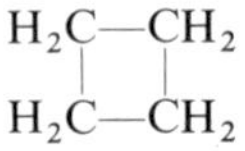 H_2C-CH_2 H_2C-CH_2
Cyclopentane	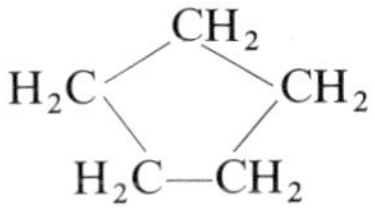 CH_2 $H_2C \quad CH_2$ H_2C-CH_2
Cyclohexane	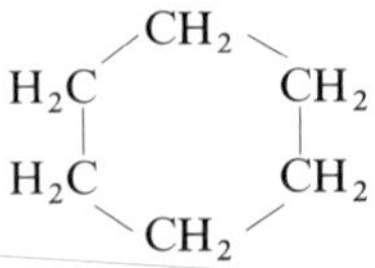 CH_2 $H_2C \quad CH_2$ $H_2C \quad CH_2$ CH_2
Cyclopentene	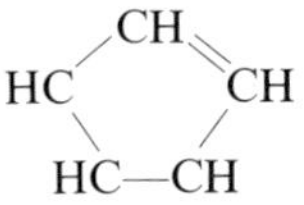 CH $HC \quad CH$ $HC-CH$
Cyclohexene	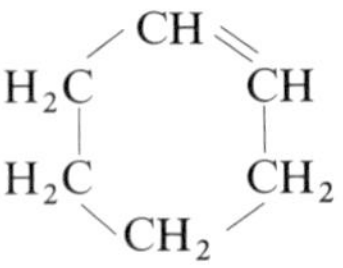 CH $H_2C \quad CH$ $H_2C \quad CH_2$ CH_2

NOTE: Cycloalkynes seldom form because the triply bonded carbon atoms must have a linear arrangement of bonding partners. This is an extremely difficult geometry to attain in a ring compound.

Example 15.13   Name the compound:

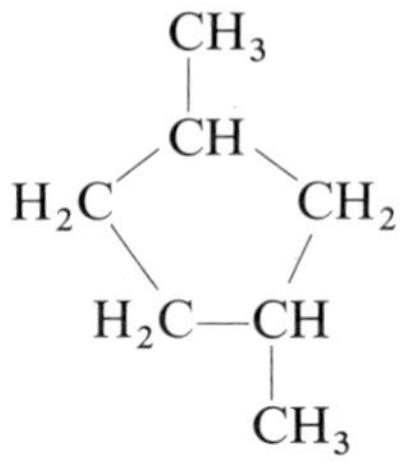

$$CH_3$$
$$CH$$
$$H_2C \qquad CH_2$$
$$H_2C-CH$$
$$CH_3$$

Step 1   Count the carbons in the ring and write the name, prefixing it with *cyclo-* and noting the presence or absence of double bonds: cyclopentane.

Step 2 Number the carbon atoms on the ring to get the lowest possible values on substituents:

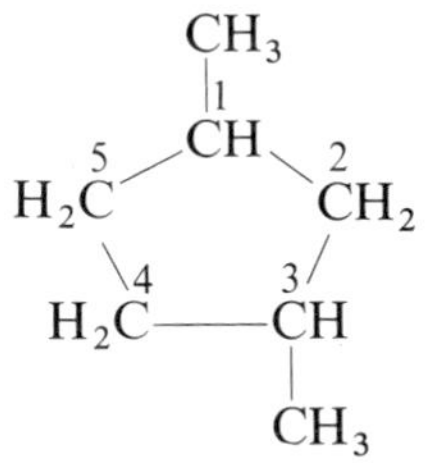

$$CH_3$$

$$
\begin{array}{c}
CH_3 \\
|1 \\
CH \\
\overset{5}{H_2C} \qquad \overset{2}{CH_2} \\
\overset{4}{\diagdown} \qquad \overset{3}{\diagup} \\
H_2C \!-\!\!-\! CH \\
| \\
CH_3
\end{array}
$$

Step 3 Name the groups and their locations on the ring: 1,3-dimethyl-cyclopentane.

Example 15.14 Name the compound:

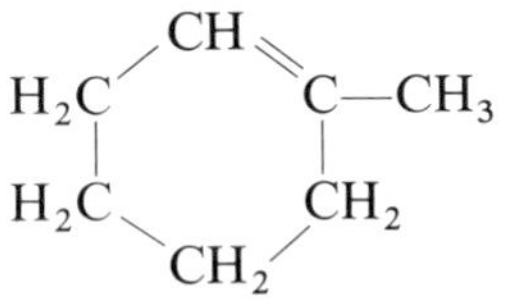

$$
\begin{array}{c}
CH \\
H_2C \diagup \quad \diagdown C\!-\!CH_3 \\
| \qquad\qquad | \\
H_2C \diagdown \quad \diagup CH_2 \\
CH_2
\end{array}
$$

Step 1 Cyclohexene.

$$
\begin{array}{c}
\overset{1}{CH} \\
\overset{6}{H_2C} \diagup \quad \overset{2}{\diagdown} C\!-\!CH_3 \\
| \qquad\qquad \overset{3}{|} \\
H_2\underset{5}{C} \diagdown \quad \diagup H_2C \\
CH_2 \\
4
\end{array}
$$

Step 2

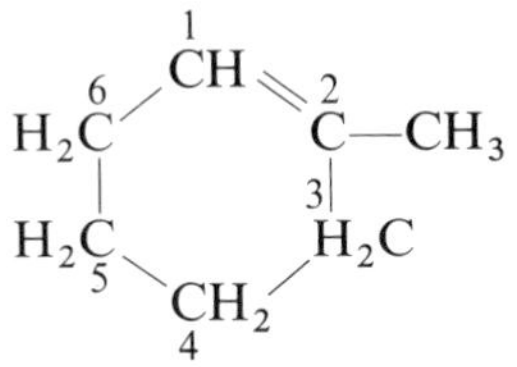

Step 3 2-methyl-1-cyclohexene.

There is one other big class of hydrocarbons. These are the **aromatic hydrocarbons**. The name was originally given to this group because of the distinctive odors of the compounds in the group. The compounds are special because all have one common feature in their electronic structures that causes them to behave alike chemically. The special feature is a ring structure with a double bond between every other carbon in the ring. The simplest aromatic hydrocarbon is benzene. It can be drawn like this:

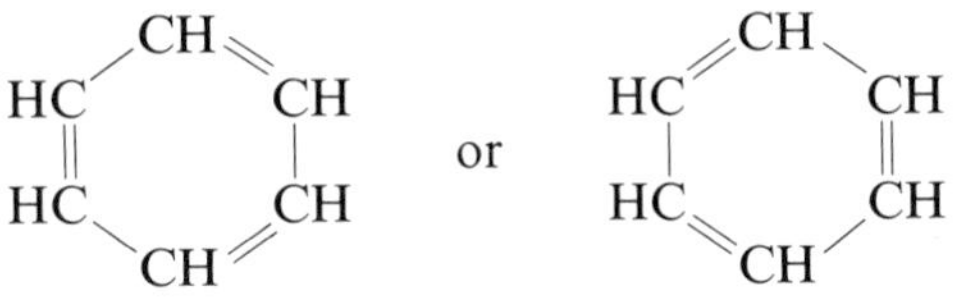

$$
\begin{array}{c}
CH \\
HC \diagup \quad \diagdown CH \\
\| \qquad\qquad | \\
HC \diagdown \quad \diagup CH \\
CH
\end{array}
\quad \text{or} \quad
\begin{array}{c}
CH \\
HC \diagup \quad \diagdown CH \\
| \qquad\qquad \| \\
HC \diagdown \quad \diagup CH \\
CH
\end{array}
$$

Figure 15.11 In benzene and other aromatics, the electrons in the double bonds are distributed over the whole molecule. In the case of benzene, they are above and below the molecule and do not stay in the rigid, double-bonded structure.

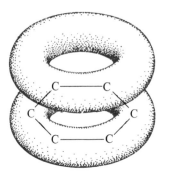

Although these are different representations of structure, they show the same compound. This is an old-fashioned way of showing benzene. The electrons are really spread all around the ring as shown in Figure 15.11. Thus, chemists often draw the structure of benzene as

Each of the six points in the figure represents a —C— group.

Mothballs are an example of another aromatic hydrocarbon, called naphthalene. The chemical structure, consisting of two fused benzene rings, can be symbolized

Compounds of benzene and naphthalene produced by substituting various groups for hydrogen atoms are named similarly to other ring compounds.

Example 15.15   Name the compound:

$$CH_3$$

$$—CH_2—CH_2—CH_3$$

Step 1   Name the ring involved: benzene.

Step 2   Number the carbon atoms on the ring to get the lowest possible values on the substituents:

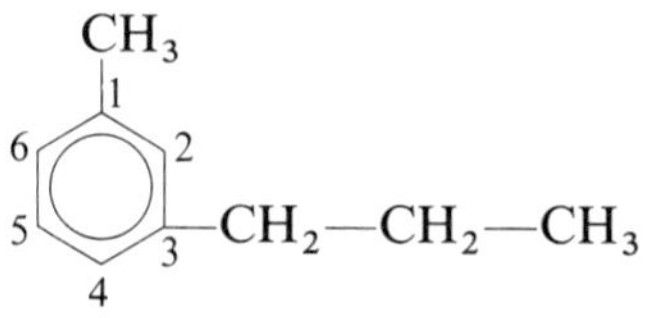

$$CH_3$$

Step 3   Name the groups and their locations on the ring, remembering the alphabetical rule: 1-methyl-3-propylbenzene.

Example 15.16   Name the compound:

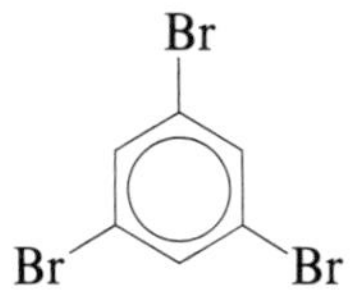

Step 1   Benzene.

Step 2

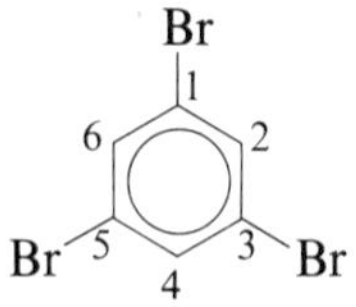

Step 3   1,3,5-tribromobenzene.

Example 15.17   Name the compound:

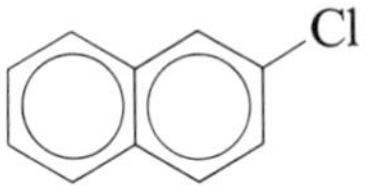

Step 1   Naphthalene.

Step 2

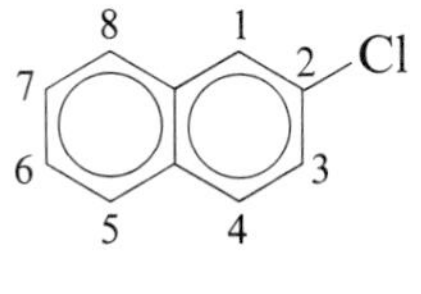

Step 3   2-chloronaphthalene.

Example 15.18   Name the compound:

$$\text{C}_6\text{H}_5-\text{CH}_2-\text{CH}_2-\text{CH}_3$$

Step 1   Benzene.

Step 2

$$\underset{4}{\overset{5}{\underset{3}{\overset{6}{\bigcirc}}}}^1-\text{CH}_2-\text{CH}_2-\text{CH}_3$$

Step 3   Propylbenzene. This compound could also be named 1-phenylpropane.

The benzene group is called phenyl when it is named as a substituent. The choice of naming here is arbitrary.

15.4   Sources of Hydrocarbons

Hydrocarbons extensively affect our environment and our lives. Our modern society depends heavily on oil for energy. Crude oil is a mixture of many hydrocarbons; as many as 295 different hydrocarbons have been found in one sample of crude oil. Products from oil provide fuel for automobiles, fuel for electrical generating plants, starting materials for production of most plastics, starting materials for synthetic rubber, and source material for many other products.

The components of crude oil must be separated before the oil is very useful. This is accomplished by **fractional distillation**, a process in which crude oil is placed in a furnace and heated (Figure 15.12). As the oil is heated, the components that boil at the lowest temperature go up the column and out of the top, where they are collected. These components are compounds ranging in size from methane (CH_4) to butane (C_4H_{10}). Another group of hydrocarbons, ranging in composition from 5 carbons to 12 carbons, is collected in the middle of the tower. The higher-molecular-weight hydrocarbons do not vaporize easily and are drained off into another furnace, where they are heated under vacuum. Using a vacuum allows separating hydrocarbons containing many carbons in the same way as low-molecular-weight hydrocarbons, except that

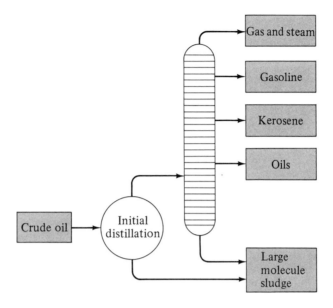

Figure 15.12 A fractionating tower and plant for the vacuum distillation of oil.

under vacuum the passage of these hydrocarbons up the tower is made easier. Table 15.6 shows some products of this fractional distillation and their uses.

Society has a tremendous need for gasoline to supply the ever growing number of automobiles and trucks that are manufactured and used. The natural supply of gasoline from crude oil is not nearly enough to supply the need, so a way of producing more gasoline has been devised. This process is called **cracking** (Figure 15.13). The portion of the crude oil that contains 12 to 18 carbons is heated in a vacuum, and the large molecules break apart to form smaller molecules containing between 5 and 12 carbons each. This greatly increases the fraction of crude oil that can be used for gasoline and also produces unsaturated hydrocarbons that can be used by the petrochemical industry to make plastics, detergents, and many other products.

Another important source of hydrocarbon fuel is coal. Millions of tons of coal are mined each year to provide fuel to drive electrical generators and

Table 15.6 Crude Oil Fractions

Fraction	Hydrocarbon Range	Typical Uses
Gas	CH_4–C_4H_{10}	Fuel
Gasoline	C_5H_{12}–$C_{12}H_{26}$	Fuel, solvents
Kerosene	$C_{12}H_{26}$–$C_{16}H_{34}$	Diesel fuel, cracking to gasoline
Heating oil	$C_{15}H_{32}$–$C_{18}H_{38}$	Heating-cracking to gasoline
Lubricating oil	$C_{17}H_{36}$–up	Lubricants
Residue	$C_{20}H_{42}$–up	Paraffin, asphalt

Figure 15.13 A fluid catalytic cracking plant at Sun Oil Company's Marcus Hook, Pa., refinery towers 20 stories high and covers $2\frac{1}{2}$ acres. This refining unit has a daily capacity of 84,000 barrels. It circulates about eight million pounds of catalyst every hour—the equivalent of 100 car loads. (Photo courtesy of Sun Company, Inc.)

to supply starting materials for chemical products. Coal tar is an even more complicated mixture than crude oil. Thousands of different compounds have been found in coal tar and many more have not been identified.

15.5   Alkane Reactions

Many hydrocarbons react with chlorine, and chlorinated derivatives of those compounds are the products. To understand these reactions and organic reactions in general, one must realize that when an organic compound takes part in a reaction, more than one product may form. When chlorine and methane, for example, are mixed and a spark is passed through the mixture, the following reactions are most likely:

$$CH_4 + Cl_2 \xrightarrow{\text{spark}} CH_3Cl + HCl$$

$$CH_4 + 2Cl_2 \xrightarrow{\text{spark}} CH_2Cl_2 + 2HCl$$

$$CH_4 + 3Cl_2 \xrightarrow{\text{spark}} CHCl_3 + 3HCl$$

$$CH_4 + 4Cl_2 \xrightarrow{\text{spark}} CCl_4 + 4HCl$$

Still other reactions are possible, but their yield is very small.

The four main products of this set of reactions are

CH_3Cl CH_2Cl_2 $CHCl_3$ CCl_4

chloromethane   dichloromethane   trichloromethane,   tetrachloromethane,
                                   or chloroform   or carbon tetrachloride

Chlorination of ethane yields more possible products, some of which are shown:

$$CH_3-CH_3 + nCl_2 \xrightarrow{\text{spark}} \begin{cases} CH_2Cl-CH_3 \\ CHCl_2-CH_3 \\ CH_2Cl-CH_2Cl \\ CCl_3-CH_3 \\ CHCl_2-CH_2Cl \\ CCl_3-CH_2Cl \\ CHCl_2-CHCl_2 \\ CCl_3-CHCl_2 \end{cases}$$

ethane

As the number of carbon atoms in the hydrocarbon is higher, the number of possible products is greater also. For any set of reactants in an organic reaction, numerous products are possible. Therefore, when chemists write equations for organic reactions, they show only one or two principal products. Under certain conditions in the chlorination of propane, for example, the reaction equation is written

$$CH_3-CH_2-CH_2 \xrightarrow{Cl_2} \overset{\overset{\displaystyle Cl}{|}}{CH_2}-CH_2-CH_3 + CH_3-\overset{\overset{\displaystyle Cl}{|}}{CH}-CH_3$$

The main products are shown. Writing the Cl_2 above the arrow means that the propane is in the presence of Cl_2; the quantity of Cl_2 is left unspecified. Thus, we must remember two things in writing organic reaction equations: (1) We write only the chief products. (2) Reactants are shown above the arrow if quantities are meant to remain unspecified.

The reaction just shown can be applied to any alkane, even cycloalkanes. The reaction can be generally written

$$-\overset{|}{\underset{H}{C}}- \xrightarrow{Cl_2} -\overset{|}{\underset{Cl}{C}}-$$

Examples of this reaction are:

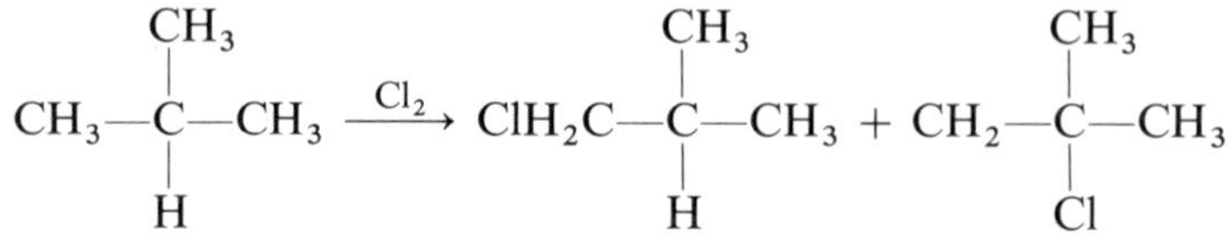

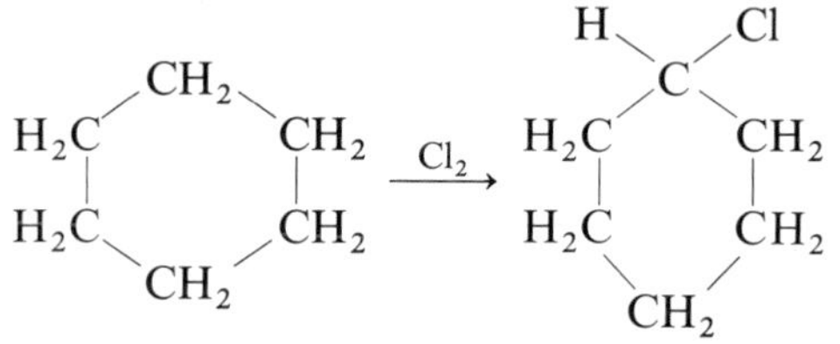

$$CH_3-\underset{\underset{H}{|}}{\overset{\overset{CH_3}{|}}{C}}-CH_3 \xrightarrow{Cl_2} ClH_2C-\underset{\underset{H}{|}}{\overset{\overset{CH_3}{|}}{C}}-CH_3 + CH_2-\underset{\underset{Cl}{|}}{\overset{\overset{CH_3}{|}}{C}}-CH_3$$

Fluorination and bromination of hydrocarbons occurs in similar reactions. Chlorinated hydrocarbons have an important history as industrial and medical chemicals. Carbon tetrachloride was an important cleaning fluid and fire extinguisher until scientists learned that CCl_4, entering the body through lungs and skin, destroys human liver tissue. Chloroform ($CHCl_3$) was used as a surgical anesthetic until physicians realized that the lethal dose of chloroform and the anesthetic dose were almost equal. Saturated hydrocarbons like cyclopropane are now often used as general anesthetics. Finally, DDT, the chlorinated hydrocarbon of the structure as shown, was widely used as an

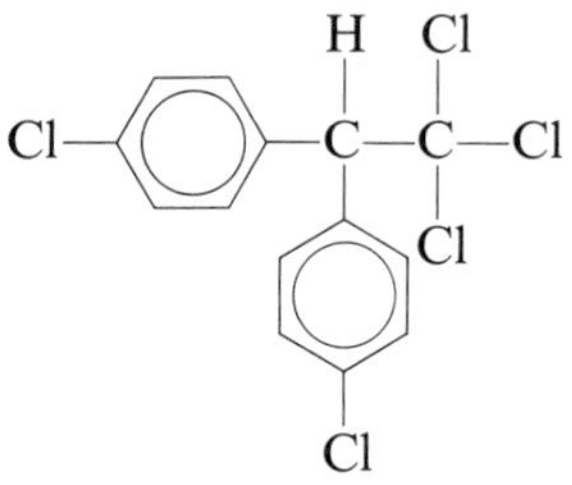

insecticide until scientists realized that it was responsible for destroying entire bird and small-animal populations in the areas in which it was used. Thus, DDT has been banned internationally for several years. It has the credit, however, of being such an effective insecticide that it has controlled malaria-carrying mosquitoes in many countries.

Chlorine- and fluorine-substituted hydrocarbons are also important. The Freon family of compounds, a few of which are shown herewith, were once important as dispersing agents in aerosol cans. These are the gases that under pressure pushed deodorant, synthetic whipped cream, cleanser, and an assortment of other useful substances out of spray cans. Until recently, the Freons were thought to be harmless. Several experiments, however, have indicated that

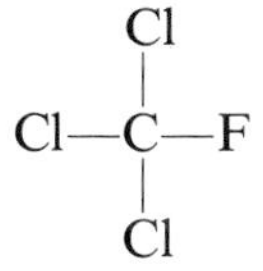

Trichlorofluoromethane
Freon 11

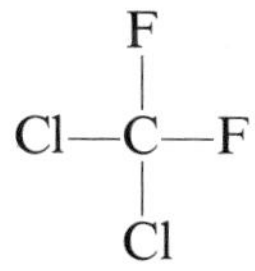

Dichlorodifluoromethane
Freon 12

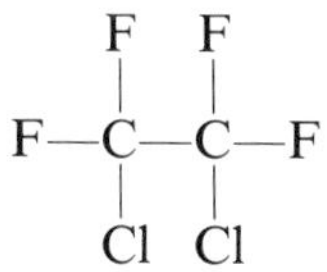

1,2-Dichloro-1,1,2,2-tetrafluoroethane
Freon 114

Freons in the upper atmosphere take part in a reaction that reduces the amount of ozone (O_3) present at those levels. The ozone layer protects the earth from searing ultraviolet radiation. Depleting this layer would seriously threaten our lives. Thus, these hydrocarbons are no longer used as aerosol propellants. The total effect of the presence of Freon in the upper atmosphere is not yet known; however, there is constant experimentation to determine the extent to which the various Freon compounds interact with the atmosphere.

15.6 Some Reactions of Alkenes and Alkynes

In connection with the halogenation of alkanes, we remarked that the halogen atom (most commonly chlorine) can be substituted for a hydrogen on the hydrocarbon. Alkenes and alkynes also react with halogens; these reactions are additions rather than substitutions, however.

The reaction in which chlorine and ethene are mixed is shown diagrammatically in Figure 15.14. Notice that the carbon–carbon double bond has been replaced with a carbon–carbon single bond. The two electrons from the double bond have split and one is present in each of the carbon-chlorine bonds.

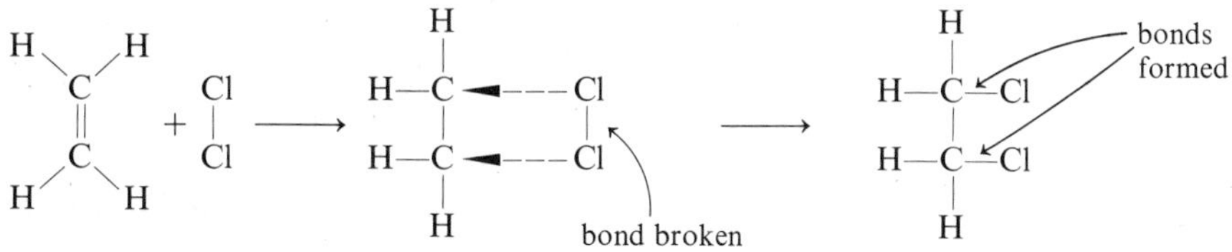

Figure 15.14 The mixing of chlorine and ethene.

Alkynes undergo similar reactions; however, two chlorine molecules can add across a triple bond. The reaction is shown for chlorine added to propyne:

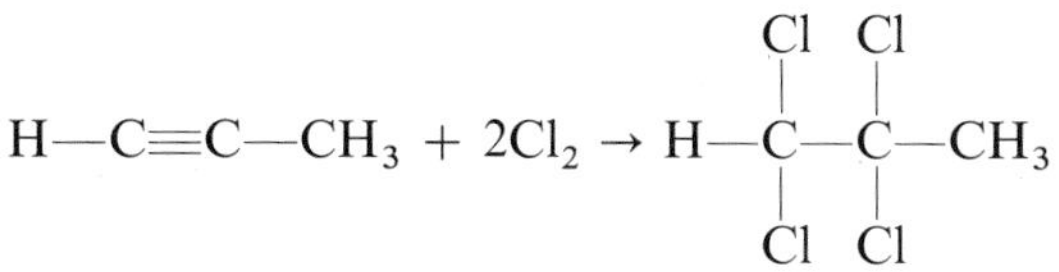

$$H-C\equiv C-CH_3 + 2Cl_2 \rightarrow H-\underset{\underset{Cl}{|}}{\overset{\overset{Cl}{|}}{C}}-\underset{\underset{Cl}{|}}{\overset{\overset{Cl}{|}}{C}}-CH_3$$

Bromine and iodine can also add across the multiple bond in alkenes and alkynes.

Example 15.19   Prepare Freon 114

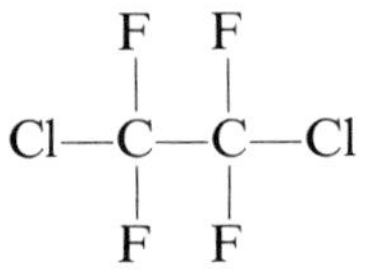

$$Cl-\underset{\underset{\displaystyle F}{|}}{\overset{\overset{\displaystyle F}{|}}{C}}-\underset{\underset{\displaystyle F}{|}}{\overset{\overset{\displaystyle F}{|}}{C}}-Cl \text{ from chlorine}$$

and tetrafluoroethene

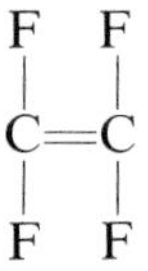

$$\underset{\underset{\displaystyle F}{|}}{\overset{\overset{\displaystyle F}{|}}{C}}=\underset{\underset{\displaystyle F}{|}}{\overset{\overset{\displaystyle F}{|}}{C}}$$

Step 1   Write the reactants indicating the addition of one compound to another:

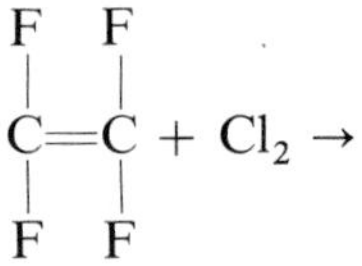

$$\underset{\underset{\displaystyle F}{|}}{\overset{\overset{\displaystyle F}{|}}{C}}=\underset{\underset{\displaystyle F}{|}}{\overset{\overset{\displaystyle F}{|}}{C}} + Cl_2 \rightarrow$$

Step 2   The product is the result of adding one Cl to each carbon involved in the double bond:

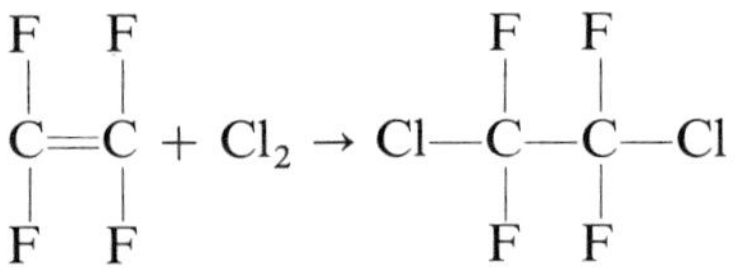

$$\underset{\underset{\displaystyle F}{|}}{\overset{\overset{\displaystyle F}{|}}{C}}=\underset{\underset{\displaystyle F}{|}}{\overset{\overset{\displaystyle F}{|}}{C}} + Cl_2 \rightarrow Cl-\underset{\underset{\displaystyle F}{|}}{\overset{\overset{\displaystyle F}{|}}{C}}-\underset{\underset{\displaystyle F}{|}}{\overset{\overset{\displaystyle F}{|}}{C}}-Cl$$

Example 15.20   What is the principal product formed when bromine is added to 2-butene?

Step 1 $CH_3-CH=CH-CH_3 + Br_2 \rightarrow$

Step 2 $CH_3-CH=CH-CH_3 + Br_2 \rightarrow CH_3-\underset{\underset{\displaystyle Br}{|}}{CH}-\underset{\underset{\displaystyle Br}{|}}{CH}-CH_3$

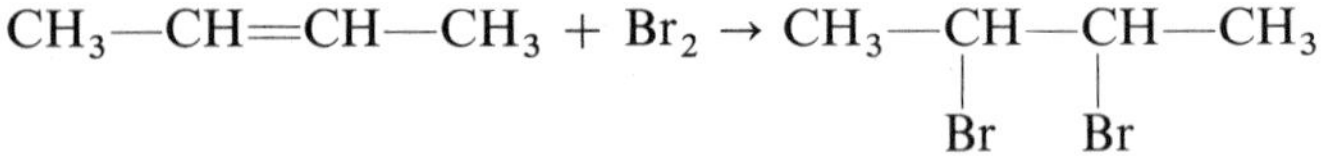

2,3-Dibromobutane

Other inorganic compounds can also add across double bonds. The substances HCl, HBr, and HI add across double bonds giving compounds that have one more halogen and one more hydrogen than the reactant alkene. The HBr adds across the double bond so that the bromine is attached to the carbon that has associated with it the fewest hydrogen atoms. This is a general rule for adding hydrogen-containing substances to double and triple bonds.

Example 15.21   What is the product when HBr is added to CH_2=CH—CH_3?

   Step 1   Write the reactants, indicating the addition of one compound to another:

$$CH_2=CH—CH_3 + HBr \rightarrow$$

   Step 2   Add H to the carbon atom in the double bond that has associated with it the most hydrogen atoms and Br to the remaining carbon of the double bond:

$$CH_2=CH—CH_3 + HBr \rightarrow \overset{\displaystyle H}{\underset{|}{CH_2}}—\overset{\displaystyle Br}{\underset{|}{CH}}—CH_2$$

2-Bromopropane

Example 15.22   What is the product when HCl is added to 1-butene?

   Step 1 CH_2=CH—CH_2—CH_3 + HCl →

   Step 2 $CH_2=CH—CH_2—CH_3 + HCl \rightarrow \overset{\displaystyle H}{\underset{|}{CH_2}}—\overset{\displaystyle Cl}{\underset{|}{CH}}—CH_2—CH_3$

2-Chlorobutane

Example 15.23   What is the product when HBr is added to propyne?

   Step 1 CH≡C—CH_3 + HBr →

   Step 2 $CH≡C—CH_3 + HBr \rightarrow \overset{\displaystyle H}{\underset{|}{CH}}=\overset{\displaystyle Br}{\underset{|}{C}}—CH_3$

2-Bromopropene

A double bond remains; thus HBr continues to add in the same way.

$$\text{Step 3} \quad CH_2{=}\overset{\overset{\displaystyle Br}{|}}{C}{-}CH_3 + HBr \rightarrow \overset{\overset{\displaystyle H}{|}}{C}H_2{-}\overset{\overset{\displaystyle Br}{|}}{\underset{\underset{\displaystyle Br}{|}}{C}}{-}CH_3$$

2,2-Dibromopropane

15.7   Alcohols

Water (H—OH) can also add to alkenes in the presence of acid. The compounds formed are called **alcohols**. Thus, alcohols can be formed from hydrocarbons and are considered derivatives of hydrocarbons; they are characterized by an —OH group attached to a carbon atom in the compound. Examples of

$$H_2C{=}CH_2 + H_2O \xrightarrow{H^+} H{-}\overset{\overset{\displaystyle H}{|}}{\underset{\underset{\displaystyle H}{|}}{C}}{-}\overset{\overset{\displaystyle H}{|}}{\underset{\underset{\displaystyle OH}{|}}{C}}{-}H$$

$$CH_2{=}\overset{\overset{\displaystyle CH_3}{|}}{C}{-}CH_3 + H_2O \xrightarrow{H^+} CH_3{-}\overset{\overset{\displaystyle CH_3}{|}}{\underset{\underset{\displaystyle OH}{|}}{C}}{-}CH_3$$

$$\underset{\underset{\displaystyle H_2C{-}CH_2}{}}{H\,C\overset{\displaystyle {=}CH}{\diagdown}CH} + H_2O \xrightarrow{H^+} \underset{\underset{\displaystyle H_2C{-}CH_2}{}}{H_2C\overset{\displaystyle \overset{H\diagup \diagdown OH}{C}}{\diagdown}CH_2}$$

reactions in which alcohols form are shown. The H^+ above the arrow means that these reactions are carried out in acid solution. The hydrogen ion acts as a catalyst.

    In the IUPAC system, alcohols are named by starting with the parent alkane and changing the name ending to -ol. Wood alcohol, which has a structure like methane, is named methanol. The structure CH_3CH_2—OH represents ethanol. The common names for alcohols are used frequently. The names *methyl alcohol* and *ethyl alcohol* are often seen, for example. Common names for alcohols are derived by changing the -ane in the alkane to -yl and adding the word *alcohol*.

Example 15.24   Name the compound: $CH_3CH_2CH_2CH_2CH_2$—OH

  Step 1   Name the parent compound, changing the ending to *-ol*: pentanol.
  Step 2   Number the carbons so that the lowest number is on the carbon that has the —OH group:

$$\overset{5}{C}H_3—\overset{4}{C}H_2—\overset{3}{C}H_2—\overset{2}{C}H_2—\overset{1}{C}H_2—OH$$

  Step 3   Locate the position of any groups attached to the parent compound and the position of the —OH group: 1-pentanol.

Example 15.25   Name the compound: $CH_3CH_2CH_2CHCH_3$
$$\qquad\qquad\qquad\qquad\qquad | $$
$$\qquad\qquad\qquad\qquad\quad OH$$

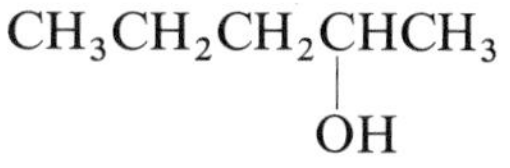

  Step 1   Pentanol.

  Step 2 $\overset{5}{C}H_3\overset{4}{C}H_2\overset{3}{C}H_2\overset{2}{C}H—\overset{1}{C}H_3$
$$\qquad\qquad\qquad\quad | $$
$$\qquad\qquad\qquad\; OH$$

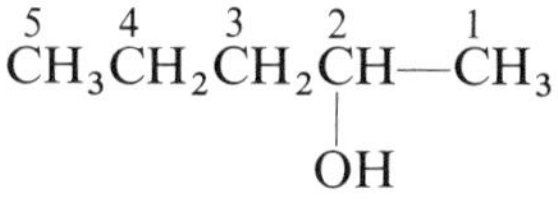

  Step 3   2-pentanol.

Example 15.26   Name the compound:

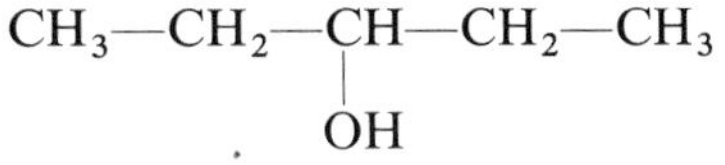

$$CH_3—CH_2—CH—CH_2—CH_3$$
$$\qquad\qquad\quad\; |$$
$$\qquad\qquad\quad OH$$

  Step 1   Pentanol.

  Step 2 $\overset{1}{C}H_3—\overset{2}{C}H_2—\overset{3}{C}H—\overset{4}{C}H_2—\overset{5}{C}H_3$
$$\qquad\qquad\qquad\qquad | $$
$$\qquad\qquad\qquad\; OH$$

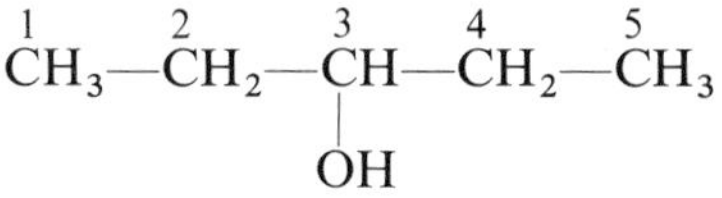

  Step 3   3-pentanol.

Example 15.27   Name the compound:

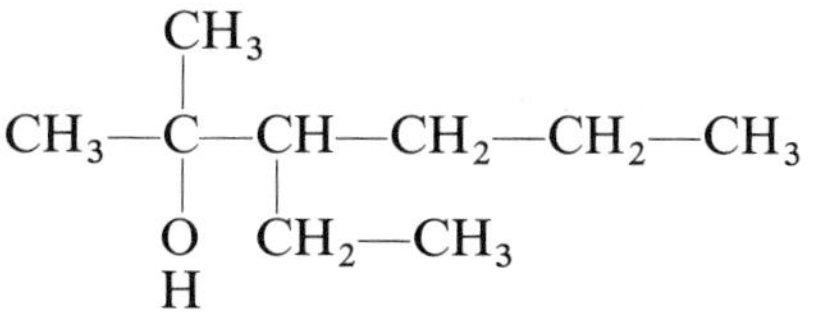

$$CH_3$$
$$|$$
$$CH_3—C—CH—CH_2—CH_2—CH_3$$
$$\qquad\; | \qquad |$$
$$\qquad\; O \quad CH_2—CH_3$$
$$\qquad\; H$$

Step 1   Hexanol.

$$
\underset{\substack{| \\ \underset{H}{O}}}{\overset{\overset{CH_3}{|}}{\underset{1}{CH_3}-\overset{2}{C}-\overset{3}{CH}-\overset{4}{CH_2}-\overset{5}{CH_2}-\overset{6}{CH_3}}}
$$

Step 2 $CH_3 \overset{CH_3}{\underset{\underset{H}{O}}{-C-}} \overset{}{\underset{CH_2-CH_3}{CH}} - CH_2 - CH_2 - CH_3$

Step 3   3-ethyl-2-methyl-2-hexanol.

Alcohols are widely used in our society. Many are used for their properties as alcohols, and many more are used as starting materials in making other compounds. Table 15.7 lists some common alcohols.

Table 15.7 Common Alcohols

Alcohol	*Structure*
Methanol Wood alcohol, methyl alcohol	CH_3OH
Ethanol Grain alcohol, ethyl alcohol	CH_3CH_2OH

2-Propanol
   Isopropyl alcohol
   Rubbing alcohol
	$CH_3\underset{\underset{OH}{\|}}{CH}CH_3$

1,2-Ethanediol Ethylene glycol	$HO-CH_2CH_2-OH$
1,2,3-Propanetriol Glycerol, or glycerine	$HO-CH_2\underset{\underset{OH}{\|}}{CH}CH_2-OH$
1-Butanol Butyl alcohol	$CH_3-CH_2-CH_2-CH_2OH$

Methanol

The simplest alcohol is methanol (H_3C-OH; wood alcohol). It is called wood alcohol because this compound can be obtained from wood by heating it to high temperatures with little oxygen present. The process is called the destructive distillation of wood.

    Huge quantities of methanol are used in the United States each year. Methanol is the main ingredient in Sterno (a brand of canned heat). Methanol can also be used in pure form as a fuel; a fondue pot might be heated with methanol, for example. Several years ago methanol was a common antifreeze for car radiators. Because it has a very low boiling point, however, it boils away as the car runs; thus, it must be continually replaced during the winter months. Large quantities of methanol are converted to formaldehyde ($H_2C{=}O$), which is used as an ingredient in making Formica, a very tough plastic material, and as the starting material for many other chemicals.

Drinking methanol is a bad idea. The methanol itself is not highly toxic, but the human body converts methanol to formaldehyde, which is very poisonous. Formaldehyde in the tissues can cause blindness and death. For this reason, methyl alcohol is often labeled *Methanol* (and *POISON*), so the average person (who is not aware of the difference between alcohols) will not be tempted to drink it, mistaking it for ethyl (or grain) alcohol.

Ethanol

Ethanol is the alcohol with which most people are familiar. It is the intoxicating ingredient in all alcoholic beverages. Man has been making ethyl alcohol since prehistoric times; sometimes the preparation was inadvertent—as when sugared pineapple or a bottle of apple cider was left standing too long.

The action of yeast on sugar produces ethyl alcohol and carbon dioxide:

$$C_6H_{12}O_6 \xrightarrow{\text{yeast}} 2CO_2 + 2C_2H_5OH$$

The process is called fermentation. It is very common and is often a part of preparing food. When bread or rolls are made, yeast produces alcohol and carbon dioxide. The carbon dioxide trapped in the bread dough causes the dough to rise. When the bread is baked, the ethyl alcohol is boiled away.

With fuel shortages prevalent in the United States, ethanol is viewed as a practical fuel for motor vehicles. Ethanol can be produced cheaply from organic waste materials by fermentation and by adding water in the presence of acid to ethene:

$$CH_2{=}CH_2 + H_2O \xrightarrow{H+} CH_3{-}CH_2{-}OH$$

(This reaction was discussed earlier.) The ethanol produced can be mixed with gasoline to create gasohol. Intensive study into this method of extending petroleum fuel resources was begun in 1979.

Ethyl alcohol has a variety of other uses (as a solvent and as a starting material for making other organic compounds). These uses lead to a problem for the government. Alcoholic beverages are very heavily taxed. It costs only about $3 to make a gallon of ethyl alcohol, but the taxes on the same alcohol raise the price to about \$32 a gallon. Alcohol used for other purposes besides drinking is not taxed to this extent, and thus its use is controlled closely by the government. It is very costly for the government to maintain this control, but the taxes more than cover the costs.

The concentration of ethyl alcohol solutions is measured in proof gallons, where 200 proof is equated with 100 percent ethyl alcohol. A beverage labeled 80 proof contains 40 percent alcohol. Ethyl alcohol, like other alcohols, is poisonous in the sense that it is changed to the aldehyde ethanal ($CH_3CH{=}O$) in the body. Excessive drinking of ethyl alcohol over a long period will cause a person loss of memory and damage to liver tissue. A person who drank a pint of pure ethyl alcohol rapidly would have essentially no chance of survival. Ethyl alcohol is also used in such things as cosmetics, paints, and perfumes, and as a general solvent.

Other Alcohols

Isopropyl alcohol (2-propanol), when diluted with water, is often called rubbing alcohol. It has a wide household use as a germicide. Isopropyl alcohol is also used as a solvent, and large quantities are used to make acetone

$$CH_3-\overset{\overset{\textstyle O}{\|}}{C}-CH_3$$

Isopropyl alcohol is poisonous, but the body will generally reject this alcohol by vomiting before concentration in the blood becomes high enough to cause death.

Ethylene glycol ($HO-CH_2-CH_2-OH$) is an example of a glycol (a dialcohol). It has found use as a permanent antifreeze for car radiators. Unlike other alcohols, it has a high boiling point and can be used the year round in car radiators without evaporating. Most commercial antifreeze contains about 50 percent ethylene glycol. This mixture is diluted further in your car radiator to give the required protection against freezing.

Glycerine or glycerol, is a trialcohol,

$$HO-CH_2-\overset{\overset{\textstyle }{|}}{\underset{\underset{\textstyle OH}{|}}{CH}}-CH_2-OH$$

It is the primary ingredient in many hand lotions, lipsticks, and other cosmetics. Glycerine is by far the least toxic of the alcohols mentioned. If large quantities of glycerine are consumed, the main effect is laxative.

15.8

Ethers

Another group of compounds that are related to alcohols, the ethers, is characterized by a

$$-\overset{|}{\underset{|}{C}}-O-\overset{|}{\underset{|}{C}}-$$

structure within a molecule. Several simple ethers are shown in Table 15.8. Diethyl ether (CH_3—CH_2—O—CH_2—CH_3) can be made from two ethyl alcohol molecules:

$$\begin{array}{l} CH_3-CH_2-\boxed{OH} \\ CH_3-CH_2-O\boxed{H} \end{array} \xrightarrow[\text{H}^+]{\text{heat}} CH_3-CH_2-O-CH_2-CH_3 + H_2O$$

Many ethers are prepared industrially in this way. This reaction works well only for symmetrical ethers, which are ethers that have the same hydrocarbon group on each side of the oxygen. Consider what might happen if methyl ethyl

Table 15.8 Common Ethers

Name	Structural Formula
CH_3—O—CH_3	Dimethyl ether
CH_3—O—CH_2—CH_3	Methyl ethyl ether
CH_3—CH_2—O—CH_2—CH_3	Diethyl ether
HC—CH HC CH O	Furan
H_2C—CH_2 H_2C CH_2 O	Tetrahydrofuran
O H_2C CH_2 H_2C CH_2 O	Dioxane

ether were made by splitting out a water molecule:

$$CH_3OH + CH_3—CH_2OH \xrightarrow[\text{heat}]{H^+} CH_3—O—CH_2—CH_3$$

The desired product forms, but two other products are possible and form in significant quantities: $CH_3—O—CH_3$ and $CH_3—CH_2—O—CH_2—CH_3$. These compounds form in the reactions:

$$CH_3OH + CH_3OH \xrightarrow[\text{heat}]{H^+} CH_3—O—CH_3$$

$$CH_3—CH_2OH + CH_3—CH_2OH \xrightarrow[\text{heat}]{H^+} CH_3—CH_2—O—CH_2—CH_3$$

When ethers are prepared from two different alcohols by adding acid and heat, all products are about equally probable. Thus, using this reaction to make any single product is not efficient. Another, more efficient way of preparing methyl ethyl ether is to cause the sodium salt of methanol to react with iodoethane:

$$CH_3O^-Na^+ + I—CH_2CH_3 \rightarrow H_3C—O—CH_2CH_3 + NaI$$

Simple ethers are named by specifying the groups on either side of the oxygen and adding the word *ether*. Ring ethers have special names, which must be memorized. The following examples help explain naming.

Example 15.28   Name the compound:

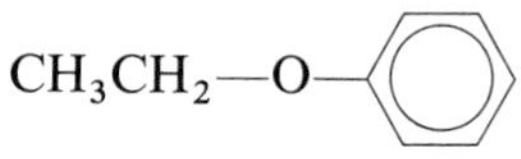

$$CH_3CH_2—O—\bigcirc$$

Step 1   Name the groups on either side of the oxygen atom: ethyl and phenyl.
Step 2   Combine the names and add the word *ether*: ethyl phenyl ether.

Example 15.29   Name the compound:

$$CH_3CH_2CH_2CH_2—O—\overset{\overset{\displaystyle CH_3}{|}}{CH}—CH_3$$

Step 1   Isopropyl and butyl.
Step 2   Isopropyl butyl ether.

Ethers are nonreactive compounds used primarily as solvents for other organic reactions. One ether, diethyl ether, has a special use as a general anesthetic. It has been so used since 1846 but is slowly being replaced by low-formula-weight hydrocarbons.

15.9 Aldehydes and Ketones

Aldehydes and ketones have very similar structures. Both contain the structure

$$-\overset{\overset{\displaystyle O}{\|}}{C}-,$$

where the carbon atom may be bonded to one or more carbon atoms or to one or more hydrogen atoms. If the oxygen is attached to a carbon atom located at the end of a carbon chain, as shown by the first four compounds listed in Table 15.9, the compound is classified as an **aldehyde**. If the oxygen is attached to a carbon atom located within the carbon chain, as shown in the

Table 15.9 Common Aldehydes and Ketones

Name	Structural Formula
Methanal (Formaldehyde)	$H-\overset{\overset{\displaystyle }{\underset{\underset{\displaystyle H}{\|}}{}}}{C}=O$
Ethanal	$CH_3-\overset{\underset{\underset{\displaystyle H}{\|}}{}}{C}=O$
Propanal	$CH_3-CH_2-\overset{\underset{\underset{\displaystyle H}{\|}}{}}{C}=O$
Butanal	$CH_3-CH_2-CH_2-\overset{\underset{\underset{\displaystyle H}{\|}}{}}{C}=O$
Propanone	$CH_3-\overset{\overset{\displaystyle O}{\|}}{C}-CH_3$
Butanone	$CH_3-\overset{\overset{\displaystyle O}{\|}}{C}-CH_2-CH_3$
2-Pentanone	$CH_3-\overset{\overset{\displaystyle O}{\|}}{C}-CH_2-CH_2-CH_3$
3-Pentanone	$CH_3-CH_2-\overset{\overset{\displaystyle O}{\|}}{C}-CH_2-CH_3$

second four compounds listed in Table 15.9, the compound is classified as a **ketone**.

Aldehydes are named by replacing the -*ane* ending on the corresponding alkane with -*al*. Thus, 2-methyl propanal would be pictured

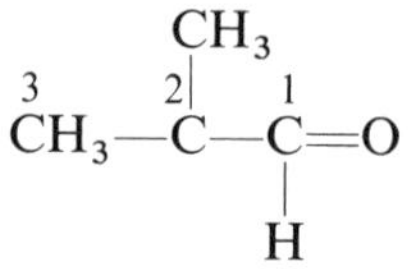

$$\underset{3}{CH_3}-\underset{2}{\overset{\overset{\displaystyle CH_3}{|}}{C}}-\underset{1}{\underset{\underset{\displaystyle H}{|}}{C}}=O$$

Also, we have the name 3-chloro-5-phenylhexanal for

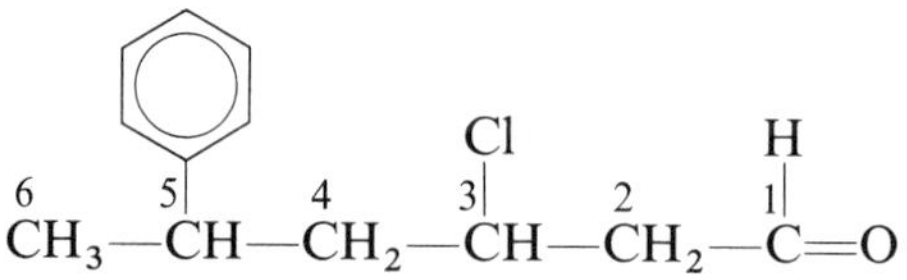

$$\underset{6}{CH_3}-\underset{5}{CH}-\underset{4}{CH_2}-\underset{3}{\overset{\overset{\displaystyle Cl}{|}}{CH}}-\underset{2}{CH_2}-\underset{1}{\underset{\underset{\displaystyle}{}}{\overset{\overset{\displaystyle H}{|}}{C}}}=O$$

Ketones are named by replacing the -*ane* ending on the corresponding alkane with -*one*. Thus, we have 3-phenyl-2-butanone,

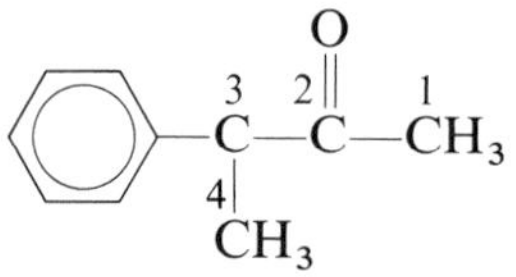

$$\bigcirc-\underset{3}{C}-\underset{2}{\overset{\overset{\displaystyle O}{||}}{C}}-\underset{1}{CH_3}$$
$$\underset{4}{\overset{|}{CH_3}}$$

Sugars are aldehydes and ketones; the chemistry of sugars depends on the aldehyde part of their structures. The following structures are examples:

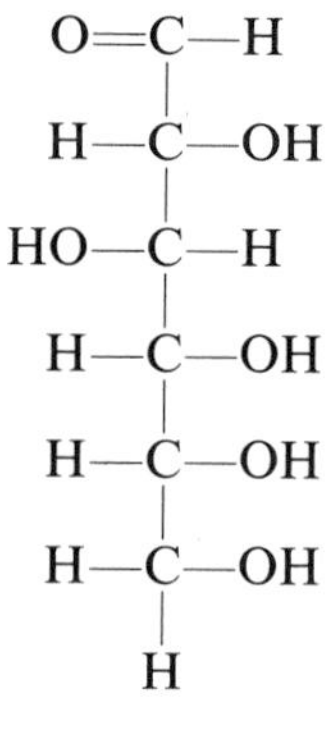

Glucose

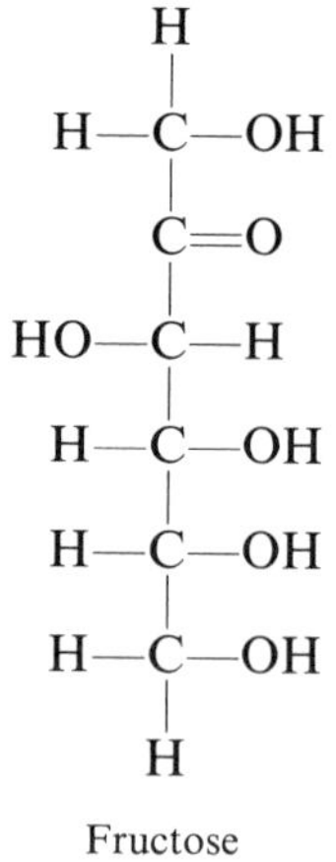

Fructose

Sugars are the basic structural units of cellulose and starch. Cellulose and starch are compounds that constitute the reserve food supply in plants.

15.10

Organic Acids and Esters

Organic Acids

Organic acids are characterized by molecules that contain the carboxyl group,

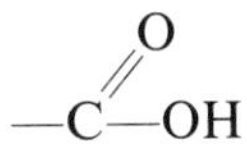

$$-C\overset{O}{\underset{OH}{\diagup}}$$

Several common acids are listed in Table 15.10. Substituted organic acids are named as derivatives of acids with the IUPAC names shown in Table 15.10. Thus,

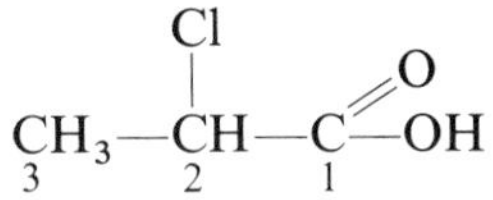

$$CH_3\underset{3}{-}\underset{2}{CH}\underset{1}{-}C\overset{O}{\underset{OH}{\diagup}}$$
$$\underset{Cl}{|}$$

is called 2-chloropropanoic acid. Also,

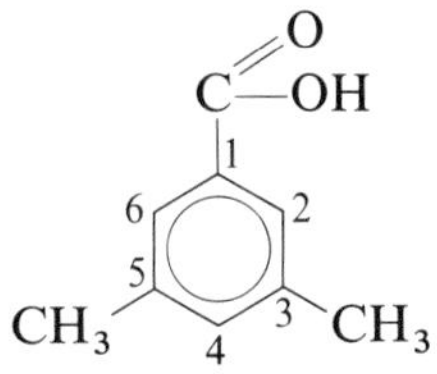

is called 3,5-dimethylbenzoic acid.

Organic acids are prepared from alcohols by oxidation. Thus, for acetic acid to be prepared from ethyl alcohol, the following reaction can be used:

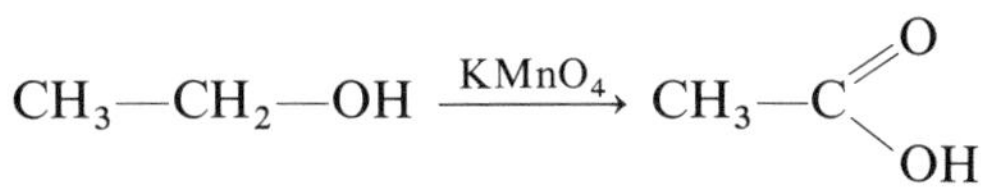

$$CH_3-CH_2-OH \xrightarrow{\text{KMnO}_4} CH_3-C\overset{O}{\underset{OH}{\diagup}}$$

This reaction is effective only when the —OH is attached to the last carbon in the chain.

Organic acids are common in our surroundings. The bite of an ant or a bee includes injection of formic acid (methanoic acid)

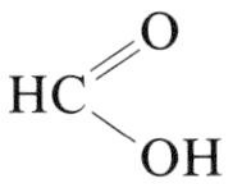

$$HC\overset{O}{\underset{OH}{\diagup}}$$

Table 15.10 Common Organic Acids

Name[a]	Structural Formula
Methanoic acid (Formic acid)	$H{-}C\begin{smallmatrix}\nearrow O\\\searrow OH\end{smallmatrix}$
Ethanoic acid (Acetic acid)	$CH_3{-}C\begin{smallmatrix}\nearrow O\\\searrow OH\end{smallmatrix}$
Propanoic acid	$CH_3{-}CH_2{-}C\begin{smallmatrix}\nearrow O\\\searrow OH\end{smallmatrix}$
Butanoic acid (Butyric acid)	$CH_3{-}CH_2{-}CH_2{-}C\begin{smallmatrix}\nearrow O\\\searrow OH\end{smallmatrix}$
Benzoic acid	

[a] The first names shown are the IUPAC names, and in parentheses are the common names.

into the skin. Notice that formic acid looks very much like formaldehyde ($H_2C{=}O$). It can be made by oxidizing formaldehyde, according to the equation

$$H{-}\overset{\displaystyle \overset{H}{|}}{C}{=}O \xrightarrow{\text{KMnO}_4} H{-}C\begin{smallmatrix}\nearrow O\\\searrow OH\end{smallmatrix}$$

Acetic acid (ethanoic acid)

$$CH_3{-}C\begin{smallmatrix}\nearrow O\\\searrow OH\end{smallmatrix}$$

is also a common acid. A dilute solution of acetic acid in water is vinegar. In a home winemaking project, if the wine is allowed to remain in the air for too long, the ethyl alcohol produced is oxidized by air to acetic acid. Wine vinegar is produced instead of wine.

High-molecular-weight acids tend to have very bad odors. Butanoic acid (also called butyric acid)

$$CH_3{-}CH_2{-}CH_2{-}C\begin{smallmatrix}\nearrow O\\\searrow OH\end{smallmatrix}$$

is the principal odorous material in rancid butter. Butanoic acid is also one of the compounds that causes body odor. The smell of goats results from a mixture of pentanoic acid and hexanoic acid:

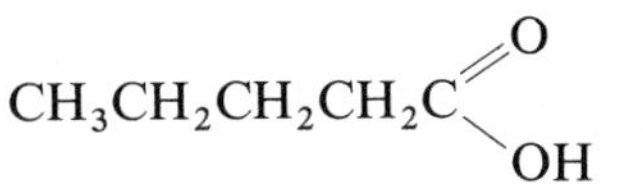

$$CH_3CH_2CH_2CH_2C\overset{O}{\underset{OH}{\diagup}}$$

Pentanoic acid

$$CH_3CH_2CH_2CH_2CH_2C\overset{O}{\underset{OH}{\diagup}}$$

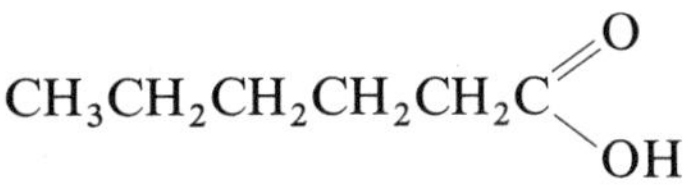

Hexanoic acid

There are many other common organic acids. Acetylsalicylic acid is the main ingredient in all aspirin:

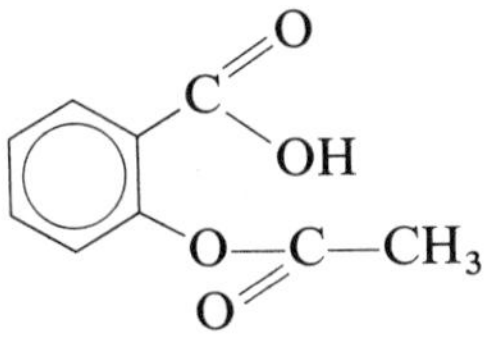

Acetylsalicylic acid(aspirin)

Note the carboxyl group in the complicated structure. Lactic acid, a combination alcohol and acid,

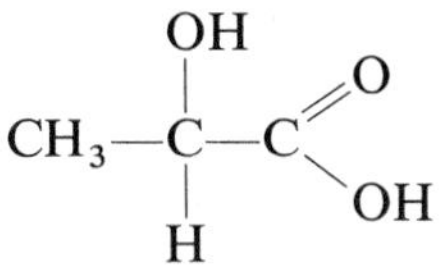

is formed when muscles contract. If contraction is maintained or severe, lactic acid accumulates, and pain and cramping result. Citric acid is what gives the sour taste to lemons, limes, and other citrus fruits. Notice that citric acid is a triacid.

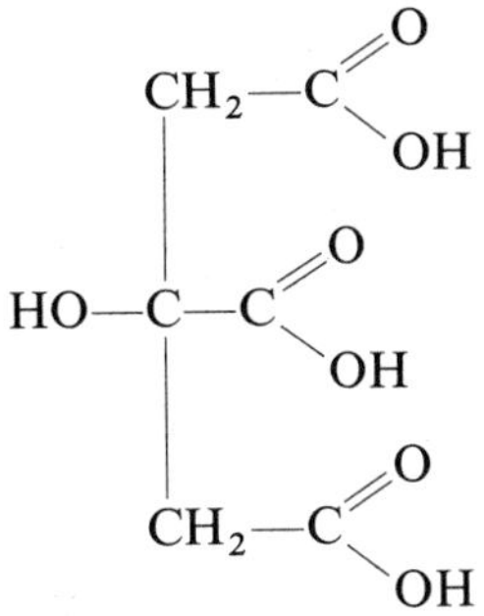

Citric acid

Esters

Alcohols react with organic acids to form esters. **Esters** are, therefore, organic compounds. The reaction of acetic acid with methanol yields methyl ethanoate:

$$CH_3-C{\overset{O}{\underset{OH}{}}} \; + \; HO-CH_3 \; \xrightarrow{H^+} \; CH_3-C{\overset{O}{\underset{O-CH_3}{}}} \; + \; H_2O$$

Methyl ethanoate

Several esters are shown in Table 15.11. Esters are named by first specifying the group attached to the acid and then changing the acid -*ic* ending to -*ate*. Common names are often used for esters, as shown in Table 15.11.

Naming esters resembles naming other organic compounds. Thus,

$$\overset{4}{CH_3}-\overset{3}{\underset{\underset{CH_3}{|}}{CH}}-\overset{2}{CH_2}-\overset{1}{C}{\overset{O}{\underset{O-\underset{\underset{CH_3}{|}}{CH}-CH_3}{}}}$$

Table 15.11 Selected Esters

Name[a]	Structural Formula
Methyl methanoate (Methyl formate)	$HC{\overset{O}{\underset{O-CH_3}{}}}$
Ethyl methanoate (Ethyl formate)	$HC{\overset{O}{\underset{O-CH_2-CH_3}{}}}$
Ethyl ethanoate (Ethyl acetate)	$CH_3-C{\overset{O}{\underset{O-CH_2-CH_3}{}}}$
Ethyl butanoate (Ethyl butyrate)	$CH_3-CH_2-CH_2-C{\overset{O}{\underset{O-CH_2-CH_3}{}}}$
Methyl benzoate	$C_6H_5-C{\overset{O}{\underset{O-CH_3}{}}}$

[a] The first names shown are the IUPAC names, with the common names given in parentheses.

is called isopropyl 3-methylbutanoate, and

is called chloromethyl-2,4-dibromobenzoate.

Esters, unlike the corresponding organic acids, usually have a pleasant odor and are often used in perfumes and artificial flavorings. Some familiar esters are shown in Table 15.12.

Table 15.12 Selected Familiar Esters

Name[a]	Structural Formula	Comment
Pentyl ethanoate (Pentyl acetate)		Banana oil
Isobutyl methanoate (Isobutyl formate)		Rasberry oil
Isobutyl propanoate		Rum flavor
3-Methylbutyl ethanoate (Isopentyl acetate)		Pear flavor
Acetyl salicylic acid		Aspirin
Methyl salicylate		Oil of wintergreen
Benzyl ethanoate		Oil of jasmine

[a] The first names given are IUPAC names, the common names being given in parentheses.

15.11   Amines and Amides

Amines

Amines are organic compounds that contain the group $-C-NH_2$. Several typical amines are shown in Table 15.13. The nomenclature of amines is also based on the parent hydrocarbon. For instance,

$$\overset{3}{CH_3}-\overset{\overset{\displaystyle CH_3}{|}}{\underset{2}{CH}}-\overset{1}{CH_2}-NH_2$$

is called 2-methylpropylamine, and

$$\overset{3}{CH_3}-\overset{\overset{\displaystyle Cl}{|}}{\underset{2}{CH}}-\overset{1}{CH_2}-NH-CH_3$$

is called 2-chloropropyl methylamine.

Amines are an important set of compounds. Some are potent stimulants. These include the amphetamines, three of which are shown.

Amphetamine   Methamphetamine   Benzamphetamine

Table 15.13   Selected Amines

Name	Structural Formula
Methylamine	CH_3-NH_2
Ethylamine	$CH_3-CH_2-NH_2$
Ethylmethylamine	$CH_3-CH_2-NH-CH_3$
Dimethylamine	$CH_3-NH-CH_3$
Trimethylamine	CH_3-N-CH_3 $\quad\quad\ \ |$ $\quad\quad CH_3$
Phenylamine (Aniline)	$\langle O \rangle -NH_2$

Some are powerful pain killers like benzocaine and novocaine:

Ethyl-4-aminobenzoate (Benzocaine)   Novocaine

Some cause the disgusting odor of decaying flesh:

$$NH_2-CH_2-CH_2-CH_2-CH_2-NH_2 \qquad NH_2-CH_2-CH_2-CH_2-CH_2-CH_2-NH_2$$

Putrescine (1,4-diaminobutane)   Cadaverine (1,5-diaminopentane)

Others, like aniline (phenylamine) are important organic solvents. Still others are industrial dyes, like 4-aminoazobenzene, a yellow dye,

Amides

Amides are related to both amines and carboxylic acids. **Amides** contain the structure

The importance of amides can be seen in the basic linkage in proteins, the building-block molecules of the body. Proteins consist of many linked amino acids. Several typical amino acids are shown.

Alanine   Glycine   Serine

There are over twenty natural amino acids that link into proteins. The linkages are called peptide linkages and are amide structures. In a single protein, there can be hundreds or thousands of amino acids.

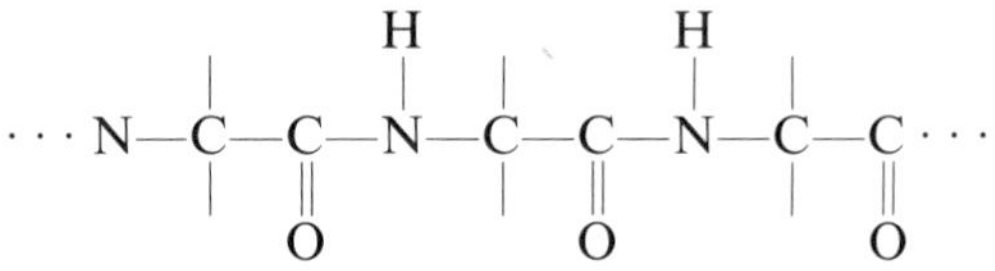

$$\cdots N-C-C-N-C-C-N-C-C \cdots$$

15.12

Polymers

Our short examination of proteins leads to a look at other large molecules. Proteins, long chains of amino acids, are called macromolecules because they are extremely large. The amino acids, which make up proteins, are linked in chains, and these chains contain many different amino acids. Polymers are also chains of molecules that are linked. **Polymers**, however, are composed of identical repeating units. Polyethylene, the material from which most plastic bags are made, consists of chains of ethene molecules:

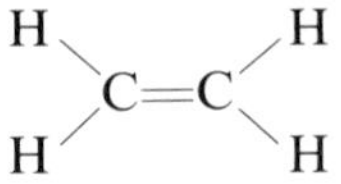

Ethene (ethylene)

which have linked to form an extremely long hydrocarbon chain:

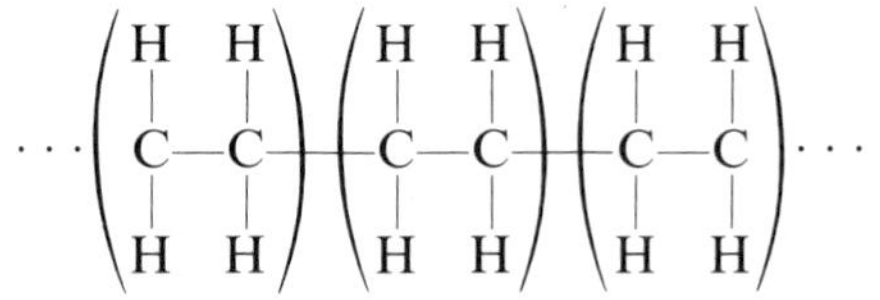

The formation of the polymer (called polymerization) can be visualized as shown in Figure 15.15. The length of polyethylene chains varies from a few hundred to several thousand molecules. Polyethylene can be an extremely flexible plastic or a relatively rigid material, depending on how the polymer is made. A relatively rigid material forms when the polymer chains are straight.

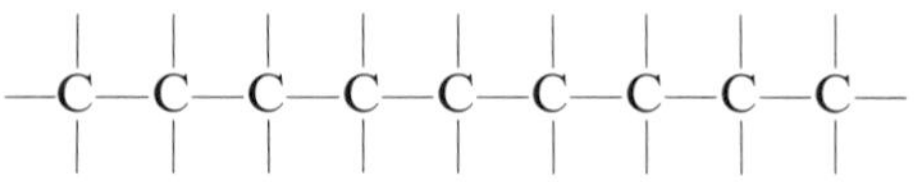

Figure 15.15 Diagram
of the formation of
polyethylene.

H H   H H   H H
··· C=C—H   H—C=C—H   H—C=C—H ···
    H

H H H H H H
··· C—C—C—C—C—C ···
H H H H H H

new bonds

These straight chains can pack closely together, giving a rigid structure (Figure 15.16). More flexible polyethylene exists when the polymer forms side chains

Figure 15.16 A rigid
material results from the
close packing of many
polymer chains.

and cross-links between chains. The chains cannot pack so close together under these conditions, and a more flexible material results.

Polymers that are related to polyethylene can also be made. These materials differ slightly in their properties from polyethylene. Several are shown in Table 15.14. These polymers are thermoplastic polymers—they can be heated, melted, and re-formed into any desired shape. Another kind of polymer is the thermosetting polymer; this polymer forms in a specific way and cannot be

Table 15.14 Selected Polymers of the Polyethylene Type

Name	Structure	Starting Compound	Uses
Polyvinylchloride	H H H H H H ∿C—C—C—C—C—C∿ H Cl H Cl H Cl	$\underset{H}{\overset{H}{>}}C=C\underset{Cl}{\overset{H}{<}}$	Phonograph records, leather-substitute containers
Polypropylene	H H H H H H ∿C—C—C—C—C—C∿ H CH$_3$ H CH$_3$ H CH$_3$	$\underset{H}{\overset{H}{>}}C=C\underset{CH_3}{\overset{H}{<}}$	Indoor-outdoor carpeting, kitchenware
Styron (Polystyrene)	H H H H H H ∿C—C—C—C—C—C∿ H ⬡ H ⬡ H ⬡	$\underset{H}{\overset{H}{>}}C=C\underset{⬡}{\overset{H}{<}}$	Styrofoam, packaging materials
Saran (Polyvinylidene chloride)	H Cl H Cl H Cl ∿C—C—C—C—C—C∿ H Cl H Cl H Cl	$\underset{H}{\overset{H}{>}}C=C\underset{Cl}{\overset{Cl}{<}}$	Food wrap
Teflon (Polytetrafluoro-ethylene)	F F F F F F ∿C—C—C—C—C—C∿ F F F F F F	$\underset{F}{\overset{F}{>}}C=C\underset{F}{\overset{F}{<}}$	Nonstick coating

heated and re-formed. Such polymers are combinations of two or more polymerizing units. For example, Bakelite, the first thermosetting polymer discovered, is made from formaldehyde and phenol units.

4-Methylphenol (p-Cresol)   Methanal (Formaldehyde)

These combine in the reaction

The products then combine and split off water:

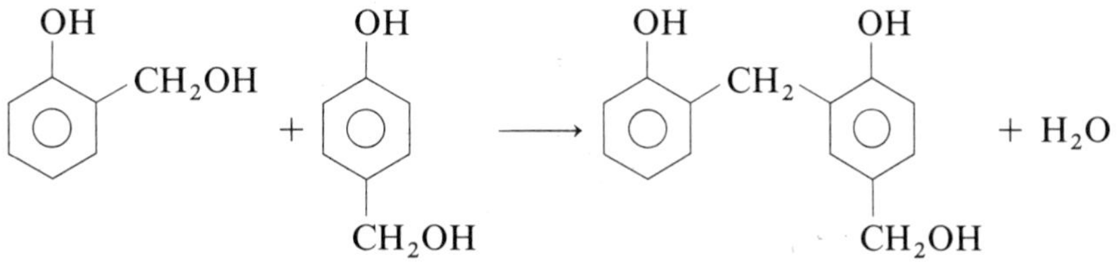

The ultimate product is a polymer, the structure of which is shown. Such polymers are widely used in almost all aspects of present-day technological society; the plastics industry is one of the largest in the American economy.

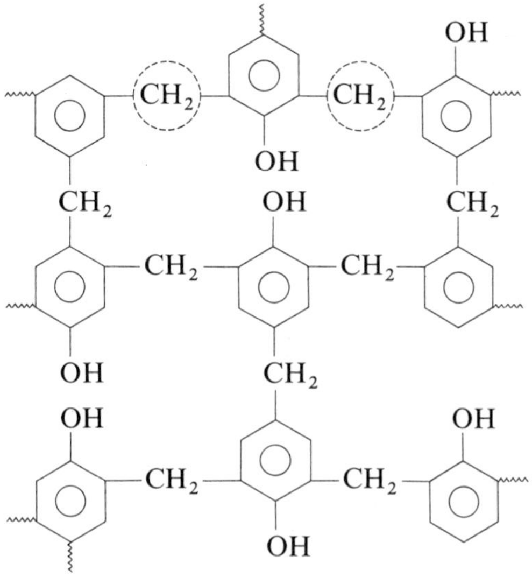

Glossary

Alcohol　　　　An organic compound whose molecules contain the group

$$-\overset{|}{\underset{|}{C}}-OH$$

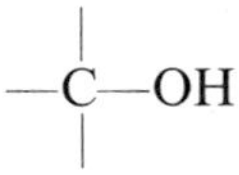

Aldehyde　　　　An organic compound whose molecules contain the group

$$-C\overset{O}{\underset{H}{\diagdown}}$$

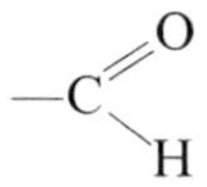

Alkane	A hydrocarbon compound whose molecules contain only single bonds.
Alkene	A hydrocarbon compound whose molecules contain one or more carbon-to-carbon double bonds.
Alkyne	A hydrocarbon compound whose molecules contain one or more carbon-to-carbon triple bonds.
Amide	An organic compound whose molecules contain the group

$$-C\underset{\textstyle NH_2}{\overset{\textstyle O}{\Big\langle}}$$

Amine   An organic compound whose molecules contain the group

$$-\overset{|}{\underset{|}{C}}-NH_2$$

Aromatic compounds	Compounds whose molecules contain one or more benzene rings.
Cracking	Heating organic material in a vacuum to break apart high molecular weight compounds.
Ester	An organic compound whose molecules contain the group

$$-\overset{\textstyle O}{\overset{\textstyle \|}{C}}-O-\overset{|}{\underset{|}{C}}-$$

Ether   An organic compound whose molecules contain the group

$$-\overset{|}{\underset{|}{C}}-O-\overset{|}{\underset{|}{C}}-$$

Fractional distillation	Heating organic material to separate components with varying molecular weights.
Isomers	Organic compounds whose molecules have the same molecular formulas but different structural formulas.
Hydrocarbon	A compound whose molecules contain only carbon and hydrogen.

Ketone	An organic compound whose molecules contain the group

$$-\overset{\displaystyle |}{\underset{\displaystyle |}{C}}-\overset{\displaystyle \overset{O}{\|}}{C}-\overset{\displaystyle |}{\underset{\displaystyle |}{C}}-$$

Organic acid	An organic compound whose molecules contain the group

$$-C\!\!\begin{array}{c}\diagup O\\ \diagdown OH\end{array}$$

Organic chemistry	The study of carbon-containing compounds.
Polymer	Chains of linked identical repeating units of atoms and molecules.
Saturated hydrocarbon	A compound whose molecules contain only single-bonded carbons.
Structural formula	A formula that shows the arrangement of atoms in a molecule.
Unsaturated hydrocarbon	A hydrocarbon compound whose molecules contain double- or triple-bonded carbons.

Problems

1. Draw isomers for the following compounds:
   (a) C_3H_8 (b) C_4H_{10} (c) C_5H_{12}
   (d) C_4H_8 (e) C_5H_8 (f) C_4H_7Cl
   (g) C_6H_6

2. Name the following compounds:
   (a) $CH_3CH_2CH_3$

   (b) CH_3—$\overset{\displaystyle CH}{\underset{\displaystyle |}{}}$—$CH_3$
            $|$
          CH_3

   (c) CH_3CH_2—OH

   (d) $CH_3CH_2CH_2C\!\!\begin{array}{c}\diagup O\\ \diagdown OH\end{array}$

   (e) CH_2=CH—CH_3

   (f) CH_3CH_2—O—CH_2CH_3

   (g) CCl_4

   (h) $CH_3CH_2C\!\!\begin{array}{c}\diagup O\\ \diagdown OCH_3\end{array}$

   (i) CH_3—$\overset{\displaystyle CH}{\underset{\displaystyle |}{}}$—$CH_2CH_3$
           $\overset{Cl}{|}$

   (j) $HC\!\equiv\!C$—CH_3

3. Name the following compounds:
   (a) $CH_3CH_2\overset{\displaystyle \overset{CH_3}{|}}{C}$——$\overset{\displaystyle \overset{CH_3}{|}}{CH}$—$CH_3$
                 $\underset{CH_3}{|}$

   (b) CH_3—$\overset{\displaystyle \overset{OH}{|}}{CH}$—$CH_3$

   (c) $\overset{\displaystyle \overset{OH}{|}}{CH_2}$—$\overset{\displaystyle \overset{OH}{|}}{CH}$—$\overset{\displaystyle \overset{OH}{|}}{CH_2}$

(d) $CH_3CH{=}O$

(e) $CH_3CH_2CH{=}O$

(f) $CH_3{-}\overset{\overset{\displaystyle O}{\|}}{C}{-}CH_3$

(g) $CH_3{-}CH_2{-}\overset{\overset{\displaystyle O}{\|}}{C}{-}CH_3$

(h) $HC\overset{\displaystyle O}{\underset{\displaystyle OH}{}}$

(i) $CH_3{-}C\overset{\displaystyle O}{\underset{\displaystyle OH}{}}$

(j) $CH_3{-}O{-}CH_2CH_3$

4. Name the following compounds:

(a) $CH_3CH_2{-}NH_2$

(b) $CH_3CH_2{-}\overset{\overset{\displaystyle H}{|}}{N}{-}CH_3$

(c) $CH_3{-}\underset{\underset{\displaystyle CH_3}{|}}{N}{-}CH_3$

(d) $CH_3{-}\underset{\underset{\displaystyle NH_2}{|}}{C}{-}CH_3$

(e) $CH_2{=}CH_2$

(f) 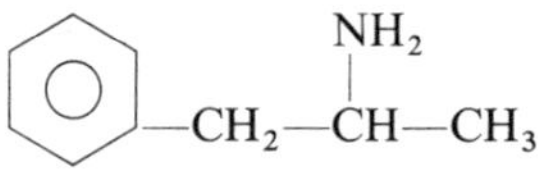 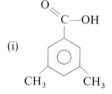 —$CH_2{-}\underset{\underset{\displaystyle NH_2}{|}}{CH}{-}CH_3$

(g) $CH_3{-}\underset{\underset{\displaystyle Cl}{|}}{CH}{-}CH_2{-}NH{-}CH_3$

(h) $CH_3CH_2CH_2C\overset{\displaystyle O}{\underset{\displaystyle O{-}CH_2CH_3}{}}$

(i)

(j) $CH_3{-}C{\equiv}C{-}CH_2{-}\underset{\underset{\displaystyle CH_3}{|}}{\overset{\overset{\displaystyle CH_3}{|}}{C}}{-}C\overset{\displaystyle O}{\underset{\displaystyle OH}{}}$

5. Draw structures for the following compounds:

(a) 3-Methylhexane   (b) 3-Ethylhexane
(c) 2-Propanol   (d) Pentanoic acid
(e) Ethyl acetate   (f) 1-Chloro-2-butene
(g) 2-Pentyne   (h) 2-Methylhexane

6. Draw structures for the following compounds:

(a) Ethylamine
(b) Dimethylamine
(c) Phenylamine
(d) 3-Methylbutyl amine
(e) Acetic acid
(f) Acetyl salicylic acid
(g) Methyl methanoate
(h) Citric acid
(i) 3-Methylbutanoic acid
(j) Hexanoic acid

7. Draw structures for the following compounds:

(a) Dimethyl ether
(b) Phenyl ethyl ether
(c) Ethylene glycol
(d) Ethanol
(e) Pentanol
(f) 4-Methyl-3,3-dichloro-1-heptene
(g) 1,2,3-Propanetriol
(h) Cyclopentanol
(i) 1,2-Dichloro-1,1,2,2-tetrafluoroethane

8. Predict the main products of the following reactions.

(a) $CH_4 + Cl_2 \xrightarrow{\text{spark}}$

(b) $CH_3CH{=}CH_2 + Cl_2 \rightarrow$

(c) $CH_3CH_2CH{=}CH_2 + HCl \rightarrow$

(d) $CH_3CH_2C{\equiv}CH + 2HBr \rightarrow$

(e) $CH_3{-}C{\equiv}C{-}CH_3 + 2Br_2 \rightarrow$

9. Predict the main products of the following reactions:

(a) $CH_3CH{=}CH_2 + H_2O \xrightarrow{H^+}$

(b)

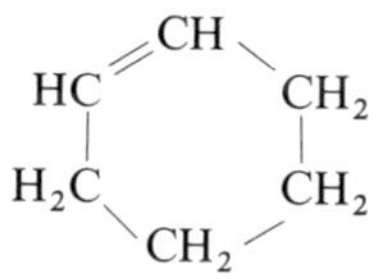

$$\text{HC} \overset{\text{CH}}{\underset{\text{CH}_2}{\overbrace{}}} \quad + \text{H}_2\text{O} \xrightarrow{\text{H}^+}$$

(the structure shows a cyclohexene-type ring: HC=CH at top, H$_2$C and CH$_2$ on the sides, CH$_2$ at bottom)

(c) $\text{CH}_2{=}\text{CH}_2 + \text{H}_2\text{O} \xrightarrow{\text{H}^+}$

(d) $\text{CH}_3\text{OH} + \text{CH}_3\text{OH} \xrightarrow[\text{heat}]{\text{H}^+}$

(e) $\text{CH}_3\text{OH} + \text{CH}_3\text{CH}_2\text{OH} \xrightarrow[\text{heat}]{\text{H}^+}$

10. Predict the main products of the following reactions:

(a) $\text{CH}_3\text{ONa} + \text{CH}_3\text{CH}_2\text{I} \rightarrow$

(b) ⟨◯⟩$-\text{CH}_2\text{ONa} + \text{CH}_3\text{I} \rightarrow$

(c) 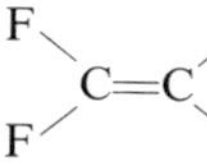 $\underset{\text{F}}{\overset{\text{F}}{>}}\text{C}{=}\text{C}\underset{\text{F}}{\overset{\text{F}}{<}} + \text{Cl}_2 \rightarrow$

(d) $\text{I}{-}\text{CH}_2{-}\text{CH}_2{-}\text{CH}_2{-}\text{CH}_2\text{ONa} \rightarrow$

(e) $\text{CH}_3{-}\text{C}{\equiv}\text{C}{-}\text{CH}_3 + 2\text{HCl} \rightarrow$

Learning Objectives for Chapter 16

Name the chief constituents of pollutants in the atmosphere that have been generated by human activity.

Define the conditions necessary for a temperature inversion.

Explain the general effect of a temperature inversion.

List the important sources of the pollutant hydrocarbons, nitrogen oxide, and carbon monoxide in the atmosphere.

List the important sources of the pollutant sulfur oxides and particulates in the atmosphere.

List the methods for removing particulates from smokestacks.

Describe the function of a tertiary sewage plant.

Describe how water is purified for drinking.

List five general categories of food additives.

Identify three flavoring agents.

Identify three preservative agents.

Identify an emulsifier.

16 POLLUTION

16.1   Air Pollution

Have you ever been in a city and noticed that the air around you is heavy, that it seems to sting your eyes, or that you are having trouble breathing? If you are healthy, such discomfort may be caused by air pollution—impurities in the air that are often not natural products but the products of society.

Air surrounds us. We walk through it, breathe it, fly planes in it, feel its pressure, and use it in chemical reactions. But what is air? We have learned that air is a mixture of gases. The composition of dry air in percentage by volume is shown in Table 16.1.

Krypton, ozone, and xenon are also present in smaller amounts along with many trace impurities. Water vapor is a common constituent of natural air but the amount varies widely from one place to another.

Table 16.1 refers to "pure" air. Pure air is air that has not been exposed to the by-products and waste products of human society; also it does not contain the products of decay and volcanic activity. Much of the difference between pure air and the air we breathe is caused by industries and automobiles. In most areas, volcanic activity and decay make only a small contribution.

In almost every city in the world, where large populations exist in small areas, the air becomes heavily polluted. Three hundred years ago, pollution was not as commonplace as it is today. The air was nearly as clear around cities as in the country. Some pollution has always existed around cities because

Table 16.1 Composition of "Pure" Dry Air in Percentage by Volume

Constituent	Percentage
N_2	78.08
O_2	20.95
Ar	0.92
CO_2	0.035
H_2	0.01
Ne	0.0018
He	0.0005

Figure 16.1 Nitrogen and sulfur oxides, carbon monoxides, unburned hydrocarbons, and particulates react with sunlight to produce the reddish-brown photo-chemical haze seen in this photograph of Boston. (Photo courtesy of Massachusetts Audubon Society, Allen H. Morgan, photographer)

people have always burned coal for heat and cooking. In the last fifty years or so, however, pollutants have been produced much faster and in greater quantities than ever before.

In many cases, changes in the air can be seen. People flying from east to west across the United States always notice the heavy brown haze when they cross the mountains 70 miles west of Los Angeles. New York and the East Coast are equally murky (Figure 16.1).

The difference between air pollution 300 years ago and today is the effect of industries, power plants that produce electricity, and automobiles. Millions of tons of air pollutants are dumped into the atmosphere each year from these three sources, and the amount seems to be increasing. The atmosphere, which is usually able to cleanse itself of impurities by the action of sun, wind, and rain, is unable to keep up.

The main constituents of man-made pollutants in the atmosphere are:

1. Hydrocarbons and organics
2. Carbon monoxide (CO)
3. Nitrogen oxides (NO, NO_2)
4. Sulfur oxides (SO_2, SO_3)
5. Particulates

These five categories account for 90 percent of the pollution in the atmosphere. We shall examine these pollutants one at a time. First, however, an important phenomenon called a temperature inversion must be explained. Temperature inversions restrict the dispersion of air pollutants.

16.2   Temperature Inversion

In a vertical direction through the atmosphere away from the earth, two distinctive physical changes are evident. First, the air becomes less dense; and second, the air becomes cooler. These two phenomena can be seen in the Rocky Mountains. On days when the temperature is quite warm on the plains, perhaps in the 90s, snow can be seen on the high mountains. A person accustomed to low altitudes who might be playing in that snow at 14,000 feet would quickly notice a shortness of breath. The cause would be the low concentration of air (oxygen in particular) at the higher altitude. The air is simply less dense at high altitudes.

During a normal day, as the sun shines, it heats the air and the ground. The ground traps much more energy than the air, becoming relatively warmer and heating the air right above it. As the air close to the ground becomes warmer, it becomes less dense and begins to rise, carrying along any pollutants present. The result is that the ground-level pollutants are dissipated into the upper atmosphere. This dissipation is effected as the hot air rises and is replaced by cooler air and the generated breeze widely disperses the remaining pollutants.

Now suppose a city is built in an area whose geological formation causes it to be shaped like a huge bowl. Examples of such cities are Los Angeles, which has hills on three sides and the Pacific Ocean on the other, and Denver, with the Rocky Mountains to the west and the plains to the east. This kind of topography limits the lateral movement of air. In Los Angeles, the bowl shape allows movement only toward the sea. In Denver, the high mountains act as a barrier to air movement. The extreme temperature differences between high and low altitudes primarily determine air movement. In the spring, when the air in the mountains is much cooler than the air on the plains, air tends to move from the mountains onto the plains, creating very high winds. At other times of the year, the mountains act as a wall, a barrier to movement of air toward them.

Now add to these situations a layer of air 150 to 300 meters above the ground that is warmer than the air on the ground. See Figure 16.2.

This is a temperature inversion, not a normal situation. When a **temperature inversion** exists, air heated by the earth will rise only until it reaches warmer air above, then it will stop, trapped by the warmer, less dense air above. Vertical movement of the air is cut off. The result is that air pollutants have nowhere to go and thus continue to increase in concentration. If a temperature inversion lasts for several days, serious health hazards can result.

How is a temperature inversion possible? In Colorado, temperature inversions often follow snowstorms. The snow accumulated on the ground holds the temperature of the earth near 0 °C, regardless of how much the sun shines. The sun, however, warms the air above the ground, a temperature inversion is created, and atmospheric pollution becomes a problem.

Figure 16.2 A simple temperature inversion, showing a layer of cooler air being trapped by a layer of warmer air. Since the vertical movement of air has halted due to the inversion, smog has built up in the cooler layer.

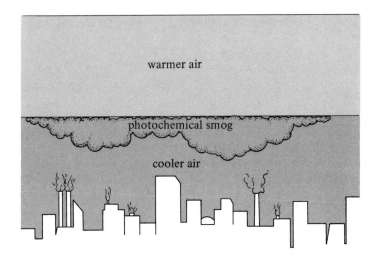

In Los Angeles, the inversion is not caused by such a drastic weather condition but is more subtle. In the evening, the earth cools more rapidly than the air. As the night progresses, the air near the surface cools substantially, while the layer immediately above the surface air cools only a little. The result is a layer of warm air sandwiched between two layers of cool air. This is the Los Angeles situation. It happens so frequently that temperature inversions exist in Los Angeles as often as 270 days in a year.

16.3 Hydrocarbons

The gasoline engine is undoubtedly the chief contributor of hydrocarbons to the atmosphere. For example, 0.5 percent of all gasoline consumed is unburned as it leaves the tailpipe of a car, 0.2 percent passes through the crankcase ventilation system, and 0.1 percent is lost to evaporation. These may seem like small amounts, until one considers the amount of gasoline consumed daily. Around Los Angeles alone, over 7 million gallons of gasoline are consumed in a day; this means that 63,000 gallons daily are lost by the methods listed. It is little wonder that California has led the nation in requiring positive ventilation controls on crankcases, catalytic burners for exhaust, and suction devices on gasoline pumps.

What are the sources of hydrocarbon emission? At present, 63 percent of the hydrocarbons in the air comes from vehicles, 5.3 percent from fuel combustion in power plants, 21 percent from other industrial processes, 5.3 percent from solid waste disposal, and 5.3 percent from heaters. It is easy to see that automobiles are indeed a serious offender in polluting the air.

Hydrocarbons supply the world with much-needed energy, but the price is high in terms of contaminated air.

The hydrocarbons in the atmosphere are not particularly hazardous themselves, but their oxidation products are dangerous. These substances are produced by the interaction of hydrocarbons with ozone, atomic oxygen, and excited oxygen. The whole chain is very complicated, with each part depending on other contaminants in the air, as shown in Figure 16.3. By far the most dangerous of the oxidation products involve a group of compounds given the name **PANs**.

The formation of these compounds requires strong sunlight. On cloudy days or during the winter, the quantity of PANs in the atmosphere is greatly reduced. This observation leads to the term *photochemical smog* since strong light is involved. These compounds are structurally somewhat like esters; they differ in containing a nitrate group instead of the hydrogen on the—OH part of the acid. The PANs result from a reaction of hydrocarbons with ozone in the air. The simplest one is called *p*eroxy*a*cetyl*n*itrate; hence the acronym PAN.

$$CH_3-C\!\!\begin{array}{c} \diagup\!\!^O \\[-4pt] \diagdown\!\!_{O-O-NO_2} \end{array}$$

The name PAN refers to a whole series of related compounds. Many times it is the PANs in the air that are responsible for red eyes and sore throats. PANs have been found to be particularly damaging to plants; if a plant is exposed to PANs for just a few hours at a concentration of 0.05 ppm, it will become damaged.

Figure 16.3 The chain of events which leads to photochemical smog is a complicated one.

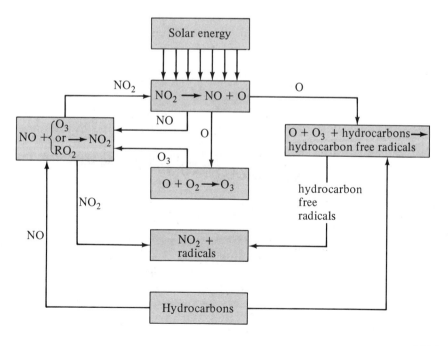

16.4 Carbon Monoxide and Carbon Dioxide

When any hydrocarbon is burned completely, carbon dioxide is produced. An example, is

$$C_5H_{12} + 8O_2 \rightarrow 5CO_2 + 6H_2O$$

If not enough oxygen is present, and this is true for many automobile engines, some carbon monoxide is produced instead of carbon dioxide. This is the source of most of the carbon monoxide polluting the air. The reaction is

$$2C_5H_{12} + 11O_2 \rightarrow 10CO + 12H_2O$$

Carbon monoxide is a poisonous gas and is also involved in reactions that produce other very dangerous air pollutants. It is so dangerous that when only 5.0 ppm in air is present, people begin to show ill effects. In general, 64 percent of all of the CO in air comes from cars, another 17 percent comes from burning, and the rest comes from industries.

Levels of carbon monoxide of 50 ppm are frequent on city streets. Poorly ventilated tunnels have been reported at several hundred parts per million of carbon monoxide. A 15-min exposure to this concentration visibly impairs mental function.

Carbon dioxide is not nearly so toxic as carbon monoxide, but it is much more abundant and its effect may be more subtle. Plants and trees tend to use up carbon dioxide in the summer; it is returned to the air in the winter when plant material decays. Burning fossil fuels year after year, however, creates a huge surplus of carbon dioxide, much of which ends up in the ocean. Another portion of this CO_2 finds its way to the upper atmosphere. Some scientists feel that more CO_2 in the upper atmosphere will cause increased heating of the earth. This projected phenomenon is known popularly as the "greenhouse effect." As the oceans heat, they release more CO_2 and inevitably sponsor more heating. A catastrophic cycle is thus envisioned for the earth should its average temperature increase beyond livable limits. The theory has not yet been verified.

16.5 Nitrogen Oxides

Carbon monoxide is produced when organic fuels in automobile engines burn incompletely. Nitrogen oxides, too, are produced in automobile engines. Air is composed of about 80 percent nitrogen, a stable substance; it therefore does not take part in most chemical reactions on the surface of the earth. In the piston engine, however, very high pressures and high temperatures (1200–1800 °C) cause the following reaction after air is drawn into the cylinder:

$$N_2 + O_2 \rightarrow 2NO$$

Nitric oxide (NO) is formed. When the NO leaves the exhaust pipe and hits the light of day, another reaction causes nitrogen dioxide (NO_2) to form:

$$2NO + O_2 \xrightarrow{\text{sunlight}} 2NO_2$$

It is interesting that natural processes—bacterial action and decay—produce most of the nitrogen oxides in the world. This process has little effect on the human population since the nitrogen oxides produced are so evenly distributed. The formation of nitrogen oxides begins to have an effect when a large quantity is produced in a very small area. Cars produce about 40 percent of the man-made nitrogen oxides, and industries produce about 50 percent. Concentrations of 100 ppm of NO_2 have caused death in laboratory animals; and concentrations of as little as 5 ppm in air have resulted in the paralysis of the breathing mechanism.

16.6   Oxides of Sulfur

Burning any sulfur-containing material causes sulfur oxides to form according to the following reactions:

$$S + O_2 \longrightarrow SO_2$$

$$2SO_2 + O_2 \xrightarrow{\text{sunlight}} 2SO_3$$

Most sulfur oxides entering the atmosphere come from natural sources. Sulfur compounds are present in high concentrations in ocean water, and they are released by sea spray. Decay of biological materials is another natural process for releasing sulfur compounds into the atmosphere.

About a third of the sulfur oxides in the atmosphere are man-made. Again, the problem is with how man's waste products are distributed. High concentrations in small areas can cause dangerous conditions.

About two-thirds of the man-made sulfur oxides entering the atmosphere result from the burning of fossil fuels to produce electricity (Figure 16.4). Coal usually contains a small amount of sulfur; but from the large quantity of coal burned, 20 million tons of sulfur oxides are dumped into the atmosphere each year. Thus coal of a low sulfur content has become valuable. Great deposits of low-sulfur coal are in the western Dakotas and eastern Montana, and industries have been strip-mining such places.

Figure 16.4 One of the most modern coal mines in the United States, the Pike Mine in Pike County, Kentucky. (Photo courtesy of Bethlehem Steel.)

The sulfur oxides are serious health hazards. Concentrations of 20 ppm of SO_2 can cause eye irritation and coughing, and very long exposure to 50 ppm can cause death. Sulfur dioxide is usually pointed to as the cause of many deaths in the London "killer fogs" of 1956 and 1957.

Effects of sulfur trioxide (SO_3) on humans are not so well known; however, SO_3 reacts with water vapor in the air and in lungs according to the equation

$$SO_3 + H_2O \rightarrow H_2SO_4$$

to form sulfuric acid. Sulfuric acid irritates both eyes and throat.

16.7   Particulates

Particulate contaminants in the air include matter like ashes, soot, and smoke. Particulates can also come from dust kicked up by windstorms or thrown out by volcanoes. Most of the problems result from high concentrations of particulates in small areas. The main source of artificially created particulates is burning. Industrial and electrical plants especially have contributed to the problem.

Most industrial plants have significantly reduced the amount of particulate matter released to the atmosphere by placing a device on their smokestacks to trap the particles. This may be as simple as placing a filter in the gas stream to collect the particles. Another, more sophisticated device is the **mechanical cyclone** (Figure 16.5), which whirls the gas, forcing particles to the outside

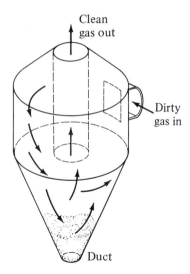

Figure 16.5 Schematic of a mechanical cyclone, which uses centrifugal force to separate particulate matter from gases.

Clean gas out

Dirty gas in

Duct

edges, where they can fall into a collector. **Wet scrubbers** pass the gases through a fine water spray, which collects the particles in the water drops. The most sophisticated method involves the **electrostatic precipator** (Figure 16.6). It uses an electrode that is run down the center of the collector, and a high voltage is applied between this center electrode and the sides of the collector. The particles passing through the electric field pick up a negative charge and are attracted to the sides of the container. The container is periodically shaken, and the particles fall to the bottom, from which they are removed.

Figure 16.6 Schematic of an electrostatic precipitator. A high voltage is applied across the gases which causes the solid particles to pick up electrons and become attracted to the positive electrode.

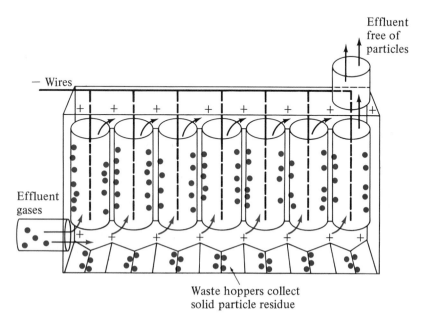

Effluent free of particles

− Wires

Effluent gases

Waste hoppers collect solid particle residue

16.8 Water Pollution

Anything that is added to the water by people can be thought of as a pollutant. This can mean empty beer cans, fertilizer that runs into the streams or lakes from a farmer's field or somebody's lawn, sewage material, or industrial waste. These pollutants have different effects on the water. If the pollutants are junk, cans, old tires, or wrecked cars dumped into streams, the effect is extreme unsightliness.

If the pollutants consist of fertilizer running into streams and lakes, the effect is an abnormal growth of algae, which turns the water green. In addition, the algae die and decompose. Decomposition of algae uses up the oxygen in the water and aquatic animal life dies. As the cycle continues, more plants and animals die, and more oxygen is used. In extreme cases the water becomes completely putrid and highly malodorous.

Sewage material creates much the same problem. It has the added complication of infecting the water with bacteria that may be dangerous to human health. The water can no longer be used for swimming or other water sports. Industrial wastes add many chemicals that cannot be removed naturally and thus may stay in the water supply for years, destroying aquatic life. Many heavy metals such as mercury and cadmium are dumped into the water by industrial companies. These metals, when they accumulate, affect all kinds of animal life, including man.

A serious and pressing problem that the United States, together with other countries, is facing today is supplying enough drinking water. The average city family uses about 300 gal of water each day; and since it all comes from the same pipes, it all must be of drinking quality. Industry uses millions of gallons of water, 10 gal for each can of vegetables on the grocery shelf, 25,000 gal for each ton of steel produced, and 50,000 gal for each ton of paper made. Since the water used by industry ends up unfit to drink, obviously providing enough drinkable water by purifying polluted water is linked to the amount industries use. Used water must be repurified. Most cities locate their drinking water intake above the city and discharge the sewage below the city. The next city downstream does the same thing, and by the time the end of the river is reached, the last city must purify water extensively before it is drinkable.

A stream has the ability to purify itself if it is not overloaded with pollutants. As waste material is dumped into the stream, the heavy particles settle to the bottom, where bacteria slowly decompose any organic matter. Other particles and soluble material are carried downstream and are exposed to sunlight and air. As the material is mixed with air, bacteria attack the pollutants, and the water is eventually purified. These processes need oxygen, and the pollutant concentration is often measured by the amount of oxygen necessary for the processes to continue. The term **BOD (biological oxygen demand)** is used for this measurement. It is the expression of the amount of oxygen needed for oxidation of the organic material in the water. As the organic material in the water goes up, the BOD goes up. When the quantities of pollutants in the water become too large, the streams and rivers simply cannot purify themselves.

16.9 Sewage Plants

Man has studied the ways water is purified naturally to develop ways of handling sewage. Sewage plants break the handling of sewage into three parts: primary, secondary and tertiary systems (Figure 16.7). The **primary sewage system** takes care of large solid wastes, the **secondary system** takes care of colloidal pollutants, and the **tertiary system** gets at dissolved pollutants and any remaining suspended material. Most cities have at least a primary sewage treatment plant, although there are still areas of the country in which raw sewage (untreated sewage) is dumped into a river.

In a typical sewage plant, incoming sewage is passed through screens to remove the larger chunks of material and then passed into settling tanks, where the denser materials settle out. This step has a very large BOD. Often, all the oxygen in the water being treated may be used up and there is anaerobic decomposition; this means that bacteria work on organic material in the absence of air. Effluent from this treatment still contains a lot of suspended organic

Figure 16.7 Diagram of a sewage treatment plant.

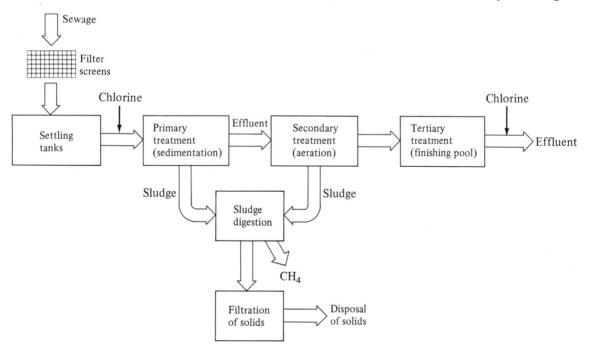

material. If the sewage plant has only primary treatment, the effluent is treated with chlorine and returned to the stream. A sewage plant that has secondary treatment facilities passes the primary effluent into large aerated tanks that contain activated sludge. The activated sludge is the solid material that settles out and contains the bacteria that are aerobic; such bacteria work on organic material in air. Sewage is allowed to stand in these tanks while a continual supply of air is provided and the bacteria decompose the organic material. This effluent is then treated with chlorine and returned to the river. If a plant has tertiary facilities, the effluent from the secondary treatment is passed into a finishing lagoon, where the remaining organic material and most phosphates and nitrates are allowed to decompose. The water is then filtered, chlorinated, and returned to the river. Few sewage plants render all three treatments. All three phases yield such effective treatment, however, that some plants (like the Lake Tahoe tertiary treatment plant) claim that water coming from the tertiary system is pure enough to be used as drinking water.

16.10 Drinking Water

Because any city downriver from another city must use some of the sewage effluent from the upstream cities, the water must be purified before it is drinkable. This is usually done by allowing the water to stand in a settling basin, where it is treated with calcium hydroxide and aluminum sulfate. These compounds react to form aluminum hydroxide, which precipitates from the water. As the aluminum hydroxide precipitates, it carries with it dirt and bacteria. The water is then filtered through sand and gravel. It may also be sprayed into the air or filtered through charcoal to remove odors and color. The water is then treated with chlorine to kill bacteria. If much chlorine must be added, its taste in the water is obvious (Figure 16.8).

Figure 16.8 Diagram of water purification.

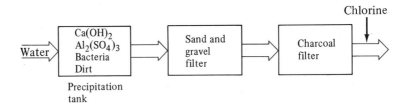

16.11 Heavy Metals as Pollutants

Inorganic materials, like heavy metals dissolved in the water, have become a very serious problem. Mercury pollution in particular has been thoroughly investigated. Mercury and mercury compounds are used in many different industrial processes, including paper, plastic, and paint production, and also in coal-burning power plants. Mercury compounds have even been used to treat seeds to prevent mildew.

Mercury itself, if it stayed as elemental mercury, would not affect man too much. Although mercury as a metal is harmful to humans, it would not spread very far or in very large quantities in that form. The main problem arises when certain microorganisms convert the mercury into organic mercury compounds that contain the methyl mercury group (H_3C—Hg—) and when seeds are coated with compounds that contain methyl mercury. Animals that live in the water readily assimilate mercury in this form. These animals are often eaten by people. A human who accumulates too much methyl mercury in the body becomes irritable, loses motor control, often loses hair, suffers decaying teeth, and untreated, eventually will die. The Food and Drug Administration is trying to keep mercury-contaminated foods from reaching the consumer.

16.12 Food Additives

The use of chemical additives in food has become controversial of late. Since the world population is constantly increasing and the supply of food constantly decreasing, there is little doubt that man will continue to use food additives. The questions that must be considered relative to adding chemicals to our food supply are: (1) Is the added material safe? and (2) Is it necessary to add this chemical?

Although generally we consider **food additives** chemical compounds added to food for enhancing flavor, improving color, extending shelf life, and protecting nutritional value, no universally agreed-on definition has ever been established. Since man has known and used fire, smoking food has been a method of preservation. This process involves adding complex organic molecules via smoke to the food. The net effect is preservation of the food and the ingestion of many foreign compounds. It seems that a definition of food additive must involve the following questions:

1. Is there a difference between natural and man-made chemicals?
2. Are added chemicals poisonous?
3. How is the safety of a food additive evaluated?
4. Is the food supply safe?

Concerning question 1, common table sugar, sucrose, can be obtained from sugar cane merely by sucking on sections of the mature plant. Recovering sucrose from sugar beets involves a long, tedious chemical process. The net result of both processes is no different from the sucrose that could be synthesized in a student's flask from other compounds. To say that any one of the three compounds is not sucrose would be incorrect. The question is further complicated by considering compounds such as sodium propionate, which is natural to Swiss cheese but an additive in bread, to inhibit mold. Should sodium propionate be considered an additive, or a natural product and thus, a candidate for the organic grocery shelf? These questions will be reevaluated and reargued for years.

Perhaps more important is evaluating the remaining three questions. Concerning safety of natural products, mushrooms are commonly eaten and enjoyed by people everywhere; however, the compound amanitine produced by the mushroom *Amanita phalloides* is an extremely deadly poison. Many plants have been shown to be toxic. The leaves of the common rhubarb plant often sicken children who eat them. If one stops to consider the multitude of poisonous plants, it will be readily apparent that nature did not intend everything to be edible.

Concerning question 3, chemical additives must be evaluated to determine both short-term and long-term effects on the organism ingesting the material. This is the job of thousands of chemists throughout the world. Nearly all companies that produce additives for food run extensive programs to evaluate the safety and effectiveness of the particular product. These programs are checked and expanded by the Food and Drug Administration, which constantly monitors new materials on the market. Unfortunately, there are so many new materials that little time is devoted to investigating compounds that have been on the market for several years. It is clear that many compounds have been marketed without proper tests.

Concerning question 4, the safety of foods and additives must be evaluated in terms of quantities consumed. One must remember to keep chemicals in food in proper perspective. Chemicals such as common table salt (NaCl), copper, manganese, and zinc, and also compounds like vitamins are essential to life and must be consumed on a regular basis. However, an overdose of any one of these materials can be fatal.

Food additives can be classified in five general categories of compounds: (1) flavoring, (2) coloring, (3) preservation, (4) texture, and (5) miscellaneous, a category that is a catchall for anything that does not fall into the first four.

Flavoring Agents

Well over a thousand different flavoring agents are extant, and most have not been extensively investigated for physiological safety. Many of these are natural compounds, which often have artificial counterparts synthesized in the laboratory. Vanilla, lemon, orange, peppermint, and wintergreen are natural compounds, and these flavors are not commonly synthesized. Acetaldehyde, benzaldehyde, ethyl acetate, ethyl vanillin, glycerol, tributyrate, and piperonal are examples of synthetic flavors that the U.S. Food and Drug Administration has approved.

The compound monosodium glutamate, MSG, is classified with flavoring compounds. Although it is not a flavoring agent as such, it is considered a flavor enhancer and is widely marketed around the world. One study has shown, however, that large doses of MSG produce brain lesions in newborn animals. This is a typical example of the problem scientists face in trying to extrapolate data obtained from high-level ingestion by animals to low-level use by humans.

Coloring Agents

Colors are put in food primarily to produce a more appetizing or pleasing appearance. A person spreading margarine on bread wants to see a yellow color. In most instances, the yellow color is from a coloring agent. During the late 1940s, the butter industry succeeded in having laws passed prohibiting the sale of yellow margarine. If a family wanted margarine, they either used it white or mixed in a prepared coloring agent. The mere color of the margarine was sufficient to retard margarine sales. Repeal of the laws governing the addition of coloring agents to margarine occurred within a few years and we may now buy yellow margarine.

In producing a coloring agent, not only must the manufacturer consider the desired color but also the compound must be stable during storage, cooking, and interaction with other compounds. Names such as amaranth (red), tartrazine (yellow), benylviolet (violet), and indigatine (blue) on labels indicate those coloring additives.

Preservative Agents

Preservatives reduce food spoilage caused by microorganisms. It has been estimated that nearly 20 percent of the food supply is lost because of spoilage. Common methods of food preservation include freezing, drying, salting, heating, and souring. All these methods are somewhat effective. The role of additives as preservatives is to lengthen the safe-storage time of foods. Compounds such as sodium diacetate, lactic acid, sodium propionate, and calcium phosphate are added to bread products to prevent mold spores from becoming active in warm humid weather. Sorbic acid prevents mold in cheese and syrups. The names *benzoic acid* and *sodium benzoate* are found on the labels of many juices, vegetables, and margarines. Many preservatives come under the general heading of antioxidants and are added to foods containing fats to prevent the food from becoming rancid. Compounds like propyl gallate and butylated hydroxytoluene are added to margarine, cooking oils, cereals, and potato chips. Ascorbic acid (Vitamin C) is often added with one of the antioxidants to increase the effect and also to prevent discoloration of foods over time.

Antibiotics have also been used as preservatives. The United States has discouraged this practice because microorganisms have a tendency to adapt to accommodate the particular antibiotic; its medical effectiveness is thus lost to people consuming food in which such adaptation has been made.

Texture Agents

Texture agents are compounds used as emulsifiers, stabilizers, and thickening agents. They are used extensively in ice cream, whipped products, bread, candy, and some soft drinks. An emulsifier keeps oil dispersed in water. This allows a manufacturer to produce a smooth, even texture of any desired thickness. Compounds such as cholic acid, glucocholic acid, monosodium phosphate, and propylene are used as emulsifiers. A very common natural compound in this category is pectin. Many a well-intentioned homemaker has had to use strawberry jam as syrup for pancakes because enough pectin for "setting" the jam was not present. Pectin is found naturally in many fruits, but must be added to many others for suitable thickening in cooking.

Miscellaneous Agents

This category includes such substances as acids, alkalis, and buffers. The pH of a foodstuff is often important, particularly in soft drinks, chocolate, and processed cheese. Bleaching agents are used on flour. Anticaking agents keep salt and other powders free-flowing. Foaming agents allow canning whipped cream. Clarifying agents are used in vinegar. Caffeine is extracted from coffee with various solvents.

Food additives have numerous uses, but unfortunately, some uses are intended to bilk the public. Several years ago a fish dealer in Philadelphia used large amounts of sodium nitrate to cover the spoilage of a batch of fish. Sodium nitrate is normally an innocuous compound, well tolerated by the body. On this occasion, however, such large amounts were used that over 180 persons became ill and one died.

Cases of this kind should not close the door on food additives, but should encourage the public to monitor the use of additives closely. With proper management, they are a boon to mankind.

Glossary

Biological oxygen demand (BOD)	A phrase that expresses the quantity of oxygen required to decompose organic matter in aqueous solution.

Electrostatic precipitator	A device for removing particulate matter from gases. A high potential is put across the gas stream, whereby a charge on the particles is created. The charged particles migrate to the positive electrode, where they collect.
Food additives	Chemical compounds added to food for such purposes as enhancing flavor, improving color, extending shelf life, and protecting nutritional value.
Mechanical cyclone	A device for removing particulate matter from gases. It works by forcing the heavier particles to the outside of the device; there they fall from the gases and are collected.
PAN (peroxyacetylnitrate)	A class of organic pollutants whose molecules contain the group

Particulate pollutant	Air pollution by tiny particles of liquids and solids.
Primary sewage treatment	The treatment of sewage that consists in allowing the solid matter to settle from the liquid sewage (first stage in sewage treatment).
Secondary sewage treatment	The treatment of sewage that consists in removing colloidal particles from the liquid sewage (second stage in sewage treatment).
Temperature inversion	An atmospheric condition whereby the temperature increases rather than decreases as the altitude becomes higher. Temperature inversions trap air pollutants, thereby worsening pollution.
Tertiary sewage treatment	The treatment of sewage that consists in removing residual suspended matter and dissolved pollutants (third stage in sewage treatment).
Wet scrubber	A device for removing particulate matter from gases by collecting the particles in a fine spray of water.

Problems

1. The air pollution index is listed in most large newspapers throughout the country. Graph all or part of the data given for one week. Note corresponding weather patterns and see what correlations you can make.

2. Find out about your community's sewage system. Is it primary, secondary, or tertiary? Is it large enough to handle all sewage, even during peak hours of use? A visit to your local sewage plant is an eye-opening experience. Arrange a trip if possible.

3. Where does your community's drinking water come from? Is it extensively purified before chlorination?

4. From packaged food available to you, list all additives present. Try to place the additives in one of the five categories outlined.

Learning Objectives for Chapter 17

Define **radioactivity, beta particle, positron, gamma ray, alpha particle, electron capture, half-life, chain reaction.**

Write the symbol for an element and properly indicate its mass number and atomic number.

Determine which elements are naturally radioactive.

Write nuclear equations indicating products formed.

Explain a decay series for a radioactive element.

Predict products formed when alpha particles and neutrons bombard atomic nuclei in man-made reactions.

Explain how new elements can be made.

Explain how a nuclear power plant generates electricity.

Describe how fission reactions are controlled.

Show how more fuel for a reactor can be made while the reactor is generating electricity.

List some possible environmental problems connected with nuclear power.

Explain how the effect of radiation on humans is measured.

Explain nuclear fusion.

17 NUCLEAR ENERGY

17.1 Energy for Everyone?

If you have ever been to the top of the Empire State Building and looked over Manhattan, you might have been impressed with the number of buildings, apartments, and people located on this small island. You might have wondered what made it possible for so many people to live and work in such a small area. It must take a tremendous amount of energy in the form of electricity to operate all the lights, elevators, air-conditioners, and even the blinking lights on telephones. It has become evident in the past few years that there is not always enough electricity to supply the requirements of the city. Brownouts and blackouts have become commonplace during the hot summer months in New York, and the problem is getting worse. Such shortage of electrical energy has hit almost every large population area in the United States.

What will happen to people if enough power cannot be supplied to meet requirements? Will the quality of life decline as more and more people have less and less energy to consume? It seems that with the world population expanding at a rate unequaled in recorded history, the population cannot be supported, and a shortage of resources may force us to return to the way of life of our forefathers.

Science and technology have created a way of life that has fostered many modern problems. Science and technology must now lead the way in solving the problems they have helped to create. If an attempt is made to solve the power crisis exclusively by building more power plants fueled with coal and oil, one price will be more and more polluted air. Because of polluted air some people die sooner than they would otherwise—not just from lung cancer but from many other causes. In addition, the supply of oil in the world is limited, and ultimately, so is the supply of coal. Scientists, engineers, and managers must look for new ways of generating and conserving power, ways that will not pollute the atmosphere, and ways that will serve humanity when oil and coal have been depleted.

Many different ways of solving this problem are being investigated. Energy conservation is one very important strategy. Also, scientists are studying methods of converting **solar energy** (energy from the sun) to electrical power to be used by man. **Geothermal energy** (energy from the earth's core) is being investigated. The ocean tides have been used to generate electricity.

These sources of power hold promise for the future, but much technology must be developed before significant contributions can be realized. There is, however, already available a nearly unending supply of energy in nuclear power. The technology is currently available to tap this power.

17.2   The Nuclear Atom

The accepted model of the atom is a very small dense core (the nucleus) surrounded by a cloud of electrons. To understand the tremendous energy stored in the atom, it is necessary to closely study the nucleus, in which this energy is stored. If nuclear reactions are understood, producing and using nuclear energy for power can be better understood (Figure 17.1).

The nucleus contains primarily protons (positive charges) and neutrons (no charge); and the neutron is only slightly heavier than the proton. Many individual types of subatomic particles in the nucleus have been identified, all held together by very strong forces. The subjects of immediate interest are the protons and the neutrons, and the effect of the forces holding these particles in the nucleus. It is these strong nuclear forces that are tapped to supply nuclear energy for use by society.

Figure 17.1 Nuclear energy can be used for other purposes besides power. The photo shows a linear accelerator which uses nuclear energy, in the form of radiation, to treat cancer. (Photo courtesy of American Cancer Society.)

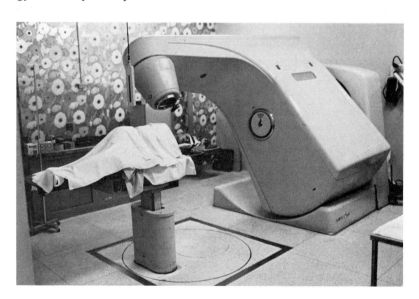

The atomic number Z equals the number of protons in the nucleus. When nuclear scientists refer to different isotopes of elements, they commonly refer to the mass numbers of the isotopes. The mass number A is the sum of the protons and neutrons in the nucleus. Isotopes are forms of an element that differ only in the number of neutrons contained in the nucleus.

Scientists have worked out a system of identifying elements and isotopes using the element's symbol. The mass number is placed in the upper left-hand corner of the element's symbol, and the atomic number is placed in the lower left-hand corner:

$$\,_{Z}^{A}X$$

(Remember that A is the total number of protons and neutrons in a given isotope, not the average number in nature.)

Subatomic particles can also be represented by these symbols. The neutron can be shown as

$$\,_{0}^{1}n$$

since it has a mass number of one unit and zero charge. The proton can be shown as

$$\,_{1}^{1}p$$

since it has a mass number of one unit and a charge (number of protons) equal to 1. The electron can be represented as

$$\,_{-1}^{0}e$$

indicating that it contains no protons or neutrons, and that it has a charge equal and opposite to the charge on the proton.

This symbolism helps distinguish between two or more different isotopes, such as $\,_{92}^{238}U$ and $\,_{92}^{235}U$.

17.3 What Happens When A Nucleus Is Unstable

Nuclear reactions occur when the nucleus is unstable. Instability can be caused by a variety of circumstances:

1. When there are too many or too few neutrons present.
2. When the nucleus is hit very hard with some other particle.
3. When the nucleus is too big to be held tightly together.
4. Numerous other circumstances not to well understood.

From the periodic chart, you can see that every element with an atomic number higher than 83, for bismuth, is radioactive. The term **radioactive** means

Table 17.1 Summary of Spontaneous Nuclear Processes

Process	Designation	Change in A	Change in Z	Example
Beta emission	$_{-1}^{0}e$	0	+1	$_{89}^{227}Ac \rightarrow \, _{90}^{227}Th + \, _{-1}^{0}e$
Positron emission	$_{1}^{0}e$	0	−1	$_{7}^{13}N \rightarrow \, _{6}^{13}C + \, _{1}^{0}e$
Electron capture	E.C.	0	−1	$_{-1}^{0}e + \, _{33}^{73}As \rightarrow \, _{32}^{73}Ge$
Isotropic transition	$_{0}^{0}\gamma$	0	0	$_{34}^{77}Se \rightarrow \, _{34}^{77}Se + \, _{0}^{0}\gamma$
Alpha emission	$_{2}^{4}\alpha$	−4	−2	$_{84}^{210}Po \rightarrow \, _{82}^{206}Pb + \, _{2}^{4}\alpha$

that individual atoms emit particles or electromagnetic radiation, often resulting in the disintegration of the original atom. Radioactive atoms are called **radioactive nuclides**. This means that the nuclei of these atoms are unstable, and various kinds of reactions will result from the tendency of the nuclei to reach stable arrangements.

Isotopes of many lighter elements can also be radioactive. Most isotopes of iodine, for example, are stable, but one isotope of iodine, iodine-131 ($_{53}^{131}I$) is radioactive. This isotope is used in medicine to diagnose thyroid-gland problems. An isotope of carbon, $_{6}^{14}C$, is used to determine the age of ancient relics. Cobalt-60 ($_{27}^{60}Co$) is used in treating cancer.

What kinds of reactions take place in unstable nuclei to enable them to become more stable? Table 17.1 summarizes spontaneous nuclear processes, those that are not forced.

Beta Emission

An isotope of hydrogen called tritium, $_{1}^{3}H$, contains one proton (atomic number 1) and two neutrons. This is a very high neutron-to-proton ratio for a small atom; thus the nucleus is unstable. Tritium can give off a beta particle ($_{-1}^{0}e$), an act that has the effect of converting a neutron to a proton. The nucleus now contains two protons and one neutron instead of one proton and two neutrons. A new element has been formed, which is an isotope of helium. The nuclear reaction is

$$_{1}^{3}H \rightarrow \, _{-1}^{0}e + \, _{2}^{3}He$$

A **beta particle** has the same charge and mass as an electron (Figure 17.2). Because it comes from the nucleus, however, it has much more energy than an electron in an orbital. It is moving much faster than electrons in the orbitals and escapes from the atom to go shooting off into space.

Whenever a radiochemical equation like the one shown is written, the mass numbers and charges on one side of the equation must always add up

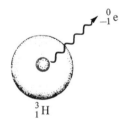

$_{-1}^{0}e$

$_{1}^{3}H$

Figure 17.2 Tritium emits a $_{-1}^{0}e$ particle to become the more stable $_{2}^{3}He$.

438

to the mass numbers and charges on the other. For example, in the equation

$$^3_1H \rightarrow \,_{-1}^{0}e + \,^3_2He$$

the mass number of the hydrogen on the left-hand side of the equation, 3, must equal the total number of protons and neutrons on the right-hand side of the equation. Because the beta particle contains no neutrons or protons, it contributes nothing to the mass number. The helium on the right side of the equation contains two protons and one neutron, so the mass numbers balance— three on the left and three on the right. In shorthand, it looks like this:

$$\text{Mass-number balance} \qquad 3 = 0 + 3$$

The nuclear charges are balanced in the following manner. Hydrogen on the left has one proton ($+1$). Helium on the right has two protons ($+2$) but a beta particle (-1) has been emitted. Therefore the $+1$ charge on the left equals the $+2$ charge and the -1 charge on the right, or in shorthand,

$$\text{Nuclear charge-number balance} \qquad +1 = (+2) - 1 = +1$$

Whenever a beta particle is emitted from the nucleus, the effect is of converting a neutron to a proton. This causes the atomic number to increase by 1 (in this case from 1 to 2) while the mass number remains the same. Remember, the mass number is the sum of the neutrons and the protons. Some more examples of beta emission are:

$$^{111}_{47}Ag \rightarrow \,^{111}_{48}Cd + \,_{-1}^{0}e$$

$$^{59}_{26}Fe \rightarrow \,^{59}_{27}Co + \,_{-1}^{0}e$$

$$^{154}_{63}Eu \rightarrow \,^{154}_{64}Gd + \,_{-1}^{0}e$$

Positron Emission

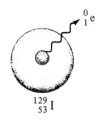

The oppositely charged counterpart of a beta particle is the **positron** (^0_1e). It has exactly the same rest mass as the beta particle but a $+1$ charge. It is sometimes referred to as a positive electron. Emission of a positron has the effect of converting a proton to a neutron. The end result is one fewer proton and one more neutron in the nucleus, so the atomic number goes down by 1 while the mass number remains the same (Figure 17.3). For example,

$$^{129}_{53}I \rightarrow \,^0_1e + \,^{129}_{52}Te$$

$$^{58}_{27}Co \rightarrow \,^0_1e + \,^{58}_{26}Fe$$

$$^{65}_{30}Zn \rightarrow \,^0_1e + \,^{65}_{29}Cu$$

Figure 17.3 $^{129}_{53}I$ emits a positron to become $^{129}_{52}Te$.

$^{129}_{53}I$

Positron emission is spontaneous but only after the nucleus has been hit with something (Section 17.7).

How is it possible to lose the small amount of mass of a beta particle or a positron and still keep the mass of the product particle the same? A partial answer to this can be got by realizing that the mass of an electron is only $\frac{1}{1836}$ the mass of a proton. Thus, the mass involved when a beta particle or positron is lost or gained does not significantly affect the mass number of an atom.

Electron Capture

$^{197}_{80}$ Hg

Figure 17.4 $^{197}_{80}$Hg undergoes electron capture to form $^{197}_{79}$Au.

Electron capture is a form of decay in which the nucleus of an atom captures an orbital electron. The captured electron converts a proton into a neutron. Electron capture has the same effect as positron emission, but the process is different (Figure 17.4). Sometimes the nucleus has too many protons to be stable. If that condition exists, an electron can be pulled into the nucleus from the electron cloud. This neutralizes the charge on a proton. The combining of positive and negative charges forms the neutral neutron. The result is that the atomic number goes down by 1 and the mass number remains the same. Some examples are:

$$_{-1}^{0}e + {}^{242}_{95}Am \xrightarrow{\text{E.C.}} {}^{242}_{94}Pu$$

$$_{-1}^{0}e + {}^{204}_{81}Tl \xrightarrow{\text{E.C.}} {}^{204}_{80}Hg$$

$$_{-1}^{0}e + {}^{197}_{80}Hg \xrightarrow{\text{E.C.}} {}^{197}_{79}Au$$

Gamma Rays

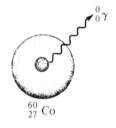

$^{60}_{27}$ Co

Figure 17.5 $^{60}_{27}$Co emits a gamma ray and does *not* change into another element.

Often, unstable atoms produce a packet of energy called a gamma ray ($^{0}_{0}\gamma$). The **gamma ray** is not a particle but a bundle of electromagnetic energy that comes from the nucleus. It has no mass and no charge. The gamma ray comes from a nucleus that contains excess energy. With excess energy, the nucleus is unstable, so this energy is emitted in the form of a gamma ray. The loss of energy does not affect the atomic number or the mass number of the atom. The atom will simply have a less energetic nucleus. Gamma rays are very much like X rays and can be used for the same purposes (Figure 17.5).

Here are some examples of gamma emissions:

$$^{110}_{47}Ag \rightarrow {}^{110}_{47}Ag + {}^{0}_{0}\gamma$$

$$^{60}_{27}Co \rightarrow {}^{60}_{27}Co + {}^{0}_{0}\gamma$$

$$^{22}_{11}Na \rightarrow {}^{22}_{11}Na + {}^{0}_{0}\gamma$$

A stable nucleus cannot be formed by gamma emission alone; gamma emission is always accompanied by emission of some other particle.

Alpha Emission

The largest particle that can be emitted from the nucleus is the **alpha particle** ($_2^4\alpha$). An alpha particle contains two protons and two neutrons. Hence, it is written in radiochemical symbols

$$_2^4\alpha$$

Remember that the charge on the alpha particle is $+2$, since it has no electrons. The alpha particle is a helium nucleus. When an alpha particle leaves the nucleus, the atomic number goes down by 2, and the mass number goes down by 4 (Figure 17.6). Some examples are:

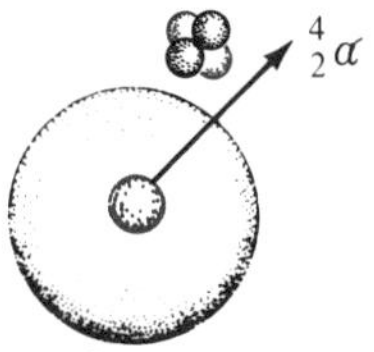

$$_{92}^{238}U \rightarrow _2^4\alpha + _{90}^{234}Th$$

$$_{88}^{226}Ra \rightarrow _2^4\alpha + _{86}^{222}Rn$$

$$_{84}^{218}Po \rightarrow _2^4\alpha + _{82}^{214}Pb$$

Figure 17.6 $_{92}^{238}U$ emits an alpha particle to become $_{90}^{234}Th$.

Here also, the mass numbers add up on both sides of the equation, as the nuclear charge numbers do. For the reaction

$$_{84}^{218}Po \rightarrow _2^4\alpha + _{82}^{214}Pb$$

the balanced mass numbers are

$$218 = 214 + 4$$

and the nuclear charge numbers are

$$84 = 82 + 2$$

17.4 Relative Penetrating Power of Emissions

Alpha, beta, and gamma emissions are the three most common kinds of nuclear emissions. The relative penetrating power of these emissions varies considerably. Alpha particles, since they are very highly charged, cannot travel very far without being attracted to something; and they are easily stopped when they travel near almost anything. An alpha particle can travel about 6 in.

in air before it picks up some electrons from molecules in the air and is converted to helium. If alpha particles were bombarding the skin, the individual would not be in serious danger of a radiation burn because the dead layer of skin that covers the body would stop the alpha-particles. If, however, some material that emits alpha particles were ingested, serious consequences would result. There is no internal layer of dead skin to stop the particles, only living tissue. The alpha particles would therefore quickly destroy those cells that they hit.

Beta particles can travel much further than alpha particles, but because of their charge and light weight, can be easily stopped. A sheet of paper is usually all that is required to stop beta particles. Beta particles are sufficiently dangerous that handling very large quantities of a material that emits them must be avoided.

The gamma ray is by far the most penetrating of the three. Since it has no mass and no charge, it can travel long distances before it is stopped. This means that it can penetrate the body and perhaps damage internal organs. The gamma ray can pass through several feet of concrete; substances such as lead (which is very dense) are often used to protect people from gamma rays.

17.5 Nuclear Equations

Table 17.2 will be useful in writing nuclear equations. The following examples illustrate the use of this table.

Table 17.2 Summary of Nuclear Changes

Mass Number Change	Atomic Number Change	Type of Emission
0	+1	$_{-1}^{0}e$
0	-1	Positron ($_{1}^{0}e$) or electron capture
0	0	$_{0}^{0}\gamma$
-4	-2	$_{2}^{4}\alpha$

Example 17.1

Plutonium-239 undergoes spontaneous emission to form uranium-235. What particle is emitted?

Step 1 Identify the change in atomic number:

$$_{94}Pu - _{92}U: \text{change of 2 in atomic number}$$

Step 2 Identify the change in mass number:

$$^{239}\text{Pu} - {}^{235}\text{U}: \text{change of 4 in mass number}$$

Step 3 Correlate change in atomic number and change in mass number with possible nuclear processes listed in Table 17.2. Mass no. -4, atomic no. -2, correlates to an alpha particle ${}^{4}_{2}\alpha$.

$$^{239}_{94}\text{Pu} \rightarrow {}^{235}_{92}\text{U} + {}^{4}_{2}\alpha$$

Example 17.2

Fluorine-18 emits a beta particle. What element is formed?

Step 1 By Table 17.2, a beta particle increases the atomic number by 1 and does not affect the mass number.

Step 2 Adding 1 to the atomic number of fluorine, 9, produces the element neon (atomic no. 10):

$$^{18}_{9}\text{F} \rightarrow {}^{18}_{10}\text{Ne} + {}^{0}_{-1}\text{e}$$

Example 17.3

Chromium-51 spontaneously forms vanadium-51. What is the reaction?

Step 1 Identify the change in atomic number:

$$_{24}\text{Cr} - {}_{23}\text{V}: \text{decrease of 1 in atomic number}$$

Step 2 Identify the change in mass number:

$$^{51}\text{Cr} - {}^{51}\text{V}: 0 \text{ change in mass number}$$

Step 3 Use Table 17.2 to identify the particle. Table 17.2 indicates that this process may be either an electron capture or a positron emission. From the information given, it is not possible to determine which. Experiments show that the process actually involves electron capture; thus the reaction is

$$_{-1}^{0}\text{e} + {}^{51}_{24}\text{Cr} \xrightarrow{\text{E.C.}} {}^{51}_{23}\text{V}$$

Example 17.4

Actinium-227 spontaneously forms thorium-227. What is the reaction?

Step 1 The change in atomic number is

$$_{89}\text{Ac} - {}_{90}\text{Th}: \text{increase of 1}$$

Step 2 The change in mass number is

$$^{227}\text{Ac} - {}^{227}\text{Th}: 0$$

Step 3   Table 17.2 indicates the emission of a beta particle $_{-1}^{0}e$; thus,

$$_{89}^{227}Ac \rightarrow {}_{90}^{227}Th + {}_{-1}^{0}e$$

Example 17.5   Nitrogen-13 spontaneously forms carbon-13. What is the reaction?

Step 1   The change in atomic number is

$$_{7}N - {}_{6}C: \text{decrease of } 1$$

Step 2   The change is mass number is

$$^{13}N - {}^{13}C: 0$$

Step 3   Table 17.2 indicates either electron capture or positron emission. Further information from experiment indicates that the reaction is

$$_{7}^{13}N \rightarrow {}_{6}^{13}C + {}_{1}^{0}e$$

Example 17.6   Selenium-77 spontaneously emits energy in the form of a gamma ray. What is the reaction?

Step 1   Table 17.2 indicates that a gamma ray affects neither the atomic number nor the mass number of an element; thus no change in either value is indicated.

Step 2 $$_{34}^{77}Se \rightarrow {}_{34}^{77}Se + {}_{0}^{0}\gamma$$

Example 17.7   Polonium-210 spontaneously forms lead-206. What is the reaction?

Step 1   The change in atomic number:

$$_{84}Po - {}_{82}Pb: \text{decrease of } 2$$

Step 2   The change in mass number is

$$^{210}Po - {}^{206}Pb: \text{decrease of } 4$$

Step 3   Table 17.2 indicates that an alpha particle has been emitted.

$$_{84}^{210}Po \rightarrow {}_{82}^{206}Pb + {}_{2}^{4}\alpha$$

17.6

Decay

Decay Series and Times

What happens to an unstable nucleus that emits a particle and forms a new atom that is also unstable? A whole series of emissions evolves until a new atom is reached that has a stable nucleus. This series of emissions is called a **decay series**.

Figure 17.7 shows the decay series for $^{238}_{92}U$. A whole series of alpha and beta emissions results in the final stable element, which is $^{206}_{82}Pb$.

Figure 17.7 The uranium-238 decay series. Many radioactive elements undergo more than one decay. They will jump from one element to another until they become stable.

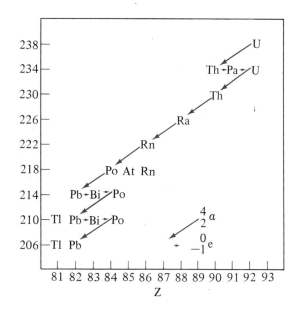

Half-life

How long does nuclear decay take? The length of time it takes for different elements to undergo the nuclear processes discussed varies from element to element. The people who work with these kinds of reactions have defined a term to represent how long it takes a given group of radioactive nuclei to decompose. This term is called the **half-life** of the element. The **half-life** is defined as the time it takes for one-half of a given quantity of material to decompose by a single nuclear process. It works like this. From an initial 1 kg of $^{131}_{53}I$ that has a half-life of eight days, there will be 500 g of $^{131}_{53}I$ left after

Figure 17.8 If a man goes to the well by halves, where each step is half the length of the preceding step, theoretically he will never get there. However, we *say* that he is there once his arm can reach the well. With radioactive half-lives, the element is gone for all practical purposes when we can no longer measure its presence.

eight days. The other 500 g has been converted to $^{131}_{54}Xe$, according to the reaction

$$^{131}_{53}I \rightarrow {}^{131}_{54}Xe + {}^{0}_{-1}e$$

After eight more days, half of the 500 remaining grams of $^{131}_{53}I$ will decompose, leaving 250 g. In eight more days, half of that will be gone, leaving 125 g.

Theoretically, all the material will never be gone. In reality, eventually such a small amount will be left that it can no longer be measured. At this time, it will be deemed all gone.

The half-life idea is like the thirsty man trying to get a drink of water. If he is 100 m from the water, and he can cover one-half the distance between himself and the water each minute, he would never reach the water. That is, after 1 min, he would be 50 m away; 2 min, 25 m; 3 min, 12.5 m (Figure 17.8). Continuing this process, after 11 min he would be only 4.9 cm away, which is close enough to get the drink if he has a long tongue. The half-life of radioactive elements can vary from 10^{-7} to 10^{15} yr. That is quite a spread of time. Some of these are shown in Table 17.3.

17.7   Man-made Nuclear Reactions

If a nucleus can emit particles, there is no reason why these particles cannot be used to bombard another nucleus, thus causing different kinds of reactions. For instance, if you were to shoot an alpha particle at an atom of $^{207}_{82}Pb$, the lead might absorb the alpha particle, forming another element, $^{211}_{84}Po$ (atomic number up 2, mass number up 4).

Table 17.3 Some Radioactive Isotopes and Their Half-lives

Isotope	Half-life	Isotope	Half-life
$^{3}_{1}H$	12.26 yr	$^{131}_{53}I$	8.1 d
$^{8}_{3}Li$	0.84 s	$^{198}_{79}Au$	2.7 d
$^{7}_{4}Be$	53.1 d	$^{226}_{88}Ra$	1620 yr
$^{8}_{5}B$	0.77 s	$^{238}_{92}U$	4.5×10^{9} yr
$^{14}_{6}C$	5745 yr	$^{237}_{93}Np$	2.2×10^{6} yr
$^{13}_{7}N$	10.0 min	$^{244}_{94}Pu$	7.6×10^{7} yr
$^{15}_{8}O$	2.0 min	$^{243}_{95}Am$	7.6×10^{3} yr
$^{18}_{9}F$	1.8 h	$^{248}_{96}Cm$	4.7×10^{5} yr
$^{24}_{11}Na$	15.0 h	$^{247}_{97}Bk$	1.4×10^{3} yr
$^{32}_{15}P$	14.3 d	$^{251}_{98}Cf$	800 yr
$^{35}_{16}S$	87 d	$^{252}_{99}Es$	140 d
$^{40}_{19}K$	1.4×10^{9} yr	$^{253}_{100}Fm$	5 d
$^{51}_{24}Cr$	28 d	$^{256}_{101}Md$	1.5 h
$^{64}_{29}Cu$	12.8 h	$^{256}_{102}No$	2.7 s
$^{67}_{31}Ga$	79 h	$^{256}_{103}Lw$	45 s
$^{90}_{38}Sr$	28 yr		

NOTE: s = second; min = minute; d = day; yr = year.

$$^{207}_{82}Pb + ^{4}_{2}\alpha \rightarrow ^{211}_{84}Po$$

This is the way nuclear scientists make new elements. All the elements with higher atomic numbers than uranium are artificially made. They did not previously exist in measurable amounts on the surface of the earth.

The nuclear scientist can take streams of small ions and get them going very fast in an accelerator, which also aims them. The accelerator is a tube that contains charged plates that can attract charged particles. If these particles are pulled toward a charged plate and pass through a hole, they will be accelerated. One only has to place a target in front of the beam and nuclear reactions can be incited. This type of accelerator is called a **linear accelerator** (Figure 17.9).

Figure 17.9 Sketch of a linear accelerator. Charged particles are accelerated along the length of the tube.

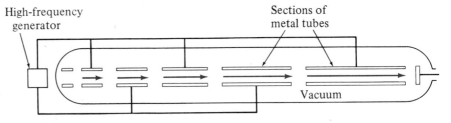

High-frequency generator

Sections of metal tubes

Vacuum

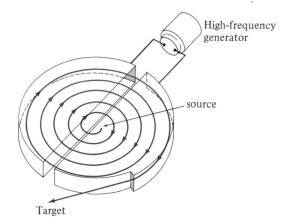

Figure 17.10 Sketch of a cyclotron. Charged particles are accelerated and pass along the path shown by the arrow.

High-frequency generator

source

Target

Another kind of accelerator is a cyclotron; which is built circularly. With this construction, scientists can use combinations of electric and magnetic fields to make particles go much faster than they would in a linear accelerator. The high speed is possible because the particles can go around the cyclotron many times, gaining speed with each circle, and spiraling out from the center so that they do not collide with other accelerating particles (Figure 17.10).

Often when a particle hits a nucleus, the nucleus becomes unstable and spontaneously decomposes, that is, falls apart. It is very much like a bullet shot at a board. The bullet hits the board and as it passes through the back of the board, it creates splinters. The nucleus can act similarly when it is hit by a particle. Pieces can fly out.

As an example of this, element 105, hahnium, was prepared by shooting a nitrogen nucleus at a californium atom. This can be done in the following manner. The atom $^{250}_{98}Cf$ is hit by $^{15}_{7}N$. The nitrogen contains 7 protons and 8 neutrons. If this particle were absorbed when it hit the californium nucleus, it would add 15 to the mass number and 7 to the atomic number. In the collision, however, 4 neutrons are knocked out, and the resulting product is $^{261}_{105}Ha$:

$$^{250}_{98}Cf + ^{15}_{7}N \rightarrow ^{261}_{105}Ha + 4^{1}_{0}n$$

Another isotope of hahnium can be made by bombarding $^{209}_{97}Bk$ with $^{18}_{8}O$, according to

$$^{249}_{97}Bk + ^{18}_{8}O \rightarrow ^{262}_{105}Ha + 5^{1}_{0}n.$$

Neutron Bombardment

Many new elements have been made by bombarding other elements with atomic nuclei. Nuclear scientists have found that instead of shooting charged particles like the alpha particle or a nitrogen nucleus at a target, however, it is sometimes better to shoot neutrons at the target. The advantage is that while positive particles tend to repel each other because of their similar charges, neutrons have no charge and are not repelled as much by the nucleus at which they are aimed.

Plutonium-239, a very important element in the nuclear industry, is made in this way. The isotope $^{238}_{92}U$ is used as the target material; it is bombarded with a neutron. This creates $^{239}_{92}U$.

$$^{238}_{92}U + ^{1}_{0}n \rightarrow ^{239}_{92}U$$

The $^{239}_{92}U$ nucleus is unstable and emits a $^{0}_{-1}e$ particle, forming neptunium,

$$^{239}_{92}U \rightarrow ^{239}_{93}Np + ^{0}_{-1}e$$

The $^{239}_{93}Np$ is also unstable and emits another $^{0}_{-1}e$ particle, forming $^{239}_{94}Pu$,

$$^{239}_{93}Np \rightarrow ^{239}_{94}Pu + ^{0}_{-1}e$$

The whole series of reactions can be written as

$$^{238}_{92}U + ^{1}_{0}n \rightarrow ^{239}_{92}U$$

$$^{239}_{92}U \rightarrow ^{239}_{93}Np + ^{0}_{-1}e$$

$$^{239}_{93}Np \rightarrow ^{239}_{94}Pu + ^{0}_{-1}e$$

The more numerous the neutrons shot at a target, the better the chance that something will happen, so nuclear scientists are looking for ways to increase the number of neutrons they can produce.

Table 17.4 illustrates reactions involved in the formation of several man-made elements and the year they were produced.

The Chain Reaction

The operation of a nuclear power plant depends directly on producing neutrons. It was discovered that one particular isotope of uranium, $^{235}_{92}U$, undergoes a special type of reaction when it is hit by a neutron. The special kind of reaction involves the splitting of the uranium nucleus (called nuclear fission) to produce different, smaller nuclei and more neutrons. The following equation is an example of what happens:

$$^{235}_{92}U + ^{1}_{0}n \rightarrow ^{143}_{54}Xe + ^{90}_{38}Sr + 3^{1}_{0}n + energy$$

If this happens to one $^{235}_{92}U$ nucleus, the 3 neutrons given off can hit 3 more uranium atoms, which in turn would each give off 3 neutrons to hit 9

Table 17.4 Reactions for Several Man-made Elements

Element	Nuclear Reactions Involved	Year Discovered
Np	$^{238}_{92}U + ^{1}_{0}n \rightarrow ^{239}_{92}U$ $^{239}_{92}U \rightarrow ^{239}_{93}Np + ^{0}_{-1}e$	1940
Pu	$^{239}_{93}Np \rightarrow ^{239}_{94}Pu + ^{0}_{-1}e$	1941
Am	$^{239}_{94}Pu + 2^{1}_{0}n \rightarrow ^{241}_{94}Pu$ $^{241}_{94}Pu \rightarrow ^{241}_{95}Am + ^{0}_{-1}e$	1945
Cm	$^{241}_{95}Am + ^{1}_{0}n \rightarrow ^{242}_{95}Am$ $^{242}_{95}Am \rightarrow ^{242}_{96}Cm + ^{0}_{-1}e$	1946
Bk	$^{242}_{96}Cm + 7^{1}_{0}n \rightarrow ^{249}_{96}Cm$ $^{249}_{96}Cm \rightarrow ^{249}_{97}Bk + ^{0}_{-1}e$	1950
Cf	$^{249}_{97}Bk + ^{1}_{0}n \rightarrow ^{250}_{97}Bk$ $^{250}_{97}Bk \rightarrow ^{250}_{98}Cf + ^{0}_{-1}e$	1950
Es	$^{250}_{98}Cf + 3^{1}_{0}n \rightarrow ^{253}_{98}Cf$ $^{253}_{98}Cf \rightarrow ^{253}_{99}Es + ^{0}_{-1}e$	1954
Fm	$^{253}_{99}Es + ^{1}_{0}n \rightarrow ^{254}_{99}Es$ $^{254}_{99}Es \rightarrow ^{254}_{100}Fm + ^{0}_{-1}e$	1954
Md	$^{253}_{99}Es + ^{4}_{2}He \rightarrow ^{256}_{101}Md + ^{1}_{0}n$	1954
No	$^{246}_{96}Cm + ^{12}_{6}C \rightarrow ^{254}_{102}No + 4^{1}_{0}n$	1957
Lw	$^{250}_{98}Cf + ^{10}_{5}B \rightarrow ^{256}_{103}Lr + 4^{1}_{0}n$	1961

more atoms; these then give off 3 neutrons each, to hit 27 atoms and so on. This is the famous **chain reaction**. Figure 17.11 illustrates this process.

If such a reaction were allowed to go uncontrolled, huge numbers of uranium atoms would be split in a fraction of a second, and tremendous quantities of energy would be released. This happens in an atomic bomb. The very same reaction, however, when controlled, can produce usable energy.

17.8   Nuclear Power Plants

One pound of uranium-235 can produce as much energy as 4 million pounds of coal and do so without dumping soot, nitrogen oxides, or sulfur oxides into the air. Nuclear energy can satisfactorily be tapped for peaceful purposes. Figure 17.12 is a diagram of the high-temperature gas-cooled reactor system

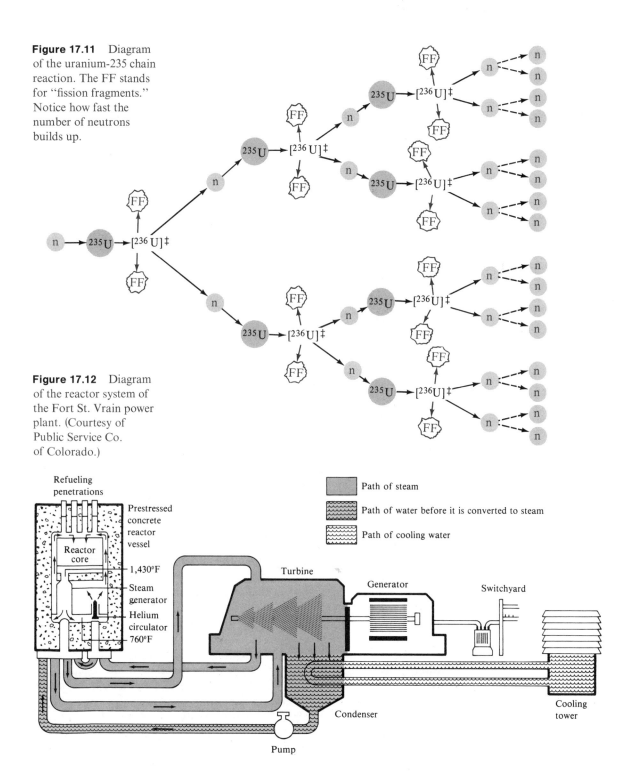

Figure 17.11 Diagram of the uranium-235 chain reaction. The FF stands for "fission fragments." Notice how fast the number of neutrons builds up.

Figure 17.12 Diagram of the reactor system of the Fort St. Vrain power plant. (Courtesy of Public Service Co. of Colorado.)

Path of steam

Path of water before it is converted to steam

Path of cooling water

Refueling penetrations

Prestressed concrete reactor vessel

Reactor core

1,430°F

Steam generator

Helium circulator

760°F

Turbine

Generator

Switchyard

Condenser

Pump

Cooling tower

Figure 17.13 The Fort
St. Vrain power plant.
(Photo courtesy of
Public Service Co. of
Colorado.)

recently built in conjunction with the Public Service Company of Colorado. It
is the Fort St. Vrain nuclear generating station. This type of nuclear power
generator is the most advanced in the country today. Figure 17.13 shows the
exterior of the plant.

Nuclear power plants work by using the heat generated from a controlled
chain reaction to create steam, which drives a turbine to produce electricity. It
works like this. Helium is circulated through the reactor core. The core heats
the helium to about 1430° F. As the helium is circulated, it comes in contact
with a series of pipes that contain water. This water is converted to steam by
the heated helium. The steam is heated to approximately 1000° F. The water
and steam never come in contact with the reactor core. The steam generated is
used to drive a turbine that is connected to the electrical generator.

After the steam has passed through the turbine, it is condensed back to
water and recirculated back to the steam generator. The steam is condensed
back to water by a cooling system that is completely isolated from the steam
used to drive the turbine. The water used to condense the steam is cooled by
evaporation in a cooling tower and recirculated to condense more steam.

This type of reactor has many advantages. The radioactive core never
comes in contact with the water it is heating; thus, there is little chance for
radiation to leak from the reactor. The cooling water is in an independent
system and is recycled. This kind of setup uses the minimum amount of water
and produces little or no thermal (heat) pollution of streams.

The Fort St. Vrain Nuclear Generating Station is designed to produce
330,000 kilowatts of electricity continuously. This is enough electricity to light
3.3 million 100 watt light bulbs.

Reactor Core

The heart of the system is the reactor core. It is the site of the chain reaction, where the heat is produced. The fuel used in the reactor core is a mixture of $^{235}_{92}U$ and $^{232}_{90}Th$ dicarbides, $^{235}_{92}UC_2$, and $^{232}_{90}ThC_2$. These materials are compressed into fuel particles that are inserted into graphite fuel elements. **Control rods** made of boron carbide and graphite are located in the reactor.

The idea is that there is enough uranium in each fuel element to give off some neutrons but not enough to initiate the chain reaction, since some neutrons are always lost (Figure 17.14). If several fuel rods are placed close to each other, the amount of uranium needed to carry on the chain reaction is present because neutrons can pass from one fuel element to another. The control rods are placed between the fuel elements. The control rods absorb neutrons passing from one fuel element to another.

As the control rods are pulled out, more neutrons can pass between fuel elements and the reaction proceeds. The further the control rods are pulled out, the faster the reaction. The further in they are pushed, the slower the re-action. The moderator graphite is used to slow down the neutrons so they can be more effectively captured by other $^{235}_{92}U$ atom (Figure 17.15). In general, it is a very simple idea.

In the reactor, there is present about 20 times as much thorium as $^{235}_{92}U$. What does this thorium do? Uranium-235 is relatively scarce: less than 1 percent

Figure 17.14 Schematic diagram of a reactor core with fuel, moderator, and control rods. Moderator rods slow down the neutrons. They are in the reactor permanently. (Courtesy of Public Service Co. of Colorado.)

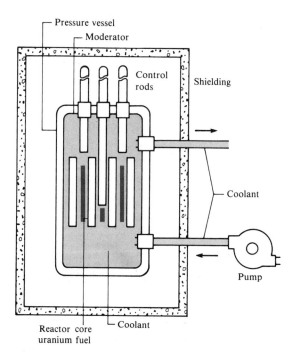

Figure 17.15 In the core of a reactor, neutrons are given off by the fuel rods, absorbed by the control rods, and slowed by the moderator rods.

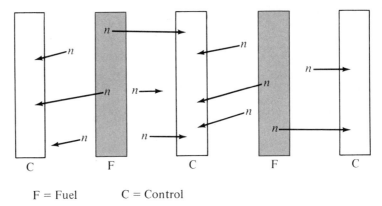

F = Fuel   C = Control

of all the uranium mined is the proper isotope, $^{235}_{92}U$. This makes the cost of $^{235}_{92}U$ very high. When the $^{232}_{90}Th$ is mixed with the $^{235}_{92}U$, the following reactions take place:

$$^{232}_{90}Th + ^{1}_{0}n \rightarrow ^{233}_{90}Th$$

$$^{233}_{90}Th \rightarrow ^{0}_{-1}e + ^{233}_{91}Pa$$

$$^{233}_{91}Pa \rightarrow ^{0}_{-1}e + ^{233}_{92}U$$

The isotope $^{233}_{92}U$ is very similar to $^{235}_{92}U$ in that it also undergoes the same sort of chain reaction as the $^{235}_{92}U$. The reactor is thus continually making more fuel for itself as it runs. Since thorium is relatively cheap, the cost of running a reactor is lowered considerably.

Since $^{235}_{92}U$ is fairly rare, the supply will eventually be depleted, just as with other types of fuel. The nuclear reactor, however, has another method of perpetuating itself. Even though the supply of $^{235}_{92}U$ is low, the supply of $^{238}_{92}U$ (the most common isotope of uranium) is high. If large quantities of $^{238}_{92}U$ are placed in the reactor, the $^{238}_{92}U$ is converted to $^{239}_{94}Pu$. And $^{239}_{94}Pu$ can carry on the same type of chain reaction as $^{235}_{92}U$ and $^{233}_{92}U$. Thus, one $^{235}_{92}U$ reactor can produce more fuel than it consumes from the large supply of $^{238}_{92}U$. Such a reactor is called a **breeder reactor**, and it is a potential source of fuel for years and years to come. Processes are being investigated to increase the efficiency of this reaction.

Power Output

In 1976, nuclear-power capacity from installations with operating permits in the United States was about 41,594 megawatts, representing 8.3 percent of the total electrical output in this country. This percentage is supposed to rise to 33 percent by 1980 and 50 percent by 2000. It seems evident, in light of the 1979 nuclear-power-plant accident at Three Mile Island in Pennsylvania, that neither of these projections will be correct.

17.9

Nuclear Power and the Environment

What kinds of things are people concerned about as nuclear power plants become increasingly common. The first relevant question might be, "Will a nuclear power plant blow up like a big bomb?"

It is completely impossible for an atomic power plant to act like an atomic bomb. A bomb works by compressing pure fissionable material very rapidly into a dense mass. The mass must then be held together for a short period so the chain reaction can move through the mass. Reactors do not have this arrangement. The fuel is relatively dilute and mixed with other things, so creating a dense enough mass of the fissionable isotope is impossible. It is also impossible to hold the fuel in close contact, which is necessary for the bomb.

Measuring Radiation

Another question involving nuclear power plants is, "What happens to the products of a chain reaction, and how dangerous are they?" To answer this question, it is first necessary to have a meaningful way of measuring the amount of radioactivity present. Scientists usually express amounts of radioactivity in **curies**, a measure of the number of atomic distintegrations per second. This term was named after Marie Curie, who discovered radium. The problem with just measuring the number of disintegrations per second is that the different types of radiation behave differently.

Look at the difference between the alpha particle and the gamma ray. The alpha particle is not too dangerous under some circumstances, whereas the gamma ray is very dangerous. To overcome this measuring problem, scientists have defined a new unit, called a rem. A **rem** is a unit that takes into account the different types of radiation and the radiation's effect on animals. If there were no nuclear explosions or nuclear power plants in the world, a person could expect to be hit by about 125 millirems of radiation a year at sea level and about 300 millirems of radiation a year in Colorado, 1 mile high. A millirem is one thousandth of a rem (1 mrem = 0.001 rem). This radiation comes from cosmic rays and natural radiation on the earth; all the elements above bismuth on the periodic chart are radioactive. A person is also exposed to other man-made radiation —X rays, television sets, and luminescent watch dials. A complete dental X ray exposes a person to about 5000 millirems over the natural background. Right next to a power plant, background radiation increases about 5 millirems.

Waste Disposal

What happens to the fission byproducts from a nuclear reactor? A very large reactor might contain 50 to 100 tons of fuel. As the fuel is used up and other products are formed, the used fuel elements are removed and stored under water in a large pool for several months. This allows those elements that have very short half-lives to disappear, and the fuel "cools" down considerably. The fuel is then reprocessed to recover all the unreacted fuel, which is then put back into the reactor. The remaining radioactive fission products must then be disposed of. This is the biggest problem with nuclear reactors. Many of these products are now being buried in Idaho, but new ways of disposing of the material are continually being sought.

R. Philip Hammond has proposed various criteria for safety in radioactive waste storage.* Dr. Hammond proposes that storage facilities must be designed to accommodate the following points.

1. The waste must be reliably contained at all times.

2. The containers must be retrievable and maintainable.

3. The storage facility must provide isolation from external events and must also permit careful control of human access.

*__American Scientist__ 67, March–April 1979, pp. 146–50.

Figure 17.16 An artist's conception of a proposed storage system for nuclear wastes. Such a storage system allows ready access to canisters in which waste materials are stored, thus aiding in the prevention of undetected or irreparable radiation leakage. (Courtesy of *American Scientist.*)

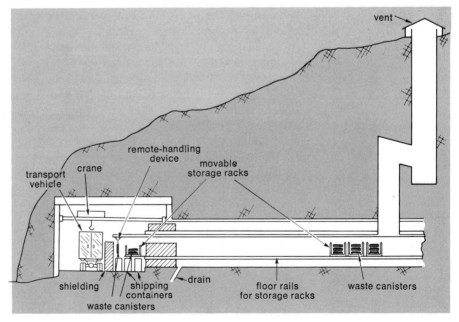

4. The storage facility and the containers must have plausible or demonstrable likelihood of lasting for 100 years.

5. The storage system should be able to accept and retrieve both processed waste and spent fuel elements interchangeably.

An artist's conception of Dr. Hammond's proposed storage system is shown in Figure 17.16.

17.10 Nuclear Energy For the Future

The hydrogen bomb is different from the atomic bomb. The difference is that in a hydrogen bomb, nuclei are put together instead of broken apart. The process is called **fusion**, instead of fission, and involves very small atoms instead of very large ones. Some of the reactions in a hydrogen bomb are:

$$^1_1H + ^1_1H \rightarrow ^2_1H + ^0_1e$$

$$^2_1H + ^1_1H \rightarrow ^3_2He + ^0_0\gamma + energy$$

Much more energy is obtained from putting together light atoms than from breaking apart heavy atoms. Such a process is continually happening naturally in the sun. The advantages of fusion compared with fission are the substantially smaller amount of radioactive waste and the potentially enormous supply of fuel. It has been projected that the heavy isotope of hydrogen, deuterium (^2_1H), from the oceans would suffice to produce all the world's electricity for the next 20,000 million years. If scientists could harness the power of the hydrogen bomb, an energy crisis would no longer exist.

The problems involved in harnessing the power of fusion are enormous, but bit by bit, scientists are solving them. The first problem involves the supply of fuel for such a reaction. The most likely process is probably the reaction of deuterium and tritium of form helium. This reaction goes on at temperatures lower than those required for the lighter isotopes of hydrogen.

$$^2_1H + ^3_1H \rightarrow ^1_0n + ^4_2He + energy$$

The reaction needs a constant supply of tritium (^3_1H), which does not exist naturally in significant amounts. It is proposed that the tritium needed for fueling a fusion reactor could be gotten from lithium by these reactions:

$$^6_3Li + ^1_0n \rightarrow ^7_3Li$$

$$^6_3Li + ^1_0n \rightarrow ^3_1H + ^4_2He$$

$$^7_3Li + ^1_0n \rightarrow ^3_1H + ^4_2He + ^1_0n$$

To fuse deuterium and tritium effectively, a plasma containing these elements at 100 million degrees Kelvin must be controlled. The approaches for accomplishing this feat are being intensively investigated.

Glossary

Alpha particle	Helium nucleus consisting of two protons and two neutrons.
Beta particle	A particle equivalent in mass and charge to an electron. The beta particle results from a nuclear disintegration.
Breeder Reactor	A nuclear reactor capable of producing more fuel than it consumes.
Control rod	A rod in a nuclear reactor used to regulate the chain reaction.
Curie	A measure of the number of atomic disintegrations per second.
Cyclotron	A device that uses electric and magnetic fields to accelerate particles. The particles are accelerated in a spiral.
Decay series	A series of spontaneous emissions from the nucleus of an atom that continue until a stable nucleus is obtained.
Electron capture	The decay in which the nucleus of an atom captures an orbital electron. The captured electron converts a proton into a neutron.
Fuel rod	In a nuclear reactor, a rod that contains the fissionable material used to generate heat.
Gamma ray	Electromagnetic radiation of short wavelength.
Geothermal energy	Energy derived from the earth's core.
Half-life	A measure of the rate of radioactive decay. The time required for half of a given quantity of radioactive material to decompose by a single decay reaction.
Linear accelerator	A device for accelerating charged particles in a straight line toward a target.
Positron	A particle having the same mass as an electron but a positive charge equal and opposite to the negative charge on the electron.
Radioactive nuclides	Atoms that disintegrate by emitting particles or electromagnetic radiation.
Rem	The measure of radiation that considers different types of radiation and the effect of radiation on animals.
Solar energy	Energy derived from the sun.

Problems

1. Complete the following reactions:
   (a) $^{11}_{4}Be \rightarrow {}^{11}_{5}B + ?$
   (b) $^{8}_{5}B \rightarrow {}^{8}_{4}Be + ?$
   (c) $^{19}_{8}O \rightarrow ? + {}^{0}_{-1}e$
   (d) $^{129}_{54}Xe \rightarrow {}^{129}_{54}Xe + ?$
   (e) $^{150}_{64}Gd \rightarrow {}^{4}_{2}\alpha + ?$
   (f) $^{152}_{64}Gd \rightarrow {}^{148}_{62}Sm + ?$

   (g) $^{149}_{65}Tb + {}^{0}_{-1}e \xrightarrow{E.C.} ?$
   (h) $^{158}_{65}Tb \rightarrow {}^{0}_{0}\gamma + ?$
   (i) $^{174}_{72}Hf \rightarrow {}^{4}_{2}\alpha + ?$
   (j) $? \rightarrow {}^{112}_{46}Pd + {}^{0}_{-1}e$
   (k) $? \rightarrow {}^{102}_{47}Ag + {}^{0}_{1}e$
   (l) $? \rightarrow {}^{235}_{92}U + {}^{4}_{2}\alpha$

2. The following could be man-made reactions. Predict the indicated species.
   (a) $^{58}_{28}Ni + {}^{1}_{0}n \rightarrow ?$
   (b) $^{103}_{45}Rh + {}^{1}_{0}n \rightarrow {}^{104}_{46}Pd + ?$
   (c) $^{98}_{46}Pd + {}^{1}_{0}n \rightarrow {}^{0}_{1}e + ?$
   (d) $^{88}_{41}Nb + {}^{1}_{0}n + {}^{0}_{-1}e \rightarrow ?$
   (e) $^{82}_{35}Br + {}^{4}_{2}\alpha \rightarrow ?$
   (f) $^{198}_{79}Au + ? \rightarrow {}^{200}_{79}Au$
   (g) $^{131}_{53}I + 5{}^{1}_{0}n \rightarrow ? + {}^{136}_{55}Cs$

3. Explain how elements can have unstable nuclei.

4. Write the symbols for alpha, beta, gamma, and positron emission and explain what composes each particle or ray.

5. How does electron capture differ from positron emission?

6. Explain the decay series for $^{238}_{92}U$.

7. The element $^{14}_{6}C$, having the half-life 5770 yr, is used to determine the age of ancient materials. A piece of wood initially containing 0.020 g of $^{14}_{6}C$ was analyzed and found to contain 0.0010 g of $^{14}_{6}C$. How old was the wood?

8. The half-life of tritium is 12.26 yr. For an initial amount of 10. g of tritium, how many years of decay will it take to have only 0.078 g of tritium left?

9. Explain how the high-temperature gas-cooled reactor generates electricity.

10. What is required to generate heat in a reactor?

11. Write equations for two different methods of producing nuclear fuel from a nuclear reactor.

12. List several possible environmental problems connected with nuclear reactors.

13. Predict a way of making a new element, number 110.

A BALANCING REDOX EQUATIONS

It is fairly easy to balance oxidation-reduction (redox) equations if a simple set of rules for balancing is followed. There are two different ways of balancing oxidation-reduction equations, the **electron transfer method** and the **half-reaction method.** Let's consider the electron transfer method first and work through a few examples.

Electron Transfer Method

Step 1   Write the formulas for the reactants and the products. Remember, you must use the actual reactants and products that are involved.

$$K_2Cr_2O_7 + FeCl_2 + HCl = CrCl_3 + FeCl_3 + KCl + H_2O$$

Step 2   Find each element undergoing a change in oxidation number and write the oxidation number of the element above the element.

$$K_2 \overset{+6}{Cr_2}O_7 + \overset{+2}{Fe}Cl_2 + HCl = \overset{+3}{Cr}Cl_3 + \overset{+3}{Fe}Cl_3 + KCl + H_2O$$

Step 3   Draw lines from the reactant to the corresponding product to tie together the elements which undergo changes in oxidation number. Place the number of electrons changed *per atom* in parentheses above these tie lines

$$K_2 \overset{+6}{Cr_2}O_7 + \overset{+2}{Fe}Cl_2 + HCl = \overset{+3}{Cr}Cl_3 + \overset{+3}{Fe}Cl_3 + KCl + H_2O$$

(3e)

(1e)

Step 4   Equate the total number of electrons gained to the total number of electrons lost. Care must be taken at this point to consider the whole compound that is losing electrons. The chromium in $K_2Cr_2O_7$ gains three electrons per chromium but there are two chromiums. This means that the total formula unit gains six electrons. You must therefore multiply the three electrons changed per chromium by two chromiums to get the six electrons gained. Those six electrons must come from the iron so multiply the electron changes per iron by 6. This step can be shown as follows:

$$2 \times (3e)$$

$$K_2Cr_2O_7 + FeCl_2 + HCl = CrCl_3 + FeCl_3 + KCl + H_2O$$

$$6 \times (1e)$$

Notice that the chromium compound gained six electrons, and the iron compound lost six electrons. The electrons lost must always equal the electrons gained. To do this we multiplied the (1e) by 6 and the (3e) by 2.

Step 5   Place correct coefficients on each formula unit involved in the oxidation-reduction by using the multiplier numbers (the numbers by which the electron changes were multiplied). For example, the multiplier number 2 tells us we need two chromiums, and $K_2Cr_2O_7$ contains exactly that so place a 1 in front of $K_2Cr_2O_7$. The $CrCl_3$ must also yield 2 chromiums, so place a 2 in front of $CrCl_3$. Place a 6 in front of each iron compound to give the right number of irons according to their multiplier number.

$$K_2Cr_2O_7 + 6 \, FeCl_2 + HCl = 2 \, CrCl_3 + 6FeCl_3 + KCl + H_2O$$

Step 6   The oxidation-reduction portion of the equation is now balanced. The rest of the equation is balanced by inspection. The only potassiums on the left side occur in $K_2Cr_2O_7$ that has a coefficient of 1; therefore, 2 KCls are needed on the right. This makes 26 Cls total on the right and only 12 Cls on the left. To balance the Cl put 14 in front of the HCl, and the Cls are balanced.

$$K_2Cr_2O_7 + 6 \, FeCl_2 + 14 \, HCl = 2 \, CrCl_3 + 6 \, FeCl_3 + 2KCl + H_2O$$

The only hydrogens on the left are in HCl, 14 of them so 14 H are needed on the right. These can be obtained by placing a 7 in front of the H_2O. The equation is balanced. Notice that the oxygens came out balanced; seven on the left and seven on the right.

$$K_2Cr_2O_7 + 6 FeCl_2 + 14 HCl = 2 CrCl_3 + 6 FeCl_3 + 2 KCl + 7 H_2O$$

Let's look at one more equation balanced by this method.

Step 1 Correct formulas for all reactants and products.

$$CdS + I_2 + HCl = CdCl_2 + HI + S$$

Step 2 Find elements changing oxidation number and indicate the oxidation numbers.

$$\overset{-2}{Cd}S + \overset{0}{I_2} + HCl = CdCl_2 + H\overset{-1}{I} + \overset{0}{S}$$

Step 3 Connect the reactants and products and indicate the number of electrons changed.

$$(2e)$$
$$\overset{-2}{Cd}S + \overset{0}{I_2} + HCl = CdCl_2\ H\overset{-1}{I} + \overset{0}{S}$$
$$(1e)$$

Step 4 Equate electrons gained with electrons lost.

$$1 \times (2e)$$
$$CdS + I_2 + HCl = CdCl_2\ HI + S$$
$$2 \times (1e)$$

Step 5 Place the correct multiplier number in front of compounds.

$$CdS + I_2 + HCl = CdCl_2 + 2 HI + S$$

Step 6 Complete the balancing by inspection.

$$CdS + I_2 + 2 HCl = CdCl_2 + 2 HI + S$$

Half-Reaction Method

This method is popular with chemists who are working in electro-chemistry and with chemists dealing with organic oxidation-reduction equations where it is often very hard to assign oxidation numbers. The balancing is done in steps. Let's look at an equation that was done by the electron transfer method.

Step 1   Write the formulas for the reactants and the products.

$$K_2Cr_2O_7 + FeCl_2 + HCl = CrCl_3 + FeCl_3 + KCl + H_2O$$

Step 2   Write the equation in ionic form omitting the ions that do not change in oxidation number.

$$Cr_2O_7^{2-} + Fe^{2+} = Cr^{3+} + Fe^{3+}$$

Step 3   Write the half reactions for the compounds oxidized and reduced and balance by inspection.

$$Cr_2O_7^{2-} = 2Cr^{3+}$$
$$Fe^{2+} = Fe^{3+}$$

Step 4   Add electrons that are gained or lost in each half reaction.

$$Cr_2O_7^{2-} + 6e^- = 2Cr^{3+}$$
$$Fe^{2+} = Fe^{3+} + e^-$$

Step 5   Balance the hydrogens and oxygens by adding H^+ or OH^- and water. If the solution is acidic as this one is because of the HCl, you may add hydrogen ions and water as needed.

You cannot add OH^- ions into the equation if the solution is acidic. If the solution were basic you would have to use OH^- ions and water to balance the equation. You could not use H^+ ions.

Let's see how this works for this example. Since $Cr_2O_7^{2-}$ half reaction has seven oxygen atoms on the left, you must put seven oxygen atoms on the right. This is done by putting 7 H_2O on the right. You now have 14 hydrogens on the right so you need 14 hydrogens on the left. Add 14 H^+ to the left. The two half-reaction equations now look like this

$$Cr_2O_7^{2-} + 6e^- + 14H^+ = 2Cr^{3+} + 7H_2O$$
$$Fe^{2+} = Fe^{3+} + e^-$$

There are no hydrogens or oxygens involved in iron's half reaction. Notice also that in each half reaction the charges are the same on each side of the equal sign. The left hand side of the first equation adds to six plus charges and the right to six plus charges. In the second equation the left adds to two plus charges and the right side adds to two plus charges. It is very important for a balanced equation to have the charges balanced as well as the atoms balanced.

Step 6 Add the two equations together so that the electrons balance. This means that you will have to multiply the iron equation through by 6 to get six electrons lost so when the equations are added together there will be six electrons on each side, and they will cancel each other.

$$Cr_2O_7^{2-} + 6e^- + 14H^+ = 2Cr^{3+} + 7H_2O$$
$$6 \times (Fe^{2+} = Fe^{3+} + e^-)$$

or

$$Cr_2O_7^{2-} + 6e^- + 14H^+ = 2Cr^{3+} + 7H_2O$$
$$6Fe^{2+} \qquad\qquad = 6Fe^{3+} + 6e^-$$
$$\overline{Cr_2O_7^{2-} + 6Fe^{2+} + 14H^+ + \cancel{6e^-} = 2Cr^{3+} + 7H_2O + 6Fe^{3+} + \cancel{6e^-}}$$
$$Cr_2O_7^{2-} + 6Fe^{2+} + 14H^+ = 2Cr^{3+} + 7H_2O + 6Fe^{3+}$$

Step 7 Add the ions back to the equation that you removed in the second step (the ions not undergoing change) and finish balancing the equation.

$$K_2Cr_2O_7 + 6FeCl_2 + 14HCl = 2CrCl_3 + 7H_2O + 6FeCl_3$$

There are two potassiums on the left and none on the right so put the 2KCl back in on the right and you are through.

$$K_2Cr_2O_7 + 6FeCl_2 + 14HCl$$
$$= 2CrCl_3 + 7H_2O + 6FeCl_3 + 2KCl$$

Many times when an equation is balanced by the half-reaction method, there is only interest in the ionic equation and not in an equation that contains ions which are not directly involved in the reaction. Let's look at an example like this.

Steps 1 and 2 The equation is given in ionic form.

$$Cr(OH)_4^- + BrO^- = CrO_4^{2-} + Br^- \text{ in basic solution}$$

Step 3 Write the half reactions

$$Cr(OH)_4^- = CrO_4^{2-}$$
$$BrO^- = Br^-$$

Step 4 Add the electrons gained and lost.

$$Cr(OH)_4^- = CrO_4^{2-} + 3e^-$$
$$BrO^- + 2e^- = Br^-$$

Step 5 Balance the oxygen and hydrogen with OH$^-$ and water because this is a basic solution.

$$Cr(OH)_4^- + 4OH^- = CrO_4^{2-} + 3e^- + 4H_2O$$
$$H_2O + BrO^- + 2e^- = Br^- + 2OH^-$$

The easy way to tell the side to add the OH$^-$ and the number of OH$^-$ is to count the charges on both sides of the equations and add OH$^-$ so that they come out the same. Water is then added to the other side to balance the atoms.

Step 6 Equate electrons gained with electrons lost by multiplying each equation by the appropriate number.

$$2[Cr(OH)_4^- + 4OH^- = CrO_4^{2-} + 3e^- + 4H_2O]$$
$$3[H_2O + BrO^- + 2e^- = Br^- + 2OH^-]$$

or

$$2Cr(OH)_4^- + 8OH^- = 2CrO_4^{2-} + 6e^- + 8H_2O$$
$$\underline{3H_2O + 3BrO^- + 6e^- = 3Br^- + 6OH^-}$$
$$2Cr(OH)_4^- + 8OH^- + 3H_2O + 3BrO^- + \cancel{6e^-}$$
$$= 2CrO_4^{2-} + 3Br^- + 8H_2O + 6OH^- + \cancel{6e^-}$$

Notice also that some of the OH$^-$ and H$_2$O groups can be cancelled by subtracting from both sides.

$$2\text{Cr(OH)}_4^- + \overset{2\text{OH}-}{\cancel{8\text{OH}^-}} + \cancel{3\text{H}_2\text{O}} + 3\text{BrO}^-$$
$$= 2\text{CrO}_4^{2-} + 3\text{Br}^- + \overset{5\text{H}_2\text{O}}{\cancel{8\text{H}_2\text{O}}} + \cancel{6\text{OH}^-}$$

The final equation is:

$$2\text{Cr(OH)}_4^- + 2\text{OH}^- + 3\text{BrO}^- = 2\text{CrO}_4^{2-} + 3\text{Br}^- + 5\text{H}_2\text{O}$$

B ANSWERS TO SELECTED PROBLEMS

Chapter 2, page 57

1. (a) 7.53×10^8 (c) 7.6×10^{-4}
(e) 7×10^0 (g) 8.76395421×10^8
(i) 7.93×10^{-2}

2. (a) 0.000001 (c) 873,200,000
(e) 5 (g) 0.00000005839125
(i) 50

3. (a) 2 (c) 2
(e) 4 (g) 5

4. (a) 21.66 (c) 40.00

5. (a) $\dfrac{1 \text{ yd}}{36 \text{ in.}} = 1 = \dfrac{36 \text{ in.}}{1 \text{ yd}}$

(c) $\dfrac{2 \text{ pt}}{1 \text{ qt}} = 1 = \dfrac{1 \text{ qt}}{2 \text{ pt}}$

(e) $\dfrac{4 \text{ qt}}{1 \text{ gal}} = 1 = \dfrac{1 \text{ gal}}{4 \text{ qt}}$

7. (a) $\dfrac{1 \text{ cm}}{10 \text{ mm}} = 1 = \dfrac{10 \text{ mm}}{1 \text{ cm}}$

(c) $\dfrac{1 \text{ L}}{1000 \text{ mL}} = 1 = \dfrac{1000 \text{ mL}}{1 \text{ L}}$

(e) $\dfrac{1 \text{ g}}{1000 \text{ mg}} = 1 = \dfrac{1000 \text{ mg}}{1 \text{ g}}$

8. (a) 0.1 cm (c) 1000 mm
(e) 0.01 m

9. (a) 0.1 dL (c) 0.1 dkL
(e) 1×10^6 mL

10. (a) 0.001 g (c) 1000 g
(e) 1×10^3 cg

11. (a) 7.89×10^{-3} mi (c) 3.00×10^3 cc

12. (a) 0.805 km (c) 0.176 oz
(e) 2.27×10^7 mg

13. (a) 61.0 cm (c) 11.4 kg
(e) 437.8 yd

15. 6.25×10^{-5} tons

17. 10 oranges

19. 7.00×10^4 g; 154 lb

23. 27.4 m

25. 1.30×10^7 in^2; 8.39×10^7 cm^2

27. (a) $2.0 \dfrac{\text{oz}}{\text{qt}}$ (c) $8.3 \dfrac{\text{lb}}{\text{gal}}$

29. 870 cm^3

31. 1.13×10^6 g

33. (a) 32 °C (c) −189 °F
(e) 1033 K

35. −40 °F

37. 194 °F 363 K

Chapter 3, page 93

5. (a) H (c) Au
(e) Cu (g) I
(i) N (k) Fe
(m) C (o) Na

6. (a) Platinum (c) Zinc
(e) Cobalt (g) Chlorine
(i) Silicon (k) Rhodium
(m) Zirconium (o) Plutonium

8. (a) 78   (c) 30
   (e) 27   (g) 17
   (i) 14   (k) 45
   (m) 40   (o) 94

9. (a) 78   (c) 30
   (e) 27   (g) 17
   (i) 14   (k) 45
   (m) 40   (o) 94

12. (a) 13, 14   (c) 35, 45
   (e) 11, 12

13. (a) 24, 24, 28   (c) 92, 92, 146
   (e) 37, 37, 49   (g) 23, 23, 28
   (i) 74, 74, 110

15. (a) $5f$: ☐ ☐ ☐ ☐ ☐ ☐ ☐
   (c) $3d$: ☐ ☐ ☐ ☐ ☐

16. (a) Li: $1s^2 2s^1$
   (c) Ga: $1s^2 2s^2 2p^6 3s^2 3p^6 4s^2 3d^{10} 4p^1$
   (e) Sn: $1s^2 2s^2 2p^6 3s^2 3p^6 4s^2 3d^{10} 4p^6 5s^2 4d^{10} 5p^2$
   (g) Cl: $1s^2 2s^2 2p^6 3s^2 3p^5$
   (i) Cr: $1s^2 2s^2 2p^6 3s^2 3p^6 4s^1 3d^5$ (Remember the stability of half filled subshells)

17. (a) Li   (c) Mn
   (e) As

18. (a) Pt: $5d$ (c) Sr: $5s$
   (e) Rn: $6p$ (g) Gd: $4f$
   (i) Cm: $5f$

21. Hydrogen isotopes contain 0, 1, and 2 neutrons respectively.

24. (c) Hg: liquid, metallic (e) O: gas, nonmetallic
   (g) U: solid, metallic (i) Ar: gas, nonmetallic

25. (a) 6.02×10^{23} atoms Na
   (c) 1.2×10^{24} atoms Na

26. (a) 1.00 mole Be   (c) 0.5000 mole U
   (e) 0.1249 mole Ag   (g) 10.0 mole Y
   (i) 0.200 mole Ge

27. (a) 6.02×10^{23} atoms Be
   (c) 3.01×10^{23} atoms U
   (e) 7.52×10^{22} atoms Ag
   (g) 6.02×10^{24} atoms Y
   (i) 1.20×10^{23} atoms Ge

Chapter 4, page 131

2. (a) 2   (c) 3
   (e) 8   (g) 13
   (i) 6

3. (a) O^{2-}: $1s^2 2s^2 2p^6$
   (c) Na^+: $1s^2 2s^2 2p^6$
   (e) Br^-: $1s^2 2s^2 2p^6 3s^2 3p^6 4s^2 3d^{10} 4p^6$
   (g) Al^{3+}: $1s^2 2s^2 2p^6$
   (i) B^{3+}: $1s^2$

5. (a) 1 atom of C; 4 atoms of Br
   (c) 2 atoms of K; 1 atom of O
   (e) 3 atoms of Ba; 2 atoms of N
   (g) 1 atom of Be; 2 atoms of I
   (i) 1 atom of F; 1 atom of F

6. (a) Sr: Sr^{2+} (c) F: F^-
   (e) K: K^+

7. (a) Charge: -1; Mg   (c) Charge: $+2$; Xe
   (e) Charge: -5; Zn

9. (a) H·   (c) Ȧl·
   (e) ·C̈·   (g) :B̈r·
   (i) K·

10. (a) H loses or shares 1 electron to form a full or empty $1s$ sublevel.
   (c) Al loses 3 electrons to form a full $2p$ sublevel.
   (e) C shares 4 electrons to form a full $2p$ sublevel.
   (g) Br gains or shares one electron to form a full $4p$ sublevel.
   (i) K loses 1 electron to form a full $3p$ sublevel.

11. (a) Na^+ (c) B^{3+}
   (e) Si^{4+} (g) $:\ddot{B}r:^-$
   (i) Cs^+

12. (a) $:\ddot{F}:\ddot{F}:$ (c) $:\ddot{C}l:$
$\qquad\qquad\qquad\qquad\qquad :\ddot{C}l:P:\ddot{C}l:$

   (e) $:\ddot{C}l:$
$\qquad :\ddot{C}l:C:\ddot{C}l:$
$\qquad\qquad :\ddot{C}l:$

   (g) $\left(\begin{array}{c} :\ddot{O}: \\ :\ddot{O}:S:\ddot{O}: \end{array} \right)^{2-}$

(i) $: \overset{\cdot\cdot}{\underset{\cdot\cdot}{Cl}} : Zn : \overset{\cdot\cdot}{\underset{\cdot\cdot}{Cl}} :$

(k) H
$\qquad H : \overset{\cdot\cdot}{\underset{\cdot\cdot}{P}} : H$

(m) $\qquad : \overset{\cdot\cdot}{\underset{\cdot\cdot}{F}} :$
$\qquad : \overset{\cdot\cdot}{\underset{\cdot\cdot}{F}} : As : \overset{\cdot\cdot}{\underset{\cdot\cdot}{F}} :$

14. (a) covalent
(c) ionic
(e) covalent
(g) S–O bonds covalent; H–O bonds covalent
(i) covalent
(k) ionic

15. (a) two double bonds
(c) one double bond, one single bond
(e) one single bond
(g) one double bond, four single bonds.

16. (a) K^+ is larger than Li^+
(c) Br^- is larger than F^-
(e) Br^- is larger than Sr^{2+}

17. (a) $\left(\overset{:O:}{\underset{}{:\overset{\cdot\cdot}{\underset{\cdot\cdot}{O}}: C :: \overset{\cdot\cdot}{\underset{\cdot\cdot}{O}}}} \right)^{2-}$ or $\left(\overset{:O:}{:\overset{\cdot\cdot}{\underset{\cdot\cdot}{O}}: C : \overset{\cdot\cdot}{\underset{\cdot\cdot}{O}} :} \right)^{2-}$

or $\left(\overset{:\overset{\cdot\cdot}{O}:}{\underset{}{O :: C : \overset{\cdot\cdot}{\underset{\cdot\cdot}{O}}:}} \right)^{2-}$

(c) $\left(: \overset{\cdot\cdot}{\underset{\cdot\cdot}{O}} : N :: \overset{\cdot\cdot}{\underset{\cdot\cdot}{O}} \right)^-$ or $\left(\overset{\cdot\cdot}{\underset{\cdot\cdot}{O}} :: N : \overset{\cdot\cdot}{\underset{\cdot\cdot}{O}} : \right)^-$

18. (a) pyramidal   (c) tetrahedral
(e) pyramidal   (g) linear
(i) tetrahedral

19. Co_2; linear

21. $: \overset{\cdot\cdot}{O} :: Si :: \overset{\cdot\cdot}{O} :$; linear

Chapter 5, page 146

1. (a) chlorine   (c) cadmium chloride
(e) magnesium sulfide   (g) aluminum oxide
(i) phosphorus   (k) ammonia
trichloride

2. (a) sodium chloride   (c) beryllium nitride
(e) mercury(II) oxide   (g) tin(IV) sulfide
(i) iron(III) oxide   (k) lithium sulfide

3. (a) rubidium phosphide
(c) potassium sulfide
(e) phosphorus pentachloride
(g) magnesium oxide
(i) mercury(I) chloride
(k) lithium iodide

4. (a) potassium bicarbonate
(c) magnesium sulfate
(e) potassium permanganate
(g) sodium dichromate
(i) ammonium nitrate
(k) sodium hypochlorite

5. (a) iron(III) phosphate
(c) aluminum bicarbonate
(e) potassium nitrate
(g) sodium bicarbonate
(i) sodium hydroxide
(k) barium hydroxide

6. (a) sodium acetate
(c) carbonic acid (hydrogen carbonate)
(e) magnesium nitrite
(g) sulfurous acid (hydrogen sulfite)
(i) titanium(IV) sulfate
(k) ammonium hydroxide

7. (a) $CuBr$ (c) Na_2O
(e) MgS (g) AlP
(i) SO_3

8. (a) Rb_2S (c) MnF_4
(e) NiS (g) FeI_2
(i) Hg_2O

9. (a) NH_4HCO_3 (c) $Mg(C_2H_3O_2)_2$
(e) $Ca_3(PO_4)_2$ (g) $Al_2(SO_4)_3$
(i) $AgNO_3$

10. (a) FeS (c) $Pb(OH)_4$
(e) $KMnO_4$ (g) $Na_2Cr_2O_7$
(i) Li_2CrO_4

11. (a) H_2S (c) $CuSO_4$
(e) HNO_2 (g) $Fe(OH)_2$
(i) $Sn(NO_3)_4$

12. (a) hydrogen oxide
(c) hydrogen sulfate
(e) hydrogen chloride or hydrochloric acid

13. (a) $MgCl_2$ magnesium chloride
       MgO magnesium oxide
       $MgSO_4$ magnesium sulfate
       $Mg(NO_2)_2$ magnesium nitrite
       $Mg(ClO_4)_2$ magnesium perchlorate
       $Mg_3(PO_4)_2$ magnesium phosphate
       $MgCO_3$ magnesium carbonate

   (c) $CoCl_2$ cobalt(II) chloride
       CoO cobalt(II) oxide
       $CoSO_4$ cobalt(II) sulfate
       $Co(NO_2)_2$ cobalt(II) nitrite
       $Co(ClO_4)_2$ cobalt(II) perchlorate
       $Co_3(PO_4)_2$ cobalt(II) phosphate
       $CoCO_3$ cobalt(II) carbonate

   (e) NH_4Cl ammonium chloride
       $(NH_4)_2O$ ammonium oxide
       $(NH_4)_2SO_4$ ammonium sulfate
       NH_4NO_2 ammonium nitrite
       NH_4ClO_4 ammonium perchlorate
       $(NH_4)_3PO_4$ ammonium phosphate
       $(NH_4)_2CO_3$ ammonium carbonate

   (g) $LiCl$ lithium chloride
       Li_2O lithium oxide
       Li_2SO_4 lithium sulfate
       $LiNO_2$ lithium nitrite
       $LiClO_4$ lithium perchlorate
       Li_3PO_4 lithium phosphate
       Li_2CO_3 lithium carbonate

14. (a) KF, K_2S, $KClO_3$, $KMnO_4$, KOH
    (c) AlF_3, Al_2S_3, $Al(ClO_3)_3$, $Al(MnO_4)_3$,
        $Al(OH)_3$
    (e) NH_4F, $(NH_4)_2S$, NH_4ClO_3, NH_4MnO_4,
        NH_4OH

Chapter 6, page 162

2. (a) 28.1   (c) 38.0
   (e) 127.9   (g) 40.0
   (i) 310.3

3. (a) 124.0   (c) 52.0
   (e) 102.0   (g) 374.1
   (i) 342.3

4. (a) 0.185 mol Al   (c) 5.0 mol H_2
   (e) 7×10^{-4} mol Ba

5. (a) 0.633 mol H_3PO_4 (c) 1.2 mol $BaCl_2$
   (e) 0.128 mol $Al(OH)_3$

6. (a) 6×10^{23} atoms Si
   (c) 4.39×10^{24} atoms U
   (e) 3.9×10^{25} formula units CaI_2

7. (a) 1.5×10^{24} formula units HCl
   (c) 6.02×10^{21} formula units $Ca(OH)_2$
   (e) 1.01×10^{26} formula units CO_2

8. (a) 1.16×10^{22} atoms Cr
   (c) 6×10^{20} formula units N_2
   (e) 6.92×10^{44} formula units Cl_2O

9. (a) 2×10^{24} formula units $HClO_3$
   (c) 2.83×10^{22} formula units $Al(NO_3)_3$
   (e) 1.00×10^{12} formula units SiO_2

10. (a) 2×10^{24} atoms
    (c) 1.2×10^{26} atoms
    (e) 3225 atoms

11. (a) %Ba = 66.0%
        %Cl = 34.0%
    (c) %Al = 20.2%
        %Cl = 79.8%
    (e) %Fe = 34.4%
        %Cl = 65.6%

12. (a) %K = 69.7%
        %O = 28.5%
        %H = 1.8%
    (c) %Al = 22.1%
        %P = 25.4%
        %O = 52.5%
    (e) %K = 24.7%
        %Mn = 34.8%
        %O = 40.5%

14. (a) C_4H_8O

15. (a) $MgCl_2$

16. (a) $AlCl_3$

17. (a) Hg_2Cl_2 (c) SiO_2
    (e) N_4O_8

19. Al_2Cl_6

Chapter 7, page 178

2. (a) 1 mole of HCl reacts with one mole of
       NaOH to form 1 mole of NaCl and 1 mole
       of H_2O
   (c) 1 mole of Ca reacts with 2 moles of H_2O to
       form 1 mole of $Ca(OH)_2$ and 1 mole H_2

(e) 4 moles of FeS react with 7 moles of O_2 to form 2 moles of Fe_2O_3 and 4 moles of SO_2

(g) 3 moles CuS react with 8 moles of HNO_3 to form 3 moles of $Cu(NO_3)_2$ and 3 moles of S and 2 moles of NO and 4 moles of H_2O

(i) 2 moles of $Pb(NO_3)_2$ react to form 2 moles of PbO and 4 moles of NO_2 and 1 mole of O_2

3. (a) 1 molecule of HCl reacts with 1 formula unit of NaOH to form 1 formula unit of NaCl and 1 molecule of water

(c) 1 atom of Ca reacts with 2 molecules of water to form 1 formula unit of $Ca(OH)_2$ and 1 molecule of H_2

(e) 4 formula units of FeS react with 7 molecules of O_2 to form 2 formula units of Fe_2O_3 and 4 molecules of SO_2

(g) 3 formula units of CuS react with 8 formula units of HNO_3 to form 3 formula units of $Cu(NO_3)_2$ and 3 atoms of S and 2 molecules of NO and 4 molecules of H_2O

(i) 2 formula units of $Pb(NO_3)_2$ react to form 2 formula units of PbO and 4 molecules of NO_2 and 1 molecule of O_2

4. (a) 36.5 g HCl react with 40.0 g NaOH to form 58.5 g NaCl and 18.0 g H_2O

(c) 40.1 g Ca react with 36.0 g H_2O to form 74.1 g $Ca(OH)_2$ and 2.0 g H_2

(e) 351.6 g FeS react with 224.0 g O_2 to form 319.2 g Fe_2O_3 and 256.4 g SO_2

(g) 286.8 g CuS react with 504.0 g HNO_3 to form 562.5 g $Cu(NO_3)_2$ and 96.3 g S and 60.0 g NO and 72.0 g H_2O

(i) 662.4 g $Pb(NO_3)_2$ react to form 446.4 g PbO and 184.0 g NO_2 and 32.0 g O_2

5. (a) $NaCl + AgNO_3 \rightarrow AgCl + NaNO_3$
(c) $FeCl_3 + 3NaOH \rightarrow Fe(OH)_3 + 3NaCl$
(e) $Cr_2O_3 + 3H_2 \rightarrow 2Cr + 3H_2O$

6. (a) $2Al + 6HCl \rightarrow 3H_2 + 2AlCl_3$
(c) $CaO + H_2O \rightarrow Ca(OH)_2$
(e) $F_2 + 2NaCl \rightarrow 2NaF + Cl_2$
(g) $2CS_2 + 5O_2 \rightarrow 2CO + 4SO_2$
(i) $Na_3As + 3NH_4Br \rightarrow (NH_4)_3As + 3NaBr$

7. (a) $3Mg + N_2 \rightarrow Mg_3N_2$
(c) $Ca(OH)_2 + Na_2CO_3 \rightarrow 2NaOH + CaCO_3$
(e) $2NH_4Cl + CaO \rightarrow 2NH_3 + H_2O + CaCl_2$

(g) $MnO_2 + 4HCl \rightarrow MnCl_2 + Cl_2 + 2H_2O$
(i) $2Cu_2S + 3O_2 \rightarrow 2Cu_2O + 2SO_2$
(k) $2HgO \rightarrow 2Hg + O_2$
(m) $3CuO + 2NH_3 \rightarrow 3Cu + 3H_2O + N_2$
(o) $2H_2S + 3O_2 \rightarrow 2SO_2 + 2H_2O$
(q) $4Al + 3O_2 \rightarrow 2Al_2O_3$
(s) $P_4 + 5O_2 \rightarrow P_4O_{10}$
(u) $2AgNO_3 + MgCl_2 \rightarrow 2AgCl + Mg(NO_3)_2$
(w) $H_3PO_4 + 3KOH \rightarrow K_3PO_4 + 3H_2O$
(y) $K_2O + H_2O \rightarrow 2KOH$

8. (a) exothermic   (c) exothermic
(e) endothermic

Chapter 8, page 193

1. (a) $\dfrac{4\text{ mole }NH_3}{5\text{ mole }O_2} = 1 = \dfrac{5\text{ mole }O_2}{4\text{ mole }NH_3}$

$\dfrac{4\text{ mole }NH_3}{4\text{ mole }NO} = 1 = \dfrac{4\text{ mole }NO}{4\text{ mole }NH_3}$

$\dfrac{4\text{ mole }NH_3}{6\text{ mole }H_2O} = 1 = \dfrac{6\text{ mole }H_2O}{4\text{ mole }NH_3}$

$\dfrac{5\text{ mole }O_2}{4\text{ mole }NO} = 1 = \dfrac{4\text{ mole }NO}{5\text{ mole }O_2}$

$\dfrac{5\text{ mole }O_2}{6\text{ mole }H_2O} = 1 = \dfrac{6\text{ mole }H_2O}{5\text{ mole }O_2}$

$\dfrac{4\text{ mole }NO}{6\text{ mole }H_2O} = 1 = \dfrac{6\text{ mole }H_2O}{4\text{ mole }NO}$

(b) 5.00 mole O_2 (c) 1.25 mole O_2
(d) 1.50 mole H_2O (e) 120. g NO
(f) 21.6 g H_2O (g) 15 g NO
(h) 24 g O_2

3. 0.787 kg SO_2

5. 60. g NO_2

7. 450 g $Ca(H_2PO_4)_2$

9. 22 g $CaCO_3$

11. 45 g $AlCl_3$
19 g Al remaining

13. 250 g CS_2

15. 51.2 g H_2O

17. 41 g Cl_2

19. 58% pure CuO in sample

1. (a) combination of elements; oxidation-reduction reaction
   (c) replacement reaction; oxidation-reduction reaction
   (e) replacement reaction; oxidation-reduction reaction
   (g) oxidation-reduction reaction
   (i) decomposition reaction; oxidation-reduction reaction
   (k) replacement reaction; oxidation-reduction reaction
   (m) oxidation-reduction reaction
   (o) replacement reaction; acid-base reaction

2. (a) $Mg + 2AgNO_3 \rightarrow Mg(NO_3)_2 + 2Ag$
   (c) $2Na + 2H_2O \rightarrow 2NaOH + H_2$
   (e) $Fe + Al_2(SO_4)_3 \rightarrow$ No reaction
   (g) $CuSO_4 + H_2S \rightarrow CuS(s) + H_2SO_4$
   (i) $Na_2CO_3 + CaCl_2 \rightarrow CaCO_3(s) + 2NaCl$
   (k) $Pb(NO_3)_2 + 2KCl \rightarrow PbCl_2(s) + 2KNO_3$
   (m) $Na_2SO_3 + 2HCl \rightarrow$
   $$2NaCl + H_2O + SO_2(g)$$
   (o) $(NH_4)_2CO_3 + Ca(C_2H_3O_2)_2 \rightarrow$
   $$2NH_4C_2H_3O_2 + CaCO_3(s)$$
   (q) $H_2SO_4 + Ca(OH)_2 \rightarrow 2H_2O + CaSO_4$
   (s) $2AgNO_3 + BaCl_2 \rightarrow 2AgCl(s) + Ba(NO_3)_2$

3. (a) F: -1 (c) F: -1
       H: $+1$ S: $+6$
   (e) O: -2 (g) H: $+1$
       Mn: $+7$ O: -1
   (i) O: -2 (k) Cl: -1
       P: $+5$ H: $+1$ N: -3
   (m) O: -2 (o) H: -1
       N: $+4$ Mg $+2$
   (q) Fe: $+2$ (s) O: -2
       O: -2 Cr: $+6$
       C: $+4$

4. (a) Oxidized: H_2 H: $0 \rightarrow +1$
       Reduced: FeO   Fe: $+2 \rightarrow 0$
   (c) Oxidized: Al   Al: $0 \rightarrow +3$
       Reduced: $AgNO_3$ Ag: $+1 \rightarrow 0$
   (e) Oxidized: Br_2 Br: $0 \rightarrow +5$
       Reduced: Br_2 Br: $0 \rightarrow -1$
   (g) Oxidized: Al   Al: $0 \rightarrow +3$
       Reduced: $CuSO_4$ Cu: $+2 \rightarrow 0$
   (i) Oxidized: I_2 I: $0 \rightarrow +5$
       Reduced: HNO_3 N: $+5 \rightarrow +4$

5.

		Arrhenius	Brønsted-Lowry	Lewis
(a)	Base	x	x	x
(c)	Base	x	x	x
(e)	Base	x	x	x
(g)	Acid or	x	x	x
	Base		x	x
(i)	Base		x	x
(k)	Acid			x
(m)	Acid	x	x	x
(o)	Base	x	x	x
(q)	Acid	x	x	x
(s)	Acid	x	x	x

(a) $Fe(OH)_2 + 2HCl \rightarrow FeCl_2 + 2H_2O$
(c) $KOH + HCl \rightarrow KCl + H_2O$
(e) $Ca(OH)_2 + 2HCl \rightarrow CaCl_2 + 2H_2O$
(g) $NaHCO_3 + HCl \rightarrow$
$$NaCl + H_2CO_3 \rightarrow NaCl + H_2O + CO_2$$
$$NaHCO_3 + NaOH \rightarrow Na_2CO_3 + H_2O$$
(i) $PH_3 + HCl \rightarrow PH_4Cl$
(k) $AlBr_3 + NaOH \rightarrow Na(AlBr_3OH)$
(m) $HBr + NaOH \rightarrow NaBr + H_2O$
(o) $Ba(OH)_2 + 2HCl \rightarrow BaCl_2 + 2H_2O$
(q) $H_3PO_4 + 3NaOH \rightarrow Na_3PO_4 + 3H_2O$
(s) $HNO_3 + NaOH \rightarrow NaNO_3 + H_2$

6. See answers to Problem 5. In Problem 5, only (f) and (k) are not Brønsted-Lowry acids or bases.

7. (a) NH_3 (c) HCl

Chapter 10, page 257

2. (a) 76 cm Hg   (c) 270 cm Hg
   (e) 1.9 atm   (g) 62 cm Hg
   (i) 1.7×10^{-3} atm

5. (a) 298K   (c) 233K
   (e) 573K

6. (a) 0.6 L   (c) 430 mm Hg
   (e) 1.8 atm

9. 10 L

15. 1000 mL

19. 1.1 L

23. 29 L

25. (a) 0.903 L   (b) 2.54 g P_2O_5

Chapter 11, page 294

1. 13%

3. 25 g glucose

5. 160 g H_2O

7. 15%

9. 0.034 mol NaOH

11. 0.29 M

13. 0.23 mol $FeCl_3$

15. 55 g HCl

17. 6%

19. Begin with 250 mL of 12 M HCl and dilute with 250 mL water to make 500 mL of solution.

21. 50 L

23. 31.50 mL

25. 0.43 g Al_2S_3

27. (a) 36.5 g   (c) 40.0 g
    (e) 26.0 g   (g) 45.0 g

28. (a) NaOH: 40.0
         HCl: 36.5
    (c) H_2CO_3: 31.0
         NaOH: 40.0

29. (a) 0.2 N (c) 6×10^{-10} N

31. 0.03 g H_2

33. (a) 4.0 M (c) 0.025 M

Chapter 12, page 312

6. (a) 10   (c) 7
   (e) 12

7. (a) $[H+] = 1 \times 10^{-2}$
        pH = 2
   (c) $[H+] = 1 \times 10^{-7}$
        pH = 7
   (e) $[H+] = 1 \times 10^{-4}$
        pH = 4

8. (a) 1×10^{-5} (c) 1×10^{-12}
   (e) 1×10^{-2}

9. (a) acidic   (c) basic
   (e) acidic

10. (a) 1×10^{-12} (c) 1×10^{-3}
    (e) 1×10^{-6}

11. (a) acidic   (c) basic
    (e) basic

Chapter 13, page 339

5. rate = K (number of open doors) (number of calls from girlfriends)^2

7. rate = K (A) (B)

9. (a) $K = \dfrac{P^2_{NO_2}}{P^2_{NO} P_{O_2}}$

   (c) $K = \dfrac{P_{H_2} P_{CO}}{P_{H_2O}}$

   (e) $K = \dfrac{P_{H_2S}}{P_{HCl}}$

11. (a) right   (b) left
    (c) right   (d) left
    (e) right

Chapter 14, page 361

3. (a) cathode: Na
        anode: Cl_2
   (c) cathode: Cu
        anode: O_2
   (e) cathode: H_2
        anode: O_2

4. (a) H_2 (c) H_2
   (e) H_2

6. (a) Cell potential = 0.49V
        Oxidation: $Cr \rightarrow Cr^{3+} + 3e^-$: anode
        Reduction: $Ni^{2+} + 2e^- \rightarrow Ni$: cathode
   (c) Cell potential = 5.95V
        Oxidation: $Li \rightarrow Li^+ + e^-$: anode
        Reduction: $F_2 + 2e^- \rightarrow 2F^-$: cathode
   (e) Cell potential: 0.37V
        Oxidation: $Pd \rightarrow Pd^{2+} + 2e^-$: anode
        Reduction: $Cl_2 + 2e^- \rightarrow 2Cl^-$: cathode

7. (a) Au, Pt, Pd, Ag, Hg, Cu

1. (a) CH₃-CH₂-CH₃

   (c) CH₃-CH₂-CH₂-CH₂-CH₃

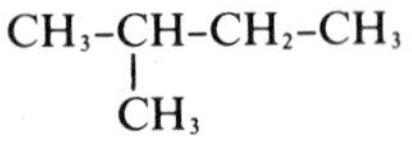

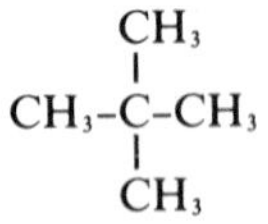

   CH₃-CH-CH₂-CH₃
       |
       CH₃

       CH₃
       |
   CH₃-C-CH₃
       |
       CH₃

   (e) CH≡C-CH₂-CH₂-CH₃
   CH₃-C≡C-CH₂-CH₃

   CH₂=CH-CH₂-CH=CH₂
   CH₂=CH-CH=CH-CH₃

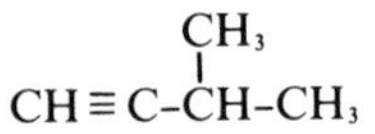

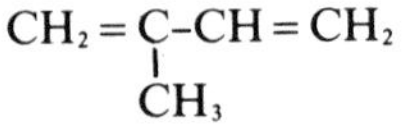

       CH₃   CH₂=C-CH=CH₂
       | |
   CH≡C-CH-CH₃   CH₃

   plus more obscure structures

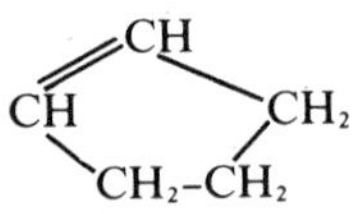

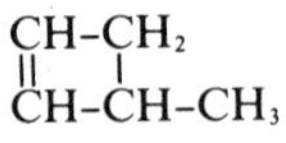

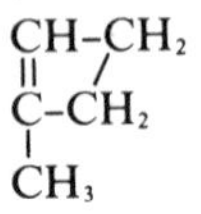

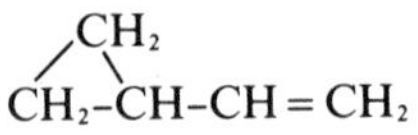

   (g) CH≡C-C≡C-CH₂-CH₃
   CH≡C-CH₂-C≡C-CH₃
   CH≡C-CH-C≡CH
         |
         CH₃
   CH≡C-CH₂-CH₂-C≡CH

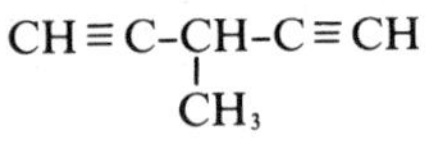

   plus more obscure structures

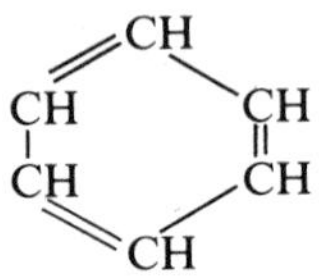

2. (a) propane   (c) ethanol
   (e) propene
   (g) tetrachloromethane or carbon tetrachloride
   (i) 2–chlorobutane

3. (a) 2,3,3–trimethylpentane
   (c) 1,2,3 propanetriol or glycerol
   (e) propanal
   (g) butanone
   (i) ethanoic acid or acetic acid

4. (a) ethylamine (c) trimethylamine
   (e) ethene
   (g) 2–chloropropyl methylamine
   (i) 3,5–dimethyl benzoic acid

5. (a) CH₃-CH₂-CH-CH₂-CH₂-CH₃
               |
               CH₃

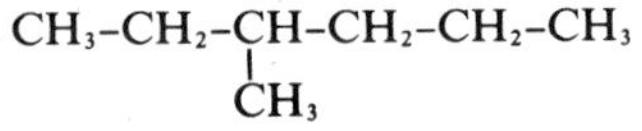

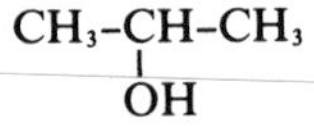

   (c) CH₃-CH-CH₃
           |
           OH

   (e)   O
            ||
       CH₃-C-O-CH₂-CH₃

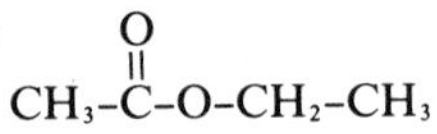

   (g) CH₃-C≡C-CH₂-CH₃

6. (a) CH₃-CH₂-NH₂

   (c) NH₂

   (e)   O
            ||
       CH-C-OH

   (g)   O
            ⁄⁄
       HC
           \
           O-CH₃

   (i)   O
                  ⁄⁄
       CH₃-CH-CH₂-C
           | \
           CH₃   OH

7. (a) CH₃-O-CH₃

   (c) CH₂-CH₂
       | |
       OH OH

   (e) CH₃-CH₂-CH₂-CH₂-CH₂OH

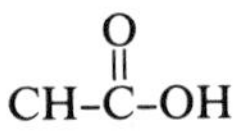

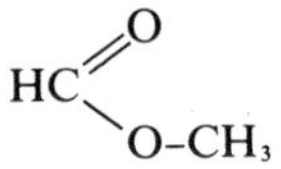

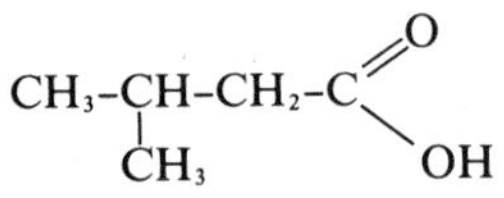

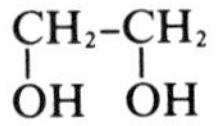

   (g) CH₂-CH-CH₂
       | | |
       OH OH OH

   (i)   Cl Cl
          | |
       F-C-C-F
          | |
          F F

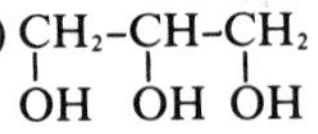

8. (a) $CH_3Cl + CH_2Cl_2 + CHCl_3 + CCl_4$
in order of decreasing quantity

(c) $CH_3-CH_2-\underset{\underset{Cl}{|}}{CH}-CH_3$

(e)
$$CH_3-\underset{\underset{Br}{|}}{\overset{\overset{Br}{|}}{C}}-\underset{\underset{Br}{|}}{\overset{\overset{Br}{|}}{C}}-CH_3$$

9. (a) $CH_3-\underset{\underset{OH}{|}}{CH}-CH_3$ (c) CH_3-CH_2-OH

(e) $CH_3-O-CH_2-CH_3 +$
$CH_3CH_2-O-CH_2-CH_3 + CH_3-O-CH_3$

10. (a) $CH_3-O-CH_2-CH_3$

(c)
$$F-\underset{\underset{F}{|}}{\overset{\overset{Cl}{|}}{C}}-\underset{\underset{F}{|}}{\overset{\overset{Cl}{|}}{C}}-F$$

(e)
$$CH_3-\underset{\underset{Cl}{|}}{\overset{\overset{Cl}{|}}{C}}-CH_2-CH_3$$

Chapter 16, page 433

All problems are discussion questions.

Chapter 17, page 459

1. (a) $_{-1}^{0}e$ (c) $_{9}^{19}F$

(e) $_{62}^{146}Sm$ (g) $_{64}^{149}Gd$

(i) $_{70}^{170}Yb$ (k) $_{48}^{102}Cd$

2. (a) $_{28}^{59}Ni$ (c) $_{45}^{99}Rh$

(e) $_{37}^{86}Rb$ (g) $2 _{-1}^{0}e$

7. 23000 years

INDEX

Parts per million, 270, 293
Parts per thousand, 270, 293
Periodic chart, 68
Periodic property, 77
pH, 308, 312
Phase diagram, 252, 256
Photochemical smog, 421
Physical change, 4, 11
Physical chemistry, 5
Physical property, 297, 312
Physics, 5, 11
Polar bond, 128, 131
Pollution
    air, 417
    carbon dioxide, 422
    carbon monoxide, 422
    heavy metals, 428
    hydrocarbon, 420
    nitrogen oxides, 422
    particulates, 424
    sewage, 426
    sulfur oxides, 423
Polyatomic ion, 116, 131, 143, 146
Polymer, 408, 413
Positron, 439, 458
Positron emission, 439
Power, 15
Precipitation, 213, 221
Preservative agent, food, 431
Pressure, 228, 256
    atmospheric, 229, 255
    osmotic, 312
    standard, 239
    vapor, 249, 257
Primary cell, 359, 361
Primary sewage treatment, 427, 433
Product, 165, 178
Proton, 64, 65, 92

Radioactive nuclide, 438, 458
Radioactivity, 437
Raoult's law, 299, 312
Rate law, 325, 339
Rate of reaction, 317
Reactant, 165, 178
Reaction
    chemical, 177
    combination, 201, 221
    decomposition, 204, 221

Reaction *(continued)*
    double replacement, 212, 221
    endothermic, 175, 177
    exothermic, 175, 178
    nonspontaneous, 173
    oxidation-reduction, 197, 211, 221
    rate of, 317
    redox, 197
    single replacement, 206, 222
    spontaneous, 173, 178
Reagent, 189
Redox, 221
Redox reaction, 197, 461
Reducing agent, 198, 222
Reduction, 197, 222
Rem, 455, 458
Representative elements, 89
Resistance, 344
Resonance, 121
Rutherford scattering experiment, 66
Rutherford, E., 66

s orbital, 77
Salt, 216, 222
Salt bridge, 353, 361
Saturated hydrocarbon, 371, 413
Saturated solution, 263, 293
Scientific method, 5
Scientific notation, 15
Secondary sewage treatment, 427, 433
Semipermeable membrane, 302, 312
Sewage treatment, 427
SHE, 355, 361
SI, 14, 55, 57
Significant figures, 19, 57
    multiplication and division, 23
    sums and differences, 22
Single replacement reaction, 206, 222
Solar energy, 436, 458
Solid, 4, 225, 256
Solubility, 264, 293
    product constant, 333, 339
    rules, 213
Solute, 262, 293
Solution, 261, 293
Solvation, 293
Solvent, 262, 293
Specific gravity, 45, 57
Specific heat, 54, 57